3. 20

Hopress

P 22, 23, 24, 25

Chap II 34-34 On

10ᵗ illustrated Booklet
Gulf Hanstery
1531 Basel St
Mobile, Ala.

QUALITATIVE ANALYSIS
AND
CHEMICAL EQUILIBRIUM

THIRD EDITION

BY

T. R. HOGNESS
PROFESSOR OF CHEMISTRY
UNIVERSITY OF CHICAGO

AND

WARREN C. JOHNSON
PROFESSOR OF CHEMISTRY
CHAIRMAN OF THE DEPARTMENT OF CHEMISTRY
UNIVERSITY OF CHICAGO

NEW YORK
HENRY HOLT AND COMPANY

PRINTED IN THE
UNITED STATES OF AMERICA

PREFACE TO THE THIRD EDITION

When we decided to write the first edition of *Qualitative Analysis and Chemical Equilibrium* we were motivated by the desire to divert the emphasis in the conventional course in qualitative analysis from the more technological and practical bases to those of pure science. The tendency of too many instructors was to regard the aim of this course solely as that of giving instruction in analytical procedures and techniques. But with the more advanced techniques of spectroscopy becoming fully developed in their application to qualitative analysis, the wet analysis became outmoded and, considering that perhaps less than one per cent of the students would ever make practical application of the detailed laboratory knowledge of this course, we were faced with the question of either trying to eliminate this course altogether from the curriculum or changing it so drastically that the laboratory work would be an adjunct but nevertheless an excellent practical illustration of one of the basic principles of chemistry, namely, chemical equilibrium. We chose the latter procedure, and hence the title of the book.

We recognized, however, that the attainment of certain techniques is necessary in the training of a scientist and that perhaps the conventional course in qualitative analysis served in this way. On the other hand, a brief visit to almost any qualitative analysis laboratory will convince one that the purpose of training in technique was not being achieved, particularly when one contrasted the condition of the qualitative analysis laboratory, for example, with that of the botany laboratory.

With Pregel as its inspiration, quantitative analysis had shifted its emphasis more and more toward microanalysis and micro techniques. Milligrams, rather than grams, became the common units of weight, and the question was often asked, could not qualitative analysis follow this same course? There were two principal objections to the instituting of micro techniques in the qualitative laboratory: (1) the cost of micro equipment was beyond the means of the average school, and (2) the student in his early and formative years could not be expected to become suddenly ultra-careful.

Since neither the macro nor the micro methods were practical, we adopted the intermediate scale or semi-micro qualitative methods, and the result of this experiment in teaching has been most gratifying. The qualitative analysis laboratory no longer smells excessively of hydrogen sulfide, the student's desk and habits of work have become neater and therefore technically much better and the laboratory costs have been much reduced. We are told that this movement has become so popular that in a few years more than half the colleges of the country have adopted the semi-micro method of laboratory teaching and there is a tendency to expand this method to other courses in chemistry.

No procedure of qualitative analysis will ever suit every teacher. There are so many variations possible and so many teachers who have personal preferences that a universally accepted method is practically impossible of attainment. We have in the past few years had much constructive criticism and many compliments, for which we are very grateful. Criticisms have been noted; wherever practicable they have been tried out; and when satisfactory, they have been adopted. The text has therefore been kept under constant revision. The result of this revision now appears in the third edition. In making these revisions, we have avoided the use of organic reagents as much as possible and have weighed the psychological effect of the perfect analytical scheme against the effect of the student's inability to comprehend completely all steps in the process.

The theoretical part of the text has also been modified. The first chapter has been changed and expanded into two chapters with the hope of giving the student (1) a better idea of what material we consider should receive the greatest emphasis, (2) a better correlation between general chemistry and qualitative analysis, (3) an improved presentation of the basis of the fundamental concepts of chemistry, and (4) inspiration to explore the subject further. In the carrying out of these objectives several significant changes have been made. Of these there should be mentioned the increase in emphasis on the electronic structure of atoms, molecules and ions, which makes it possible for the student to consider the properties of these particles in terms of structure. The chapter on oxidation and reduction, as it appeared in the earlier editions, has been broken into two parts, and that part dealing with the balancing of equations has been moved forward. Additions are also made in the chapters including discussion of complex ions and amphoteric substances. The problems have been improved and a number of new ones have been added.

In the preparation of the second and third editions we are particularly indebted to Dr. F. A. Long, of Cornell University; Professor A. R. Armstrong, of the College of William and Mary; Professor A. B. Burg, of the University of Southern California; and Professor James B. Parsons and Miss Virginia Mayo, of the University of Chicago, for their constructive criticisms and suggestions. For their helpful comments and interest we also wish to express our gratitude to Mr. George Fawcett, of Wright Junior College; Mr. L. A. Johnson, of Virginia (Minnesota) Junior College; Professor H. I. Schlesinger, of the University of Chicago; Professor H. L. Brown, of Wayne University; Professor L. J. Desha, of Washington and Lee University; Professor E. L. Haenisch, of Villanova University; Professor M. G. Burford, of Wesleyan University; Professor H. N. Alyea, of Princeton University; and Professor W. C. Pierce, of Pomona College.

T. R. H.
W. C. J.

The University of Chicago
November 15, 1946

PREFACE TO THE FIRST EDITION

The ever-increasing growth of knowledge in science and the attempt on the part of teachers to keep pace with this growth has brought us face to face with the dilemma that less time is allowed the student to acquire more knowledge and information. It has become necessary to evaluate the entire chemistry curriculum more critically with a view toward a redistribution of the fundamental units of the subject and toward an alteration in the emphasis. As a result, qualitative analysis is one of the subjects that is receiving increased attention.

The primary aim of a course in qualitative analysis some few years ago was chiefly to give instruction in analytical procedure and technique. More recently, however, there has developed a marked tendency to place more and more emphasis on the application of the fundamental concepts of solutions to the laboratory work. Apparently this movement is still growing, and attempts are being made to adjust the subject matter of the course accordingly.

In the elementary chemistry course the student gains some idea of the properties of ions and some acquaintance with the concept of equilibrium. Yet it has been our experience that this training alone is not sufficient to serve as a basis for later work in chemistry and its related fields. In its newer development qualitative analysis offers an excellent opportunity for the student (1) to get a better knowledge of the properties of ions and their compounds, (2) to acquire a thorough understanding of the principle of chemical equilibrium and (3) to acquire training in experimental technique, especially that involving the use of small amounts of material.

Although the text is formally divided into two parts, (I) considerations of general principles and (II) chemistry

vii

of the ions, experiments and analytical procedures, this separation is somewhat artificial. Theory and practice are coordinated at every opportunity.

Of all the general principles of science, chemical equilibrium is unquestionably one of the most important. Problems in chemistry, physics, astronomy, animal and plant biology, medicine, and engineering very often involve considerations of chemical equilibrium. The general applicability of the subject requires a more thorough knowledge than is usually obtained from the course in elementary chemistry. The concept should be so deeply ingrained in the student's mind that it becomes the first consideration in attacking any chemical problem.

With a subject so widespreading in its ramifications as this, it is obvious that an extensive treatment cannot be given to its applicability, which would cover most of the present subject matter of chemistry. Rather, a thorough understanding of the principle itself becomes one of the main objectives of this course. Although it is here applied to qualitative analysis, its later application to any other field can be made relatively easily.

It is assumed that the student is familiar with the atomic theory, the kinetic molecular hypothesis and its application to the behavior of gases, the meaning of atomic and molecular weights, the balancing of simple chemical equations, the most general properties of solutions, and, in an elementary way, the periodic system. The subject of solutions and solubility is introduced by way of a consideration of the forces between ions and solvent molecules. Only enough electronic structure theory is given to enable the student to understand in a general way the nature of ions and molecules and the forces that operate between them. The strong electrolytes are treated from the generally accepted standpoint of complete ionization. This concept leads to the use of ionic equations throughout the text. The confusing notation often applied to a description of the phenomena and the methods of measuring conductances has been avoided.

We believe that the simpler treatment of this subject found in this text is entirely adequate.

Throughout years of experience we have often observed that the student has considerable difficulty in obtaining a clear understanding of the derivation of the Law of Mass Action as it is usually presented. We hope that this difficulty has been overcome by the simple graphical treatment given in Chapter II. Likewise, we have found that the use of electrode potentials in the treatment of oxidation and reduction, and the consequent use of the Nernst equation relating potential to concentration is most confusing to the student of qualitative analysis. It is impossible to understand fully the relationship between potential and concentration without recourse to thermodynamics. The treatment of oxidation-reduction equilibria as given in Chapter IX follows, to the best of our knowledge, an entirely new method of approach. These equilibria are considered in a manner quite analogous to those already familiar to the student at this point in the course. Instead of the usual single-electrode potentials, we have introduced equilibrium constants for half-reactions the combinations of which permit simple calculations to be made for the determination of the course of any of the common oxidation-reduction reactions.

No attempt has been made to introduce the concept of activity or activity coefficients. This subject is not essential to a fundamental understanding of chemical equilibrium, nor is the student prepared to interpret its significance. In numerical calculations in this course its contribution is of no importance. Nor do we believe that the modern theories of acids and bases offer sufficient advantages to be included here.

Descriptive material is interwoven with the presentation of the theoretical aspects of the subject, both of which are applied in numerous instances to qualitative analysis and general problems of chemistry. Each chapter concludes with a set of questions and problems. The questions serve as a guide for study and review of the subject matter. The problems deal essentially with equilibria of solutions. It is our conviction that the student cannot acquire an adequate understanding of chemical equilibrium and its application without dealing with numerical calculations involving this principle. It is not necessary that these calculations be mathematically difficult. Accordingly, special effort has been made to select relatively simple problems which are arranged in the order of increasing difficulty. Examples of all types of problems and their complete solutions are given at the end of each chapter. Answers to all problems and an ample section on mathematical operations are included in the Appendix as a guide for the student. New problems may easily be constructed from those given in the text.

Part II is to be studied simultaneously with Part I of the text. This second part includes descriptive material which covers the chemistry of the ions and their compounds, experiments to illustrate the principles of equilibrium and qualitative analysis, and the analytical procedure. Experiments, preliminary to the analytical procedure for each group, that are designed to acquaint the student with the colors of precipitates, and that give only descriptive information concerning reactions, have been reduced in number. Instead, other experiments are introduced to show the rôles that equilibrium and reaction velocity play in the separation and identification of the ions. Many of these experiments demand the exercise of some originality and constructive effort on the part of the student. The descriptive material pertaining to the group of ions studied is given in concise form, and precedes both the experiments and the analytical procedures. The laboratory study is interspersed with questions designed to correlate the principles with the work at hand. The student is expected to answer these questions as they are presented.

One of the aims of a course in qualitative analysis is to guide the student in developing technique in the usual operations of chemistry, but with the amounts of material ordinarily employed in the laboratory work this aim is seldom accomplished to the desired extent. We do not believe that in the past full advantage has been taken of the opportunities offered by laboratory work in the more elementary courses to develop the technical ability of the student. The future scientist, the student of today, as he inquires more deeply into the problems of chemistry, physics and biology, will be confronted with the necessity of working with smaller objects and smaller amounts of material, and consequently he must acquire a "micro" technique to cope with this situation.

In this course a step has been taken in the "micro" direction by reducing the amounts of materials employed to a minimum consistent with easily available and standard apparatus. The volume of the "unknown" solution has been reduced to three milliliters, with the concentration of each ion not greater than .02 molar (5 to 15 milligrams of a salt). One-milliliter medicine droppers are used to handle reagents and to wash precipitates; the funnels, test-tubes and flasks are of correspondingly small size. To go farther in this direction would require special apparatus and reagents, and would involve reactions that the student is not prepared to understand. Furthermore, the training in working with small amounts of material should not be so specialized that it is not generally applicable.

There are many advantages to be gained by basing the laboratory work on minimum amounts of material. The student learns that care and neatness are essential, and of necessity develops these qualities. In the usual analytical procedures the student spends an inordinate amount of time filtering solutions and washing precipitates. In the procedure outlined in this text the time required for these operations is reduced manyfold. The contamination of the laboratory air with hydrogen sulfide is no longer a serious problem. Very much smaller amounts of this gas and much less time are required to saturate the solutions. Another significant advantage is the reduced cost of equipment, supplies and laboratory maintenance.

The analytical procedure, with few variations, is essentially that developed by Fresenius. Radical departure from this procedure is unnecessary and offers no special advantages. However, we have made a slight change in the usual order of the analytical groups in that the alkali metal group is considered first instead of last. The order of presentation of all analytical groups is the same as that followed in the systematic general procedure. The ammonium ion is identified by the usual method, while sodium and potassium ions are detected by flame tests only. Therefore no separation of this group is necessary. This scheme has been adopted to allow opportunity for better correlation between theory and practice.

Even with the greatest care in the production of a textbook, small errors seem to be inevitable. We shall be very grateful to readers who offer corrections, suggestions and criticism.

We take pleasure in acknowledging our indebtedness to the works of Prescott and Johnson, Latimer and Hildebrand, Stieglitz, and A. A. Noyes. We are particularly grateful to Professor H. I. Schlesinger and Mr. Harry H. Wood for their criticisms and helpful suggestions. We are also indebted to many students of the laboratory for their assistance in the selection of data, checking numerical calculations and laboratory procedures, and in the reading of proof.

T. R. H.
W. C. J.

THE UNIVERSITY OF CHICAGO
April, 1937

CONTENTS

PART I

PART II

To the Instructor

We have tried to design this course in such a way that the theoretical considerations contained in the first part of this book keep pace with the laboratory work. But that objective cannot be strictly achieved unless the beginning of the laboratory work is unduly delayed. The extent of the lag between theory and the laboratory work, in the first part of the course, can be determined by the instructor and is left to his discretion.

The first three chapters are partly review and partly an elaboration of concepts already presented to the student. The extent to which these chapters are in the nature of review will depend entirely upon the emphasis given the subject matter in the student's previous training. Therefore, to bring about a satisfactory adjustment between theory and the laboratory work as soon as possible, the instructor may assign any one or all three of these chapters, or even parts of chapters, as extra reading; he may defer attention to these chapters until a later time in the course; or in exceptional cases he may even omit them altogether. Certain parts of the second chapter may seem to be extraneous to qualitative analysis. We have inserted these parts in the hope that they may have some inspirational value for the curious and more ambitious student.

CHAPTER I

Electrolytes and Non-Electrolytes

The authors have assumed that the student beginning a course in qualitative analysis and chemical equilibrium has a good background in general chemistry. However, there are a few principles in chemistry with which we shall deal so often that, although they may have been considered in a previous course, we believe that it will be advantageous to restate, elaborate and emphasize them in this chapter.

Our object is to enlarge on the concepts of electrolytes, both strong and weak, and non-electrolytes. In so doing we shall consider the problem of polarity of molecules and the theory of ionization, and with the object of producing a better picture of these phenomena in the mind's eye, we shall consider in the next chapter some of the rudimentary phases of atomic and molecular structure.

To the well-trained, experienced and imaginative chemist, a chemical equation implies much more than the mere stoichiometric relationships (weight relationships of substances concerned). To illustrate, let us consider the reaction which takes place in the neutralization of acetic acid (HAc)* by ammonium hydroxide (NH_4OH) in water solution to form ammonium acetate and water.

$$HAc + NH_4OH = NH_4^+ + Ac^- + H_2O \qquad (1)$$

This equation not only tells us that for every molecule of acetic acid reacting with one molecule of ammonium hydroxide one ammonium ion, one acetate ion, and one molecule of water are formed, but it also suggests a host of correlated principles and facts which give us a mental picture of the sub-microscopic process involved in the reaction. This picture in all its details includes such phenomena as

---

* We shall use acetic acid and acetates so frequently throughout this text that it will be convenient to abbreviate the formula for the acid to HAc, the Ac referring to the acetate radical, CH_3COO.

hydrolysis, the ionization of weak acids and weak bases, the complete ionization of salts, the equilibrium between hydrogen ion, hydroxide ion and water, and the hydration of ions and molecules. An extension of this picture into its still finer details takes into account the polarity and the electronic structure of the molecules and ions themselves.

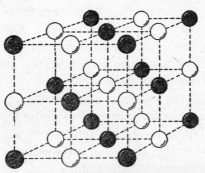

Figure 1. Schematic Representation of a Crystal of Sodium Chloride

We shall then want to know something about these phenomena and theories so that our later work will have more meaning and thereby become easier to grasp.

The Nature of Solids. We shall not enter into any prolonged discussion on the definition of a solid. There are some scientists who say that glass, for example, is a supercooled liquid and therefore it is not a solid, but certainly the common concept of glass at room temperature is that of a solid. We do not sacrifice scientific accuracy if we conceive of a solid merely as that state of matter which retains its shape over an extended period of time.

A more important distinction than that which exists between liquids and solids is that between crystalline and non-crystalline solids. Solids may be classified into two general divisions, glasses and crystals. In crystals the molecules, atoms or particles occupy definite positions with respect to each other, while in glasses the positions of the molecules or atoms are fixed in no very definite structural form. From X-ray diffraction photographs it has been shown that in a crystal of sodium chloride, a typical crystalline solid, the ultimate sodium and chlorine particles are so arranged that each sodium particle is surrounded by six of chlorine and each chlorine by six of sodium; that is, each sodium and each chlorine has six neighbors. The arrangement of the particles in such a crystal is shown in Figure 1. Again, from the analysis of X-ray photographs we know that the molecules in a glass have no very definite and orderly arrangement. The generally accepted concept of the arrangement of particles in quartz glass is shown in Figure 2, which is a representation in only two dimensions.

In each case, glass or crystal, the particles are regarded as being fixed in position; the difference between the glass and the crystal lies in the difference in the orderliness of the particle arrangement.

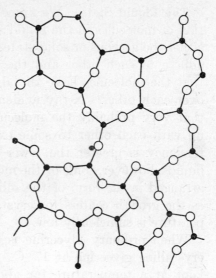

Figure 2. Schematic Representation of Quartz Glass. The shaded circles represent silicon and the unshaded, oxygen particles. (According to Zachariasen)

When heat is applied to a crystal, a definite temperature is reached at which the crystal melts. This temperature is known as the melting point. Above this temperature the substance in question is a liquid; below this temperature, it is crystalline. A glass, on the other hand, when heated has no definite melting point but gradually becomes softer and less viscous until finally it becomes a liquid. Because of this gradual change from a solid to a liquid state and vice versa, a glass is often regarded as a super-cooled liquid.

Very few substances form glasses. Practically all those substances with which we are to deal are of a crystalline nature. With very few possible exceptions all substances that are precipitated from solution are crystalline even though they may not appear so to the naked eye.

The Liquid State. We know much less about the condition of molecules in the liquid state than we do for that in either the gaseous or solid states. The molecules of a liquid adhere to each other and the fluidity of liquids indicates that the molecules have the ability to move about or slip over each other. X-ray evidence again supports the view that very probably the molecules in a liquid tend to line up with each other to some extent and that this aligning tendency is greater the lower the temperature. In most liquids, however, some of the molecules are probably already arranged in the form of the solid crystal. These nuclei act as the growth centers for crystal formation when the temperature is sufficiently low.

When ordinary glycerine is cooled, it solidifies to form crystalline glycerine at 17° C. On the other hand, if it is kept at a temperature far above its melting point for a protracted time and then is cooled below the melting point, the glycerine gradually becomes more and more viscous until a glass is formed. If the glass is now melted and subsequently cooled, a glass is formed again, unless the liquid is seeded by the addition of glycerine crystals or of glycerine which itself will crystallize on cooling. Evidently, ordinary glycerine contains some nuclei or incipient crystals which act as the starting point for crystallization but which are destroyed at high temperatures. Liquids differ markedly in their ability to form glasses or supercooled liquids (i.e., cooled below the freezing point.)

Molecules in both the liquid and solid states are regarded as having vibrational motion, which motion increases with increasing temperature. When the vibrational motion within a crystal becomes sufficiently great, the molecules or particles no longer can remain in a fixed position and the crystal melts. In a glass we believe that this vibrational motion, when increased by heating, gradually gives the molecules the ability to move about; hence the glass gradually softens.

Polarity of Molecules. Suppose that two large sheets of metal are connected electrically with a battery B, a switch

and a current-measuring instrument as shown in Figure 3.
When the switch S is closed, the plate connected to the
negative pole of the battery becomes negatively charged
and the plate connected to the positive pole of the battery
positively charged. Just at the moment the switch is closed
the small current charging the plates will flow through and
be measured by the current-measuring instrument. The
positive charges on the one plate attract the negative charges
of the other and vice versa, and this attraction builds up

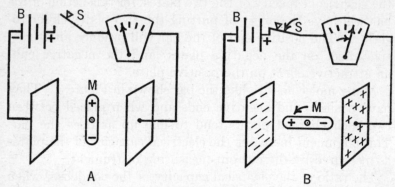

Figure 3. Action of Electric Field on Polar Molecule

the charge-holding ability or capacity of the two plates.
If the size of the plates is increased, it is obvious that the
two plates will hold a greater electric charge, that is, the
capacity will be increased.

The nearer two oppositely charged objects are to each
other the greater is the attractive force between them. If
the two plates are moved closer together the attractive force
which holds the charge on the surface of each plate becomes
greater and the two plates therefore have a greater capacity.
One might argue that as the charge increases on each of the
plates the attractive force will also increase, resulting in an
accumulatively greater capacity. There is an opposing
force, however, which stops this accumulative effect. Like
charges *on the same plate* repel each other and this repulsive
force, which is greater as the charge on each plate is in-

creased, prevents any indefinite accumulation of charge on any one plate. Such an arrangement of plates is known as a condenser.

Suppose that a bar M which can pivot about its center and which has one end positively charged and one end negatively charged is placed between the two plates. When the plates are now charged the bar will be found to tilt in such a position that the positive end will move toward the negative plate (Figure 3B). Such a bar will increase the electrical capacity of the two plates, for this action of the bar will have the effect of putting the two plates closer together. The positive end of the bar will produce an attractive effect on the negative plate; and the negative end, an attractive effect on the positive plate.

Many molecules are like the bar shown in Figure 3. They have positive and negative ends and when placed between two such charged plates tend to line up as does the bar. This alignment increases the electrical capacity of the plates as measured by the current-measuring instrument.

The ratio of the electrical capacity of the condenser when some substance is placed between its plates to the electrical capacity when there is a vacuum between these same plates is known as the **dielectric constant** of the substance.

$$\frac{\text{capacity with substance}}{\text{capacity in vacuum}} = \text{dielectric constant}$$

The greater the separation of the positive and negative charges in a molecule, the greater will be the turning effect on the molecule in the condenser, and therefore the greater will be the capacity of the condenser and the greater the dielectric constant of the substance. In Figure 4, the molecule B has a greater turning effect than molecule A. Since a greater separation of charge produces a greater torque or electrical leverage, molecule B can be more easily turned than molecule A. Therefore B has a greater dielectric constant than A. The dielectric constant is then a measure of the separation of the charges in a molecule.

Not all molecules when placed between the plates of a condenser are turned at right angles to the plates as shown in the case of the charged bar (Figure 3). The thermal agitation of the molecules prevents perfect alignment. We can deduce that the lower the temperature the less will be the thermal agitation and the greater will be the alignment. The dielectric constant of a polar molecule should therefore decrease with increasing temperature. This conclusion is completely verified by experiment.

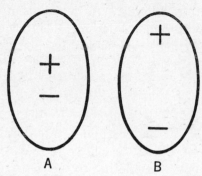

A   B

Figure 4. Schematic Representation of Two Polar Molecules. *B* More Polar than *A*

Polar and Non-Polar Substances. Those substances which have a large dielectric constant, that is, a large separation in the charges, are known as polar substances and those which have little or no separation in charges as non-polar substances. Water is a polar substance and methane, CH_4, and hexane, C_6H_{14}, a constituent of gasoline, are non-polar substances. We shall have more to say regarding such substances at a later time.

The Problem of Solubility. Some substances are soluble in each other in all proportions, while some are only so slightly soluble that we say they are insoluble. This difference in solubility of various substances in the same or different solvents has been a subject of the greatest concern for the chemist. It is a problem which is so complex that its quantitative solution offers great difficulties, yet the fundamental principles involved are not at all out of our reach.

Let us consider two liquids which are practically insoluble in each other. There are a great many systems of pairs of liquids which conform to this condition of low mutual solubility, but as a specific example we shall choose water and carbon tetrachloride. The water molecules are polar and those of carbon tetrachloride are non-polar. By virtue of their polarity, the water molecules have a greater tendency to adhere to each other (the positive end of one adhering to the negative end of another) than to molecules of carbon tetrachloride. As a result of the attractive forces of the water molecules for each other, any molecules of carbon tetrachloride which happen to be mixed with the water molecules are squeezed out. Due to thermal agitation, a few water molecules will probably break through the water surface in contact with carbon tetrachloride and wander off into this medium. For this reason, we cannot say that water and carbon tetrachloride are absolutely immiscible (absolutely insoluble in each other). The water molecules prefer each other to the molecules of carbon tetrachloride as neighbors. Likewise the molecules of carbon tetrachloride prefer each other. The polar dissimilarity of these two types of molecules, in a general way, accounts for the insolubility of water and carbon tetrachloride in each other.

Let us next consider a solution of two substances the molecules of both of which are polar. Water and ordinary alcohol are two such substances. The water molecules are somewhat more polar than the alcohol molecules. In this case the water molecules do not have any very great tendency to prefer each other as neighbors and the same is true of the alcohol molecules. The water molecules adhere to the alcohol molecules almost as strongly as they do to each other. Now there is no tendency for the water molecules to squeeze the alcohol molecules out of solution, nor do the alcohol molecules have this tendency toward water molecules. The result is that water and alcohol are soluble in each other in all proportions.

Non-polar substances are also soluble in each other, for there is no great tendency for the like molecules to prefer each other as neighbors; hence no "squeezing-out" effect.

No new considerations need be introduced in the problem of the solubility of solids in liquids. The attractive forces of the particles for each other in the crystal, in general, are very great; nevertheless there will be competition between the crystal and the solvent for the particles of the solid. The stronger the crystal forces operating between the atoms or particles of the solid and the greater the "squeezing-out" tendency of the solvent, the less soluble will be the solid in question.

It is possible to arrange substances in a series or table in order of the attractive forces operating between the molecules. An example of such a series is given in the following table. The non-polar substances appear at the top of the table and the polar substances at the bottom. Two substances lying close together in the series are very soluble in each other; those far apart are relatively insoluble in each other.

TABLE 1

RELATIVE ATTRACTIVE FORCES BETWEEN MOLECULES

Hexane
Carbon tetrachloride
Benzene
Toluene
Chloroform
Naphthalene
Anthracene
Nitrobenzene
Pyridine
Carbon bisulfide
Acetone
Acetic acid
Ethyl alcohol
Methyl alcohol
Water

POLAR

NON-POLAR

Some organic molecules are so complicated in structure that parts of the molecule may be regarded as polar and other parts as non-polar. With such substances the problem of solubility is necessarily a much more complex one.

The compound, $CH_3CH_2CH_2CH_2CH_2CH_2CH_2CH_2OH$, octyl alcohol, for example, consists of a long chain of carbon atoms, to one end of which is attached an OH radical. This OH end of the molecule is polar and the other end is non-polar. When placed in contact with water, only one end of the molecule is squeezed out of solution and the other end remains in contact with the water. The result is that the octyl alcohol molecule is squeezed to the surface of the water, with one end out of solution. Such phenomena are common and are of great interest in the study of surface chemistry.

There is one type of solution, electrolytic solution, which we have not yet considered and to which we shall later largely confine our attention. Before going on with the problems of solubility pertaining to such solutions, we must first deal with some of their properties.

The Concentration of a Solution. The simplest kind of a solution is made up of two components, the **solvent** and the **solute.** In general, the component present in the larger amount is known as the solvent, the other component, the solute. Thus, for a solution consisting of a large amount of water and a small amount of alcohol, water is the solvent and alcohol, the solute. If the alcohol were present in the larger amount, it would be the solvent and the water would be designated as the solute. However, for solutions consisting of water and an inorganic substance we shall arbitrarily refer to water as the solvent in all cases. A solution of sulfuric acid may be so concentrated that water is present in the smaller amount; nevertheless, we shall still regard the water as the solvent. In this course we shall be concerned chiefly with only three types of solutions, namely, gases, liquids and solids dissolved in water.

The amount of the solute dissolved in a given quantity of water determines the **concentration** of the solution. The quantitative expression for the concentration may be defined in a number of ways.

Weight-percent Solutions. The concentration of a weight-percent solution is expressed in terms of the number of parts of solute by weight contained in 100 parts of the solution. Thus 100 grams of a 36% solution of hydrochloric acid by weight contains 36 grams of HCl and 64 grams of water.

Molal Solutions. The **molal** concentration of a solution is defined as the number of gram-molecular-weights or gram-formula-weights of solute dissolved in 1000 grams of water. In qualitative analysis we shall have no need to use solutions the concentrations of which are defined in this way.

Molar Solutions. The **molar** concentration of a solution is defined as the number of gram-molecular-weights (**moles**) or gram-formula-weights dissolved in one liter of *solution*, i.e., in enough water to produce one liter of solution. Thus, a 2 molar solution of NaCl may be prepared by adding enough water to 116.92 (2×58.46) grams of NaCl so that the final volume is exactly one liter. The **molarity** (moles per liter) of this solution is 2 moles NaCl per liter or 2 M NaCl. A 2 M NaCl solution could also be prepared by adding enough water to 11.692 grams of NaCl to make 100 ml. (0.1 liter) of solution.

The concentration of a solution bears no relation to the amount of solution. If the concentration of a solution is designated as 2 M then every drop, every milliliter, every liter or even every barrel of that solution has the same concentration, 2 M.

The number of moles of a solute contained in a given amount of solution is never equal to the molarity of that solution unless the volume should happen to be exactly one liter. The number of moles of a solute contained in any solution is equal to the molarity multiplied by the volume of the solution expressed in liters. In one ml. of a 2 M NaCl solution there is present $.001 \times 2$ moles or .002 moles of NaCl. It is to be observed that a 2 M solution may also be defined as one which contains 2 *millimoles* per *milliliter* (a millimole is .001 mole and a milliliter is .001 liter).

$$\frac{.002 \text{ mole}}{.001 \text{ liter}} = \frac{2 \text{ moles}}{1 \text{ liter}} = 2 \, M$$

In this text the concentrations of solutions will always be expressed in terms of molarity.

Normal Solutions. The concentration of a solution is said to be 1 normal (1 N) when enough water is added to 1 gram-equivalent-weight * of the solute to make 1 liter of the solution. Concentrations expressed in terms of normality are very convenient in quantitative volumetric analysis, but use of normal rather than molar solutions offers no decided advantage in this course. We shall therefore not be concerned with this method for expressing concentration.

Conductance of Electricity by Solutions — Electrolytes and Non-Electrolytes. We shall compare the conductance of electricity by solutions of different substances. Such a comparison will allow us to divide practically all substances into two general classes, **electrolytes** and **non-electrolytes**. The conductance of any substance is the inverse of the resistance offered by the substance to the passage of the electric current, that is, $C = 1/R$, where C and R represent the conductance and resistance respectively. Conductance, like resistance, is determined by measuring the electric current passing through the substance when a definite voltage is applied between the two terminals of the containing cell. For a given voltage the amount of current is proportional to the conductance, that is, a solution having twice the conductance of another will allow twice as much current to pass through it for the same applied voltage.

In order to compare the conductances of solutions it is necessary that we consider the same number of equivalents of solute in each case. What we really wish to know is the *conductance per equivalent weight of solute.*

Consider a conductance cell of the type illustrated in Fig-

---

* The student is referred to any general chemistry text for a definition of this term.

ure 5. The cell itself is constructed of some non-conductor such as glass. The two electrodes A and B consist of metal strips which fit closely between the sides of the cell. The top is open. G is a current-measuring instrument such as an ammeter or a galvanometer and should be very sensitive if we wish to measure very small currents. For very rough measurements a light bulb may be used instead of the am-

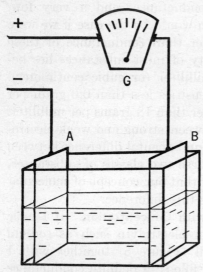

meter. If a conducting solution is placed in this box and a voltage applied to the electrodes, any current which passes from A to B must pass through the solution. If a sugar solution is placed in this cell together with any additional amount of water, the mixture shows no appreciable conductance. The same is true of solutions of alcohol, ether, glycerine and many similar substances. On the other hand, if sodium chloride in water is placed in this cell, the solution is a very good conductor of elec-

Figure 5. Conductance Cell and Measuring Instrument

tricity. Solutions of many solutes such as HCl, H_2SO_4, NaOH and K_2SO_4 show a high conductance, while only a relatively small number of compounds give solutions which are slightly conducting.

The great majority of solutions fall into one of two distinct classes, very good conductors and non-conductors. Substances the solutions of which are good conductors of electricity are called **electrolytes,** and substances that are non-conductors in solution, **non-electrolytes.** The difference in conductance shown by electrolytes and non-electrolytes is not merely a difference of degree. It is a *difference of kind*. If we were to classify all substances according to ability to

conduct an electric current, we should find a great number
which show practically no conductance; almost all the rest
show high conductance, with only a relatively few substances falling between these two classes. Were the difference between non-electrolytes and electrolytes one of degree
rather than one of kind, we should expect most substances
to show about the same conductance, with only a relatively
few displaying very high conductance, and a very few,
almost no conductance. Such would be the case if we were
to consider the density rather than conductance of these
same substances. The density of most substances lies between 2 and 5 grams per milliliter (or cubic centimeter).
Very few substances have densities less than 0.6 gram per
milliliter, and very few, greater than 18 grams per milliliter.

The difference of kind between strong and weak electrolytes suggests that there is a fundamental difference between
the molecular structures of these two classes of substances.
At a later time we shall show that our concept of molecular
structure adequately explains this difference.

Variation of Conductance with Concentration. If 1 mole
(gram formula weight) of an electrolyte such as sodium
chloride is placed in the cell (Figure 5) together with 1
liter of water (the cell is not filled), a definite conductance
will be observed. Upon the addition of more water, the
solution will be diluted but the same amount of sodium
chloride will remain between the plates. However, it is
observed that the conductance is increased. The fact that
the conductance increases with dilution may at first sight
seem to be an anomaly, since by dilution the concentration
decreases, but it must be borne in mind that we are not
considering the conductance of a solution with a fixed cross
section. As water is added to the cell the surface of the
electrode exposed to the solution increases, as does the cross
section of the conducting solution.

The conductance of an electrolyte increases with increasing dilution as shown in Figure 6. As the solution is diluted
the concentration decreases (from right to left along the

horizontal axis). After considering the next section on "The Lowering of the Freezing Point" we shall give an explanation of this phenomenon.

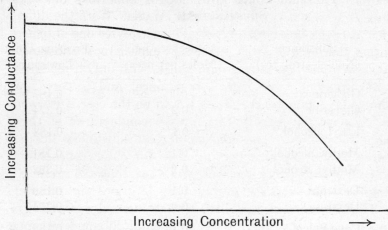

Figure 6. Change in Conductance with Concentration

The Lowering of the Freezing Point. The freezing point of water is lowered by the addition of a solute. The difference between electrolytes and non-electrolytes in this respect is well demonstrated in Table 2. The second column of the table gives the concentration of the solute in question in terms of moles or gram formula weights per liter of water, while the third column lists the freezing point lowering, i.e., freezing point of solution in degrees below 0° C.

We see that for non-electrolytes 0.1 mole of any substance dissolved in 1 liter of water lowers the freezing point about 0.186° C, and 0.2 mole per liter has twice this effect. It is to be observed that there is some variation in the effects of different solutes, but this variation is a relatively small one (methyl alcohol 0.181° C). The conclusion we can immediately draw is that the total number of moles per liter or the total number of molecules per liter of non-electrolytes is the principal determining factor in the lowering of the freezing point. The kind of molecule has little or no effect. If electrolytes behaved like non-electrolytes in solution, we

TABLE 2

Freezing Point Lowering of Solutions of Substances in Water

Substance (Non-electrolytes)	Concentration (Moles per liter)	Freezing Point Lowering
Glycerine	0.1	0.187
Glycerine	0.2	0.374
Ethyl alcohol	0.1	0.183
Methyl alcohol	0.1	0.181
Methyl alcohol	0.2	0.362
Dextrose	0.1	0.186
Dextrose	0.2	0.374
Cane Sugar	0.1	0.188
Hydrogen peroxide	0.1	0.184
Sugar 0.05 Glycerine 0.05	0.1	0.187
Average of a large number of non-electrolytes	0.1	0.186
(Electrolytes)		
HCl	0.1	0.352
KNO$_3$	0.1	0.331
KCl	0.1	0.345
NaCl	0.1	0.348
Na$_2$SO$_4$	0.1	0.434
CaCl$_2$	0.1	0.494
NiCl$_2$	0.1	0.538

should expect that their freezing point lowerings would be the same. More specifically, if sodium chloride in solution consisted of molecules, each of which contained one atom of sodium and one atom of chlorine, a gram formula weight would be the same as a mole and we should expect that the lowering of the freezing point would be the same as for non-electrolytes. Instead the lowering of the freezing point for HCl, KNO_3, KCl and NaCl is almost twice that for non-electrolytes; and for Na_2SO_4, $CaCl_2$ and $NiCl_2$ more than twice and almost three times that of non-electrolytes. Again we see a difference in kind between electrolytes and non-electrolytes.

Interpretation of the Foregoing Facts by the Theory of Ionization. Our problem is to interpret the fact that electrolytes give a greater lowering of the freezing point — almost two and sometimes three times as great as that of non-electrolytes. In a general way, we already know the answer — the theory of ionization — yet let us follow the logic of the argument to determine what the assumptions are and to judge the justification of any conclusions we may draw. In order to explain the fact that the lowering of the freezing point of some electrolytes like NaCl is almost twice that for non-electrolytes, we assume that the electrolyte is present in the solution as ions, not as molecules. If sodium chloride existed in solution as uncharged molecules of NaCl we should expect a lowering of the freezing point of $0.186°$ per 0.1 formula weight. Twice this lowering would mean twice as many particles, which effect could be explained only by the presence of sodium and chlorine particles existing separately in solution. Since a solution of sodium chloride is a good conductor we also assume that the particles are charged; one kind to be positively charged and one kind negatively charged.

In a general way the explanation seems to be a satisfactory one. However, we may ask why the lowering of the freezing point of sodium chloride and similar substances is not more nearly twice that of non-electrolytes. There are two possible ways of explaining this latter fact. Let us consider a 0.1 molal solution (0.1 formula weight per 1000 grams of water — refer to page 12) of sodium chloride as an example. For this solution the freezing point lowering is $0.348°$ C. If all the sodium chloride existed as Na^+ and Cl^- ions we would ex pect the freezing point lowering to be $2 \times 0.186°$ or $0.372°$ C, *if ions behaved exactly like neutral particles or molecules in solution.* If ions behaved like molecules in solution we can calculate that about 13% of the Na^+ and Cl^- ions are united in the form of uncharged NaCl molecules, i.e., 87% of all the sodium chloride in a 0.1 M solution is in the form of ions and 13% in the form of molecules.

How does this explanation apply to the experimental results of conductance? If the assumption that only part of the sodium chloride (87%) is in the form of ions is valid, then we should expect that at very great dilutions all or almost all of the sodium chloride would be in the ionic form, for at great dilutions the ions would be relatively far apart and would not have the same chance of combining with each other to form molecules. The molar or equivalent conductance would therefore increase with increasing dilution, as it does. If further we assume that ions move with the same velocity in dilute as in the more concentrated solutions, then the conductance of a 0.1 M sodium chloride solution should be 87% of that of an exceedingly dilute one. As a matter of fact the conductance is about 90% that of the very dilute solution. The agreement between experiment and prediction, in this case, is not perfect but good enough to have led chemists to this view, which they retained over thirty years. Today the idea of partial ionization of *strong* electrolytes is no longer considered tenable in spite of the reasonable agreement referred to above. Chemists now regard practically *all* the sodium chloride in 0.1 M solution to be present as ions, not to the extent of 87% or 90%, but *100% as ions.* How then are we to explain the fact that the lowering of the freezing point is not $2 \times 0.186°$ instead of $0.348°$ and how are we to explain the increased conductance of sodium chloride with increasing dilution?

Let us first get a picture of what we mean by the sodium ion or chloride ion in solution. The sodium ion is designated by the symbol Na^+ and from this it might be inferred that we believe that the sodium ion exists alone and unattached

to other molecules in the solution. Evidence from conductance experiments tells us, however, that the sodium ion
has several molecules of water quite firmly attached to it.
The number is somewhat variable and is dependent upon the
concentration of the sodium chloride and upon the temperature of the solution. From what we said previously regarding the polarity of water molecules we might expect such a
process to take place. We might expect that the negative
ends of the water molecules would be attached to the posi-

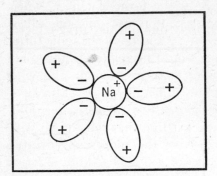

Figure 7. Concept of the Hydrated
Na⁺ Ion

tive sodium ion and form a
blanket around it. Such a
condition is illustrated in
Figure 7. The same con-
cept is held for the negative
chloride ion and in general
for all ions.

Let us now examine
closely the assumptions
made in drawing conclu-
sions regarding the partial
ionization of sodium chlo-
ride to determine, if possible, the weak point of the argument. Two assumptions were implicitly made: (1) that
charged particles (ions) behave like neutral molecules in
lowering the freezing point of water and (2) that ions under
the influence of an electric field move with the same velocity
in the dilute as in the more concentrated solutions. Contrary to the first assumption we might expect that ions
in solution with their greater attractions for the polar molecules of water would not behave exactly like neutral molecules. The second assumption does not seem reasonable,
since a positive ion will certainly be hindered in its movement
toward the negative electrode by the proximity of negative
ions. The negative ions will act as a "drag" upon the positive ions and vice versa, tending to retard them. For this
reason alone we should expect the conductance of concentrated solutions to be less than that of dilute solutions.

The concept of ionic conductance and the effect of the close proximity of oppositely charged ions is illustrated in Figure 8. The attractive force between positively and negatively charged particles tends to keep them near each other and to prevent the easy flow of these ions when they are placed between the two charged plates of a conductance cell. The nearer the particles are to each other (the more concentrated the solution), the greater is this hindrance to flow, or the greater the "drag-effect" becomes.

We can assume that the lowering of the conductance with increasing concentration is entirely due to this "drag-effect" and that the molecules are completely dissociated. Further evidence in support of the theory of complete dissociation is presented in Chapter III. Evidence which we cannot present here has further strengthened this view until it has become almost universally accepted by chemists. Therefore we shall consider most strong electrolytes to exist in solution entirely in the form of ions.

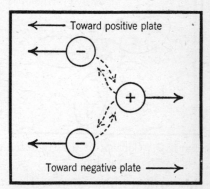

Figure 8. The Attractive Force between the Ions Prevents Easy Flow

Of all the common acids that we encounter in the laboratory, H_2SO_4, HNO_3 and HCl are 100% ionized (strong). All other common acids are partially ionized (weak). The hydroxides of the alkali and alkaline earth metals are strong bases. All salts are strong electrolytes with the exception of the halides of zinc, cadmium and mercury and a few of the salts of lead.

There are other arguments which support the theory of ionization, as it was first proposed by Arrhenius. These include the transfer of matter by electricity in solutions of electrolytes, Faraday's Law which was used to assign the number of charges on each ion, and the common color of the

same ion in solutions of different salts.   A consideration of
these phenomena may be found in almost any textbook of
general chemistry.

The Solubility of Electrolytes in Water. In considering
the solubility of electrolytes we must first regard the substances in solution to be in the form of ions and not mole-

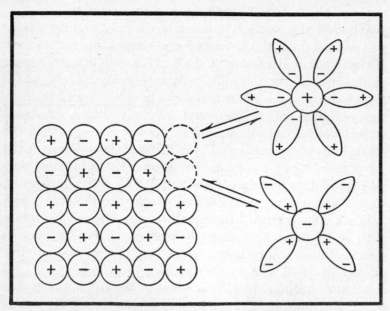

Figure 9.   Schematic View of the Process of Solution and
Crystallization of Sodium Chloride

cules.   Experiment supports the view that in the crystal
form the electrolyte also exists as positive and negative ions
regularly arranged with respect to each other.   The sodium
chloride crystal, for example, is built up of sodium ions and
chloride ions, alternately spaced in such a way that each
sodium ion is surrounded by six negative chloride ions and
each chloride ion by six positive sodium ions.   The difference in state between the ions in the crystal and those in
solution is the close regular packing in the crystal and the
hydration as well as random distribution of the ions in solution.   The process of solution of sodium chloride is given in

Figure 9. The positive sodium ions leave the crystal and become surrounded by the polar water molecules, and the same is true of the negative chloride ions. The same number of chloride ions as of sodium ions enters the solution but nowhere is it necessary to assume that the sodium and chloride ions leave the crystal as molecules. The same picture would apply to the reverse process, that of precipitation.

Whether any electrolyte is soluble or only slightly soluble will depend upon the nature of the competition for its ions. If the forces of attraction of the ions for each other are great in the crystal, the solubility will necessarily be less, but if the tendency of the water molecules to hold the ions is great, the solubility will be increased. To say that a substance is very soluble means, according to our concept, that the crystal forces are small and that the attractive forces of the water molecules for the ions are great. Hydrated ions may be regarded as having some similarity to water molecules, since they have water molecules attached to them.

Weak Electrolytes. Inasmuch as any strong electrolyte is to be regarded as completely ionized, its conductance in water solution will be equal to the sum of the conductances of its individual ions. For example, the conductance of a solution of sodium chloride is equal to the conductance due to the Na^+ ion plus the conductance due to the Cl^- ion. If in very dilute solution all ions were to move independently of each other and with the same velocity when subjected to the same conditions, it would follow that the equivalent conductance values of all electrolytes would be identical. Since the conductance values are not the same for all electrolytes of the same type we must conclude that some ions travel faster than others. Thus it might be expected that the light and small H^+ ion would travel faster than the heavy and large Cs^+ ion.

In very dilute solutions we might expect that the "drag-effect" would be inappreciably small and that, when subjected to the same electric field (same voltage per centimeter length of cell), each ion would move with a definite velocity which is independent of the nature of the ion with which it is associated. For example, the chloride ion would move with the same velocity in a dilute solution of potassium chloride as it would in a dilute solution of sodium chloride. In other words, the conductance contributed by the chloride ion is the same in both solutions.

However, in solutions of potassium chloride and sodium chloride the sodium ion would not travel with the same velocity as the potassium ion, nor would either of these ions necessarily travel with the same velocity as the negative chloride ion. At first sight it may be confusing to have a condition in which positive and negative ions travel with different velocities. One might argue that positive or negative ions would accumulate at one end of the conductance cell. It must be borne in mind that reactions take place at the electrodes which will offset any such accumulation and keep the number of positive and negative charges the same in all parts of the cell.

Let us assume that in dilute solution the ions are independent of each other in their current-carrying capacities, and follow the method of determining the conductance of nitric acid from the conductance values of solutions of sodium nitrate, sodium chloride, and hydrochloric acid. Let us imagine that we are using a cell such as that described on page 14 and that in all of the experiments we impose the same potential between the two electrodes. Under these conditions the current carried by any electrolyte is proportional to its conductance. We shall designate the current carried by one equivalent of any substance as L. Since sodium nitrate is completely ionized, the current carried by this substance is equal to the current carried by the sodium ion plus the current carried by the nitrate ion.

$$L(\text{NaNO}_3 \text{ soln.}) = L(\text{Na}^+) + L(\text{NO}_3^-) \qquad (2)$$
$$L(\text{HCl soln.}) \quad = L(\text{H}^+) \quad + L(\text{Cl}^-) \qquad (3)$$

By adding these two equations we obtain the conductance of a solution containing one equivalent each of sodium nitrate and of hydrochloric acid. The total conductance is the sum of the conductances of all four ions.

$L(\text{NaNO}_3 + \text{HCl soln.})$
$$= L(\text{Na}^+) + L(\text{H}^+) + L(\text{NO}_3^-) + L(\text{Cl}^-) \quad (4)$$

If we could remove the sodium and chloride ions from this solution, a solution of nitric acid would be left. However, it is not necessary to remove these ions to obtain the conductance of a solution containing H^+ and NO_3^- ions. Since the conductance of a solution of sodium chloride is

$$L(\text{NaCl soln.}) = L(\text{Na}^+) + L(\text{Cl}^-) \quad (5)$$

we need only subtract equation (5) from equation (4) to obtain the desired result, $L(\text{H}^+) + L(\text{NO}_3^-)$, which is equal to the conductance of a dilute solution of nitric acid. Making this calculation quantitatively, we find that the value so calculated for the conductance of a nitric acid solution agrees with that obtained experimentally. Thus we have evidence that our assumption regarding the independent movement or current-carrying capacity of the ions is a reasonably valid one when applied to dilute solutions.

In the same way we can calculate the conductance that a solution of acetic acid (HAc) would have if it were a strong electrolyte. This is the sum of the conductances of the hydrogen and acetate ions, which we can determine in the following manner:

$$L(\text{NaAc soln.}) = L(\text{Na}^+) + L(\text{Ac}^-) \quad (6)$$
$$L(\text{HCl soln.}) \ = L(\text{H}^+) \ + L(\text{Cl}^-) \quad (7)$$
$$L(\text{NaCl soln.}) = L(\text{Na}^+) + L(\text{Cl}^-) \quad (8)$$

Adding equations (6) and (7) and subtracting (8) we obtain

$$(6) + (7) - (8) = L(\text{H}^+) + L(\text{Ac}^-) \quad (9)$$

The value so calculated would be the conductance of a dilute acetic acid solution *if acetic acid were completely ionized.*

Comparing the value for the conductance of an acetic acid solution, as calculated above, with that determined experimentally for a 0.1 M solution, we find that the experimentally determined conductance is only about 1% of the value calculated. The value of the conductance of a 0.1 M sodium chloride solution is about 90% that for a very dilute solution. This fact we explained by the "drag-effect" due to the attractions of the positive and negative ions for each other. With acetic acid, however, the ratio of the conductance of a 0.1 M solution to that of a very dilute solution is of another order of magnitude (1%) and we cannot explain this in the same way. We must now assume that acetic acid exists in solution chiefly as acetic acid molecules and that only about 1% of these molecules is dissociated into hydrogen and acetate ions. There are quite a number of substances, particularly organic acids and bases, which are only partially ionized. Such substances are known as **weak electrolytes** and are intermediate between non-electrolytes and strong electrolytes. While such substances are not as numerous, by any means, as either the **strong electrolytes** (sodium chloride type) or as the non-electrolytes, they are nevertheless a very important class of substances with which we shall be very much concerned.*

The Use of Ionic Equations. If a solution of sodium hydroxide is neutralized by one of hydrochloric acid the resulting solution will be one of sodium chloride. The hydroxide ion, OH⁻, of the sodium hydroxide solution reacts with the hydrogen ion of the hydrochloric acid solution to produce water; no reaction takes place between the sodium and the chloride ions. If the equation we are to use to represent the change taking place in this reaction is to include only those substances which disappear and those which are

* The terms **strong** and **weak** must not be confused with **dilute** and **concentrated.** A strong electrolyte is completely or almost completely ionized in solution, while a weak electrolyte is ionized to only a small extent. A concentrated solution is one which contains a relatively large amount of solute per unit volume, regardless of whether the solute is strong, weak or a non-electrolyte. A dilute solution contains a relatively small amount of the solute.

formed we may express the above change by

$$H^+ + OH^- = H_2O \tag{10}$$

Brønsted: $H_3O^+ + OH^- = 2H_2O$ (11)

Some prefer to express this change as

$$HCl + NaOH = NaCl + H_2O \tag{12}$$

or if the substances involved are to be expressed as ions,

$$H^+ + Cl^- + Na^+ + OH^- = Na^+ + Cl^- + H_2O \tag{13}$$

In the last equation the ions Na^+ and Cl^- appear on both sides and may be cancelled to give equation (10), or if equation (13) were written in the Brønsted terminology the result, with cancellation, would be equation (11). It is true that this last equation does not give information as to what particular kind of solutions were used, for the neutralization of solutions of potassium hydroxide and nitric acid would be expressed by the same equation. On the other hand, the use of the simple equation (10) includes only those substances that enter into the reaction and gives the information that strong electrolytes are involved. *This equation also tells us that the substances involved are in solution.* If gaseous hydrogen chloride were to react with solid sodium hydroxide to give steam and solid sodium chloride, the equation for the reaction would be more properly expressed by (12). For these reasons we shall use ionic equations whenever ions are involved in the reactions.

In writing an equation for the neutralization of a solution of acetic acid (HAc) by a solution of sodium hydroxide, we write

$$HAc + OH^- = H_2O + Ac^- \tag{14}$$

Here we write acetic acid as HAc and not as H^+ for in this case most of the acetic acid in solution is in the form of molecules and not in the form of ions. It is the molecules of acetic acid which ultimately disappear in the reaction, so it is necessary to designate them as such and to include them in the equation.

Likewise, the formation of silver chloride by the addition of a solution of silver nitrate to one of sodium chloride is written

$$Ag^+ + Cl^- = AgCl(solid) \qquad (15)$$

In this reaction only the silver and chloride ions and the precipitated silver chloride are involved; the sodium and nitrate ions take no part in the reaction whatsoever; they contribute neither to the forward nor to the reverse reaction.

EXAMPLES OF PROBLEMS

Example 1.

How many grams of KBr will be needed to make 150 ml. of a 2 M solution?

1 mole (formula weight) KBr = 39.1 + 79.9 = 119.0 g.

2 moles KBr = 2 × 119.0 = 238.0 g.

1 liter of a 2 M KBr solution contains 238.0 g.

1 ml. of a 2 M KBr solution contains 0.238 g.

150 ml. contains 150 × 0.238 = 35.7 g.

Therefore, if enough water is added to 35.7 g. KBr to make 150 ml. a 2 M solution will be obtained.

Example 2.

It is desired to make a 0.1 M solution by adding water to 5 g. of $AgNO_3$. What must be the final volume of the solution after all the water is added?

1 mole $AgNO_3$ = 107.9 + 14.0 + 3 × 16 = 169.9 g.

A 0.1 M $AgNO_3$ solution contains 16.99 g. per liter or .01699 g. per ml.

5 g. $AgNO_3$ furnishes enough for $\dfrac{5}{.01699}$ or 294 ml.

Example 3.

How many ml. of water must be added to 5 ml. of 12 M HCl solution to make a 3 M HCl solution?

NOTE: *In all dilution problems we shall assume that the final volume is equal to the volume of the initial solution plus the volume of the water added; i.e., that the volume occupied by all molecules or ions is the same in solutions of all concentrations.*

In 1 ml. of a 3 M solution there are $\frac{3}{12}$ or $\frac{1}{4}$ as many molecules as there are in 1 ml. of a 12 M solution. Therefore, enough water must be added to the 12 M solution to make its final volume 4 times as great as it was originally. In this problem the final volume must be 4×5 ml. or 20 ml. Therefore 15 ml. of water must be added. In brief, the final volume must be 5×12 ml.

The amount of water added is $5 \times \dfrac{12-3}{3} = 15$ ml. In general, the volume of water added equals the *initial volume of solution* multiplied by $\dfrac{C_2 - C_1}{C_1}$ where C_2 is the larger concentration and C_1 the smaller.

Example 4.

How many ml. of a 2 M HCl solution are necessary to neutralize 3 ml. of a 0.5 M NaOH solution?

1 mole HCl neutralizes 1 mole NaOH.

The same number of moles of HCl are required as there are moles of NaOH in 3 ml. of a 0.5 M NaOH solution.

If the HCl solution were 0.5 M, instead of 2 M, equal volumes of each would be required. But the HCl is 2 M or 4 times as concentrated as the NaOH; therefore less is required. Specifically, $\frac{1}{4}$ as much would be required as would be the case if the HCl were 0.5 M.

Number of ml. of HCl required $= 3 \times \dfrac{0.5}{2} = 0.75$ ml.

Example 5.

How many ml. of 6 M H_2SO_4 would be required to neutralize 100 ml. of 3 M NaOH?

Since the H_2SO_4 contains 2 replaceable H atoms (H^+ ions) and NaOH contains only 1 replaceable OH radical (OH^- ion), one-half as many moles H_2SO_4 are required as the number of moles of NaOH contained in 100 ml. of 3 M NaOH.

If the H_2SO_4 were 1.5 M, instead of 6 M, 100 ml. would be required, but with 6 M H_2SO_4 the amount required would be $100 \times \dfrac{1.5}{6} = 25$ ml.

Example 6.

What is the molarity of a H_2SO_4 solution which contains 33.33% H_2SO_4 by weight and which has a density of 1.25?

One liter of the solution weighs 1000×1.25 or 1250 g.

The number of grams of H_2SO_4 in 1 liter is 0.3333×1250 or 417 g.

One mole of H_2SO_4 is 98.1 g. The number of moles in 1 liter is $\frac{417}{98.1} = 4.25$ moles per liter. The solution is therefore 4.25 M.

QUESTIONS AND PROBLEMS

1. What is the distinction between a glass and a crystalline solid?

2. Account for the fact that glycerine, when cooled to a sufficiently low temperature, in some cases solidifies to form a glass, and in other cases, to form a crystalline solid.

3. What is the dielectric constant of any given substance?

4. How does a polar molecule differ from a non-polar one?

5. Taking into account the thermal agitation of molecules, explain why the dielectric constant for a given substance is lower the higher the temperature of the substance.

6. Does a molecule of solid sodium chloride consist of one ion of sodium and one of chlorine? Explain.

7. Explain why two liquids, one of which consists of polar molecules and one of non-polar molecules, are immiscible in each other.

8. What is the difference between an electrolyte and a non-electrolyte?

9. By what reasoning can we come to the conclusion that there is a sharp difference between electrolytes and non-electrolytes (e.g., a difference of kind)?

10. Is the equivalent conductance (conductance of 1 gram formula weight) of sodium chloride in solution increased or decreased if the solution is diluted with water?

11. What is the average lowering of the freezing point of water if 0.1 mole per liter of a non-electrolyte is added to it?

12. What would be the freezing point of a solution which contains .05 mole of sugar, .05 mole of glycerine and .05 mole of alcohol, all in 1 liter of the same solution?

13. Explain why a dilute solution of sodium chloride has a greater conductance (per formula weight of NaCl) than does a more concentrated solution.

14. Is it necessarily true that ions in solution will behave like neutral molecules in their effect on the lowering of the freezing point?

15. Is a sodium chloride solution regarded as containing both sodium chloride molecules and the ions Na^+ and Cl^-? Explain.

16. What is the distinction between a strong acid and a concentrated one? Name three strong acids.

17. Give a schematic picture of the process taking place when solid sodium chloride dissolves in water.

18. Give an example of a weak electrolyte.

19. The equivalent conductance of a .01 molar solution of $NaNO_3$ at 25° C is 99 reciprocal ohms; that for a .01 molar solution of HCl, 391 reciprocal ohms; and for a .01 molar solution of NaCl it is 107 reciprocal ohms. Calculate the equivalent conductance of a .01 molar solution of HNO_3 and compare with the experimental value of 384 reciprocal ohms.

20. What is the molarity of a solution which contains 5 g. HCl in 100 ml. of solution?

21. How many moles of NaOH are contained in 200 ml. of a 0.5 M solution?

22. How many grams of H_2SO_4 are there in 40 ml. of a 0.1 M H_2SO_4 solution? ($H = 1$, $S = 32$, $O = 16$)

23. If 27 ml. of water is added to 35 ml. of a 0.1 M solution of any substance, what is the molarity of the final solution?

24. (a) How many moles are 5.85 g. of NaCl? (Use 23.0 as the atomic weight of sodium and 35.5 as the atomic weight of chlorine.)

(b) If this amount of NaCl is dissolved to make one liter of solution, what is the molarity of the solution?

(c) If this amount of NaCl is dissolved to make 500 ml. of solution, what is its molarity?

25. How many grams of solute are contained in each of the following solutions?

(a) 250 ml. of 0.1 M $MnCl_2$ solution
(b) 500 ml. of 5 M H_2SO_4 solution
(c) 25 ml. of 2 M Na_2CO_3 solution
(d) 12 ml. of 0.1 M $AgNO_3$ solution
(e) 125 ml. of 0.5 M $BaCl_2$ solution

(Assume the solute to have the formula indicated in each problem, i.e., unhydrated. See inside front cover for atomic weights — use only first figure beyond decimal point.)

26. If in each of the following cases it is desired to make a 0.1 M solution, what must be the final volume of the solution after the addition of water?

(a) 10 g. NaCl, (b) 20 g. $AgNO_3$, (c) 10 g. $HgCl_2$, (d) 10 g. $Na_2SO_4 \cdot 10H_2O$, (e) 1 g. $CuSO_4 \cdot 5H_2O$

27. How many ml. of water must be added to each of the following solutions to give the desired concentration?

(a) 10 ml. 6 M HCl to give a 2 M solution
(b) 25 ml. 2 M H_2SO_4 to give a 0.1 M solution
(c) 6 ml. 0.1 M $AgNO_3$ to give a .01 M solution
(d) 35 ml. 1.5 M H_2SO_4 to give a 0.3 M solution
(e) 2 ml. 0.3 M NaCl to give a 0.25 M solution

28. How many ml. of 0.1 M $AgNO_3$ solution and how many ml. of water must be mixed to give 250 ml. of .03 M $AgNO_3$ solution?

29. How many ml. of 0.1 M HCl solution is required to neutralize 25 ml. of 0.3 M NaOH solution?

30. How many ml. of 0.1 M H_2SO_4 solution is required to neutralize 25 ml. of a 0.3 M KOH solution?

31. How many ml. of a 1.5 M HCl solution is required to neutralize 75 ml. of a 0.2 M NaOH solution?

32. How many ml. of a 0.1 M HNO_3 solution is necessary to neutralize 15 drops of a 1 M NaOH solution? (Assume that 20 drops equals 1 ml.)

33. What is the molarity of each of the following solutions?

(a) 93.1% H_2SO_4 by weight (Density is 1.835)
(b) 32.3% HNO_3 by weight (Density is 1.200)
(c) 40.0% HCl by weight (Density is 1.200)
(d) 16.0% NaOH by weight (Density is 1.180)

The following review problems cover material not treated in this text. If necessary the student should refer to any general chemistry text for help.

34. A flask is filled with NH_3 gas at 76 cm. pressure and at 25° C. After a catalyst has been placed in the flask it is sealed.

The flask is then heated and the NH_3 is completely converted into H_2 and N_2 in accordance with the equation

$$2NH_3 = 3H_2 + N_2$$

What is the total pressure of the mixed gases after the flask has again been cooled to 25° C?

35. What per cent of lead is there in each of the following oxides: (a) PbO, (b) PbO_2, (c) PbO_3, and (d) Pb_3O_4?

36. Ten grams of $CuSO_4 \cdot 5H_2O$ is heated to drive off the water of crystallization. After dehydration what is the weight of the anhydrous $CuSO_4$?

37. One hundred grams of iron combine with 30.1 liters of oxygen, measured at standard conditions, to form a solid oxide. What is the formula of the oxide?

38. Lead oxide decomposes to form oxygen in accordance with the following equation

$$2PbO_2 = 2PbO + O_2$$

How many grams of PbO_2 are necessary to give 22.4 liters of O_2, measured at standard conditions?

39. How many grams of oxygen will combine with 10 g. of magnesium to form MgO?

40. Assuming that a certain iron ore were pure Fe_2O_3 calculate the maximum number of pounds of iron that could be obtained from one ton of this ore.

41. 1.000 g. of copper is placed in a crucible covered with sulfur and heated out of contact with air. A reaction takes place between the copper and the sulfur. After the reaction is complete the excess sulfur is burned off as SO_2. The residue in the crucible now weighs 1.253 g. How many atoms of copper combine with one atom of sulfur? What is the formula for the sulfide of copper?

42. An oxide of chromium contains 68.4% chromium and 31.6% oxygen. What is its formula?

43. The chloride of a certain metal contains 64.1% of chlorine. What is the equivalent weight of the metal?

44. A 68.0 weight per cent solution of sulfuric acid has a specific gravity of 1.587. What is the molarity of this solution?

45. What volume of the solution in question 44 would be necessary to make 1 liter of a 0.1 M solution?

46. What volume of 0.1 M HCl would be necessary to precipitate all the silver from a solution containing 1.00 g. of $AgNO_3$? (Assume that all the silver in solution will be precipitated as AgCl.)

47. Beginning with 0.1 M solutions of $AgNO_3$, $Pb(NO_3)_2$ and $Hg_2(NO_3)_2$, how many ml. of each must be used to make 1 liter of a solution which is .02 M with respect to each of the ions, Ag^+, Pb^{++} and Hg_2^{++}?

CHAPTER II

The Structure of Atoms and Molecules

The concepts of polarity and of electrolytes and non-electrolytes, presented in the last chapter, as well as the concepts of valence and the stability of molecules can be pictured in greater detail and explained by considerations of the electronic structures of atoms and molecules.

To help us visualize atoms and molecules in our mind's eye and thus help us understand the phenomena of chemistry, we shall, in this chapter, devote our attention to this experimentally verified and accepted theory.

General Concepts. All the experiments of chemistry and physics are consistent with the view that atoms are built up of positively charged nuclei surrounded by negative electrons. The nucleus of the atom possesses a charge which is equal in magnitude to the total charge of all the electrons surrounding the nucleus. This charge is known as the **atomic number** of the atom.

To account for the classification of the elements into the periodic system it is assumed that (1) the electrons in the atom are arranged in concentric shells; (2) the number of electrons in each shell is definitely limited; (3) the inner shells of an atom are filled while the outermost shell, except in the case of the rare gases, is not filled; and (4), the chemical properties of the atom depend upon the number of electrons in the outermost shell.

The charge on the nucleus, hence the number of electrons surrounding it, increases by one unit in passing from one element to the next element of higher atomic weight. When the number of electrons in the outermost shell becomes filled, a new shell is begun. The first or innermost shell requires two electrons to fill it. The next outer shell requires eight electrons and the other shells still more. The electrons of the filled shells are so tightly bound that they cannot be loosened sufficiently to form chemical bonds. Atoms are

34

attached to each other to form molecules through transfer of electrons from one atom to another, or through sharing of common electrons by two atoms. Since only the electrons of the outermost shell undergo such transfer or sharing and thus account for the chemical properties of the atom, our attention shall be largely confined to these electrons.

The Inert Gas Structures. As we all know, the inert gases do not form any compounds — a fact which was of great significance to the chemists and physicists who first formulated their ideas of atomic structure. Evidently there is something about their structures that makes them particularly stable; the stability of their electronic structures cannot be enhanced through combination with other atoms as is the case with other elements. The distributions of electrons in the various shells about the nuclei of these elements are given in Table 3.

TABLE 3

ELECTRONIC STRUCTURES OF INERT GASES

Atomic Number	Element	Number of Electrons in Shell					
		K	L	M	N	O	P
2	Helium	2					
10	Neon	2	8				
18	Argon	2	8	8			
36	Krypton	2	8	18	8		
54	Xenon	2	8	18	18	8	
86	Radon	2	8	18	32	18	8

(*The designations* K, L, M, *etc., are arbitrary.*)

The number of electrons in each shell from the nucleus outward for any given atom is read horizontally. Thus the innermost shell (K shell) of radon contains 2 electrons, the next shell (L shell) 8 electrons, then 18, 32, 18 and finally 8. Note particularly that (1) with the exception of helium, each of the outermost shells of all these atoms contains 8 electrons; (2) each of these atoms has two electrons in the K shell and 8 in the L shell; and (3) the stable filled shells contain 2, 8, 18 or 32 electrons.

The Structures of Group I. The main group I of the periodic table (see back cover) consists of H, Li, Na, K, Rb, Cs and 87 (sometimes referred to as virginium). We shall consider the structures of these atoms and note the difference between these and the structures of the inert gases.

TABLE 4

ELECTRONIC STRUCTURES OF GROUP I

Atomic Number	Element	Number of Electrons in Shell						
		K	L	M	N	O	P	Q
1	Hydrogen	1						
3	Lithium	2	1					
11	Sodium	2	8	1				
19	Potassium	2	8	8	1			
37	Rubidium	2	8	18	8	1		
55	Caesium	2	8	18	18	8	1	
87	(Virginium)	2	8	18	32	18	8	1

Neglecting hydrogen, which we shall consider later, we see that, except for the single electron in the outermost shell, the structures are the same as those for the inert gases. Were these atoms to lose their outermost electrons through chemical reaction then they would revert to the stable structure of the inert gases. That is just what they do when they react to form the ions Li^+, Na^+, K^+ etc. Nor would we expect any of them to lose another electron from the next shell to form doubly charged ions, since the inert gases do not do so.

The Electronic Structures of Group VII. Let us contrast the electronic structures of the electro-positive elements in

Group I with those of the electro-negative elements of Group VII.

TABLE 5

ELECTRONIC STRUCTURES OF GROUP VII

Atomic Number	Element	Number of Electrons in Shells					
		K	L	M	N	O	P
9	Fluorine	2	7				
17	Chlorine	2	8	7			
35	Bromine	2	8	18	7		
53	Iodine	2	8	18	18	7	
85	( )	2	8	18	32	18	7

We note that each of these atoms has 7 electrons in the outermost shell. If each of them should acquire one electron to form a negative ion (for example, Cl⁻ ion), the structures of these negative ions would correspond to the stable inert gas structures as given in Table 3. It is well known, of course, that each of these elements forms singly charged negative ions. The positive elements lose electrons and the negative elements acquire electrons to form the stable inert gas structures.

Electronic Structures of the Second Series. As we proceed along any horizontal row (series) of the main group elements, in the periodic table, the core of the atoms considered remain the same and only the number of electrons in the outer shell changes. The core of the atom is to be distinguished from the nucleus in that it contains the nucleus and all the electrons except those in the outermost shell. The electronic structures for the second series is given in Table 6.

We should expect those elements on the extreme left side of this table (except Ne) to have a tendency to lose electrons, to revert to the neon structure, thus forming positive

TABLE 6

ELECTRONIC STRUCTURES OF THE SECOND SERIES

Element and Atomic Number	Ne 10	Na 11	Mg 12	Al 13	Si 14	P 15	S 16	Cl 17
K shell	2	2	2	2	2	2	2	2
M shell	8	8	8	8	8	8	8	8
N shell	0	1	2	3	4	5	6	7

ions; and those elements on the right to acquire electrons, forming negative ions or negative valences and thus acquiring the stable krypton structure. The chemical facts are in accord with these expectations.

Since it is only the outermost electrons that are of significance from a chemical standpoint, it has become customary to represent the electronic structure of an atom by its symbol surrounded by as many dots as there are valence or outside electrons. In such a case the symbol alone represents the core of the atom. Thus, Na represents the sodium atom, and :Cl· the chlorine atom.

Compound Formation Caused by the Transfer of Electrons. When equal numbers of sodium and chlorine atoms combine to form sodium chloride, a typical electrolyte, the one outermost electron of each sodium atom is taken up by the chlorine atom, thus forming in the crystal positively charged sodium ions and negatively charged chloride ions. A crystal of sodium chloride then consists, not of sodium and chlorine atoms, but of sodium and chloride ions. The electronic structures of these ions are shown in Figure 10. Note in Figure 10 that each ion has an outermost shell of eight

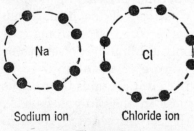

Sodium ion   Chloride ion

Figure 10

electrons complete in itself. Likewise, when sulfur $\overset{..}{\underset{.}{S}}:$ combines with sodium $\overset{.}{N}a$ we should expect the compound Na_2S to be formed, for the sulfur atom requires two electrons to form the stable group of eight electrons, and each sodium atom can contribute only one of these.

We find that those compounds formed by the transfer of electrons (as contrasted with the sharing of electrons) are strong electrolytes.

The Sharing of Electrons and the Covalent Bond. Carbon tetrachloride, a non-electrolyte, consists of a carbon atom surrounded by four chlorine atoms. The carbon atom by itself has four electrons in the outermost shell. These can supply the vacancies in the outermost shells of the chlorine atoms in carbon tetrachloride, one electron for each chlorine. With the extra electron furnished by the carbon atom, each chlorine atom will have a completed group of eight electrons as its outermost shell. But the carbon atom also must have eight electrons surrounding it, so two electrons must be shared by it and by each chlorine atom. That is, the carbon atom contributes four electrons and each chlorine atom one of its seven electrons to make a total of eight electrons about the carbon. All of these electrons then are shared between the carbon and the chlorine. This condition is illustrated in Figure 11a.

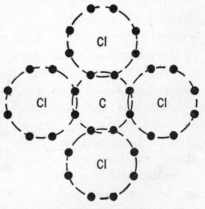

Figure 11a. Electronic Structure of Carbon Tetrachloride

The electronic structure of methane, another non-electrolyte, is shown in Figure 11b. In this case each hydrogen atom supplies one electron and the carbon four electrons. These electrons are shared by both the hydrogen and carbon. There are only two electrons for each hydrogen atom but this is also a rare gas structure, that of helium.

Iodine chloride is a compound of iodine and chlorine having the formula ICl. Both the chlorine and the iodine

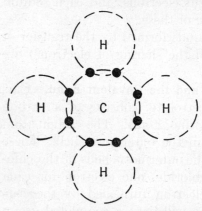

atoms have seven electrons in the outermost shell, and to produce an electronic structure for which each atom has eight electrons surrounding it, it is necessary that two electrons be shared by the two atoms in question. The structure of this compound is given in Figure 12a.

Figure 11b. Electronic Structure of Methane

By referring to both Figures 10 and 12a, the difference between electrolytes and non-electrolytes becomes apparent. Each atom of an electrolyte has a group of eight electrons about it which has been completed without the necessity of sharing any of these electrons with any other atom. The atoms of non-electrolytes are bound together by shared electrons. When electrolytes dissolve in water the ions can separate and still retain the group of eight about each ion. The atoms of non-electrolytes are held together so strongly by the shared electrons that they cannot easily exist as separate ions. If iodine chloride were to dissociate

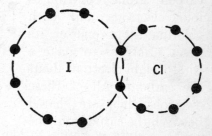

Figure 12a. Electronic Structure of Iodine Chloride

in solution to produce one positive and one negative ion it would be necessary for the positive ion to have but six electrons about it. Such a condition is not necessary for the production of Na^+ and Cl^- ions. Iodine chloride, since it is a compound produced by the sharing of electrons, is not an electrolyte.

Sodium sulfate is an electrolyte which exists in solution as sodium ions, Na^+, and sulfate ions, SO_4^{--}. The sulfate ion does not dissociate into smaller fragments for it is held together by shared electrons. Its structure is shown in Figure 12b. The sulfate ion, however, does not require the sharing of two of its elec-

trons with each sodium particle and therefore it can
exist by itself in solution as
an ion. The sulfur and oxygen atoms belong to the
sixth group of the periodic
system and therefore each
furnishes to the whole structure six valence or outside
electrons. These five atoms
then furnish thirty electrons
but thirty-two are necessary
for all the groups of eight
shown in Figure 12b. The

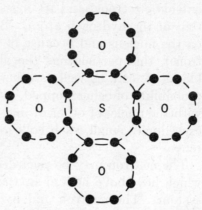

Figure 12b. Electronic Structure of the Sulfate Ion (Dotted Circles Indicate Completed Shells)

two additional electrons are furnished by the atoms with which this radical is associated in the particular compound in question; for example, the two sodium atoms supply these in the compound Na_2SO_4, thus forming two sodium ions, and the two additional electrons on the sulfate ion produce a charge of -2. The sulfate ion is to be regarded as a unit with completed electronic structure. The oxygen atoms are held to the sulfur atom by shared electrons. This shared electron structure accounts for the stability of the sulfate ion; there is little tendency for the oxygen atoms to break away from the sulfur atoms. If this process were to take place, the groups of eight electrons shown in Figure 12b would be broken up.

The difference between electrolytes and non-electrolytes lies in the difference between the electronic structures of these two types of compounds; electrolytes involve the transfer of electrons and non-electrolytes the sharing of electrons, to form the stable inert gas structures.

The Neutron — Hydrogen Atoms in Combination Form both Neutron and Helium-like Structures. The neutron is one of the fundamental atomic building blocks of nature. It consists merely of a nucleus with zero charge and no outside electrons, and its mass is very nearly the same as that of the hydrogen atom. Because of the lack of charge on the nucleus and because of its small size (no outer electrons), this particle has the ability to pass through thick blocks of lead, as well as other substances, with very little probability of being stopped. It is only stopped by collisions with the nuclei of other atoms, and since the nuclei are also exceedingly small, such collisions are of improbable occurrence.

The neutron may be regarded as an atom of an *inert gas* which lies above helium in the zero group of the periodic system. The neutron and hydrogen together then constitute the first series of the periodic system. With this concept, the first three series of the periodic system are

n	H						
He	Li	Be	B	C	N	O	F
Ne	Na	Mg	Al	Si	P	S	Cl

By sharing two electrons with another atom, the hydrogen atom shows its tendency to form the helium-like structure. In the compound LiH, lithium hydride, the hydrogen atom displays this tendency in a more marked fashion, for this compound in the molten state is in the form of Li^+ and H^- ions, as may easily be shown by electrolysis.

When the hydrogen atom shows its tendency to revert to the neutron-like structure (no outside electrons), it forms a hydrogen ion.

In some combinations, such as methane, hydrogen shares electrons with the carbon atom. In acetic acid three of the hydrogen atoms are held to a carbon atom by electron sharing; the hydrogen is in the helium-like state. The hydrogen atom attached to one of the oxygen atoms behaves as though it shows the tendency to form both the helium-like and the neutron-like structure, for only part of

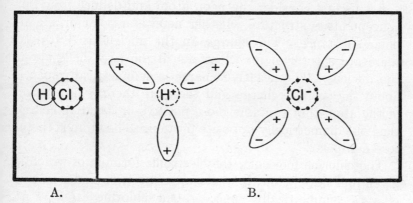

A.   B.

Figure 13

A. Hydrogen chloride molecules in the liquid state. Hydrogen takes helium-like structure.	B. Hydrogen chloride in solution. Hydrogen displays neutron-like structure.

these hydrogen atoms bound to oxygen in the acid molecule form H^+ ions by dissociation.

Liquid hydrogen chloride ($B.P. - 85°$ C) is not a good conductor of electricity. In this form it is not ionized as H^+ and Cl^- ions. The hydrogen and chlorine atoms are to be regarded as being attached to each other by electron sharing. When the molecules of hydrogen chloride are placed in water, however, the attraction of the water molecules for both the H^+ and Cl^- ions changes this tendency on the part of the hydrogen atoms, and they all revert to the neutron structure.

For the purpose of explaining this dual behavior of hydrogen, the neutron is regarded as a rare gas atom.

Explanation of the Polarity of Molecules. In discussing polar molecules in a previous section in this chapter, no insight was given as to the reason for the differences between the polarities of various kinds of molecules. Our concept and theory regarding electronic structure offer an explanation of this phenomenon. To understand this problem we must bear in mind that the seat of the positive charge of an atom lies in the nucleus, while the electrons about the nucleus constitute the negative charge.

Let us first consider the neon atom and deduce from our concept of its structure whether neon is a polar or a non-polar substance. The charge on the nucleus is + 10 and there are a total of ten electrons in the two shells about the nucleus. The negative charge is symmetrically spaced about the positive charge and therefore there is no portion of the atom that contains more positive or negative charge than the diametrically opposite portion. The atom is therefore non-polar.

The chlorine molecule, the electronic formula of which is given four lines below, is made up of positive and negative charges symmetrically spaced. One chlorine atom is no more positively charged than the other. This substance is likewise non-polar.

$$: \overset{\cdot\cdot}{\underset{\cdot\cdot}{Cl}} : \overset{\cdot\cdot}{\underset{\cdot\cdot}{Cl}} :$$

Chlorine Molecule

However, suppose one chlorine atom of the chlorine molecule is replaced by one iodine atom, we then have the molecule ICl, iodine monochloride. In this case the chlorine atom has a greater attraction for electrons than does the iodine atom and consequently a slightly greater negative charge exists about the chlorine than about the iodine atom. One end of the molecule is therefore slightly more negatively charged than the other and the molecule is slightly polar. The torque or turning effect of this molecule in an electric field would be equivalent to a positive and negative charge separated by only a small distance, and pictorially or schematically we may represent the polarity by a positive and negative charge rather close to each other, as shown in the following figure.

$$\boxed{\quad + \; - \quad}$$

Sodium chloride, as we have said, does not form molecules consisting of one atom or ion of chlorine and one of sodium either in the solid state or in solution. In the gaseous state, however, the sodium chloride molecule does consist of one particle of chlorine and one of sodium. As previously stated, the sodium atom has a tendency to give up one electron and the chlorine atom displays a tendency to acquire an electron. Therefore in the gaseous NaCl molecule we should expect that portion of the molecule occupied by the sodium to be positively charged and that portion occupied by the chlorine atom to be negatively charged. The molecule should therefore be polar with the positive and negative charges separated to a greater extent than in the ICl molecule. Schematically we might represent such a polar molecule by

$$\boxed{\quad + \quad - \quad}$$

A relatively large effective distance exists between the charges.

The water molecule is a highly polar one. The polarity on the part of this molecule gives us some insight into its structure. If the water molecule consisted of two hydrogen atoms and an oxygen atom all arranged in a straight line, such as

$$H : \overset{\cdot\cdot}{\underset{\cdot\cdot}{O}} : H$$

it should display no polarity, for all positive and negative charges would be symmetrically distributed about the oxygen atom. Since the water molecule is polar, we can conclude that the above symmetrical structure is impossible. Rather, the structure of this molecule is more probably that represented by the formula given in Figure 14. Since the oxygen atom tends to hold electrons more tightly than the hydrogen atoms, that portion of the molecule containing the oxygen atom would be more negatively charged than that containing the two hydrogen atoms.

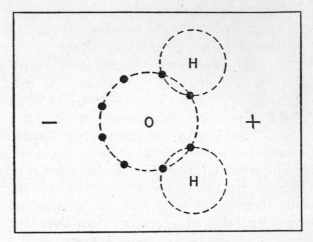

Figure 14. Water Molecule

In general, if one atom in a molecule has a greater tendency to hold electrons than any of the others, the molecule will tend to be polar unless it is symmetrical. In CCl_4, for example, the chlorine atoms are negatively charged with respect to the carbon atom but the four chlorine atoms are symmetrically placed around the carbon atom and no polarity results. Chloroform, $CHCl_3$, on the other hand, does display polarity because of lack of symmetry.

The Hydrogen Ion in Water Solution — The Hydronium Ion. The hydrogen ion or proton is unique among positive ions in that it has no valence electrons and like the neutron is very small. Like other ions it is hydrated in solution, i.e., surrounded by polarized water molecules, but because of its small size and because the water molecule also contains protons, it is assumed that for the most part the hydrogen ion does not exist in the uncombined form in water solution. Through a regular chemical binding (i.e., an electron pair) the proton may attach itself to a water molecule to form H_3O^+. This singly hydrated hydrogen ion is known as the **hydronium** ion. This ion behaves like any other positive ion in that it is also to be regarded as one which is surrounded by polarized water molecules.

The hydronium ion is the analog of the well-known ammonium ion. Liquid ammonia, NH_3, has many properties common to water. Like the water molecule the ammonia molecule is polarized, and like water ammonia dissolves many salts to form conducting solutions. If a pure acid is added to liquid ammonia, the NH_4^+ ion is produced. A typical reaction is

$$NH_3 + HNO_3 = NH_4^+ + NO_3^- \qquad (1)$$

By analogy we may argue that the proton in solution is not H^+ but H_3O^+. The addition of a pure acid to water would give the analogous reaction

$$H_2O + HNO_3 = H_3O^+ + NO_3^- \qquad (2)$$

The electronic structures of both the ammonium ion and the postulated hydronium ion are given in Figures 15 and 16 respectively. In the structure for the hydronium ion it is apparent that all three hydrogen atoms (or ions) are to be regarded as being alike, and that any one of the three can be removed. It should be pointed out, however, that these three hydrogen atoms are not in the same condition as are the two hydrogen atoms in the water molecule. The removal of one hydrogen ion from the hydronium ion re-

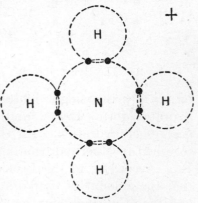

Figure 15. The Ammonium Ion

sults in the return of the two remaining hydrogens to their former condition. For example, if metallic zinc is placed into a solution containing hydronium ion (HCl solution), only one of the three protons is liberated as hydrogen gas. By the removal of one of these water is left, which we know does not react with metallic zinc.

With this concept the process of neutralization becomes

one of competition between the water molecule and the OH⁻ ion for the proton. The OH⁻ ion has the greater affinity for the proton and therefore robs the H_3O^+ ion of it. The reaction for neutralization is

$$H_3O^+ + OH^- = 2H_2O \tag{3}$$

Both the hydronium and hydroxide ions are hydrated in solution but this excess hydration is not represented in their formulae.

We may regard the reactions involving the hydrogen ion from two points of view: (1) the *transfer* of protons from water molecules to other proton acceptors, and (2) the *addition* of hydrogen ions (protons) to acceptors (such as OH⁻ ion, Ac⁻ ion, etc.). The latter viewpoint is the one which has been accepted for many years. It recognizes that the proton is hydrated and in solution may exist in the non-hydrated form, H^+, the singly hydrated form, H_3O^+, the doubly hydrated form, $H_5O_2^+$, and possibly in forms of higher degrees of hydration. All these forms have been lumped together as "the hydrogen ion," having the simple symbol H^+. According to the Brønsted * viewpoint it is assumed that the amount of unhydrated H^+ ion is extremely small and that the singly hydrated form, H_3O^+, is the principal species present in any water solution.

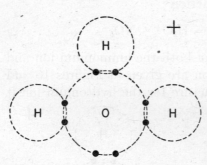

Figure 16.   The Hydronium Ion

Throughout this text we shall continue to use the simplified concept and to indicate the hydrogen ion in solution merely by the symbol H^+, except in those places where the

---

* Johannes Nicolaus Brønsted (1879–   ), a Danish physical chemist, Director of the Physico-Chemical Institute at Copenhagen, introduced new definitions and a new concept of acids and bases. These definitions will be developed at the appropriate places in the following chapters.

material in question is re-interpreted in terms of these newer definitions. As we shall see, this concept has some distinct advantages, but we shall retain the older definitions inasmuch as they have been used in the development of almost the whole of modern chemistry. As this course progresses we shall find it profitable to compare these two points of view.

The Sub-groups. In our previous discussion of electronic structure we have considered only the elements of the main groups of the periodic system. The electronic structures of these elements are all characterized by their close relationship to the structures of the inert gases. The sub-groups of the periodic system have structures which are not closely related to those of the inert gases, and this difference between the structures of the main and sub-groups accounts for the differences in their properties. To illustrate, let us consider sub-group one, the elements of which are Cu, Ag and Au. Like the elements of the main group, Li, Na etc., these elements display a valence of + 1, but there the similarity stops. The metals of the main group are very reactive. Those of the sub-group are, on the contrary, inactive; they display more than one valence; and they readily form complex ions. The electronic structures for these elements are given in Table 7.

TABLE 7

ELECTRONIC STRUCTURES OF SUB-GROUP I

Atomic Number	Element	Number of Electrons in Shell					
		K	L	M	N	O	P
29	Copper	2	8	18	1		
47	Silver	2	8	18	18	1	
79	Gold	2	8	18	32	18	1

A comparison of Table 7 with Table 4 shows that the core of the main group elements is that of a rare gas and the core of those in the sub-group is not.   The shell next to the valence shell in the sub-group elements contains 18 instead of 8 electrons and the electrons in this shell of 18 are not as tightly bound as those in the group of 8.   Therefore one or two of these may act as valence electrons, thus accounting for the formation of the ions with valences greater than plus one.   We shall have more to say about these structures in a later chapter.

The Rare Earths.   The rare earths indicated in Table 8 are in a class by themselves and do not lend themselves readily to classification in the periodic system.   They all display a principal valence of $+3$, their chemical properties are much alike and therefore they are separated from each other only with great difficulty.   These elements have usually been considered unimportant to chemists, but since some of them are formed as a result of the process of atomic fission, more attention is now being given them.

The electrons in each of the shells, other than those in the K shell, of *all atoms* are not all alike, although in the past discussion we have not differentiated between them.   The electrons in these shells have, by spectroscopic means, been classified into groups according to the spatial distribution of their orbits and energies.   The 32 electrons comprising the filled N shell, for example, are divided as follows: 2 are s electrons; 6, p electrons; 10, d electrons and 14, f electrons.   The terms s, d, p and f are spectroscopic terms which are carried over from a time before there was any theory of electronic structure and have no special significance.   The s electrons have very elliptic orbits that dive into the core near the nucleus and are more stable than the d electrons, which have less elliptical orbits; the d electrons are more stable than the p; and the f electrons are the least stable of those here mentioned.   The structures of the rare earths are given in terms of these differentiated electrons.

As can be seen from Table 8, the outer structures of all these atoms are alike and the difference lies wholly in the number of electrons in the 4f sub-shell.   In passing from

TABLE 8

ELECTRONIC STRUCTURES OF THE RARE EARTHS

Atomic Number	Element	Number of Electrons in Shells													
		K	L		M			N				O			P
		1s	2s	2p	3s	3p	3d	4s	4p	4d	4f	5s	5p	5d	6s
57	Lanthanum	2	2	6	2	6	10	2	6	10		2	6	1	2
58	Cerium	2	2	6	2	6	10	2	6	10	1	2	6	1	2
59	Praseodymium	2	2	6	2	6	10	2	6	10	2	2	6	1	2
60	Neodymium	2	2	6	2	6	10	2	6	10	3	2	6	1	2
61	Illinium	2	2	6	2	6	10	2	6	10	4	2	6	1	2
62	Samarium	2	2	6	2	6	10	2	6	10	5	2	6	1	2
63	Europium	2	2	6	2	6	10	2	6	10	6	2	6	1	2
64	Gadolinium	2	2	6	2	6	10	2	6	10	7	2	6	1	2
65	Terbium	2	2	6	2	6	10	2	6	10	8	2	6	1	2
66	Dysprosium	2	2	6	2	6	10	2	6	10	9	2	6	1	2
67	Holmium	2	2	6	2	6	10	2	6	10	10	2	6	1	2
68	Erbium	2	2	6	2	6	10	2	6	10	11	2	6	1	2
69	Thulium	2	2	6	2	6	10	2	6	10	12	2	6	1	2
70	Ytterbium	2	2	6	2	6	10	2	6	10	13	2	6	1	2
71	Lutecium	2	2	6	2	6	10	2	6	10	14	2	6	1	2

lanthanum through this series to lutecium, the N shell is increased from 18 to 32 electrons, the maximum number this shell will hold. One might expect from the structure that the valence of each of these elements would be $+2$, but the single 5d electron also acts as a valence electron. The electrons in an atom tend to pair as they do in compounds and the unpaired 5d electron is loosely held and therefore in compound formation behaves as one of the 6s electrons. Because of the unpaired electrons in some of these elements they show strong magnetic properties. A complete table of this kind for all the elements is to be found in the Appendix.

The Nucleus. Although a discussion of the electronic structures of atoms and molecules can be completed without consideration of the nucleus, the ever-increasing interest that is being displayed in nuclear chemistry makes some discussion desirable. A discussion of the nucleus becomes more pertinent when one considers that as a result of recent advances, tracer elements may in the not too distant future be used rather generally for analytical purposes.

The diameter of most atoms is about 10^{-8} cm. and that of the nucleus 10^{-12} cm. According to our present concepts, the nucleus is composed of a system of **neutrons** and **protons** (the proton is the nucleus of the hydrogen atom). When the neutrons and protons are each present in certain very definite numbers, a stable configuration results. The nuclei of elements as found on the earth possess stable configuration. It usually happens that for the same number of protons, two or more stable configurations can be formed, each having different numbers of neutrons. Thus all lithium nuclei contain 3 protons (the atomic number is 3) but some contain 3 neutrons and some 4 neutrons. Two different kinds of lithium nuclei can thus be formed. Since each proton and each neutron contribute one unit to the weight of the nucleus, the relative weights of these two different nuclei are 6 and 7. These different kinds of atoms are known as **isotopes,** and the weights 6 and 7 are known as the **mass numbers.** They exist in the ratio 7.9% Li^6, to 92.1% Li^7. The average weight of all lithium atoms is therefore 6.94, and this is the atomic weight.

Practically all elements exist in nature as isotopes. Ordinary oxygen consists of 3 isotopes, O^{16}, O^{17} and O^{18}; an uranium consists of 3, U^{234}, U^{235} and U^{238}, existing in the proportions .006%, 0.71% and 99.28% respectively. The isotopes of hydrogen are H^1 and H^2. The latter is known as **deuterium,** and the nucleus of this atom as the deuteron. The deuteron is conceived of as made up of one proton and one neutron. Heavy water is merely water the hydrogen atoms of which consist entirely of the isotope H^2.

When the proportion of neutrons to protons in any nucleus is too large for stability, the nucleus usually tends to give off **beta particles** (high-speed electrons) together with **gamma rays** (very short wave radiation). We think of the beta particle as being formed from the neutron in the nucleus by the reaction:

$$\text{neutron} \rightarrow \text{proton} + \text{electron} \tag{4}$$

This reaction cuts down the ratio of neutrons to protons, and by it, a new element with one greater positive charge on the nucleus (one greater in atomic number) is formed. On the other hand, if the ratio of neutrons to protons is too small, then the tendency is to emit an **alpha particle** (the nucleus of the helium atom) or in some cases a **positron** (like the electron but oppositely charged). When an alpha particle is emitted, the atomic number is decreased by 2 units and the mass number by 4 units. Radium, for example, is unstable, having too low a ratio of neutrons to protons, and emits an alpha particle to form the inert gas, radon. The reaction is:

$$\text{Ra}^{226} \rightarrow \text{Rn}^{222} + \text{He}^4 \tag{5}$$

The radon in turn is also unstable and emits another alpha particle, and this series continues until lead is formed. The radium emits alpha particles so slowly that for any given amount of radium one half of the atoms originally present will have decomposed or emitted alpha particles in 1590 years. This period is known as the half-life of radium 226. Radium itself is a disintegration product of uranium 238, which has a half-life of 4.51×10^9 years. In four and one-half billion years, half the uranium now present on the earth will have disappeared.

It is possible to produce radioactive elements by artificial means by the use of apparatus such as the cyclotron to impart very high speeds to charged particles. For example, Fe^{59}, an unstable form of iron, can be formed by the reaction:

$$\text{Fe}^{58} + \text{H}^2 = \text{Fe}^{59} + \text{H}^1 \tag{6}$$

If very high velocity is given the deuterons which bombard an iron target, some of the deuterons will by virtue of their high speeds overcome the repelling force of the iron nucleus and penetrate it. Fe^{59} is unstable and emits beta particles with a half-life of 47 days.

Radioactive isotopes may be used for analytical purposes. Suppose, for example, one wished to determine the amount of iron in blood by this means. The first operation would be to determine the activity of a sample of iron compound containing the isotope Fe^{59}. A definite amount of this would then be added to the blood and after the blood was dried and the organic matter decomposed, some of the iron would be precipitated out of solution (it is not necessary to precipitate all of the iron out of the sample) as $Fe(OH)_3$, which could be ignited and weighed as Fe_2O_3. Then, if the activity of this sample were determined, one could calculate the dilution of the first radioactive sample by the iron in the blood and so determine the total amount. Radioactive isotopes (known as **tracers**) can also be formed from neutrons, which are now available in relatively large concentrations in "piles" which use uranium as their source of power. Fe^{59} can be produced from cobalt in this way.

$$Co^{59} + n \rightarrow Fe^{59} + H^1 \tag{7}$$

In fact, this is a better method of producing this iron isotope.

So far, we have mentioned only the disintegration of the nucleus to form small particles such as the beta and alpha particles, but in 1939 it was discovered by Otto Hahn of Germany that the nucleus of one of the uranium isotopes when bombarded by neutrons undergoes a splitting into two parts of almost equal weight, releasing very large amounts of energy. This reaction may well change our whole social thinking or bring about the destruction of modern civilization, for it is the reaction that led to the atomic bomb.

This process is known as **nuclear fission**. It has been found that the uranium atom "fissions" in many ways and breaks up into all the elements from zinc (atomic no. 30) to gadolinium (atomic no. 64). Neutrons are also emitted in the process of fission. In one process, barium (atomic no. 56) and krypton (atomic no. 36) may be formed as a pair (sum of atomic numbers = 92, that of uranium). In another process, lanthanum and bromine may be the fission-product pair. Since neutrons are also produced in the fission process, these may serve to initiate the fissioning of other U^{235} nuclei and thus form a chain reaction or an explosion. One of the fission reactions is:

$$U^{235} + n = Ba + Kr + xn \tag{8}$$

The fission products formed in this way are very unstable, having too many neutrons, and therefore undergo a series of transformations giving off beta particles and gamma radiation until stable isotopes of other elements are produced. The fission products are therefore very radioactive. It is easy to understand that a new interest has been created in inorganic chemistry since it plays such an important role in the study of nuclear fission and atomic power.

Synthesized Elements. During the last war four new elements, all heavier than uranium, were synthesized. These are **neptunium, plutonium, americium** and **curium**; their atomic numbers are 93, 94, 95 and 96, respectively.

When a neutron enters the nucleus of U^{238} it forms an unstable U^{239}, which rather quickly gives off a beta particle (electron) from the nucleus; the positive charge on the nucleus is thereby increased by one unit and element 93, or neptunium, is formed. Neptunium is also unstable and gives off a beta particle to form the relatively stable plutonium:

$$U^{238} + n \rightarrow U^{239} \tag{9}$$
$$U^{239} \rightarrow \beta^- + Np^{239} \tag{10}$$
$$Np^{239} \rightarrow \beta^- + Pu^{239} \tag{11}$$

Plutonium 239, like U^{235}, undergoes fission when its nuclei react with neutrons. It also liberates neutrons in the fission process and as a result can sustain a chain reaction.

Americium can be made by bombarding U^{238} with helium nuclei.

$$U^{238} + He^4 \rightarrow Pu^{241} + n \tag{12}$$
$$Pu^{241} \rightarrow Am^{240} + \beta \tag{13}$$

Curium can be made by a similar reaction.

$$Pu^{239} + He^4 \rightarrow Cm^{242} + n \tag{14}$$

It might be expected that these elements would behave like those of rhenium, osmium, iridium and platinum, but the heavy elements show no chemical resemblance at all to these. Instead they show enough resemblance to the rare earths to postulate that with these elements a new rare-earth-type series is being formed.

QUESTIONS AND PROBLEMS

1. To what inert gas structure, if any, are the structures of the following atoms related:

(a) Ba   (f) Ni
(b) I   (g) Zn
(c) As   (h) Te
(d) H   (i) Al
(e) O   (j) Pd

2. Explain the fact that HCl in the pure liquefied form is not a good conductor of electricity while in aqueous solution it is.

3. Write the electronic structures (outer shells only) for the following:

(a) SO_4^{--} (f) Br_2
(b) $CHCl_3$ (g) S^{--}
(c) PO_4^{---} (h) KCl
(d) NH_4^+ (i) Na_2O
(e) CH_3CH_3 (j) NH_3

4. The uncharged radical NH_4 has been produced by the electrolysis of an aqueous solution of an ammonium salt, using mercury electrodes. From a consideration of the electronic structure of this radical, would you expect it to have properties similar to those of the gas CH_4 or to those of Na?

5. Make a table similar to Table 7 for the elements of the second sub-group (Zn, etc.). List three properties of the elements of this group that differ from those of the corresponding main group.

6. From the standpoint of electronic structure explain why the rare earths all have a valence of + 3.

7. What is

(a) a neutron
(b) a proton
(c) a beta particle
(d) an alpha particle
(e) gamma rays

(f) the nucleus
(g) isotopes
(h) a synthesized element
(i) deuterium
(j) heavy water

8. Exactly 1.000 g. of purified hemoglobin is treated with oxidizing agents to destroy the organic matter (the protein portion of the molecule). To the resulting solution is added 1 mg. (.00100 g.) of Fe_2O_3 dissolved in acid and which contains enough Fe^{59} to give 1000 counts per minute on the Geiger Muller counter. $Fe(OH)_3$ is precipitated from the resulting solution (not all the Fe need be extracted in this way). This is ignited to form Fe_2O_3 which is found to give 170 counts per minute per milligram.

(a) How much iron was there in the .00100 g. of radioactive Fe_2O_3?

(b) What was the dilution of the iron when added to that contained in the 1 g. of hemoglobin?

(c) What is the per cent iron in hemoglobin?

(Note: This problem should be reserved only for more advanced students.)

CHAPTER III

Oxidation and Reduction

All chemical reactions may be classified into two types: those which involve oxidation and reduction and those which do not. The reactions of the latter type consist of exchanges of atoms or groups of atoms without any change in the valence states of any of the reactants or, in terms of the electronic concept of matter, without any transfer of electrons. Familiar examples of reactions in water solution which do not involve any change in the valence state are:

$$Ag^+ + Cl^- = AgCl(solid) \tag{1}$$
$$Ba^{++} + SO_4^{--} = BaSO_4(solid) \tag{2}$$
$$SO_3^{--} + 2H^+ = SO_2 + H_2O \tag{3}$$
$$Cu^{++} + H_2S = CuS(solid) + 2H^+ \tag{4}$$

In each of these reactions the valence states of the atoms or groups comprising the products are the same as those of the reactants. The equations representing these reactions are relatively simple as compared with those of the oxidation-reduction type.

Since we shall encounter oxidation-reduction equations so often in our later work it is essential that we have a clear understanding of this type of reaction at the outset. We must be certain that we fully understand the balancing of oxidation-reduction equations to the extent that the balancing of any equation whatsoever will never baffle us. Once the principles of equation balancing are mastered there will never be any need to remember any equation in all its details. We shall, also, in this chapter introduce the concept of **valence number**, sometimes known as **oxidation number**, a direct consequence of our previous discussion.

58

BALANCING OF OXIDATION-REDUCTION EQUATIONS

To understand clearly oxidation-reduction processes it is essential to obtain a thorough working knowledge of a systematic scheme for balancing equations.

As an example of an oxidation-reduction reaction we shall choose the reaction of ferrous ion with chlorine in water solution.

$$2Fe^{++} + Cl_2 = 2Fe^{+++} + 2Cl^- * \qquad (5)$$

It is apparent that the condition of the iron and of the chlorine in the reactants is entirely different from that in the products. In the reactants the ferrous ion carries two positive charges while in the product the ferric ion bears three positive charges. Likewise, molecular chlorine is a reactant but the only product containing chlorine is the chloride ion. Both reactants have changed their valence states. In the course of the reaction the iron becomes more positive and the chlorine more negative. The valence number of the iron in equation (5) changes from $+2$ to $+3$, whereas that of the chlorine changes from 0 to -1. Thus, the ferrous ion loses one electron in the reaction while the chlorine atom gains one electron (the chlorine molecule accordingly gains two electrons). Substances which lose electrons are **reducing agents,** while those which gain electrons are known as **oxidizing agents.** *The oxidizing agent oxidizes the reducing agent and the reducing agent reduces the oxidizing agent.* In the reaction under discussion the ferrous ion is the reducing agent and it is oxidized to the ferric ion since it loses an electron. On the other hand, the chlorine in the zero state is the oxidizing agent and it is reduced to the chloride ion since it gains an electron. Every oxidation process is simultaneously accompanied by a reduction process; the two processes are associated with each other and

* In writing equations for oxidation-reduction reactions we shall continue to omit those substances which do not contribute in any way to the progress of the reaction. For example, in equation (5), if a solution of ferrous sulfate were the reactant employed, we would omit the sulfate ion (SO_4^{--}) from both sides of the equation.

cannot act independently. The total number of electrons gained by an oxidizing agent in a given reaction must equal the total number of electrons lost by the corresponding reducing agent. It is through this concept that we shall balance equations of the oxidation-reduction type.

The Valence Number. Before we balance equation (5) on the basis indicated above let us consider parenthetically what is meant by a change in valence state or valence number. In some cases the valence number of an atom in a molecule is equal to the charge that the atom will acquire when the molecule dissociates in water to produce ions. Thus, the valence number of iron in ferrous chloride is $+ 2$, the same as the charge on the ferrous ion (Fe^{++}) in solution. In other cases, however, the valence number of an atom in a molecule is assigned in a more arbitrary manner; its value does not correspond to the charge on any known ion of that element. The valence number of carbon in methane (CH_4) is $- 4$. A carbon ion with four negative charges is not known. In assigning a valence of $- 4$ to carbon in methane, we have quite arbitrarily assumed a valence number of $+ 1$ for hydrogen. Acids dissociate to give the hydrogen ion, H^+, which bears a $+ 1$ charge. Likewise, water to a smaller extent dissociates to give hydrogen ions as one of the products. Methane, to the best of our knowledge, does not dissociate in solution to give hydrogen ions, yet in considering the valence number of the molecule we recall the concept that hydrogen atoms have a tendency to lose one electron and produce hydrogen ions. To be consistent we therefore assign a $+ 1$ valence number to hydrogen in methane. In fact, in all compounds containing hydrogen this same valence number for the hydrogen atom is arbitrarily assumed and the valence numbers of other atoms are assigned accordingly.*

The valence number of the oxygen atom in the water molecule is $- 2$ and since the state of oxidation of the

---

* An exception to this statement is found in the case of the hydrogen compounds (hydrides) of the strongly electropositive elements such as LiH, NaH, CaH_2, etc. In these compounds the valence number is evidently $- 1$.

oxygen atom in water is the same as it is in oxides, it is assumed that the valence number of oxygen in all oxygen compounds, with the exception of the peroxides, is -2. In hydrogen peroxide, as well as in all peroxides, each oxygen atom must have a valence number of -1 if the valence number of each hydrogen atom is to be retained as $+1$.

In assigning the valence number of any atom, the only principle to be observed is that the algebraic sum of the valence numbers of all atoms in the molecule under consideration must equal zero in the case of neutral molecules, or must have the same value as the charge in the case of an ion. The following examples will serve to illustrate this point.

Substance	Atoms	Valence Number per Atom		Total Charge
Water	2 hydrogen	$+1$		$+2$
	1 oxygen	-2		-2
			Net charge	0
Sulfuric Acid	2 hydrogen	$+1$		$+2$
	4 oxygen	-2		-8
	1 sulfur	$+6$		$+6$
			Net charge	0
Ammonium ion	4 hydrogen	$+1$		$+4$
(NH_4^+)	1 nitrogen	-3		-3
			Net charge	$+1$

In the last case the net charge of $+1$ is the same as the charge on the ion.

In some cases there may be two atoms of the same element but in different valence states in one and the same molecule. For the purpose of balancing equations, either the algebraic sum or the average valence number is used. For example, consider the valence state of carbon in ethyl chloride,

$$\begin{array}{ccc} & H & H \\ & | & | \\ H\!-\!\!&C\!-\!\!C&\!-\!Cl \\ & | & | \\ & H & H \end{array}$$

From the structural formula it is apparent that one carbon atom has a valence number of -3 and the other carbon atom a valence number of -1. The sum of the valence numbers of these two carbon atoms is -4. This result could also be determined from the empirical formula, C_2H_5Cl. The algebraic sum of the valence numbers of all the atoms must equal zero. Thus, five hydrogen atoms give $+5$; one chlorine atom, -1; and the two carbon atoms must give -4 to give an algebraic sum equal to zero. Obviously the average valence number of the carbon atoms is -2 and for purposes of balancing equations this value should be used.

Atoms in the elementary state have a valence number of zero. Thus elementary copper, zinc, sodium, chlorine, hydrogen, oxygen, etc., possess atoms which as such function in reactions with a valence number of zero. In order that an atom have a positive or a negative valence number the atom must be in the form of an ion or in molecular combination.

Returning to the example of the oxidation of ferrous ion by chlorine, we may balance the equation on the basis of an equality in the number of electrons lost and gained. Writing the unbalanced equation

$$Fe^{++} + Cl_2 = Fe^{+++} + Cl^- \tag{6}$$

we see that when one ferrous ion changes to a ferric ion the process involves a loss of one electron, and when one chlorine atom in the zero valence state changes to a chloride ion, the process involves the gain of one electron. From an electronic standpoint the equation would be balanced if chlorine existed as a single atom and not as Cl_2, but since we know that elementary chlorine under ordinary conditions of temperature exists in the molecular form, as two atoms to the molecule, we must maintain it in this condition in our equation. The two chlorine atoms are held together in the molecule through a sharing of electrons, in other words, as a non-polar binding. This condition places each chlorine atom in the zero state of valence. Since two atoms of chlorine would necessarily gain a total of two electrons, and since one ferrous ion loses only one electron, equation (6) is not balanced. It may be balanced electronically, as illustrated in the following equation in which the change in valence numbers is indicated.

$$\underset{Fe^{++}}{\overset{+2}{}} + \underset{Cl_2}{\overset{0}{}} = \underset{Fe^{+++}}{\overset{+3}{}} + \underset{Cl^-}{\overset{-1}{}} \qquad (7)$$

$$\left| 2 \times 1\, e^- \text{ lost} \right| \qquad \qquad \left|$$

$$\left| 2\, e^- \text{ gained per molecule} \right|$$

For an electronic balance the gain of two electrons by the two chlorine atoms of the chlorine molecule must be equaled by a loss of two electrons by the ferrous ion. The latter process requires two ferrous ions. In this particular case the complete balancing is relatively simple since no other substances are involved in the reaction aside from the oxidizing and reducing agents and their products. Thus, the completely balanced equation is

$$2Fe^{++} + Cl_2 = 2Fe^{+++} + 2Cl^- \qquad (8)$$

In the following sections we shall present examples to illustrate the completion of more complicated equations after they have been balanced from the electronic standpoint only.

Oxidation and Reduction in Acid Solution. Many oxidation-reduction reactions take place with the production or consumption of hydrogen ions and these ions must therefore be included in the balanced equation. Among those substances which act as oxidizing agents in acid solution are included permanganate ion, MnO_4^-, dichromate ion, $Cr_2O_7^{--}$, and nitrate ion, NO_3^-. In the process of oxidation and reduction some or all of the oxygen atoms in these ions react with hydrogen ions to produce water. Thus chloride ion is oxidized by permanganate ion in acid solution to give the products shown in the following equation:

$$\underset{MnO_4^-}{\overset{+7}{}} + \underset{Cl^-}{\overset{-1}{}} + H^+ = \underset{Mn^{++}}{\overset{+2}{}} + \underset{Cl_2}{\overset{0}{}} + H_2O \qquad (9)$$

The procedure is, (1) assign valence numbers, (2) balance the equation electronically, and (3) make a complete balance. It is evident that the MnO_4^- ion is the oxidizing agent and the Cl^- ion the reducing agent; the MnO_4^- ion is reduced and the Cl^- ion is oxidized. The valence number of the manganese atom in the MnO_4^- ion is $+7$, while in the Mn^{++} ion it is $+2$. Evidently a change has taken place which involves a gain of five electrons by the MnO_4^- ion since the valence number of the oxygen is not changed in this reaction. Chloride ion, valence number -1, changes to free chlorine of zero valence number, which process can be accounted for only by a loss of one electron per Cl^- ion. The change in the electrons may now be represented as

$$\overset{+7}{MnO_4^-} + \overset{-1}{Cl^-} + H^+ = \overset{+2}{Mn^{++}} + \overset{0}{Cl_2} + H_2O \quad (10)$$

$5\ e^-$ gained

$1\ e^-$ lost

For an electronic balance the same number of electrons must be taken up by the oxidizing agent as is given up by the reducing agent. Therefore five Cl^- ions are required for each MnO_4^- ion to produce an exchange of five electrons, and therefore

$$MnO_4^- + 5Cl^- + ?H^+ = Mn^{++} + \tfrac{5}{2}Cl_2 + ?H_2O \quad (11)$$

Multiplying both sides of the equation by 2 to remove the fraction $\tfrac{5}{2}$, the equation becomes

$$2MnO_4^- + 10Cl^- + ?H^+ = 2Mn^{++} + 5Cl_2 + ?H_2O \quad (12)$$

A balance of the hydrogen and oxygen atoms is still lacking. However, it will be observed that all of the oxygen of the oxidizing agent through combination with hydrogen ions is converted into water. Since two molecules of permanganate ion contain eight oxygen atoms, eight molecules of water must be formed. In turn, eight molecules of water require sixteen hydrogen ions and the equation is finally written

$$2MnO_4^- + 10Cl^- + 16H^+ = 2Mn^{++} + 5Cl_2 + 8H_2O \quad (13)$$

When the permanganate ion acts as an oxidizing agent in acid solution the manganese is always reduced to the manganous ion, Mn^{++}.

Another very satisfactory method for completing the balancing of the equation, after the oxidation-reduction part has been taken care of, is one involving a balance of the ion charges (not necessarily valence numbers) on both sides of the equation. Beginning with equation (12) the coefficients for the hydrogen ions and water molecules may be determined as follows: On the right side of the equation the only charged particles are the two Mn^{++} ions. The total ionic charge on the right is therefore $+ 4$. The algebraic sum of the charges on the left side must also be $+ 4$. Neglecting the H^+ ion for the moment, which is not balanced, the total charge on the left side is found to be $- 12$, $(2MnO_4^- + 10Cl^-)$. Sixteen H^+ ions are necessary to make the algebraic sum $+ 4$, $(- 2 - 10 + 16 = + 4)$. The sixteen H^+ ions produce eight molecules of water. As a final check on the method the number of oxygen atoms on both sides of the equation must be the same, which is the case for the finally balanced equation (13). This method of final balance is often simpler than the alternative method previously given.

Another strong oxidizing ion in acid solution is the dichromate ion, $Cr_2O_7^{--}$, which in this medium is always reduced to the chromic ion, Cr^{+++}. Thus, iodide ion is oxidized by $Cr_2O_7^{--}$ to I_2:

$$
\begin{array}{cccccc}
2 \times (+6) & -1 & & 2 \times (+3) & 0 & \\
Cr_2O_7^{--} & + \quad I^- & + \quad H^+ & = \quad 2Cr^{+++} & + \quad I_2 & + \quad H_2O \quad (14)
\end{array}
$$

$\lfloor$ 6 e^- gained

1 e^- lost per atom

The valence number of the chromium atom in the $Cr_2O_7^{--}$ ion is $+ 6$, but since there are two chromium atoms per ion the total charge is $+ 12$. When one $Cr_2O_7^{--}$ ion is reduced to two Cr^{+++} ions there is a gain of six electrons, three electrons for each chromium atom, whereas one I^- ion loses one electron in the oxidation to an iodine atom in the iodine molecule. For an electronic balance it is evident that six I^- ions are required to take care of the gain of six electrons by the chromium atoms of the $Cr_2O_7^{--}$ ion; thus

$$Cr_2O_7^{--} + 6I^- + ?H^+ = 2Cr^{+++} + 3I_2 + ?H_2O \quad (15)$$

The equation is now balanced electronically. Making the final balance by means of the ionic charge method we find a charge of $+ 6$ on the right side of the equation due to the two Cr^{+++} ions, and a charge of $- 8$ on the left side ($Cr_2O_7^{--}$ $+ 6I^-$). To make the algebraic sum of the charges on the left equal that on the right, namely $+ 6$, it is necessary to add a charge of $+ 14$ to the left side. This is accomplished by using fourteen H^+ ions which form seven molecules of water. The final completely balanced equation is therefore

$$Cr_2O_7^{--} + 6I^- + 14H^+ = 2Cr^{+++} + 3I_2 + 7H_2O \quad (16)$$

The correctness of the balance is checked by the presence of seven oxygen atoms on each side of the equation.

The alternative method of making the final balance (beginning with equation 15) is somewhat simpler. The seven oxygen atoms on the left are completely converted into water. It is evident that in order for this to take place fourteen H^+ ions must be furnished and seven molecules of water will be formed.

Oxidation-reduction equations can be balanced without the introduction of the concept of electron change. When this is done one merely takes into account the positive or negative change in valence number. For example, in equation (14) the valence number of the chromium atoms in the $Cr_2O_7^{--}$ ion changes from $+ 12$ to $+ 6$, a net change of $- 6$, in the process of conversion to two Cr^{+++} ions. The valence number of each I^- ion changes from $- 1$ to zero, a net change of $+ 1$, in going to free iodine. To make the net positive charge equal the net negative charge six I^- ions are necessary.

We shall now consider an example of the balancing of an oxidation-reduction equation in which the reducing agent contains more than one kind of atom undergoing change in valence number. For this purpose let us choose the reaction of arsenous sulfide with nitric acid in which there is produced arsenic acid, free sulfur and nitric oxide.

$$2\times(+3)+3\times(-2) \quad +5 \qquad \qquad 2\times(+5) \quad 0 \quad +2$$
$$As_2S_3 \quad + \quad NO_3^- + H^+ = 2HAsO_3 + 3S + NO + H_2O$$

$$10\ e^-\ \text{lost}\ |(2\times 2)+(3\times 2)|$$

$$3\ e^-\ \text{gained} \qquad (17)$$

The valence number of the arsenic atom in As_2S_3 is $+3$ and the valence number of the sulfur in this molecule is -2. Both the arsenic and the sulfur change valence number and the total change for each As_2S_3 molecule is $+10$ as indicated in the above equation. On the other hand, each NO_3^- ion gains three electrons in its conversion to nitric oxide. Thus ten NO_3^- ions and three molecules of As_2S_3 are necessary to produce the same loss as gain in electrons (namely 30).

$$3As_2S_3 + 10NO_3^- + ?H^+ = 6HAsO_3 + 9S + 10NO + ?H_2O \quad (18)$$

Balancing equation (18) by the ion charge method, we find zero charge on the right side of the equation and a charge of -10 on the left (omitting the H^+ ion). Accordingly, ten H^+ ions are necessary to produce a net ionic charge on the left equal to zero. This amount of H^+ ion produces two molecules of water since six H^+ ions are required for the production of six molecules of $HAsO_3$ and the finally balanced equation becomes

$$3As_2S_3 + 10NO_3^- + 10H^+ = 6HAsO_3 + 9S + 10NO + 2H_2O \quad (19)$$

Checking the balancing by the oxygen atom count we find thirty oxygen atoms on each side of the equation.

Oxidation and Reduction in Alkaline Solution. As an example we shall choose the oxidation of chromite ion, CrO_2^-, by hypochlorite ion, ClO^-, in the presence of hydroxide ion,

OH^-. The unbalanced equation with the valence numbers indicated is

$$\overset{+3}{CrO_2^-} + \overset{+1}{ClO^-} + OH^- = \overset{+6}{CrO_4^{--}} + \overset{-1}{Cl^-} + H_2O \quad (20)$$

$2 \times 3\,e^-$ lost

$3 \times 2\,e^-$ gained

and the electronic balance is

$$2CrO_2^- + 3ClO^- + {?}OH^- = 2CrO_4^{--} + 3Cl^- + {?}H_2O \quad (21)$$

Since the algebraic sum of the charges on the ions on the right side of the equation is -7 and that on the left (leaving the OH^- out of consideration for the present) is -5, it is evident that two OH^- ions are required on the left. One molecule of water is formed and the balanced equation is

$$2CrO_2^- + 3ClO^- + 2OH^- = 2CrO_4^{--} + 3Cl^- + H_2O \quad (22)$$

Oxidation-reduction reactions in acid solution often take place with the production (not consumption) of hydrogen ions. In such cases H^+ appears on the right side of the equation. The same is true in alkaline solutions except that here we are concerned with OH^- rather than H^+ ions.

EXERCISES

Complete and balance the following equations.

(The column on the right indicates the type of solution in which the reaction takes place. H^+ or OH^- may appear on either side of the equation and when neither is necessary the solution is designated as "neutral.")

Reaction	Solution
1. $MnO_4^- + Fe^{++} = Mn^{++} + Fe^{+++}$	H^+
2. $MnO_4^- + Sn^{++} = Sn^{++++} + Mn^{++}$	H^+
3. $Cr_2O_7^{--} + Fe^{++} = Fe^{+++} + Cr^{+++}$	H^+
4. $Cr_2O_7^{--} + Sn^{++} = Sn^{++++} + Cr^{+++}$	H^+
5. $CrO_4^{--} + HSnO_2^- = HSnO_3^- + CrO_2^-$	OH^-
6. $H_2S + I_2 = S + I^-$	H^+
7. $S_2O_3^{--} + I_2 = S_4O_6^{--} + I^-$	"neutral"

	Reaction	*Solution*

8. $NO_3^- + Cu = Cu^{++} + NO$ — H^+

9. $SO_4^{--} + Cu = Cu^{++} + SO_2$ — H^+

10. $NO_3^- + Zn = Zn^{++} + NH_4^+$ — H^+

11. $H_2SO_3 + Fe^{+++} = Fe^{++} + SO_4^{--}$ — H^+

12. $CrO_2^- + ClO^- = Cl^- + CrO_4^{--}$ — OH^-

13. $MnO_4^- + H_2C_2O_4 = CO_2 + Mn^{++}$ — H^+

14. $H_2SO_3 + I_2 = SO_4^{--} + I^-$ — H^+

15. $CeO_2 + Cl^- = Ce^{+++} + Cl_2$ — H^+

16. $H_3AsO_4 + I^- = H_3AsO_3 + I_2$ — H^+

17. $O_2 + H_2O + I^- = I_2$ — OH^-

18. $CH_2O + Ag_2O = Ag + HCO_2^-$ — OH^-

19. $CH_2O + Ag(NH_3)_2^+ = Ag + HCO_2^- + NH_3$ — OH^-

20. $NO_3^- + Cu = Cu^{++} + NO_2$ — H^+

21. $NO_3^- + Ag = Ag^+ + NO_2$ — H^+

22. $NO_3^- + Ag = Ag^+ + NO$ — H^+

23. $NO_3^- + Fe^{++} = Fe^{+++} + NO$ — H^+

24. $NO_3^- + Zn = Zn^{++} + N_2$ — H^+

25. $NO_3^- + H_2S = S + NO_2$ — H^+

26. $BaO_2 + Cl^- = Cl_2 + Ba^{++}$ — H^+

27. $MnO_4^- + Br^- = Br_2 + MnO_2$ — H^+

28. $SO_4^{--} + I^- = I_2 + H_2S$ — H^+

29. $Cu^{++} + I^- = I_2 + Cu^+$ — "neutral"

30. $ClO^- + Mn(OH)_2 = MnO_2 + Cl^-$ — "neutral"

31. $Cl_2 = ClO_3^- + Cl^-$ — OH^-

32. $Fe^{+++} + H_2S = Fe^{++} + S$ — H^+

33. $NO_3^- + Fe = Fe^{+++} + NO$ — H^+

34. $ClO^- = ClO_3^- + Cl^-$ — "neutral"

35. $PbO_2 + Pb + SO_4^{--} = PbSO_4$ — H^+

36. $CN^- + MnO_4^{--} = CNO^- + MnO_2$ — OH^-

37. $CN^- + Fe(CN)_6^{---} = CNO^- + Fe(CN)_6^{----}$ — OH^-

38. $C_2H_4O + NO_3^- = NO + C_2H_4O_2$ — H^+

39. $NO_3^- + Cl^- = NOCl + Cl_2$ — H^+

40. $C_2H_3OCl + Cr_2O_7^{--} = Cr^{+++} + CO_2 + Cl^-$ — H^+

41. $CHCl_3 + MnO_4^- = Cl_2 + CO_2 + Mn^{++}$ — H^+

Reaction	*Solution*
42. $Fe_3O_4 + MnO_4^- = Fe^{+++} + Mn^{++}$	H^+
43. $SnS + S_2^{--} = SnS_3^{--}$	"neutral"
44. $As_2S_3 + S_2^{--} = AsS_4^{---} + S$	"neutral"
45. $Cu^{++} + CN^- = Cu(CN)_3^{--} + (CN)_2$	"neutral"
46. $Hg_2Cl_2 + NH_3 = Hg(NH_2)Cl + Hg + NH_4^+ + Cl^-$	"neutral"
47. $Ag^+ + AsH_3 = Ag + H_3AsO_3$	H^+
48. $CrO_2^- + H_2O_2 = CrO_4^{--}$	OH^-
49. $Sn^{++} + H_2O_2 = Sn^{++++}$	H^+

CHAPTER IV

Reaction Velocity and Chemical Equilibrium

In this chapter we shall be concerned with the problem of determining the extent to which chemical reactions take place and with the ways and means that are employed to control reactions and have them proceed as advantageously as possible. The problem can be stated more concretely by considering some specific example. For this purpose we shall choose the reaction

$$N_2 + 3H_2 = 2NH_3 \tag{1}$$

In which direction does this reaction proceed at some specified temperature and pressure? At 1000° C and at a total pressure of one atmosphere, for example, will nitrogen react with hydrogen to form ammonia or will ammonia at this same temperature and pressure decompose into its constituent elements? From the results of experiment we know that at this temperature and pressure ammonia decomposes to a very large extent (practically completely) into nitrogen and hydrogen. Therefore, at one atmosphere pressure and at 1000° C nitrogen and hydrogen cannot combine appreciably to form ammonia.

At 450° C and one atmosphere pressure about 99.7% of the ammonia decomposes but in the absence of a catalyst it is necessary to wait a very long time before the reaction reaches this point. Once this amount of decomposition has taken place, the reaction will proceed no further. This is the limit beyond which the reaction will not go. At 25° C it can be shown that only about 3% of the ammonia should decompose if the reaction proceeded rapidly enough. No means are known to the chemist of increasing the velocity of this reaction under these extreme conditions.

The limit to which any reaction can proceed is one of the important factors in determining its course. But it is apparent that there is another important factor controlling it, that of speed. These two factors, limit and speed, are sometimes confused when the "reactivity" of any substance or group of substances is considered. Reactivity usually refers to the velocity, or speed.

If only 3% of ammonia at 25° C and at one atmosphere pressure can decompose, then, conversely, hydrogen and nitrogen should combine at this same temperature and pressure to form ammonia, but this reaction also is not a feasible one because of its slow speed. Nitrogen is said to be non-reactive toward hydrogen in spite of the favorable limit of the reaction.

The subject of chemical equilibrium deals only with the limit or extent to which a reaction can take place. But a clear understanding of this subject demands a clear concept of reaction velocity and the factors which control it.

The Factors Controlling the Speed of a Reaction. Before two or more molecules can react they must collide with each other. But not every collision between reacting molecules is *effective*. In a vessel containing a mixture of hydrogen and oxygen at room temperature, billions of collisions occur each second between the molecules, yet no reaction occurs. Only those collisions which allow the molecules to penetrate deeply into each other result in reaction. This means that only collisions between fast moving molecules or between molecules having large energies with respect to each other will be effective. At room temperature there are not enough effective collisions between hydrogen and oxygen molecules to cause an appreciable number to react. How can the number of effective collisions be increased?

Effect of Temperature. From our knowledge of the kinetic theory of gases and our concept of temperature, it is easy to predict that an increase in the temperature of the reactants will increase the speed of the reaction. By increasing the temperature the velocity of the molecules is increased. Consequently, at a higher temperature there are more effective collisions, and the number of such collisions increases very rapidly as the temperature is raised. Suppose, for example, that each effective collision must involve molecules which have fifty times as much energy with respect to each other as the average energy. In such a case one in every 10^{33} * collisions, as calculated from quantitative kinetic theory considerations, would be effective at 25° C. At 100° C there would be one effective collision in every 10^{27}, an increase of one million-fold in the number of effective collisions. While the average energy of the molecules does not increase very rapidly as the temperature is increased, the number of collisions involving large energies does. In the case just considered, we assumed that an effective collision required fifty times the average molecular energy. If the effective collision required only twenty times the average energy, then at 25° C one in every 10^{13} collisions would be effective and at 100° C one in about every 10^{10}. This time the number of effective collisions increases only one thousand times in going from 25° C to 100° C.

For a large proportion of all reactions the speed approximately doubles for every 10° rise in temperature. The process of cooking food involves chemical reactions. Most of these reactions proceed at about 100° C, the boiling point of water, but the cooking process can be hastened by the use of pressure cookers since, by not allowing the steam to escape, the temperature of the water can be increased beyond 100° C. When the vapor pressure of the water in the cooker is 25 lbs. per square inch in excess of that of the atmosphere, the temperature of the water is about 130° C. If the increase in the cooking speed doubles for every 10° rise, the speed at 130° C should be about eight times (2 × 2 × 2) that at 100° C. Conversely, when the cooking is done at high altitudes in open vessels, the speed of the cooking reaction is decreased, for at decreased atmospheric pressure water boils at a lower temperature.

* For a discussion of exponential numbers refer to the Appendix.

When hydrogen and oxygen are heated to 500° C the re-action to form steam proceeds at a measurable rate. For this reaction the velocity more than doubles with every 10° rise in temperature, and at room temperature its rate is millions of millions of times slower. The combination of hydrogen with oxygen liberates a large amount of heat. If heat is generated faster than it can be removed, the re-acting substances are raised to still higher temperatures and the reaction is further accelerated. This acceleration may take place in a fraction of a second and give rise to an explosion.

The burning of fuel such as wood also evolves heat. In this case the reaction does not get out of control but the heat evolved is sufficient to keep the burning material and the air above the *kindling* temperature. This reaction is a self-sustaining one, as are many of the reactions which evolve heat. When heat is absorbed by the reaction, the reaction cannot be self-sustaining. In this case heat must be supplied to the reactants.

Reactions involving ions, such as the neutralization of a strong acid by a strong base (see equation 10, Chapter I), proceed very rapidly. For such reactions the ions have an attraction for each other and no excess energy is required for contact close enough to give rise to a reaction. Every collision or practically every collision between the ions is an effective one.

Effect of Concentration. By increasing the concentration of all or any of the reacting substances, the velocity of a reaction increases. With increased concentration any one molecule has a greater chance of colliding with another with which it may react. Hydrogen does not react as rapidly with air which is one-fifth oxygen as it does with pure oxygen. Also, a mixture of hydrogen and oxygen at very low pressures reacts more slowly than at high pressures. In fact, a mixture of hydrogen and oxygen does not explode when ignited if the total pressure of the mixture is sufficiently low. In any reaction taking place between two reactants, doubling the concentration of any one reactant doubles the number of total collisions and also doubles the number of effective collisions. Doubling the concentration of both reactants quadruples the number of collisions.

The reaction between gaseous iodine and hydrogen to form gaseous hydrogen iodide may be considered as an example to illustrate the effect of concentration on the speed of the reaction.

$$H_2 + I_2 = 2HI \qquad (2)$$

Consider first the reactants under conditions of temperature and concentration (or pressure) which allow a measurable reaction speed. If the hydrogen concentration is now doubled and the concentration of the iodine kept the same, the reaction speed will be doubled, for now each iodine atom will make twice as many collisions with hydrogen atoms, hence twice as many effective collisions. The same result would be obtained by doubling the concentration of iodine and keeping the concentration of the hydrogen the same as it was originally. If now both the concentration of the hydrogen and the concentration of the iodine are doubled, the number of effective collisions will be increased fourfold and the speed of the reaction will be four times as great. This concept will be developed more fully in the latter part of this chapter.

Effect of a Catalyst. The speed of many reactions is increased by the presence of some substance which itself undergoes no permanent chemical change during the reaction. Such a substance is known as a **catalyst.** Catalysts may be divided into two general classes: (1) contact catalysts, and (2) those which form intermediate substances which in turn react to regenerate the catalyst. The reaction of sulfur dioxide with oxygen to form sulfur trioxide in the presence of nitric oxide is an example of the latter class. Oxygen does not react with sulfur dioxide with any appreciable speed at 500° C when no other substance is present, yet in the presence of nitric oxide, NO, this reaction proceeds rapidly. The nitric oxide itself combines readily with oxygen and the product formed, NO_2, then reacts with the sulfur dioxide forming sulfur trioxide and regenerating the nitric oxide for further use as a catalyst. Known catalysts of this type are far fewer than contact catalysts.

Contact catalysts are those which provide a surface upon which the reacting substances may come in contact with each other. The catalyst has the ability to hold (adsorb) a mono-molecular layer of one or more of the reactants on its surface. When the reactant is thus adsorbed, the field of force about the adsorbed reacting molecule is so changed that the molecule with which it is to react does not have to penetrate so deeply to cause reaction. More of the collisions are therefore effective, hence the speed of the reaction is increased. Finely-divided platinum is used as a catalyst for many reactions, among which are the oxidation of sulfur dioxide to sulfur trioxide (contact process of making sulfuric acid), the addition of hydrogen to unsaturated organic compounds (hydrogenation of cottonseed oil, for example), the oxidation of methanol to formaldehyde ($2CH_3OH + O_2 = 2CH_2O + 2H_2O$), the reaction between nitrogen and hydrogen to form ammonia, the oxidation of carbon monoxide to carbon dioxide, and the reaction between hydrogen and oxygen to form water. Since the function of the platinum is to provide an active surface, the greater the surface area of the catalyst the greater is its effectiveness. The surface of the catalyst is increased by spreading the platinum over some other inert substance such as asbestos. This can be done by soaking asbestos in a solution of a platinum salt and then decomposing the salt by heat. For commercial practice a substitute for platinum is usually sought because of the high cost of the metal.

Heterogeneous and Homogeneous Reactions. All reactions may be classified as either **heterogeneous** or **homogeneous**. Those which take place at some surface are the heterogeneous reactions, examples of which were cited in the last section. In some cases the surface itself may be one of the reactants. The rusting of iron, for example, is a heterogeneous reaction in which the surface of the iron reacts with the oxygen. In this case one of the reactants is a gas and the other a solid. When manganese dioxide is placed in a solution of hydrogen peroxide, the latter substance decomposes to give water and oxygen. The manganese dioxide acts as a catalyst and the reaction is a heterogeneous one. When copper sulfate solution reacts with zinc to give zinc sulfate solution, it is the copper ion in solution which is involved in the reaction with the zinc to give zinc ions and metallic copper. This reaction also is a heterogeneous one.

Reactions which do not take place on a surface or at an interface between two different phases are called homogeneous reactions. In homogeneous reactions all reactants are gases, liquids in the same solution, or solids dissolved in each other. In other words, for homogeneous reactions there is no boundary surface between the reactants nor do the reactants combine with each other on the surface of a catalyst. The burning of illuminating gas is an example of a homogeneous reaction. All the reactants, the gas and the oxygen of the air are gaseous (of the same phase) and the reaction does not take place on a surface. However, when this reaction takes place on a Welsbach mantel, the mantel acts as a catalyst and the reaction is then a heterogeneous one. When gaseous hydrogen reacts with gaseous iodine to form gaseous hydrogen iodide (equation 2), the reaction is a homogeneous one since all the constituents are confined to a single phase.

Reactions Involving Ions. When a barium chloride solution is added to a solution of sodium sulfate a precipitate of barium sulfate immediately forms. Barium ions and the sulfate ions must eventually attach themselves to the surface of the crystal in their regular places to form the crystal of barium sulfate. The crystal of barium sulfate grows by deposition on its surface and part of the reaction at least must be heterogeneous.

The formation of the crystal nucleus, that is, the attachment of the first ions to each other, is a different kind of a reaction. Perhaps that part of the reaction is a homogeneous one. The phenomenon of supersaturation attests to the fact that this part of the reaction is different. In a supersaturated solution of sodium thiosulfate, for example, the rate of formation of crystal nuclei is so slow that crystallization cannot set in. If a crystal of solid sodium thiosulfate is added to such a solution, crystallization immediately occurs. In most ionic reactions, however, the rate of formation of crystal nuclei is very fast, as is the secondary crystallization.

The neutralization of a solution of sodium hydroxide by a solution of hydrochloric acid is an example of a homogeneous ionic reaction. As was previously stated, this reaction involves the combination of the hydrogen and hydroxide ions to form water and is confined to a single phase. The ionization of any weak acid or weak base in water solution is a homogeneous reaction of the ionic type.

Reversible Reactions. The formation of water by the combination of hydrogen with oxygen has previously been used to illustrate the different factors to be considered in an understanding of reaction velocity. It has been stated that these two elements react with each other almost completely at moderate temperatures. On the other hand, at 2000° C or above, an appreciable amount of steam is broken up into hydrogen and oxygen. Even at room temperature we may assume that some water vapor molecules dissociate into hydrogen and oxygen, but that the rate of dissociation and its extent are so small that the change cannot be detected. All reactions may be regarded as reversible. Often the amount of reversibility is so small that it cannot be determined by any known experimental method, but it would be contrary to our ideas concerning probability to suppose that any chemical reaction is absolutely irreversible. However, when no detectable amount of reversibility is ever observed it is common practice to regard the reaction as "irreversible."

When sodium reacts with water, hydrogen and a solution of sodium hydroxide are produced:

$$2Na + 2H_2O = 2NaOH + H_2 \qquad (3)$$

If the reverse process of passing hydrogen into a solution of sodium hydroxide is carried out, no detectable amount of sodium is produced, yet we may not say that not even a single atom of sodium is formed in such a process. If we were to be entirely practical, we would regard such a process as irreversible, yet from the standpoint of equilibrium, the subject we are to consider next, it will be very useful to regard every chemical reaction as having some tendency to reverse itself, however small that tendency may be.

Chemical Equilibrium. The reaction

$$2NH_3 = N_2 + 3H_2 \qquad (4)$$

was previously used to show that there is a definite limit beyond which a reaction cannot proceed. At the time the example was given, it was not made apparent why the reaction stopped before completion, but it was by no means implied that the reaction suddenly comes to a standstill. The reason for the definite limit is that the NH_3 is simultaneously being formed and finally a condition is reached in which the two opposing reactions proceed at the same rate. In this state of balance the amounts of NH_3, N_2 and H_2 present in the reaction mixture remain constant.

This condition of equilibrium, which any chemical reaction can attain, can be likened to a horse running on a treadmill which moves faster as the horse increases his speed. When the horse and the treadmill are in equilibrium, the horse is apparently stationary to an observer. If the horse runs faster, he advances a few feet, but the mill also moves faster and again he appears to be stationary. In the case in which the reaction just considered is in equilibrium the amount of NH_3, N_2 and H_2 remains constant, yet like the horse and the treadmill the reactions proceed in opposite directions with the same speed. At equilibrium the forward and reverse reactions always proceed at the same rate.

If equivalent quantities of sulfur dioxide and oxygen are both contained in the same closed vessel and heated to about 800° C at 1 atmosphere pressure, approximately one-half of the sulfur dioxide is converted to the trioxide. On the other hand, if sulfur trioxide is heated to 800° C at one atmosphere pressure about 50% of it dissociates into sulfur dioxide and oxygen. At 800° C the rate at which sulfur trioxide is formed equals the rate at which it decomposes when the concentration of the sulfur dioxide is approximately equal to that of the sulfur trioxide. The sulfur dioxide, sulfur trioxide and oxygen are in equilibrium with each other. If the temperature of the mixture is changed, equilibrium will still be maintained, but the equilibrium concentrations of the reacting substances will be different.

The Law of Mass Action. The Law of Mass Action is a quantitative statement relating the velocity of a reaction to the concentrations of its reactants. To develop the quantitative notions of chemical equilibrium, that is, to understand the Law of Mass Action, we shall consider the hypothetical reaction

$$A + B = C + D \tag{5}$$

In this reaction A molecules react with B molecules to form C and D molecules. For the A and B molecules to react it is necessary that they collide with each other. The number of molecules reacting in a given time will be proportional to the number of collisions between them. If the number of collisions between A and B molecules in one case were twice as great as that in another in a given time, then twice as many A and B molecules would react. To determine the dependence of the rate of the reaction upon the concentrations of A and B, it is only necessary to determine the manner in which the number of collisions between A and B molecules varies with their respective concentrations. To do this, consider a closed vessel containing only A and B molecules and for simplicity, suppose that there are only 4 A molecules and 4 B molecules present in the vessel. Let us determine the chance that any A molecule will collide with a B molecule in a given time. We arbitrarily indicate the chance of collision by drawing lines between A and B molecules (Figure 17). Under the conditions we have chosen, the chance that any A molecule will collide with any B molecule is 16 (16 lines). Each A molecule has

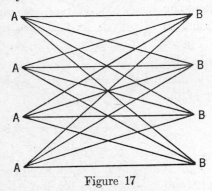

Figure 17

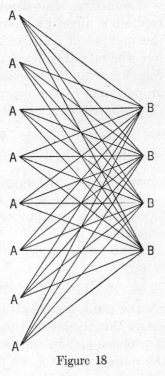

Figure 18

4 chances of colliding with a B molecule and since there are 4 A molecules the total chance becomes 4×4 or 16. It is obvious that collisions between like molecules are not to be included since they do not lead to reaction in this case.

Now suppose the concentration of A molecules is doubled, that is, there are 8 A molecules and 4 B molecules in the same container (Figure 18). The chance that any A molecule will collide with any B molecule will now be 32 (4×8 lines). The number of A molecules in the second case is now twice that in the first and the chance for collision between the A and B molecules is doubled. With 8 A molecules and 8 B molecules, the chance of collision is 64 (8×8 lines). In general, the chance of collision will be equal to $N_a \times N_b$, where N_a and N_b represent the number of A and B molecules respectively.

In all of the above cases the size of the container was the same, so N_a, expressed in proper units, is the concentration of A molecules, and N_b the concentration of B molecules. The chance for collision between A and B molecules is then proportional to the *product of the concentration of A and of B molecules.* But the rate of the reaction is directly proportional to the number of collisions. Therefore, the rate at which A molecules combine with B molecules is also proportional to the *product of the concentrations of A and B.*

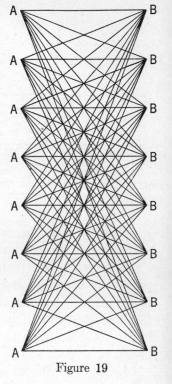

$$\text{Rate}_1 \sim (A) \times (B) \qquad (6)$$

or $\qquad \text{Rate}_1 = k_1(A) \times (B) * \qquad (7)$

where (A) and (B) represent the concentrations of A and B respectively, and k_1 is a proportionality constant.

Let us now consider the reverse reaction

$$C + D \rightarrow A + B \qquad (8)$$

By the same argument it can be shown that the rate of this reaction is proportional to the product of

Figure 19

the concentration of the C molecules and the concentration of the D molecules, that is,

$$\text{Rate}_2 = k_2(C) \times (D) \qquad (9)$$

where (C) and (D) now represent the concentrations of C and D molecules and k_2 is a proportionality constant.

When the system is in equilibrium both the reactions proceed simultaneously,

$$A + B = C + D \qquad (10)$$

* See discussion of proportion and proportionality constants in the Appendix.

and the rate in the forward direction is equal to the rate in the backward direction,

$$\text{Rate}_1 = \text{Rate}_2 \tag{11}$$

or
$$k_1(A) \times (B) = k_2(C) \times (D) \tag{12}$$

and
$$\frac{k_1}{k_2} = \frac{(C) \times (D)}{(A) \times (B)} \tag{13}$$

Since k_1 and k_2 are both constants, the ratio $\frac{k_1}{k_2}$ is also a constant.

$$\frac{(C) \times (D)}{(A) \times (B)} = K_{eq} \tag{14}$$

K_{eq} is known as the equilibrium constant for the reaction. This expression means that the concentrations of all four substances are so related that if the concentration of any one is changed, the concentrations of the others must vary through a chemical reaction in such a way as to make the value of the expression $\frac{(C) \times (D)}{(A) \times (B)}$ the same as it was originally.

Figure 20

Let us now consider another hypothetical case in which we have two molecules of the same kind reacting with each other, for example,

$$2A \to C + D \tag{15}$$

Two molecules of A react with each other to form one molecule of C and one of D. This time we shall determine the chance of collision between any two A molecules. Suppose there are 6 A molecules in the enclosed vessel. Counting the chances as was done in the previous case we find that there are 15 $(5 + 4 + 3 + 2 + 1$ lines, Figure 20), that is, the first molecule to be considered has 5 chances of collision, the next molecule has 4 chances (not counting the same chance twice), the third molecule, 3 chances, etc.

If we double the number of A molecules (now 12), we find that the chance is 66 ($11 + 10 + 9 + 8 + 7 + 6 + 5 + 4 + 3 + 2 + 1$ lines). In general, for N molecules the chance of collision will be $(N - 1) + (N - 2) + (N - 3) + \cdots + 1$. The mathematical formula for determining the sum of such a series of combinations is

$$\frac{(N - 1)N}{2} \tag{16}$$

Therefore, the number of collisions is proportional to $(N - 1) \times N$. N represents the number of molecules in the system. For all actual cases N is an exceedingly large number, so $(N - 1)$ may be considered equal to N, and $(N - 1) \times N$ is practically equal to N^2. When we recall that the lowest vacuum we can possibly obtain still contains billions of molecules per cubic centimeter, certainly one molecule more or less can make no appreciable difference, so we are quite justified in letting $N - 1$ equal N. Accordingly, we may say that the number of collisions in such a case is proportional to N^2. But since N may be expressed as the concentration of the reacting substance, in this case A molecules, the number of collisions is proportional to the concentration of A molecules squared. For this case,

$$\text{Rate}_1 = k_1(A)^2 \tag{17}$$

The reverse reaction,

$$C + D \rightarrow 2A \tag{18}$$

is similar to that already considered in the first case, and for this reaction it was shown that

$$\text{Rate}_2 = k_2(C) \times (D) \tag{19}$$

For equilibrium,

$$2A \rightleftharpoons C + D \tag{20}$$

and

$$\text{Rate}_1 = \text{Rate}_2 \tag{21}$$

Consequently,

$$\frac{k_1}{k_2} = \frac{(C) \times (D)}{(A)^2} = K_{eq} \tag{22}$$

In this case it will be noted that the equilibrium expression involves the concentration of A to the second power.

The two hypothetical cases considered are relatively simple but more complicated reactions offer no special difficulty. Thus, for the equilibrium,

$$2A + B \rightleftharpoons 2C + D \tag{23}$$

we may think of the forward reaction as taking place in two steps, the first step resulting in the formation of some intermediate compound, say A_2, which in turns reacts with B:

$$2A \rightarrow A_2 \tag{24}$$

and

$$A_2 + B \rightarrow 2C + D \tag{25}$$

The net result is the sum of equations (24) and (25),

$$2A + B \rightarrow 2C + D$$

which is the forward reaction of (23). Therefore the rate of the forward reaction is proportional to $(A)^2 \times (B)$ or

$$\text{Rate}_1 = k_1(A)^2 \times (B) \tag{26}$$

In a similar manner the reverse reaction may be thought of as taking place in two steps, and

$$\text{Rate}_2 = k_2(C)^2 \times (D) \tag{27}$$

At equilibrium, where $\text{Rate}_1 = \text{Rate}_2$,

$$\frac{(C)^2 \times (D)}{(A)^2 \times (B)} = K_{eq} \tag{28}$$

The same result could be obtained by assuming that some other intermediate compound, such as AB, is formed by the reaction

$$A + B \rightarrow AB \tag{29}$$

which in turn reacts with A:

$$AB + A \rightarrow 2C + D \tag{30}$$

In fact, it is not even necessary to assume the formation of any intermediate compound, but rather to consider the collisions between two A molecules and one B molecule simultaneously. In this case the rate in the forward direction would be proportional to the number of B molecules times the number of collisions between two A molecules. Since the number of collisions between two A molecules is proportional to $(A)^2$, then the number of collisions between two A molecules and one B molecule will be proportional to $(N_a)^2 \times N_b$. By the same arguments used previously,

$$\text{Rate}_1 = k_1(A)^2 \times (B) \tag{31}$$

and the same result for the equilibrium expression could be obtained.

In general, for the reaction

$$nA + mB \rightleftharpoons pC + rD \tag{32}$$

where n, m, p and r are small whole numbers, the expression for the equilibrium constant will be

$$K_{eq} = \frac{(C)^p \times (D)^r}{(A)^n \times (B)^m} \tag{33}$$

Expressed in mathematical language this is a generalized statement of the Law of Mass Action or the Law of Chemical Equilibrium.

In this expression it will be observed that the concentration of each reacting substance is raised to the same power as the coefficient of the respective term in the equation representing the reaction. According to convention the concentrations of the substances in the numerator of this expression are for those substances on the right side of the equation as written (products of the forward reaction), and the concentrations in the denominator are those for the substances on the left side of the equation (reactants).

Factors Influencing Equilibrium. Since at equilibrium a chemical reaction is proceeding in the forward and backward directions with equal velocities, it might be expected that those factors, such as temperature and concentration, which affect the speed of any reaction might also affect the equilibrium; that is, it might be expected that these same factors might change the balance between the two opposing reactions. To understand the problem more clearly, it might be advantageous again to consider the analogy between a chemical system in equilibrium and the horse running on a treadmill which increases its speed as the horse advances. If the horse, while running and apparently remaining stationary with respect to some fixed point, is spurred forward by a whip, he increases his speed and advances; but as he does so the speed of the treadmill also increases and again the horse comes to an apparently stationary position. For the second time, the horse and treadmill are in a state of equilibrium, but the horse has now occupied a position farther forward. If, on the other hand, a load is hitched to the horse he runs slower. Momentarily he shifts his position backward, but since the treadmill runs slower he soon assumes a new position of equilibrium. During the short interval that the horse advances or falls back the position of equilibrium is shifted.

In an analogous manner, the equilibrium position of a chemical reaction may be shifted, and it is common to speak of a **shift in equilibrium** to the right or to the left with reference to the chemical equation for the reaction taking place. Thus for the equilibrium between sulfur dioxide, oxygen and sulfur trioxide as represented by the equation

$$2SO_2 + O_2 = 2SO_3 \qquad (34)$$

all these substances are present in definite quantities and the reaction is proceeding in both directions. If now, by some influence, the equilibrium is shifted so that more sulfur trioxide is formed, we say that the equilibrium is *shifted to the right*. During the change from one equilibrium position to another the reaction proceeds momentarily faster from left to right than from right to left. The situation is analogous to the momentary shift in the position of the horse on the treadmill when he is spurred to a faster speed. With this explanatory introduction we may state the problem of this chapter more precisely. What factors shift the equilibrium of a chemical system of reacting substances?

The Effect of Changing the Concentration. The equilibrium existing in a chemical system may be shifted by increasing the speed of either the forward or backward reaction. In the hypothetical reaction

$$A + B = C + D \tag{35}$$

the forward speed depends upon the product of the concentrations of the A and B molecules while the speed of the backward reaction depends upon the product of the concentrations of the C and D molecules. If, when the system is in equilibrium, an additional amount of A or B is added, the forward rate is increased because the concentration of the reacting molecules is increased. The forward rate will momentarily be greater than the reverse rate; the system is temporarily out of equilibrium and C and D molecules will be produced faster than they disappear. But as the concentrations of C and D increase the reverse rate also increases until eventually it again becomes equal to the forward rate. A new state of equilibrium is attained. The addition of an extra amount of either A or B is like applying a whip to the horse on the treadmill. In the same manner that the horse moves forward, the equilibrium position shifts from left to right. In the second state of equilibrium the substances on the right side of the equation are present in greater concentration than originally. By increasing the concentration of either or both C and D the equilibrium can likewise be shifted to the left.

The equilibrium may also be shifted to the right by removal of either C or D. In this case the reaction from right to left is momentarily retarded and the reaction from left to right proceeds faster than that from right to left until a new equilibrium condition is again reached.

These same conclusions may be drawn by a consideration of the equilibrium constant. For the hypothetical reaction (35)

$$\frac{(C) \times (D)}{(A) \times (B)} = K_{eq} \tag{36}$$

If, when the system is in equilibrium, the concentration of A s increased, then momentarily the value of the above expression would be smaller than K_{eq}. The system must then shift so as to make the expression equal to K_{eq}. When this is done (C) and (D) increase and (B) decreases. In other words, some B molecules react with some of the A molecules that were added to form more C and D molecules.

In general, if the concentration of one of the substances appearing on the right side of the equation is increased, the equilibrium shifts from right to left and vice versa. If the concentration of one of the substances on the right side of the equation is decreased, the equilibrium shifts from left to right.

The Rule of Le Chatelier.   The effect of concentration on equilibrium, just discussed in the last section, is a special case of the general theorem known as the **Rule of Le Chatelier.**   This rule states that, for a system already in equilibrium, any change in the factors which affect this equilibrium will cause the system to shift in such a way as to neutralize the effect of this change.

The total pressure to which a system is subjected is often one of the factors affecting equilibrium. According to the Rule of Le Chatelier, if the total external pressure is increased, the system will change in such a way as to reduce this effect, that is, the equilibrium will shift so as to decrease the pressure. For a gaseous system, the shift will take place in such a way as to decrease the total number of molecules, for this would result in a smaller pressure. This effect of pressure may be illustrated by the reaction

$$2NO_2 = N_2O_4 \tag{37}$$

Consider the substances, represented by the formulae in this equation, to be in equilibrium and to be exerting a definite total pressure on the wall of the container. If the external pressure is increased, it will be momentarily balanced by the pressure exerted by the N_2O_4 and the NO_2. But by the Rule of Le Chatelier the system will change to a condition which will reduce the effect of the increased pressure. That is, the above equilibrium will shift in the direction of a fewer number of molecules, for two NO_2 molecules are required to produce one N_2O_4. In other words, an increase in the external pressure will shift the equilibrium to the right. Conversely, a decrease in total pressure (by expansion) will shift the equilibrium from right to left.

In the system consisting of ice and water in equilibrium at 0° C as much ice melts as is formed. This is an example of a physical equilibrium but it may be treated in the same manner as a chemical equilibrium. Therefore we may write

$$ice = water \qquad (38)$$

If pressure only is now applied to the system, water in equilibrium with ice, the system will change in such a way as to make the volume smaller, thereby reducing the pressure exerted on the sides of the container by its contents. Since water occupies a smaller volume than an equivalent amount of ice, some ice will melt as pressure is applied. However, as the ice melts it absorbs heat. The temperature will therefore drop and a new state of equilibrium will be reached. The melting point of ice decreases with increased pressure.

If a system of molecules in equilibrium in solution is diluted, the equilibrium will shift in such a way as to decrease the effect of dilution; that is, it will shift so as to produce more molecules or particles. Acetic acid is a weak acid which in solution consists of acetic acid molecules in equilibrium with its dissociation products, hydrogen ion and acetate ion, in accordance with the equation

$$HC_2H_3O_2 = H^+ + C_2H_3O_2^- \qquad (39)$$

Dilution decreases the concentrations of all substances but this dilution effect will be counterbalanced by the production of more particles; that is, the above reaction will shift from left to right. Conversely, if the solution is concentrated by evaporation the above equilibrium will shift from right to left.

The Effect of Temperature on Equilibrium. Let us now consider the effect on equilibrium of changing the temperature. Increasing the temperature of a reacting system in equilibrium will increase the velocities of the reactions in both directions. If the forward and backward reactions were increased by exactly the same amount by an increase in temperature there would be no change in the position of equilibrium. Returning to the analogy of the horse on the treadmill, an increase in temperature is like increasing both the speed of the horse and the mill. If the speeds of both increase by exactly the same amount the horse will remain in an apparently stationary position. If, however, the speed of the horse is increased to a greater extent than that of the mill, the horse will move forward to a new equilibrium position. Likewise, if the speeds of the forward and backward reactions are not increased by the same amount, a shift in the equilibrium position will occur.

The effect of temperature on equilibria can best be judged from the standpoint of the Rule of Le Chatelier. When any reaction proceeds in one direction, from right to left or vice versa, heat is either evolved or absorbed. Thus, when carbon monoxide reacts with oxygen to form carbon dioxide heat is evolved. This effect may be included in the equation

$$2CO + O_2 = 2CO_2 + \text{heat} \tag{40}$$

If, when all these substances are in equilibrium, the temperature is increased or heat is applied, the equilibrium will shift in such a way as to absorb the heat; that is, the equilibrium will shift from right to left, for proceeding in this direction the reaction absorbs heat. At higher temperatures, then, more CO_2 is dissociated into CO and O_2 at equilibrium than at lower temperatures.

While changing the concentration of one of the reactants and keeping the temperature constant shifts the equilibrium, it does not change the value of the equilibrium constant. The effect of temperature change, however, is to alter the value of the constant. The equilibrium expression for the reaction just considered is

$$\frac{(CO_2)^2}{(CO)^2(O_2)} = K_{eq} \tag{41}$$

K_{eq} has a definite value for each temperature and it may be deduced that the higher the temperature the lower the value of the constant. (Lower values of K_{eq} correspond to a smaller concentration of CO_2 and a larger concentration of CO and O_2).

Catalysts Cannot Shift Equilibrium. While catalysts are used to increase the speed of a reaction, they cannot shift its equilibrium position. It can be demonstrated that a shift in chemical equilibrium by a catalyst would be equivalent to a perpetual motion machine. It would only be necessary to bring the catalyst alternately in and out of the reaction mixture. Knowing that perpetual motion is impossible, we must conclude that a catalyst cannot influence the equilibrium position. The complete argument is one which falls into the scope of chemical thermodynamics and cannot be given here.

If a catalyst can increase the velocity of a reaction but not affect its equilibrium it must follow that a catalyst which increases the speed of a forward reaction also increases the speed of the reverse reaction by an equal amount. This deduction has been verified many times by experiment. Specially prepared iron, which is a good catalyst for the formation of ammonia from hydrogen and nitrogen is also a good catalyst for the decomposition of ammonia into its elements (the reverse of the formation reaction).

QUESTIONS AND PROBLEMS

1. Deduce from kinetic theory considerations that an increase in temperature will cause an increase in the velocity or rate of any given reaction.

2. If the velocity of a reaction doubles for every ten degree rise in temperature, how much faster would the reaction proceed at $100°$ C than at $20°$ C?

3. On the basis of the increase of reaction rate with increase of temperature explain why a mixture of hydrogen and oxygen explodes when ignited.

4. How much faster will the reaction, $H_2 + I_2 \rightarrow 2HI$, proceed if the partial pressures of the H_2 and I_2 are two atmospheres each than it will if their partial pressures are each one-half atmosphere (at the same temperature)?

5. What are the two classes of catalysts?

6. What is the distinction between a heterogeneous and a homogeneous reaction?

7. Is the neutralization of an acid solution by a basic solution a heterogeneous or homogeneous reaction?

8. What is meant by the term "irreversible reaction?"

9. If SO_2, O_2 and SO_3 are in equilibrium, has all reaction stopped either in the forward or reverse direction? The equation is

$$2SO_2 + O_2 = 2SO_3$$

Explain.

10. Show that for equilibrium for the hypothetical reaction

$$A + B = C + D$$

the concentrations of A, B, C and D must satisfy the condition that $\dfrac{(C) \times (D)}{(A) \times (B)}$ is equal to a constant.

11. If 5 molecules of the same kind in a given container make on the average ten collisions with each other every second, how many collisions per second would occur if 15 molecules instead of 5 were present?

12. In the equation $\dfrac{a \times b}{c \times d} = K$, where K is a constant, let the values of a, b, c and d be 3, 4, 5 and 6 respectively. What is the value of K? In each of the following cases determine the value of a, b, c or d from the value of K obtained previously and from the values of the other three letters; i.e., fill in the blanks to make the value of K the same as that previously obtained.

	a	b	c	d
(1)	3	4	10	..
(2)	3	4	20	..
(3)	..	4	5	3
(4)	..	4	5	12
(5)	3	..	5	12
(6)	3	..	5	24
(7)	6	8	5	..
(8)	12	16	5	..

13. Write the expression for the equilibrium constant for each of the following reactions:

(1) $HCN = H^+ + CN^-$
(2) $NH_4OH = NH_4^+ + OH^-$
(3) $H_2S = 2H^+ + S^{--}$
(4) $Hg_2^{++} + 2Fe^{+++} = 2Fe^{++} + 2Hg^{++}$
(5) $CO_2 + H_2 = CO + H_2O$ (gas)
(6) $2NO_2 = 2NO + O_2$
(7) $3H_2 + N_2 = 2NH_3$ (gas)

14. Consider the system represented by the equation

$$N_2 + 3H_2 = 2NH_3 + heat$$

to be in equilibrium.

(a) What will be the effect of adding more H_2 to the system? (Will the equilibrium shift to the right or left or remain stationary?)

(b) What will be the effect of adding more NH_3?

(c) What will be the effect of increasing the total pressure?

(d) What will be the effect of increasing the temperature?

15. What is the Rule of Le Chatelier?

16. Explain why a catalyst which accelerates the rate of a reaction in one direction must also accelerate the rate in the reverse direction.

17. At 60° C the solubility of KNO_3 is 110 grams per 100 grams of water, while at 20° C its solubility is 26 grams per 100 grams of water. Is heat liberated or absorbed when KNO_3 is dissolved?

18. When NH_4NO_3 dissolves in water heat is absorbed. Is NH_4NO_3 more or less soluble at high than at low temperatures?

CHAPTER V

Equilibria Involving Weak Acids and Bases

In the previous chapter we considered a generalized treatment of the Law of Mass Action or the Law of Chemical Equilibrium, which for liquid systems can be applied only to solutions of relatively insoluble substances or to solutions of weak electrolytes. Although relatively few of the known substances belong to this latter class, the majority being either strong electrolytes or non-electrolytes, yet from the standpoint of chemical equilibrium the weak electrolytes are of the greatest importance and henceforth we shall deal to a very large extent with equilibria involving this class of compounds.

Of all the weak electrolytes weak acids are the most important, not only in the subject of qualitative analysis and in problems of a purely chemical nature but also in biological systems involving the blood, the tissue and cell materials, and the glandular secretions. In many systems it is highly important that not only the hydrogen ion concentration be controlled but that a source of hydrogen ions be at hand to replace those which may be used up. The molecules of weak acids act as such a source of hydrogen ions for, as we shall see, the Law of Mass Action demands that as hydrogen ions are removed by chemical reaction, more molecules must dissociate to replace the ions that may be consumed.

The neutralization of both a strong and a weak acid by a solution of sodium hydroxide may be used to illustrate the action of a weak acid as a hydrogen ion reservoir. Hydrochloric acid and acetic acid, CH_3COOH, are typical examples of strong and weak acids respectively. Hydrochloric acid in a 1 molar solution is completely dissociated and the concentrations of the hydrogen ion and chloride ion are each 1 molar. Acetic acid in a 1 molar solution, on the other hand, is dissociated only to the extent of about 0.43%, so the hydrogen ion concentration in this solution is only .0043 molar. In spite of the difference in the hydrogen ion concentrations in the two cases cited, equal quantities of these two solutions will require the same amount of sodium hydroxide to neutralize them. When the sodium hydroxide solution is added to the solution of hydrochloric acid the reaction taking place is simply the combination of hydrogen ions and hydroxide ions of the acid and base respectively to form water, as represented by the equation

$$H^+ + OH^- = H_2O \qquad (1)$$

When sodium hydroxide is added to the solution of acetic acid we may regard the reaction as being made up of two steps or two parts. In the first place, we may regard the free hydrogen ions as combining with the hydroxide ions, the same reaction as with hydrochloric acid. As the hydrogen ions are removed, more acetic acid dissociates.

$$CH_3COOH = H^+ + CH_3COO^- \qquad (2)$$

This dissociation and combination proceeds until all the acetic acid molecules have been used up, and therefore the amount of sodium hydroxide required in the two cases will be the same. The over-all reaction for the neutralization of acetic acid by sodium hydroxide represents the summation of these two steps and is written

$$CH_3COOH + OH^- = CH_3COO^- + H_2O \qquad (3)$$

The acetic acid in solution consists principally of CH_3COOH molecules, and since it is these molecules which ultimately disappear during the course of the reaction, CH_3COOH, and not H^+ as in equation (1), must appear on the left side of the equation.

In later chapters we shall see how it is possible to calculate the hydrogen ion concentration after any given amount of sodium hydroxide has been added to the acetic acid solution.

Also, in a later chapter we shall briefly discuss the rôle of weak acids in controlling the hydrogen ion concentration in the blood.

The Ionization of Weak Acids. To illustrate the application of the Law of Chemical Equilibrium to weak acids, let us consider again acetic acid and its ions in solution. The acetic acid molecules are in equilibrium with the hydrogen ions and acetate ions, which equilibrium may be expressed by the equation

$$HAc = H^+ + Ac^- \tag{4}$$

Applying the Law of Chemical Equilibrium to this case we find that $\dfrac{Conc.\ H^+ \times Conc.\ Ac^-}{Conc.\ HAc}$ equals a constant. In a more abbreviated form this is written

$$\frac{(H^+)(Ac^-)}{(HAc)} = K_I \tag{5}$$

K_I is known as the Ionization Constant. In any Law of Mass Action expression the concentrations of the substances involved in the expression are given in terms of moles per liter, never as grams per liter or as grams per 100 ml.

In a 0.1 molar solution of acetic acid the concentrations of the H^+ and Ac^- ions are the same, and by experiment we know that their concentrations are each .00135 molar. The concentration of the undissociated acid must be 0.1 − .00135 or .09865 molar, since the total of dissociated and undissociated acid must equal 0.1 molar. (Note that the amount of undissociated acid is 0.1 − .00135 and not 0.1 − 2 × .00135, as a too hasty deduction might lead one to believe. Each molecule which dissociates produces one hydrogen ion and one acetate ion. A concentration of .00135 molar of either hydrogen ions or acetate ions in this case means that .00135 moles of acetic acid molecules are dissociated in one liter of solution.) The numerical value of the foregoing expression then becomes

$$\frac{(H^+)(Ac^-)}{(HAc)} = \frac{.00135 \times .00135}{.09865} = .0000185 \text{ or } 1.85 \times 10^{-5}$$

The value of K_I at 25° C is then 1.85×10^{-5}. At any other temperature acetic acid is not dissociated to the same extent. At 100° C, for example, the dissociation constant for acetic acid is 1.1×10^{-5}. In other words, the value of 1.85×10^{-5} holds for the temperature of 25° C only. However, at this temperature K has the same value for solutions other than 0.1 molar. For a .01 molar solution, for example, the same value of K_I is obtained. From this value of K_I it is now possible to calculate the concentrations of the H^+ and Ac^- ions in any solution of acetic acid which is not too concentrated.

In a .01 molar solution of acetic acid the total amount of acetic acid, both dissociated and undissociated, contained in one liter is .01 mole. If we let X be the concentration of the H^+ ion, then the concentration of the Ac^- ion is also X and the concentration of the undissociated acid is $.01 - X$. Then,

$$\frac{(H^+)(Ac^-)}{(HAc)} = \frac{X^2}{.01 - X} = 1.85 \times 10^{-5} \qquad (6)$$

In solving this equation for the value of X (the H^+ and Ac^- concentrations), let us first assume that X is very small as compared with .01; so small that the amount of undissociated acid $(.01 - X)$ is practically equal to .01. (X can be neglected in such equations only when it is added to or subtracted from some other number much larger than X. It cannot be neglected in the numerator of the foregoing expression.) The equation then simplifies to

$$\frac{X^2}{.01} = 1.85 \times 10^{-5}$$
$$X^2 = 1.85 \times 10^{-7} = 18.5 \times 10^{-8}$$
$$X = 4.3 \times 10^{-4} \text{ mole per liter}$$

The concentration of the H^+ and Ac^- ions is then calculated to be 4.3×10^{-4} molar. We may now inspect the original equation to see if we were justified in neglecting X in the denominator expression of $.01 - X$. $(.01 - .000431 = .009569.)$ This is almost equal to .01 and, for all practical purposes, the neglecting of X in the original expression was thus justified. If, however, X were so large that it could not be neglected (say 10% of the value from which it is subtracted or to which it is added) then the equation must be solved by the general solution of the quadratic equation (see the Appendix).

In a 0.1 molar solution of acetic acid the concentration of the H^+ ion is .00135 molar, while in a .01 molar solution we have just found it to be .000431 molar. The H^+ ion concentration is smaller in the more dilute solution. However, in the dilute solution a greater fraction of the total amount of acetic acid present is dissociated; 1.35% in the 0.1 molar solution and 4.3% in the .01 molar solution. We would be led to expect such a condition by a consideration of the processes taking place to maintain equilibrium. In the more dilute solutions the H^+ and Ac^- ions are farther apart and do not collide as often. Therefore a larger fraction of the molecules must remain in the dissociated state.

We can arrive at the same conclusion through an application of the Rule of Le Chatelier to this equilibrium (equation 4). Let us assume that we have a 0.1 molar solution in which, according to our calculations, 1.35% of the total amount of acetic acid is in the form of H^+ and Ac^- ions. These ions and the remaining undissociated acetic acid molecules are in equilibrium with each other. Now let us add some water to the solution to make it more dilute. This imposes a stress upon the equilibrium which in turn shifts in such a way as to undo its effect. The original 0.1 molar solution contained a definite number of H^+ and Ac^- ions but when water was added for dilution, temporarily the number of particles (ions plus molecules) per unit of volume became less than that originally present. To undo the effect of the stress (the dilution in this case) more acetic acid molecules dissociate to produce more ions, and since by dissociation one molecule produces two ions the net effect is to increase the total number of particles. The reaction proceeds in such a way as partially to undo the effect of the dilution. The dissociation of the acetic acid does not continue until the concentration of the ions, expressed in moles per liter, is the same as in the original 0.1 molar solution, since equilibrium is reached before dissociation has proceeded to such an extent. The removal of water from the solution would produce an opposite effect; H^+ and Ac^- ions would combine to form acetic acid molecules. There would be a shift in the equilibrium to the left (equation 4).

The Common Ion Effect. From a consideration of the Rule of Le Chatelier we can predict that the effect of adding either H^+ or Ac^- ions to a solution of acetic acid will be to shift the equilibrium in such a way as to decrease the amount of acid dissociated, i.e., to increase the amount of undissociated acid. From the Law of Chemical Equilibrium, which in fact is a more concise and exact form of the Rule of Le Chatelier, it is possible to calculate the extent to which the equilibrium is shifted and to calculate the concentrations of the H^+ and Ac^- ions present when either of these ions has been added in some form other than acetic acid. For example, let us calculate the concentration of the H^+ ion in a 0.1 molar solution of acetic acid when 0.1 mole of NaAc, sodium acetate, has been added to 1 liter of this same solution. Sodium acetate is a salt, a strong electrolyte, and is completely dissociated in this solution as well as in a solution made by adding it to pure water. The equilibrium is the same as that for the previous example except that the concentrations of the substances involved will be different. Let X equal the number of moles of HAc per liter which has dissociated. (In this case X will not have the same value as it would for a solution containing only HAc at this concentration.) The concentration of the undissociated acid is then $0.1 - X$. The dissociation of X moles of HAc produces X moles of H^+ ions and X moles of Ac^- ions, but the concentration of the Ac^- ion is not the same as that of the H^+ ion. In this case it is $0.1 + X$, since the sodium acetate supplies 0.1 mole of Ac^- ions per liter and the acetic acid supplies X moles per liter. The value of X, the H^+ ion concentration, may now be calculated.

$$\frac{(H^+)(Ac^-)}{(HAc)} = \frac{X(0.1 + X)}{(0.1 - X)} = 1.85 \times 10^{-5} \qquad (7)$$

Again simplify the expression by considering X small as compared with 0.1. Then both $0.1 + X$ and $0.1 - X$ are practically equal to 0.1, and the equation becomes

$$\frac{(X)(0.1)}{(0.1)} = 1.85 \times 10^{-5}$$

or $\qquad\qquad X = 1.85 \times 10^{-5} \qquad\qquad (8)$

We see that X is small as compared with 0.1 and we were justified in neglecting it in those terms in which it was added to and subtracted from 0.1.

The H^+ ion concentration in the acetic acid solution containing sodium acetate was found to be 1.85×10^{-5} M. In the pure acetic acid solution the H^+ ion concentration was 1.35×10^{-3} M, about 75 times larger. The dissociation of the HAc molecules was repressed by the addition of the common ion.

In the same way we could calculate the concentration of the Ac^- ion in a HAc solution to which H^+ ion has been added (as HCl, for example) and again we would find that under these conditions fewer HAc molecules dissociate. In other words, the addition of H^+ ion shifts the equilibrium again to the left as shown in equation (4).

The Law of Chemical Equilibrium Does Not Apply to Strong Acids. Hydrochloric and nitric are typical examples of strong acids. These electrolytes, like the majority of the salts, we regard as 100% ionized in solution. On the basis of the concept of complete ionization, the Law of Chemical Equilibrium cannot be applied, for in such a case the concentration of the undissociated acid would be zero and the value of the equilibrium constant, infinity. In a .01 molar solution of hydrochloric acid, for example, the concentrations of the H^+ and Cl^- ions are both .01 molar and that of the undissociated HCl molecules, zero.

$$\frac{(H^+)(Cl^-)}{(HCl)} = \frac{.01 \times .01}{0} = \text{infinity *} \tag{8}$$

The Mass Law expression applies only to systems of substances in equilibrium, and if no undissociated molecules of HCl exist, there can be no equilibrium involving this substance. However, HCl molecules were once regarded as existing in dilute solutions. As we have previously shown, solutions of HCl have a greater equivalent conductance the more dilute the solution. The fact that the more concentrated solutions do not show as high an equivalent conductance as the dilute solutions was regarded as evidence that there are relatively fewer ions present in the more concentrated solutions; hence, undissociated molecules were believed to exist. In a previous chapter it was shown that this decrease of conductance in the more concentrated solutions was due rather to a "drag-effect" (see page 20).

Following the older views for the moment, we shall tentatively regard hydrochloric acid as only partially dissociated. From conductance data together with this assumption we can calculate the fractional number of apparently undissociated and dissociated HCl molecules as well as the values for the apparent "dissociation constant" of hydrochloric acid at different concentrations. Table 9, page 103, gives the apparent "dissociation constants" of hydrochloric acid so calculated.

Passing from 0.2 molar to .001 molar the value of the dissociation constant so calculated varies more than tenfold. The same trend in the value of the equilibrium constant with varying concentration is obtained in the case of all other strong electrolytes. If we now compare these values with those obtained for acetic acid, which obeys the Law of Mass Action, we note a striking difference in the behavior of the two acids (Table 10).

* Any finite number divided by *zero* equals infinity.

TABLE 9

APPARENT DISSOCIATION CONSTANTS OF HYDROCHLORIC ACID
(Assuming Incomplete Ionization)

Concentration (Moles per Liter)	$K = \dfrac{(H^+)(Cl^-)}{(HCl)}$
0.200	1.56
0.100	1.05
0.050	0.73
0.020	0.45
0.010	0.32
0.005	0.23
0.002	0.15
0.001	0.12

TABLE 10

DISSOCIATION CONSTANTS OF ACETIC ACID
(Experimentally Determined from Conductance Data)

Concentration (Moles per Liter)	$K = \dfrac{(H^+)(Ac^-)}{(HAc)}$
0.07369	0.0000185
0.03685	0.0000186
0.01842	0.0000185
0.00921	0.0000186
0.00461	0.0000186
0.00230	0.0000186
0.00115	0.0000186
0.00057	0.0000186

In the case of acetic acid the constant has the same value well within 1% for a large range of concentrations. The lack of conformity of the strong acids and other strong electrolytes to the Law of Chemical Equilibrium was one of the chief arguments for abandoning the theory of incomplete dissociation for these substances and for adopting, instead, the theory of complete dissociation for all strong electrolytes.

The Extent of Ionization of Weak Acids. Weak acids differ considerably in their ability to ionize; the weaker acid, by definition, has a smaller tendency to dissociate. The ionization constant of an acid is of course a quantitative measure of this tendency. An acid with a very small constant has a small tendency to ionize while one with a relatively large constant ionizes to a larger extent. The following table shows a few typical weak acids together with their ionization constants at room temperature, and the per cent of ionization of their 0.1 molar aqueous solutions.

TABLE 11

TYPICAL WEAK ACIDS, THEIR IONIZATION CONSTANTS
AND EXTENT OF IONIZATION

Acid	% Ionization of 0.1 Molar Solution	K (Ionization Constant)
Dichloracetic	52	5.53×10^{-2}
Salicylic	10	1.1×10^{-3}
Nitrous	6.5	4.6×10^{-4}
Acetic	1.36	1.85×10^{-5}
Hydrocyanic	0.014	2.1×10^{-9}
Phenol	0.003	1.0×10^{-10}

The extreme variation among weak acids in the ability to ionize is well illustrated by this table; the extent of ionization of their 0.1 molar solutions varies from 52% for dichloracetic acid to .003% for phenol (carbolic acid).

The question which naturally arises is: When is an acid to be regarded as a weak acid and when a strong acid? Arbitrarily, we may answer this question in a simple way. An acid may be regarded as belonging to the weak class if its dilute solutions obey the Law of Mass Action. Such acids as hydrochloric, sulfuric and nitric are without question to be regarded as strong acids (100% ionized). When we search further for the reason that some acids are weak and some are strong, we find ourselves inquiring into the electronic structures or make-up of the molecules in question. The problem is a very complicated one which involves not only the tendencies of the different molecules to hold fast their dissociable hydrogen ions but also the tendency of surrounding water molecules to hold the dissociation products (hydrogen ions and negative ions) and thus aid the dissociation process. As we have pointed out before ions in solution do not exist independently in the condition indicated by their formulae but are surrounded by and attached, more or less firmly, to water molecules.

All Substances in the Same Solution Must Be in Equilibrium. When two or more weak acids, or in fact any weak electrolytes, are present in the same solution, they must all be in equilibrium with their respective ions. For example, if a solution contains both acetic and hydrocyanic acids, the following equilibria must be maintained:

$$HAc = H^+ + Ac^- \tag{9}$$

$$HCN = H^+ + CN^- \tag{10}$$

In this case the hydrogen ion is common to the two equilibria and since it exists in the same solution it must have only one concentration. The acetic acid ionizes to a larger extent than the hydrocyanic acid and produces more hydrogen ions, but this excess concentration of hydrogen ion represses the ionization of hydrocyanic acid and in this solution the latter is ionized to a smaller extent than it is when it exists alone in water solution. But the hydrocyanic acid also ionizes to a small extent to produce some hydrogen ions. For this reason the acetic acid is likewise ionized to a slightly smaller extent than it is in pure water. The common hydrogen ion represses the ionization of both acids in such a mixed solution. The calculation of the concentration of the hydrogen ion in a mixed solution (0.1 molar with respect to both acetic acid and hydrocyanic acid) becomes slightly more complicated than the simpler case of one acid, due to the necessity of solving simultaneous equations.

Some acids dissociate in two or more steps. Carbonic acid, H_2CO_3, is an example of this type. The first step of the dissociation of this acid results in the formation of the bicarbonate ion, HCO_3^-, and H^+ ion in accordance with the equation

$$H_2CO_3 = H^+ + HCO_3^- \tag{11}$$

The second step consists of the dissociation of the bicarbonate ion:

$$HCO_3^- = H^+ + CO_3^{--} \tag{12}$$

In any solution containing carbonic acid, both these acids (H_2CO_3 and HCO_3^-) are present and, like a mixed solution of acids, they are in complete equilibrium with each other and their common hydrogen ion. A fuller treatment of such acids will be considered in Chapter VII.

Weak Bases. Equilibria involving weak bases may be treated in the same manner as was done above in the case of weak acids with the exception, of course, that the bases dissociate to give hydroxide ions, OH^-, in solution.

TABLE 12

IONIZATION CONSTANTS OF SOME WEAK BASES

Base	% Ionization in 0.1 Molar Solution	K (Ionization Constant)
Methyl ammonium hydroxide	7.0	5.0×10^{-4}
Ammonium hydroxide	1.3	1.8×10^{-5}
Hydrazine hydroxide	0.054	3.0×10^{-6}
Phenyl ammonium hydroxide	0.0007	4.6×10^{-10}

The number of common weak bases is far smaller than that of the weak acids. The most common weak base is ammonium hydroxide, NH_4OH. This base is about as weak a base as acetic acid is a weak acid; the ionization constants are practically the same for the two substances. A few examples of weak bases appear in the table above; others together with their ionization constants are listed in the Appendix.

Just as ammonium hydroxide is known only in solution and not in the pure state, so methyl ammonium hydroxide and phenyl ammonium hydroxide are known only in solution. In the pure state these substances are known as methyl amine, CH_3NH_2, and phenyl amine, $C_6H_5NH_2$ (aniline), respectively. They are the analogues of ammonia with one hydrogen atom replaced by a methyl or phenyl group, and like ammonia, NH_3, they take up water in solution to form the hydroxide.

Indicators. Certain natural and synthetic colored substances have the property of either changing color or becoming colorless in dilute solution when the hydrogen ion concentration in the solution attains a definite and fixed value. Phenolphthalein, for example, is a colorless substance in any solution for which the hydrogen ion concentration is greater than 10^{-9} mole per liter. In solutions for which the hydrogen ion concentration is less than this value the phenolphthalein imparts a red or pink color to the solution. Methyl violet in solution is green when the hydrogen ion concentration is greater than 10^{-2} mole per liter, blue for hydrogen ion concentrations of 10^{-3} to 10^{-2} mole per liter and violet for solutions for which the hydrogen ion concentration is less than 10^{-3} mole per liter. A great number of such substances are known and enough can be selected so that the hydrogen ion concentration can be determined somewhat roughly over a wide range of concentration. The accompanying table of indicators gives such a series, together with their colors for corresponding hydrogen ion concentrations.*

Litmus, one of the first known of the indicators, changes from blue to red when the hydrogen ion concentration be-

---

* In all water solutions there is a definite relationship between the hydrogen ion and hydroxide ion concentrations. This relationship, which becomes evident from a study of the first two rows of the table, is treated fully in Chapter VIII on hydrolysis.

TABLE 13

INDICATORS

H⁺ Conc.	OH⁻ Conc.	pH														

H⁺ Conc.	1	10^{-1}	10^{-2}	10^{-3}	10^{-4}	10^{-5}	10^{-6}	10^{-7}	10^{-8}	10^{-9}	10^{-10}	10^{-11}	10^{-12}	10^{-13}	10^{-14}
OH⁻ Conc.	10^{-14}	10^{-13}	10^{-12}	10^{-11}	10^{-10}	10^{-9}	10^{-8}	10^{-7}	10^{-6}	10^{-5}	10^{-4}	10^{-3}	10^{-2}	10^{-1}	1
pH	0	1	2	3	4	5	6	7	8	9	10	11	12	13	14

Indicator	0	1	2	3	4	5	6	7	8	9	10	11	12	13	14
Methyl violet	yellow	green blue	blue						violet						
Methyl orange		red			orange				yellow						
Methyl red		red							yellow						
Brom cresol purple	yellow									purple					
Brom thymol blue	yellow						green					blue			
Phenol-phthalein		colorless										red			
Thymol blue	red				yellow							blue			
Thymol-phthalein				colorless									blue		
Tri-nitro benzene				colorless										orange	red orange

comes greater than 10^{-8} molar. The change is so gradual that it is not entirely red until the solution has a hydrogen ion concentration greater than 10^{-5} molar. Accordingly, litmus is a poor indicator for determining the hydrogen ion concentration of a solution.

In determining the hydrogen ion concentration of any solution, a number of indicators must be used and by a process of elimination the hydrogen ion concentration can be fixed within rather narrow limits. For finer work the color of the indicator in the unknown solution should be compared with its color in some solution for which the hydrogen ion concentration is known. Such solutions can be made by mixing known quantities of acids and their salts for which the hydrogen ion concentrations have been determined by other methods. The usual method of originally determining the hydrogen ion concentration of a standard solution employs the hydrogen electrode. This method cannot be discussed in this course. It is usually treated more fully in courses in quantitative analysis and in physical chemistry.

Indicators are generally considered as weak acids or weak bases, with the color of the indicator ion different from that of the undissociated compound. The general equation for the dissociation of an indicator acting as an acid is

$$Ind = Ind^- + H^+ \qquad (13)$$

With methyl orange, for example, the unionized acid (Ind) is red and the ion (Ind$^-$) is yellow. The dissociation constant for this indicator is equal to 2×10^{-4}.

$$\frac{(Ind^-)\,(H^+)}{(Ind)} = K_{Ind} = 2 \times 10^{-4} \qquad (14)$$

When the undissociated acid form and the ion form of the indicator are present in equal amounts (Ind = Ind$^-$), it is apparent that the H$^+$ concentration equals the K_{Ind}.

pH **Values.** For convenience the hydrogen ion concentration is often expressed in terms of pH values. The pH value of a solution is defined as the logarithm of the reciprocal of the hydrogen ion concentration. In other words,

$$pH = \log \frac{1}{(H^+)} \qquad (15)$$

The pH value of a solution for which the hydrogen ion concentration is 10^{-4} M, for example, is 4; the pH for a solution whose hydrogen ion concentration is 10^{-9} M is 9, etc. For a fuller treatment of this quantity the student is referred to the paragraphs on exponential numbers, logarithms and pH values in the Appendix.

pK Values. Just as it is often convenient to express the hydrogen ion concentration by pH values, it may also be desirable in some cases to express equilibrium constants by pK values. The pK for any equilibrium is defined as the logarithm, to the base 10, of the reciprocal of the equilibrium constant.

$$pK = \log \frac{1}{K_{eq}} \qquad (16)$$

Since $\qquad \log \dfrac{1}{K_{eq}} = - \log K_{eq}$

$$pK = - \log K_{eq}$$

Thus, for example, the pK for the equilibrium

$$HAc = H^+ + Ac^-$$

is equal to $- \log K_I$. The equilibrium constant for this reaction is equal to 1.85×10^{-5}. Therefore $\log K_I = \log 1.85 + \log 10^{-5} = 0.27 - 5 = - 4.73$; $pK = - (- 4.73) = 4.73$.

The equilibrium constants given in the tables (pages 484–488) in the Appendix are expressed in two ways. In the last column the value of the constant is given as a purely exponential number. The pK is the negative value of the exponent of this exponential number. The equilibrium constant for HCN, for example, is $10^{-8.7}$. The pK value for HCN is therefore 8.7.

Any equilibrium constant can be expressed in this manner.

The Brønsted Definitions of Acids and Bases. In the Brønsted system, acids and bases are defined in broader and more general terms than was commonly done in the past. The older established definitions restricted an acid to a substance producing hydrogen ions, and a base to a substance producing hydroxide ions in water solution. But it is well recognized that many substances other than hydroxides behave like bases in that they produce basic solutions and react with acids; sodium carbonate for example. Furthermore when solvents other than water are taken into consideration the number of substances which act like hydroxides in water solution increases greatly. The Brønsted definitions are so general that they include as bases all substances which combine with hydrogen ions not only in water solution but in all solvents. The definition of an acid is not greatly different from that previously used.

An acid is defined as any substance in ionic or molecular form, which produces or donates protons (H^+), while a base is any substance which accepts or acquires protons. We shall consider these definitions from the standpoint of the equilibrium existing between the proton donor and the proton acceptor, i.e., between the acid and the base. Since the equilibrium reactions are reversible neither an acid nor a base are considered separately; when an acid dissociates or transfers protons it produces a base and when a base accepts protons an acid is formed. This perhaps may be better expressed by the equation

$$\text{Acid} = H^+ + \text{Base} \qquad (17)$$

The acid produces protons (left to right) and the base acquires protons (right to left).

Since our consideration of acids and bases is to be restricted very largely to water solutions, let us consider the equilibrium existing between the proton, water, and the hydronium ion. This relationship is expressed by the equation

$$H_3O^+ = H^+ + H_2O \qquad (18)$$

Here H_3O^+, hydronium ion, is the acid (proton donor) and H_2O is the base (proton acceptor). This equilibrium is considered as being very largely in favor of H_3O^+, i.e., the concentration of free protons is very small indeed; almost all of them are attached to water molecules. Accordingly, the hydrogen ion in solution is symbolized by H_3O^+ and not by H^+. In the older established definitions all forms of the hydrogen ion, H^+, H_3O^+ and higher hydrates are represented as a group by the symbol H^+ and the equilibrium as expressed in equation (18) is never considered explicitly because it is recognized that the protons exist very largely in the hydrated form.

According to these definitions the ammonium ion is an acid.

$$NH_4^+ = H^+ + NH_3 \qquad (19)$$

In this case ammonia, NH_3, is the base. However, if this reaction takes place in water solution the protons formed attach themselves to water molecules to form hydronium ions and the complete reaction is

$$\underset{\text{Acid}_1}{NH_4^+} + \underset{\text{Base}_2}{H_2O} = \underset{\text{Acid}_2}{H_3O^+} + \underset{\text{Base}_1}{NH_3} \qquad (20)$$

In effect the proton is merely transferred from the NH_4^+ ion to the water molecule and *vice versa*. The NH_4^+ and the H_3O^+ ions are acids and H_2O and NH_3 are bases. The process is that of neutralization, with the salt formation not emphasized by the equation representing it. In this reaction, the two bases NH_3 and H_2O are competing for protons, with the NH_3 having the greater tendency to acquire them.

Water itself may act as an acid as well as a base.

$$H_2O = H^+ + OH^- \qquad (21)$$

In this case water is the acid molecule and the OH^- ion is the base. Again, this does not represent the complete reaction for according to reaction (18) the protons combine with water molecules. The reaction is rather represented by the equation

$$\underset{\text{Acid}_1}{H_2O} + \underset{\text{Base}_2}{H_2O} = \underset{\text{Acid}_2}{H_3O^+} + \underset{\text{Base}_1}{OH^-} \qquad (22)$$

In the complete reaction water acts both as an acid and as a base. It should be borne in mind that the OH⁻ ion is also hydrated but this hydration is not expressed in the formula. Hydration or combination with water is only expressed in the formulae for the hydrogen ion and for amphoteric substances some of which will be considered in a later chapter.

The fact that HCl in the pure state is virtually a non-conductor while its water solution shows a high conductivity is not as easily expressed in terms of the established definitions as it is with the newer definitions. Pure HCl, a liquid with a boiling point of $-83°$ C., dissociates into protons and chloride ions. The equation for this equilibrium is

$$HCl = H^+ + Cl^- \tag{23}$$

Both the proton and the chloride ion are probably "solvated," i.e., joined to HCl molecules. In fact we might reason by analogy that the formula of the hydrogen ion is really H_2Cl^+. On the basis of the Brønsted definitions we then can write the reaction as

$$\underset{\text{Acid}_1}{HCl} + \underset{\text{Base}_2}{HCl} = \underset{\text{Acid}_2}{H_2Cl^+} + \underset{\text{Base}_1}{Cl^-} \tag{24}$$

The reaction which takes place when pure HCl is added to water may be represented by

$$\underset{\text{Acid}_1}{HCl} + \underset{\text{Base}_2}{H_2O} = \underset{\text{Acid}_2}{H_3O^+} + \underset{\text{Base}_1}{Cl^-} \tag{25}$$

In this case the hydrogen ion is present as H_3O^+ while in pure IICl it is present as H_2Cl^+. The Cl⁻ ions are also different in the two cases but the difference is not indicated in the formula. It is apparent that HCl in the pure state and HCl in water solution are different but there is no *a priori* reason based on these definitions alone which tells us that the conductivity is very low in pure HCl, i.e., that the equilibrium in equation (24) lies largely in the direction of undissociated HCl, while in water it lies in the direction of the dissociated form (to the right in equation 25). By the older definitions both cases are represented by equation

(23); the difference between the two cases is implied and left more to the imagination or to the visualization of the experimental conditions.

Systems such as those expressed by equation (25) are known as conjugated acid-base systems. $Base_1$ is the base of $Acid_1$ and $Base_2$ is the base of $Acid_2$. A weak acid such as HAc in water solution, as indicated in the following equation, is also a part of a conjugated acid-base equilibrium system.

$$HAc + H_2O = H_3O^+ + Ac^- \qquad (26)$$

$Acid_1 \qquad Base_2 \qquad Acid_2 \qquad Base_1$

The new base indicated here is the Ac^- ion. It conforms in its properties with the definition of a base, that is, it shows a tendency to combine with the proton to produce the HAc molecule.

An acid which has a great tendency to donate protons is known as a strong acid while a base which has a great tendency to accept protons is a strong base. Acetate ion is a strong base and acetic acid is therefore a weak acid. Chloride ion in water solution is a very weak base; in fact it is so weak that in dilute solution it is no base at all, and therefore HCl in water solution is a very strong acid. In pure HCl, however, chloride ion is a strong base and HCl is a weak acid.

The ionization of a number of acids in water solution may be represented by the following equations. The order is given in decreasing strength of the acid.

$Acid_1$		$Base_2$		$Acid_2$		$Base_1$	
HSO_4^-	$+$	H_2O	$=$	H_3O^+	$+$	SO_4^{--}	(27)
H_3PO_4	$+$	H_2O	$=$	H_3O^+	$+$	$H_2PO_4^-$	(28)
HNO_2	$+$	H_2O	$=$	H_3O^+	$+$	NO_2^-	(29)
$HCNO$	$+$	H_2O	$=$	H_3O^+	$+$	CNO^-	(30)
H_2CO_3	$+$	H_2O	$=$	H_3O^+	$+$	HCO_3^-	(31)
H_2S	$+$	H_2O	$=$	H_3O^+	$+$	HS^-	(32)
$H_2PO_4^-$	$+$	H_2O	$=$	H_3O^+	$+$	HPO_4^{--}	(33)
HCN	$+$	H_2O	$=$	H_3O^+	$+$	CN^-	(34)

Acid$_1$		Base$_2$			Acid$_2$		Base$_1$	
HCO_3^-	$+$	H_2O	$=$		H_3O^+	$+$	CO_3^{--}	(35)
HPO_4^{--}	$+$	H_2O	$=$		H_3O^+	$+$	PO_4^{---}	(36)
HS^-	$+$	H_2O	$=$		H_3O^+	$+$	S^{--}	(37)

For strong acids, all of which are practically completely ionized in water solution, the following examples are cited.

Acid$_1$		Base$_2$			Acid$_2$		Base$_1$	
H_2SO_4	$+$	H_2O	$=$		H_3O^+	$+$	HSO_4^-	(38)
HNO_3	$+$	H_2O	$=$		H_3O^+	$+$	NO_3^-	(39)
HCl	$+$	H_2O	$=$		H_3O^+	$+$	Cl^-	(40)

All of the anions designated as Base$_1$ are to be regarded as bases. These are merely representative of a much larger number of anions which behave as bases in that they all show a tendency to acquire the proton. Of this group of anions, the HSO_4^-, NO_3^-, and Cl^- ions certainly show little if any tendency to acquire the proton. According to the older definitions we have already classified the corresponding acids, H_2SO_4, HNO_3, and HCl as strong and 100% ionized. How then can the anions of these acids be called bases? In water solution these acids are practically completely ionized, but in the pure state as liquids these acids show very little ionization. If we consider the reaction of Cl^- ion with the hydronium ion to form HCl gas or liquid, then there is some justification for calling the Cl^- ion a base.

Returning to equation (26), we may write the equilibrium expression as

$$\frac{(H_3O^+)(Ac^-)}{(HAc)(H_2O)} = K_{eq}^B \qquad (41)$$

The concentration of the water in the denominator remains practically constant during the course of any reaction since the water is either produced or consumed in amounts which are negligible compared to the total amount of water present. We may consider this value as constant and include it in the value for the equilibrium constant. It is therefore omitted from the expression which may now be written

$$\frac{(H_3O^+)(Ac^-)}{(HAc)} = K_1 = 1.85 \times 10^{-5} \qquad (42)$$

The symbol for the hydronium ion, H_3O^+, is merely a symbol for expressing the same particle in solution as is denoted by the simpler symbol, H^+. We may use any symbols we choose for designating particles in solution, but it is evident that the value for the equilibrium constant is independent of our method of naming the particles participating in the equilibrium. Accordingly, K_1^B of equation (42) has the same value as that given in the older established system, namely, 1.85×10^{-5}.

On the basis of the older definitions we have termed NH_4OH a weak base since it ionizes only slightly to produce NH_4^+ and OH^- ions. The equilibrium in solution is one which involves all three particles, the NH_4^+ and OH^- ions, and NH_4OH molecules. When NH_3 gas is passed into water the following equilibria are considered.

$$NH_3 + H_2O = NH_4OH = NH_4^+ + OH^- \qquad (43)$$

Whether NH_4OH molecules actually exist in solution we do not know, and as a matter of fact it makes no difference whether we consider the solution as one composed of NH_3 molecules, NH_4OH molecules, or both, since the equilibria are independent of our method of naming the particles.

Suppose we omit the intermediate NH_4OH molecule from our equation. We then have

$$NH_3 \quad + \quad H_2O \quad = \quad NH_4^+ \quad + \quad OH^- \qquad (44)$$
$$\text{Base}_1 \qquad \text{Acid}_2 \qquad \text{Acid}_1 \qquad \text{Base}_2$$

In applying our definitions of acids and bases, we see the NH_3 is a base since it combines with the proton to give NH_4^+ ion. This reaction can be considered as taking place in two steps, as can the other similar foregoing reactions.

$$H_2O = H^+ + OH^- \qquad (45)$$

and

$$NH_3 + H^+ = NH_4^+ \qquad (46)$$

The H_2O gives up H^+ ions which are then taken up by the NH_3 molecules. By adding equations (45) and (46), equation (40) is obtained.

The equilibrium expression for equation (40) is

$$\frac{(NH_4^+)(OH^-)}{(NH_3)} = K_{eq}{}^B = 1.8 \times 10^{-5} \qquad (47)$$

This expression is the same as we obtain when the ammonia in water is considered to be ammonium hydroxide, NH_4OH. The two substances, NH_3 and NH_4OH, are one and the same; different sumbols are used to designate them.

In equation (40) the reaction is one in which the two bases NH_3 and OH^- ion are competing with each other for the proton. At equilibrium the reaction will predominate either to the left or to the right depending upon whether the OH^- ion or the NH_3 molecule is the stronger base, that is, whether the OH^- ion or the ammonia molecule holds the proton more firmly.

On the basis of the proton transfer concept of acids and bases, it is apparent that the term "salt" is of little significance, since the ions of most salts may be considered either as acids or bases. These ions will either lose protons or acquire protons, and these two processes are all that is essential to conform to the definitions of acids and bases. Practically all negative ions may be considered as bases since they combine with protons. Many positive ions are acids in that they will give up protons but, on the other hand, most positive ions do not show this tendency to any marked degree. If a metallic ion is to be regarded as an acid it is apparent that its formula must include protons which it can donate. Therefore for this purpose the symbol for the hydrated form of the ion is used. Such cases will be presented later.

In the following chapters of this text we shall retain the established definitions of acids and bases, except in those sections in which we deal explicitly with the Brønsted definitions.

EXAMPLES OF PROBLEMS

Example 1.

Calculate the (H^+) in a 0.1 molar HCNO solution. What is the degree of ionization of cyanic acid in this same solution? $K_1 = 2 \times 10^{-4}$.

$$HCNO = H^+ + CNO^-$$

The concentration (0.1 molar) given for HCNO is that for the total HCNO in solution, both dissociated and undissociated.

Let $(H^+) = X$

(CNO^-) must also be X in this case, for as many CNO^- as H^+ ions are formed by the dissociation process.

$$(HCNO) = 0.1 - X$$

Substituting these values in the equilibrium expression, we have

$$\frac{(H^+)(CNO^-)}{(HCNO)} = \frac{X^2}{0.1 - X} = 2 \times 10^{-4}$$

By inspection of this equation we see that X is relatively small as compared with 0.1, therefore for all practical purposes

$$0.1 - X \approx 0.1$$

Then

$$\frac{X^2}{0.1 - X} = \frac{X^2}{0.1} = 2 \times 10^{-4}$$

$$X^2 = 2 \times 10^{-5} = 20 \times 10^{-6}$$

$$X = 4.5 \times 10^{-3}$$

$$X = .0045 \text{ mole per liter} = (H^+) = (CNO^-)$$

From the value of X so obtained we can readily see that we were justified in neglecting X as compared with 0.1, for $0.1 - .0045 = .0955$, which is near enough to 0.1 that, for the purpose of our expected accuracy, it may be neglected. If we solve the equation

$$\frac{X^2}{0.1 - X} = 2 \times 10^{-4}$$

by the use of the quadratic solution (see Appendix), we obtain a value for X of .0044 mole per liter. This again shows the justification for the simple solution.

The degree of ionization is the fractional number of molecules dissociated, or the amount per liter of the dissociated weak electrolyte divided by the total concentration (both dissociated and undissociated). Since, in this particular example, the concentration of H^+ and CNO^- is 4.5×10^{-3} mole per liter, the amount of the dissociated HCNO has this same value, for 4.5×10^{-3} mole of HCNO gives 4.5×10^{-3} mole of H^+ and 4.5×10^{-3} mole of CNO^- upon dissociation.

Degree of dissociation $= \dfrac{4.5 \times 10^{-3}}{0.1} = 4.5 \times 10^{-2}$ or 4.5%

Example 2.

In a 0.1 molar solution of a hypothetical acid, HA, the degree of dissociation is .025. Calculate the ionization constant for the acid HA.

$$HA = H^+ + A^-$$

$$.025 = \frac{\text{Concentration of dissociated HA}}{\text{Total HA}}$$

$$= \frac{(H^+)}{0.1}$$

$$(H^+) = 0.1 \times .025 = .0025 = (A^-)$$

The ionization constant $= \dfrac{(H^+)(A^-)}{(HA)}$

$$= \frac{2.5 \times 10^{-3} \times 2.5 \times 10^{-3}}{.0975}$$

$$K_I = 6.4 \times 10^{-5}$$

Example 3.

(a) What is the concentration of the H^+ in a solution containing 0.1 mole per liter HCNO and 0.1 mole NaCNO per liter?

$$HCNO = H^+ + CNO^-$$

NaCNO is completely ionized, so it contributes 0.1 mole CNO^- per liter. Let X equal the number of moles per liter of HCNO dissociated, which also equals (H^+). (CNO^-) will be $0.1 + X$ and the (HCNO) undissociated, $0.1 - X$.

$$K_1 = 2 \times 10^{-4} = \frac{(H^+)(CNO^-)}{(HCNO)}$$

$$= \frac{X(0.1 + X)}{(0.1 - X)}$$

Neglecting X in comparison with 0.1, we have

$$(0.1 + X) \approx 0.1$$
$$(0.1 - X) \approx 0.1$$

Then $\qquad \dfrac{X(0.1)}{0.1} = 2 \times 10^{-4}$

$$X = 2 \times 10^{-4} \text{ mole per liter} = (H^+)$$

(b) What is the degree of ionization of the HCNO in this solution?

The degree of ionization is the fractional number of molecules ionized. This is equivalent to the concentration of the hydrogen ion divided by the total concentration of HCNO present, both in the form of ions and unionized molecules.

$$\text{Degree of ionization} = \frac{(H^+)}{0.1} = \frac{2 \times 10^{-4}}{0.1} = .002$$

The per cent of ionization $= .002 \times 100 = 0.2$

Thus, 0.2% of the HCNO is present in solution as H^+ and CNO^- ions.

Example 4.

If 100 ml. of 0.1 M NH₄Cl solution are added to 150 ml. of 0.1 M NH₄OH solution, what is the OH^- ion concentration in the resulting solution? $K_1(NH_4OH) = 1.8 \times 10^{-5}$.

The concentration of the NH_4^+ ion is the same as it would be if the 100 ml. of 0.1 M NH₄Cl solution were diluted to 250 ml. by adding water, so the (NH_4^+) from the NH₄Cl $= 0.1 \times \frac{100}{250} = .04\ M$.

The concentration of the NH₄OH is the same as it would be if the 150 ml. of 0.1 M NH₄OH solution were diluted to 250 ml. by water, so the total NH₄OH concentration is $0.1 \times \frac{150}{250} = .06\ M$.

Substances in solution: $\text{NH}_4\text{OH} = \text{NH}_4^+ + \text{OH}^-$
Concentrations: $.06 - X \qquad .04 + X \qquad X$

$$\frac{(NH_4^+)(OH^-)}{(NH_4OH)} = \frac{(.04 + X)X}{(.06 - X)} = 1.8 \times 10^{-5}$$

Neglecting X as compared with .04 and .06,

$$\frac{(.04)X}{(.06)} = 1.8 \times 10^{-5}$$

$$X = \frac{.06}{.04} \times 1.8 \times 10^{-5} = 2.7 \times 10^{-5}\ M$$

i.e., $(OH^-) = 2.7 \times 10^{-5}\ M$

Example 5.

If 0.1 mole solid NaOH is added to 1 liter of 0.125 M HAc solution, what is the final H^+ concentration? (Assume no volume change.)

0.1 mole NaOH neutralizes 0.1 mole HAc to form 0.1 mole NaAc and leaves .025 mole HAc not neutralized in the one liter. The solution now is 0.1 M with respect to NaAc and .025 M with respect to HAc.

Substances in solution: $HAc \; = \; H^+ \; + \; Ac^-$

Concentrations: $.025 - X \quad X \quad 0.1 + X$

$$\frac{(H^+)(Ac^-)}{(HAc)} = \frac{X(0.1 + X)}{(.025 - X)} = 1.85 \times 10^{-5}$$

Neglecting X as compared with 0.1 and with .025,

$$\frac{X(0.1)}{(.025)} = 1.85 \times 10^{-5}$$

$$X = \frac{(.025)}{(0.1)} \times 1.85 \times 10^{-5}$$

$X = 0.46 \times 10^{-5} = 4.6 \times 10^{-6} \, M$ i.e., $(H^+) = 4.6 \times 10^{-6} \, M$

Example 6.

100 ml. of 0.1 M NaOH is added to 150 ml. 0.2 M HAc. Calculate the final H^+ concentration.

Before reaction, 100 ml. 0.1 M NaOH contains .01 mole NaOH.

Before reaction, 150 ml. 0.2 M HAc contains .03 mole HAc.

.01 mole NaOH neutralizes .01 mole HAc, producing .01 mole NaAc in solution and leaving .02 mole HAc not neutralized.

After reaction, the .01 mole NaAc and .02 mole HAc are contained in 250 ml. solution, so the concentrations are .04 M and .08 M respectively.

Substances in solution: $HAc \; = \; H^+ \; + \; Ac^-$

Concentrations: $.08 - X \quad X \quad .04 + X$

$$\frac{(H^+)(Ac^-)}{(HAc)} = \frac{X(.04 + X)}{(.08 - X)} = 1.85 \times 10^{-5}$$

Neglecting the X's in the terms $(.04 + X)$ and $(.08 - X)$,

$$\frac{X(.04)}{(.08)} = 1.85 \times 10^{-5}$$

$$X = \frac{(.08)}{(.04)} \times 1.85 \times 10^{-5}$$

$$X = (H^+) = 3.7 \times 10^{-5} \, M$$

Example 7.

Calculate the pH for a .01 M HCN solution.

$$K_{(HCN)} = 2.1 \times 10^{-9}$$

First calculate the (H+).

Substances in solution: HCN = H+ + CN−

Concentrations: .01 − X   X   X

$$\frac{(H^+)(CN^-)}{(HCN)} = \frac{X^2}{.01 - X} = 2.1 \times 10^{-9}$$

Neglecting X in the denominator,

$$\frac{X^2}{.01} = 2.1 \times 10^{-9}$$

$$X^2 = 2.1 \times 10^{-11} = 21 \times 10^{-12}$$

$$X = 4.6 \times 10^{-6}\ M = (H^+)$$

$$pH = \log \frac{1}{(H^+)} = - \log (H^+)$$

$$\log (H^+) = \log (4.6 \times 10^{-6}) = \log 4.6 + \log 10^{-6}$$

$$\log 4.6 = .66$$

$$\log 10^{-6} = - 6$$

$$\log (H^+) = \log (4.6 \times 10^{-6}) = .66 - 6 = - 5.34$$

$$pH = - \log (H^+) = - (- 5.34) = 5.34$$

(See also mathematical operations in the Appendix.)

Example 8.

The pH of a solution is 6.38. What is the concentration of the hydrogen ion in this solution?

$$pH = - \log (H^+) = 6.38 = - (- 6.38)$$

$$\log (H^+) = - 6.38 = - 6.00 + (- 0.38)$$

$$\log (H^+) = - 7.00 + 0.62$$

$$\text{antilog of } - 7 = 10^{-7}$$

$$\text{antilog } 0.62 = 4.17$$

$$(H^+) = 4.17 \times 10^{-7}\ M$$

Example 9.

What is the concentration of a HCN solution which is 0.2% ionized?

$$HCN = H^+ + CN^-$$

Let γ = the degree of ionization = $\dfrac{(H^+)}{C}$, where C is the total HCN concentration. Therefore

$$(H^+) = C \times \gamma$$
$$(CN^-) = (H^+) = C \times \gamma$$
$$(HCN) = C(1 - \gamma)$$
$$\frac{(H^+)(CN^-)}{(HCN)} = K_I = 2.1 \times 10^{-9}$$
$$\frac{C\gamma \times C\gamma}{C(1 - \gamma)} = \frac{C^2\gamma^2}{C(1 - \gamma)} = \frac{C\gamma^2}{1 - \gamma} = 2.1 \times 10^{-9}$$
$$\frac{C \times (.002)^2}{1 - .002} = \frac{C \times 4 \times 10^{-6}}{0.998} = 2.1 \times 10^{-9}$$
$$C = \frac{2.1 \times 10^{-9} \times 0.998}{4 \times 10^{-6}} = 5.24 \times 10^{-4} \, M \text{ HCN}$$

Example 10.

A 0.2 M HCN solution is found to have a (H^+) of $1 \times 10^{-6} \, M$. Calculate the (CN^-) necessary to maintain this (H^+).

$$HCN = H^+ + CN^-$$
$$\frac{(H^+)(CN^-)}{(HCN)} = K_I = 2.1 \times 10^{-9}$$

At equilibrium, the (HCN) has a value of $0.2 - .000001$ or $0.2 \, M$, while the (H^+) is maintained at $1 \times 10^{-6} \, M$. Then

$$\frac{(H^+)(CN^-)}{(HCN)} = \frac{1 \times 10^{-6} \, (CN^-)}{0.2} = 2.1 \times 10^{-9}$$
$$(CN^-) = \frac{0.2 \times 2.1 \times 10^{-9}}{1 \times 10^{-6}} = 4.2 \times 10^{-4} \, M$$

QUESTIONS AND PROBLEMS *

1. Will 0.1 mole of a weak acid in solution require more, less or the same amount of sodium hydroxide solution to neutralize it as 0.1 mole of a strong acid? Explain.

2. Is the percentage of molecules of HAc which are dissociated in a .001 M solution smaller, greater or the same as in a .01 M solution?

* Values for dissociation constants are given in the Appendix.

3. Considering HAc and its ions to be in a state of equilbrium,

$$HAc = H^+ + Ac^-$$

how can this equilibrium be shifted to the left and how to the right?

4. How does the application of the Law of Mass Action help support the theory of complete dissociation of strong electrolytes?

5. Which two indicators would you use to show that the hydrogen ion concentration in a given solution is less than 10^{-4} molar but greater than 10^{-7} molar?

6. Rewrite equations (1), (2), (3), (6), (7), (8), and (9) of this chapter in terms of the Brønsted definitions.

7. What pH values correspond to the following H^+ ion concentrations:

   (a) 10^{-5} (b) 10^{-9} (c) 10^{-1} (d) $10^{-7.38}$ (e) $10^{-2.1}$

8. What is the concentration of the H^+ ion in moles per liter in each of the following solutions?

   (a) 0.1 M CH_3COOH (HAc)   (f) 0.02 M HCNO
   (b) 0.01 M CH_3COOH (HAc)   (g) 0.001 M HN_3
   (c) 1 M CH_3COOH (HAc)   (h) 0.08 M $ClCH_2COOH$
   (d) 0.05 M HCN   (i) 0.004 M HCN
   (e) 0.01 M HNO_2 (j) 0.0001 M C_6H_5COOH

Use quadratic equation for (e) and (j) (see Appendix).

9. Calculate the concentration of the OH^- ion in solutions of the following:

   (a) 1 M NH_4OH (f) 0.01 M CH_3NH_3OH
   (b) 0.1 M NH_4OH (g) 0.2 M $(CH_3)_2NH_2OH$
   (c) 0.01 M NH_4OH (h) 0.1 M $C_2H_5NH_3OH$
   (d) 0.001 M NH_4OH (i) 0.002 M $C_6H_5NH_3OH$
   (e) 0.04 M NH_4OH

10. Solutions of the following weak acids and bases are ionized as indicated. Calculate the ionization constant in each case.

Solution	Per Cent Ionized
(a) 0.1 M CH_3COOH (HAc)	1.35
(b) 0.01 M CH_3COOH	4.20
(c) 0.1 M NH_4OH	1.33
(d) 0.01 M NH_4OH	4.15
(e) 0.1 M HNO_2	6.5
(f) 0.1 M HCN	0.0145
(g) 0.005 M HCN	0.065

11. Two grams of HAc are dissolved in 1 liter of water. Calculate the concentration of the H^+ ion and the Ac^- ion.

12. To the above solution (problem 11) 2 grams of NaAc are added. Now what is the concentration of the H^+ and Ac^- ions?

13. Calculate the degree of ionization of the solutes in the following aqueous solutions:

(a) $0.1 M HNO_2$ (d) $0.02 M NH_4OH$
(b) $0.01 M HCN$ (e) $0.08 M CH_3NH_3OH$
(c) $0.05 M HAc$

14. If the H^+ concentration of a solution which contains 0.1 mole of HAc and a certain amount of NaAc per liter is $.000025 M$, what must be the concentration of the Ac^- ion?

15. It is desired to make the concentration of the H^+ ion $3.5 \times 10^{-8} M$ in a $.05 M$ solution of HCN. This can be accomplished by the addition of KCN. What must be the concentration of the CN^- ion in such a solution?

16. A $0.1 M$ solution of NH_4OH, also containing some NH_4Cl, is found to have an OH^- ion concentration of $0.25 \times 10^{-5} M$. What is the concentration of the NH_4^+ ion in this solution?

17. How many moles of NH_4Cl must be added to 1 liter of a $0.1 M$ solution of NH_4OH to make the OH^- ion concentration $1 \times 10^{-5} M$ per liter?

18. If $.01$ mole HCl is added to 1 liter of the resulting solution in problem (17), what will be the OH^- ion concentration?

19. If $.01$ mole NaOH is added to 1 liter of the resulting solution in problem (17), what will be the final OH^- ion concentration?

20. A hypothetical acid, HA, dissociates as follows:

$$HA = H^+ + A^-$$

(a) If in a $0.1 M$ solution the degree of ionization is 1%, calculate the ionization constant for the acid.

(b) Calculate the concentration of the H^+ ion in a $.01 M$ solution.

(c) Calculate the degree of ionization in (b).

(d) Calculate the concentration of H^+ ion in a solution which contains $0.1 M$ of the salt NaA and $0.1 M$ of the weak acid HA, the total volume of the mixture being 1 liter.

21. Calculate the molar concentration of a solution of NH_4OH which is known to be 4% ionized.

22. What is the molar concentration of a solution of HCN which by experiment is found to be ionized to the extent of .01%?

23. Five ml. of 3 M HAc is added to 50 ml. of 1 M NaAc solution. Calculate the concentration of the H^+ ion in this solution. (The total volume is 55 ml.)

24. Five grams of NH_4Cl is added to 100 ml. of 0.1 M NH_4OH solution. Calculate the concentration of the OH^- ion.

25. Fifty ml. of 0.1 M HCl is mixed with 75 ml. of 0.1 M NH_4OH solution. Calculate the concentration of OH^- ion in the mixture.

26. Repeat problem (25) using NaOH in place of NH_4OH.

27. To 100 ml. of a .02 M solution of C_6H_5COOH is added 250 ml. of .02 M solution of sodium benzoate (C_6H_5COONa). What is the concentration of the H^+ ion in the resulting solution?

28. 4.75 g. of NH_4Cl is added to a solution already containing 2.5 g. of NH_3 and the total volume is made 500 ml. by the addition of water. What is the concentration of the OH^- ion in this solution?

29. Calculate the pH of the following solutions:
(a) 0.1 M HCl
(b) A solution containing 1 g. HCl per liter
(c) 0.1 M HAc
(d) A solution containing 0.1 M HAc and 0.1 M NaAc per liter

30. Using HAc and NaAc in different amounts in each case, give the concentrations of each of these substances for three different solutions, each solution having a H^+ ion concentration of 10^{-4}.

31. One hundred ml. of a 0.1 M HCl solution is added to 100 ml. of a 0.2 M NH_4OH solution.
(a) What fraction of the NH_4OH does the HCl neutralize?
(b) What is the concentration of the NH_4^+ ion? (Neglect that amount of NH_4^+ ion contributed by the NH_4OH not neutralized.)
(c) What is the concentration of the NH_4OH not neutralized?
(d) Calculate the OH^- ion concentration in the resulting solution.

32. In the following problem solid NaOH is to be added gradually to a solution of HAc. As the NaOH is added part of the HAc is neutralized. Even after the final addition of NaOH, the HAc will not be completely neutralized. The H$^+$ ion concentration and the pH of the solution are to be calculated after each addition of NaOH.

One-hundredth of a mole of solid NaOH is added to 1 liter of a 0.1 M HAc solution. (Neglect any volume change.)

(a) What fraction of the HAc is neutralized?

(b) What is the concentration of the Ac$^-$ ion? (Neglect that contributed by the HAc not neutralized.)

(c) What is the concentration of the HAc?

(d) Calculate the H$^+$ ion concentration.

(e) What is the pH of the solution?

To the resulting solution another .01 mole of NaOH is added. Again answer (a), (b), (c), (d), and (e). NaOH is added portion-wise (.01 mole at a time) until, in all, .07 mole has been added. After the addition of each .01 mole portion calculate the H$^+$ ion concentration and the pH of the solution.

Make a plot of pH as the ordinates (vertical axis) against the number of moles NaOH added as abscissae (horizontal axis). Note particularly that the pH does not vary greatly between .04 and .06 mole additions of NaOH. This phenomenon will be discussed in a later chapter under "Buffer Solutions."

33. From the data given in Table 13 calculate the approximate values of the indicator constants (K_{Ind}) for the following indicators, assuming them to be weak acids:

(a) methyl orange

(b) brom cresol purple

(c) brom thymol blue

(d) phenolphthalein

(e) thymolphthalein

CHAPTER VI

Heterogeneous Equilibrium — The Solubility Product — Colloids

Any equilibrium which involves some kind of boundary surface is a heterogeneous one. The evaporation of water in a closed vessel is a simple example of this type of equilibrium. Here the water vapor in the enclosing container is in contact with the liquid water through the water surface. Although all heterogeneous equilibria involve boundary surfaces, yet the concentrations of the various substances involved are independent of the area of this surface. For example, the concentration of the water vapor, or the pressure exerted by the water vapor, in any container in which liquid water is also present is independent of the amount of surface exposed by the liquid. The rate at which water evaporates from the surface is greater, the greater the extent of the surface, but the condensation of the water vapor, i.e., the return of the water molecules from the gaseous state to the liquid state, is also greater, the greater the amount of exposed liquid surface. As a result of increasing the surface both the rate of evaporation and the rate of condensation are increased in such a way that the concentration of water remaining in the vapor state is constant.

For a given temperature the rate of evaporation depends only upon the amount of surface exposed; in other words, the rate of evaporation is proportional to the amount of surface exposed. This statement may be expressed in symbols in the following manner:

$$\text{Rate of evaporation} = k_1 S \qquad (1)$$

where k_1 is some proportionality constant and S the amount of surface.

The rate of condensation is proportional to the rate at which vapor molecules strike a unit area of surface and to the amount of surface. The rate at which molecules strike unit area of surface will depend upon the pressure exerted by the vapor. (If, for any given case, the pressure exerted by the vapor is doubled, twice as many molecules strike a unit surface per second.)

$$\text{Rate on unit surface} \propto \text{pressure}$$

Therefore

$$\text{Rate of condensation} \propto P \times S$$

where P is the pressure.

Or

$$\text{Rate of condensation} = k_2 P \times S \tag{2}$$

where k_2 is some proportionality constant. At equilibrium the rate of evaporation equals the rate of condensation and

$$k_1 S = k_2 S \times P$$

Cancelling the surface term S from both sides of the equation,

$$P = \frac{k_1}{k_2} = K_{eq} \tag{3}$$

This means that for a given temperature the vapor pressure of water vapor (or of any liquid) is a constant and is independent of the surface exposed, since the surface factor S does not appear in the final equilibrium equation.

Another type of heterogeneous equilibrium with which we are to deal to a very great extent is the equilibrium between a solid and its ions in solution, i.e., the solubility of some electrolyte in water. To illustrate this type of equilibrium let us consider a specific example, the equilibrium existing between solid barium sulfate and its saturated solution, and let us apply the Law of Mass Action to this case.

According to the theory of complete ionization, the small amount of barium sulfate which exists in water is present only as barium ions and sulfate ions. Although barium sulfate is very slightly soluble in water, it is nevertheless a salt and therefore is completely ionized. It would be considered as practically completely ionized even on the basis of the theory of incomplete ionization, since its concentration is so small in the saturated solution. When equilibrium conditions are attained, that is, when the solution is saturated with the barium sulfate, the rate at which barium sulfate passes into solution from the solid crystals is equal to the rate at which barium ions and sulfate ions collide and deposit on the surface of the crystal. The rate at which barium ions and sulfate ions leave the solid barium sulfate will depend upon the amount of surface of barium sulfate in contact with the water. If in one case the surface of barium sulfate exposed to the water is three times as great as that in another case, the rate at which it enters the solution will be three times as large.

$$\text{Rate of solution} = k_1 S \tag{4}$$

where S is the amount of surface of barium sulfate exposed to the solution.

The rate of deposition of the barium sulfate will depend upon the rate at which barium ions and sulfate ions collide in juxtaposition on the surface. For a barium ion to deposit, it is also necessary that a sulfate ion deposit next to it, for in the barium sulfate crystals these ions lie next to each other. It would be impossible for only barium ions to deposit, since a positive charge would then develop on the crystal and crystals of barium sulfate could not be formed. The rate of combination of the barium and sulfate ions will then be proportional to the rate at which they collide with each other on the surface of the solid barium sulfate. The rate of formation of the crystal will then be proportional to the concentration of the barium ions, the concentration of the sulfate ions, and the surface. If the surface is doubled, twice as many collisions between barium ions and sulfate ions occur on the surface in a given period of time. We may then write

$$\text{Rate of deposition} = k_2(\text{Ba}^{++})(\text{SO}_4^{--})S \tag{5}$$

Under equilibrium conditions the rate of solution equals the rate of deposition, and

$$k_1 S = k_2 (Ba^{++})(SO_4^{--})S$$

The same amount of surface is involved in both processes of solution and deposition; the S cancels from both sides of the expression and we have

$$(Ba^{++})(SO_4^{--}) = \frac{k_1}{k_2} = K_{S.P.} \qquad (6)$$

$K_{S.P.}$ is an equilibrium constant which is designated more specifically as the solubility product constant, while the product $(Ba^{++})(SO_4^{--})$ under equilibrium conditions is known as the *solubility product*.

Analyzing this expression we see that as the concentration of the barium ion is increased, if equilibrium is to be maintained, the concentration of the sulfate ion must decrease in the inverse ratio. For example, in a saturated solution of barium sulfate in pure water the concentrations of both the barium ions and the sulfate ions are each 1×10^{-5} mole per liter. The value of $K_{S.P.}$ for barium sulfate is then $1 \times 10^{-5} \times 1 \times 10^{-5} = 1 \times 10^{-10}$. If now the concentration of the sulfate ions in this same solution is increased tenfold, that is, to 1×10^{-4} mole per liter by the addition of a small amount of sodium sulfate, then to maintain equilibrium the concentration of the barium ions must be decreased tenfold to 1×10^{-6} mole per liter, and now $(Ba^{++})(SO_4^{--}) = 10^{-6} \times 10^{-4} = 10^{-10}$.*

The product of the two concentrations must always equal 10^{-10}, the solubility product constant for the temperature in question. A decrease in the concentration of barium ions by the addition of sulfate ions, as just described, can only take place by the precipitation of barium sulfate. In other words, the barium ions can be removed from the solution only by the formation of solid barium sulfate. This general conclusion can be qualitatively deduced from a considera-

* If the coefficient in the mixed exponential number is 1 it is usually omitted. $1 \times 10^{-5} = 10^{-5}$.

tion of the Rule of Le Chatelier. The equilibrium is represented by the equation,

$$BaSO_4(\text{solid}) = Ba^{++} + SO_4^{--} \tag{7}$$

By increasing the concentration of the sulfate ions the equilibrium is shifted to the left, i.e., solid barium sulfate is formed, and this shift proceeds until a new equilibrium condition is established which, in the case cited above, results in a concentration of 10^{-4} mole per liter for sulfate ions and 10^{-6} mole per liter for barium ions.

We may apply the Law of Mass Action directly to this equilibrium without considering the rate processes involved and arrive at the same conclusion. Applying the Law of Mass Action to the equilibrium for equation (7) we may write

$$\frac{(Ba^{++})(SO_4^{--})}{(BaSO_4, \text{solid})} = k_1 \tag{8}$$

or

$$(Ba^{++})(SO_4^{--}) = k_1(BaSO_4, \text{solid})$$

But the concentration of solid barium sulfate does not change. Its concentration depends only upon the density of solid barium sulfate, which remains practically constant under all ordinary conditions. Therefore the product $k_1 \times (BaSO_4, \text{solid})$ is a constant, which we designate as $K_{\text{S.P.}}$

or

$$(Ba^{++})(SO_4^{--}) = K_{\text{S.P.}}$$

This is the same expression as that previously obtained (equation 6).

Applying these same considerations to silver chromate which dissolves slightly in water to give two silver ions for each chromate ion,

$$Ag_2CrO_4(\text{solid}) = 2Ag^+ + CrO_4^{--} \tag{9}$$

we obtain

$$(Ag^+)^2(CrO_4^{--}) = K_{\text{S.P.}} \tag{10}$$

In this case, however, for the deposition of silver chromate from its solution it is necessary that two silver ions and one chromate ion collide on the surface of the solid silver chromate, and therefore the concentration of the silver ion is squared.

Conditions Necessary for Precipitation. Every pure substance has a definite solubility in water at a given temperature. When the concentration of the substance in water solution exceeds this solubility value, either precipitation of the substance from solution or a supersaturated solution will be the result. The solubility product is a quantitative statement of the limit of solubility of any difficultly soluble substance which forms ions. When the product of the concentrations of the ions in the solution exceeds the value of the solubility product constant either precipitation will ensue or a supersaturated solution will be formed. Supersaturated solutions form with difficulty and precipitation is the usual result of excess concentration of the ions.

To illustrate this condition let us consider a specific example. If a solution contains chloride ion at a concentration of 10^{-5} mole per liter in the form of dissolved sodium chloride or calcium chloride, will a precipitate be formed when enough silver nitrate is added to make the silver ion concentration equal to 10^{-3} mole per liter? The condition necessary for precipitation is

$$(Ag^+)(Cl^-) = K_{s.p.} \tag{11}$$

The solubility product constant for silver chloride at room temperature is 1.56×10^{-10}. In the solution under consideration $(Ag^+)(Cl^-) = 10^{-3} \times 10^{-5} = 10^{-8}$, which is greater than 1.56×10^{-10}. We see that the product of the silver ion concentration and the chloride ion concentration exceeds the solubility product constant; hence, either precipitation will follow or a supersaturated solution will be formed.

If, in the above case, the concentration of the silver ion were made 10^{-5} mole per liter rather than 10^{-3} mole per liter, no precipitation would take place under any circumstances, for now the product $(Ag^+)(Cl^-)$ would be less than the solubility product constant,

$$(Ag^+)(Cl^-) = 10^{-5} \times 10^{-5} = 10^{-10} < 1.56 \times 10^{-10}$$

Supersaturation of Difficultly Soluble Substances. As we have already indicated, precipitation will not always occur when the product of the concentrations of the ions exceeds the solubility product constant, due to the slow rate of precipitation. However, once the small crystals are formed,

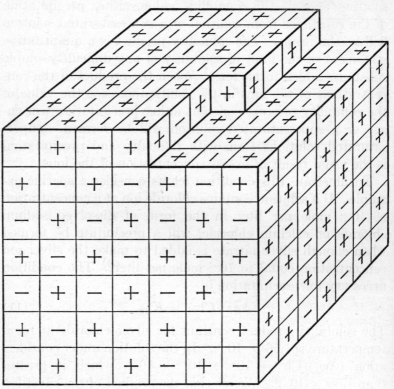

Figure 21.   Schematic Representation of a Crystal

the precipitation proceeds rapidly. The process of forming the first nucleus about which crystallization takes place is entirely different from the later crystallization. Any crystal which is within the limit of visibility even with the best microscope contains thousands of ions. Such a crystal is pictured in a general way in Figure 21.

In this case the ions only need find their regular positions and thus build up the crystal. When the crystal is started, however, the situation becomes entirely different. Figure 22 illustrates in a general way an incipient crystal. Here the

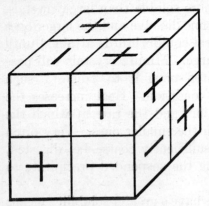

forces holding the ions are certainly different since each ion occupies a corner and edge position. An additional condition is that four or more ions be sufficiently close to each other simultaneously to allow the nucleus to form. This situation is probably rather rare. We see from these illustrations that the process of incipient crystal-lization is undoubtedly a more complicated phenome-

Figure 22. Formation of First Crystal Nucleus

non than is usually imagined. Barium oxalate, BaC_2O_4, and calcium chromate, $CaCrO_4$, are two well known examples of difficultly soluble salts which easily form supersaturated solutions.

Solubility of Very Small Crystals. Experiments have shown definitely that small crystals of any substance are more soluble than larger ones. Barium sulfate crystals, 10^{-4} cm. in diameter, are almost twice as soluble as crystals twenty times this diameter. The difference between the solubility of crystals 10^{-3} cm. in diameter and the solubility of larger crystals becomes inappreciable and it is only for very small crystals that this factor must be considered. Calculations have shown that ions in the interior of a crystal are bound with greater forces than are those on the faces or edges. Evidently a greater fraction of the ions occupy external positions for small than for larger crystals, and therefore the average tendency to enter the solution will be greater for the smaller crystal. From these considerations it can be deduced that crystals will grow in such a way as to produce as many interior ions (as few surface ions) as possible. Such a condition is attained only by the growth of larger crystals at the expense of smaller ones.

Since small crystals are more soluble than large crystals, the smallest crystals will in time dissolve and the larger ones will grow still larger. No real equilibrium is attained until the crystals are relatively large. Minute crystals will pass through filters and it is often possible to "digest" such precipitates to remove this condition. Heat increases the rate of solution, crystallization, and the rate at which the large crystals will grow from the smaller ones. Very often the precipitate will become sufficiently coarse, i.e., digested, either by heating or allowing the suspended precipitate to stand overnight.

The fact that small crystals have a greater solubility means that a different and larger solubility product constant must apply to these than to the larger crystals. The solubility product constants are calculated for solutions in contact with relatively large crystals. When calculating the concentrations of the different ions necessary for precipitation it must be borne in mind that a slight excess concentration over that demanded by the solubility product constant is required, since the first crystals formed are necessarily small. However, after crystallization has set in and relatively larger crystals are formed, the concentrations of the ions left in solution will be in accord with the solubility product constant.

Limit of Visibility of Precipitates Is Often the Determining Factor in Qualitative Analysis. Even though a precipitate may form from very dilute solutions of the reactants, yet that precipitate may exist in such small quantities that it is not visible. Such a precipitate would be of no consequence in qualitative analysis. For example, calculations show that a precipitate will be formed when a solution which contains as little as 10^{-20} mole per liter of copper ion, Cu^{++}, is saturated with hydrogen sulfide. Obviously, such a precipitate could not be seen. With silver chloride a precipitate is only visible when the solution before precipitation contains either silver ion or chloride ion at a concentration greater than 2×10^{-5} mole per liter. For the detection of a precipitate it is necessary that the ions producing the precipitate be present at concentrations sufficient to render the solid phase visible. The lower limit of "visible" concentration is about 10^{-4} mole per liter for most substances.

Increase in Solubility by the Formation of Weak Acids.
The addition of any acid to a saturated solution will increase the solubility of the salt if the hydrogen ion combines with the anion of the salt to form a weak acid. Thus, the equilibrium between silver acetate and its ions,

$$AgAc \text{ (solid)} = Ag^+ + Ac^- \qquad (12)$$

is shifted to the right by the addition of hydrogen ion in the form of a strong acid, such as nitric acid since the hydrogen ions combine with the acetate ions to form acetic acid.

All carbonates are soluble in acid solution due to the formation of the weak acid, carbonic acid, H_2CO_3 ($CO_2 + H_2O$). Barium carbonate is readily dissolved by hydrochloric and by nitric acid solutions. The solubility of barium sulfate, on the other hand, is not increased appreciably by the addition of hydrochloric acid because sulfate ions show little tendency to combine with hydrogen ions.

The solubility of any sulfide is increased by the addition of hydrogen ion, since the weak acid, hydrogen sulfide, and its weak ion, HS^-, are formed. In some cases, however, the sulfide may be so insoluble that an increase in its solubility as much as a millionfold will not be appreciable. In other words, for the very insoluble sulfides the addition of acid to the solution does not allow an appreciable amount of the sulfide to dissolve even though the solubility is increased enormously. Equilibria involving the sulfides will be considered in detail in a later chapter.

Colloids. If any relatively insoluble substance is prepared in a finely divided state and added to a liquid, such as water, a suspension of the solid in the liquid will be formed, which will ultimately settle to the bottom of the container provided that the suspended material is not too finely divided. Very finely divided suspended material will remain in continued suspension if no subsequent coagulation of the particles takes place. Such a system is a heterogeneous one and the substance in the finely divided state is known as the **dispersed phase** and the liquid, the **dispersing medium.**

When the particles in the dispersed phase are so small that they can no longer be seen or detected with the microscope, we may well ask whether this system is a suspension or a solution. If the particles were of molecular size, the system would be a solution, and if the particles were visible, a suspension or mixture would be formed. There is no sharp distinction between solutions and suspensions, and systems for which the suspended particles lie in this intermediate condition are known as **colloidal suspensions** or **colloidal solutions.** The finely divided dispersed phase in such a system is known as a **colloid.**

As we have said previously, molecules or ions at the surface of a crystal or particle behave somewhat differently from those in the interior. The properties of any substance which has a large surface compared to its volume are more like those of the surface molecules. A very finely divided substance has a very much larger surface than one consisting of large particles. Since colloidal particles are very finely divided the increased surface is responsible for some of the properties which distinguish this class of substances from substances as we ordinarily know them. For simplicity, let us consider the total surface area of the cubic particles contained in one cm.^{3} of a given substance. If only one particle is present, each edge has a length of 1 cm. and the surface area of the cube is 6 cm.^{2} By decreasing the size of the particle, the number of particles in one cm.^{3} and the surface area are greatly increased, as is demonstrated by Table 14.

TABLE 14

SURFACE OF ONE CM.³ OF MATERIAL FOR
DIFFERENT PARTICLE SIZES

Size of Cubic Particle, cm.	Surface, cm.²
1	6
0.1	60
0.01	600
0.001	6000
0.0001	60000
0.00001 *	600000
0.000001	6000000

While the limit of distinct visibility with the microscope is about 10^{-5} cm., yet particles somewhat smaller than this can be detected but not seen in outline. Such very small particles when viewed through a microscope with illumination from the side will reflect light and sparkle. Such a microscopic arrangement is known as the ultra-microscope.

The Brownian Movement. When very small particles are viewed through the microscope or ultra-microscope, they appear to be darting about in constant zig-zag motion. This motion of small particles is known as the Brownian Movement and is characteristic of all colloidal suspensions. When we seek an explanation of this motion we are led back to the kinetic theory of matter, which postulates that all molecules are in motion. Any particle in suspension is bombarded on all sides by the moving molecules of the dispersing medium. When the particles are sufficiently large the impact of the molecules on the side of the particle is not great enough to cause any appreciable movement. Furthermore, the bombardment on one side of the particle is counterbalanced by the bombardment on the opposite side, so the net result is that there is no appreciable momentum im-

* Limit of visibility.

parted to the particle in any particular direction. When the particle is very small the probability that it will be struck simultaneously with equal force on two opposite sides becomes small, and since the particle itself is small its velocity acquired by impact will be large and a visible motion results.

Classes of Colloids. Colloidal systems are not confined to the suspension of solids in liquids, although such suspensions are of most importance in qualitative analysis and in most problems in chemistry. One liquid dispersed in another is known as an emulsion; mayonnaise dressing is an example of an emulsion, essentially an oil in water. The different general types of colloidal systems are given below in tabular form.

TABLE 15

TYPES OF COLLOIDAL SYSTEMS

Dispersing Phase	Dispersed Phase	Type
gas	gas	none (homogeneous)
gas	liquid	fog
gas	solid	smoke
liquid	gas	foam
liquid	liquid	emulsion (mayonnaise dressing)
liquid	solid	suspension (muddy water)
solid	gas	solidified foam (pumice)
solid	liquid	
solid	solid	ruby glass

Adsorption. Any molecule, atom or ion may be conceived as being surrounded by a field of force, which field is not neutralized or "satisfied" when the particle is existing alone in space. This attractive force varies considerably with different particles. Thus the helium atom has a very small field, as evidenced by its very low boiling point, while the molecules of a substance having a high melting point or high boiling point possess relatively large attractive forces. When a molecule or ion is situated in the interior of a crystal these forces are neutralized or satisfied to the greatest possible extent. At the surface of a crystal, however, the attractive forces are not completely neutralized and the residual force of the surface molecules attracts other particles and holds them fast to the surface. This adherence of foreign particles to any surface is known as **adsorption.** The smaller the particle the greater the amount of surface will be and the larger the total effect of surface forces. Not all finely divided particles are perfect crystals and the less perfect the crystalline form the greater will be the adsorptive forces, for under such conditions the attractive forces of the molecules in the crystal are less satisfied by each other. Gelatinous precipitates like aluminum hydroxide and ferric hydroxide are very probably imperfectly crystallized and these substances have very great adsorptive capacities.

The small size of colloidal particles, because of the increased surface area, makes them particularly good adsorbents. Not only are neutral molecules adsorbed to their surfaces but ions as well. The adsorption of ions on the surface of colloidal particles is preferential, i.e., not all ions are adsorbed alike. In some cases negative ions are adsorbed more readily than positive ions. In such cases the colloidal particles become negatively charged. Some colloids, on the other hand, become positively charged through the adsorption of positive ions. If all the colloidal particles have the same charge, they will repel each other and prevent coagulation. The adsorption of ions of like charge, therefore, stabilizes the colloidal solution. When placed in an electric field — between two charged plates — negatively charged particles will move toward the positive plate and positively charged particles toward the negative plate. Under some conditions these particles become neutralized at the electrode and "plate out" just as ions may be plated from solution. By such a process rubber may be "plated out" of its suspension.

Finely divided barium sulfate has a great tendency to adsorb other ions from solution. In fact this tendency is so great that it becomes very difficult to obtain pure barium sulfate by precipitation.

Coagulation of Colloids. Not all colloidal suspensions are stable. Many of them tend to coagulate through the adherence of the particles for each other. When silver chloride is precipitated from solution it first forms a very finely divided suspension but in a short time these fine particles coagulate and settle to the bottom of the container. This process is hastened by heating, and in many instances this simple expedient is sufficient to cause coagulation.

When a negatively charged colloid such as arsenic trisulfide, As_2S_3, is in suspension, it may be coagulated by adding certain positive ions to the solution in the form of salts, acids or bases, which have a tendency to be adsorbed. The adsorbed positive ions neutralize the negative ions already adsorbed and the more nearly neutral particles then coagulate. In general, the hydrogen ion is highly adsorbed and the addition of an acid to this suspension precipitates it.

In general, those ions which are multiply charged are more effective in causing coagulation than singly charged ions. Aluminum ion is more effective than magnesium ion, Mg^{++}, and this ion in turn is more effective than sodium ion, Na^+.

In qualitative analysis finely divided precipitates are often very troublesome and annoying. Coagulation may often be effected by either heating or by the addition of an acid. It is evident that salts can very seldom be added to the solution, since in most cases they will interfere with the analysis.

The applications of dyestuffs to cloth fiber is usually a process of adsorption, the dyestuff being adsorbed on the fiber. Dyes will not "take" to certain fibers and in such a case the material to be dyed may be coated with a coagulant such as aluminum hydroxide or stannic acid, which in turn will adsorb the dye and bind it to the cloth fiber. Coagulants used for such purposes are known as **mordants** and the combination between the mordant and the dye is called a **lake**.

In qualitative analysis use is made of the adsorptive

properties of aluminum hydroxide in its detection. This substance possesses the property of adsorbing a dyestuff known as aluminon. When the latter is added to a suspension of aluminum hydroxide, $Al(OH)_3$, it is adsorbed preferentially by the hydroxide and the suspension, which is a lake, assumes a characteristic red color.

Catalysts. Preferential adsorption is the property that gives contact catalysts their special effectiveness. The substances which react with each other are adsorbed on the surface of the catalyst and the products formed are adsorbed to a lesser extent and thus leave the surface of activity.

The preparation of a catalyst usually greatly influences its activity. If the catalyst is prepared in such a way that the substance formed is not well crystallized, it usually becomes more active. Thus, when iron is used as a catalyst it is most active when prepared from iron oxalate. This compound is broken down at low temperatures to ferric oxide, carbon monoxide and carbon dioxide, and the ferric oxide in turn is reduced with hydrogen at a low temperature. At the low temperature perfect iron crystals form with difficulty; the imperfect crystals are the better adsorbers, hence the greater their catalytic activity. The addition of foreign substances such as sodium hydroxide or aluminum oxide often enhances this activity of the catalyst. These substances, known as **promoters,** very probably prevent the formation of perfect or large crystals by keeping the iron atoms apart.

EXAMPLES OF PROBLEMS INVOLVING THE SOLUBILITY PRODUCT PRINCIPLE

Example 1.

The solubility of $BaSO_4$ in water is .000242 g. per 100 ml. What is the value of the $K_{s.p.}$ for $BaSO_4$?

First, calculate the solubility of $BaSO_4$ in moles per liter. .000242 g. per 100 ml. is equivalent to .00242 g. per liter.

The molecular weight of $BaSO_4$ is 233.4.

$$\frac{2.42 \times 10^{-3}}{233.4} \text{ mole per liter} = 1.038 \times 10^{-5} \text{ mole per liter}$$

This means that there is 1.038×10^{-5} mole each of the barium ion and sulfate ion in solution.

The solubility product constant is therefore

$$(Ba^{++})(SO_4^{--}) = 1.038 \times 10^{-5} \times 1.038 \times 10^{-5} = 1.08 \times 10^{-10}$$

Example 2.

Silver chromate, Ag_2CrO_4, is soluble to the extent of .0431 g. per liter.   Calculate the solubility product constant.

The molecular weight of silver chromate is 331.8.   The solubility in moles per liter is

$$\frac{.0431 \text{ g. per liter}}{331.8 \text{ g. per mole}} = 1.30 \times 10^{-4} \text{ mole per liter}$$

Since silver chromate is completely ionized there is 1.30×10^{-4} mole of chromate ion and $2 \times 1.30 \times 10^{-4}$ mole of silver ion in solution.

The $K_{S.P.}$ is then

$$(Ag^+)^2(CrO_4^{--}) = (2 \times 1.30 \times 10^{-4})^2 \times 1.30 \times 10^{-4} = 9 \times 10^{-12}$$

Example 3.

Calculate the solubility of $CaSO_4$ in g. per 100 ml. from its solubility product constant. $K_{S.P.} = 6.1 \times 10^{-5}$.

Let X be the number of moles of $CaSO_4$ in 1 liter of solution.

Since $CaSO_4$ is completely dissociated, there will be X moles of Ca^{++} and X moles of SO_4^{--}.

$$CaSO_4(\text{solid}) = Ca^{++} + SO_4^{--}$$
$$X \quad \rightarrow \quad X \qquad X$$
$$(Ca^{++})(SO_4^{--}) = X^2$$
$$X^2 = 6.1 \times 10^{-5} = 61 \times 10^{-6}$$
$$X = 7.8 \times 10^{-3} \text{ mole/liter}$$

This is not only the concentration of the calcium ion and of the sulfate ion but it also represents the concentration of the total amount of calcium sulfate in solution.   The molecular weight of calcium sulfate is 136.   There are therefore

$$7.8 \times 10^{-3} \times 136 = 1.06 \text{ g. } CaSO_4/\text{liter or } 0.106 \text{ g./100 ml.}$$

Example 4.

Calculate the solubility of $Mg(OH)_2$ in g./liter from the solubility product constant. $K_{S.P.} = 1.5 \times 10^{-11} = 15 \times 10^{-12}$.

X = No. of moles of $Mg(OH)_2$ dissolved — (total)

X = No. of moles of Mg^{++}

$2X$ = No. of moles of OH^-

$$(Mg^{++})(OH^-)^2 = X(2X)^2 = 4X^3 = 15 \times 10^{-12}$$

$$X^3 = 3.75 \times 10^{-12}$$

$$X = 1.55 \times 10^{-4} \text{ mole per liter.}$$

The molecular weight of $Mg(OH)_2$ is 58.3. There are therefore $1.55 \times 10^{-4} \times 58.3 = 90.4 \times 10^{-4} = .00904$ g./liter or .009 g./liter

Example 5.

What is the concentration of Ag^+ in moles/liter left in solution if AgCl is precipitated by adding enough HCl to a solution of $AgNO_3$ to make the final Cl^- ion concentration 0.1 molar?

$$K_{S.P.}(AgCl) = 1.56 \times 10^{-10}$$

$$(Ag^+)(Cl^-) = 1.56 \times 10^{-10}$$

$$(Ag^+) \times 0.1 = 1.56 \times 10^{-10}$$

$$(Ag^+) = \frac{1.56 \times 10^{-10}}{0.1} = 1.56 \times 10^{-9} \text{ mole/liter}$$

Example 6.

(a) A solution contains .01 mole Cl^- and .001 mole CrO_4^{--} per liter. Ag^+ ion is gradually added to this solution in the form of $AgNO_3$. Which will be precipitated first, AgCl or Ag_2CrO_4?

$$K_{S.P.}(AgCl) = 1.56 \times 10^{-10}$$

$$K_{S.P.}(Ag_2CrO_4) = 9 \times 10^{-12}$$

(1) Calculate (Ag^+) necessary to precipitate AgCl.

$$(Ag^+)(Cl^-) = (Ag^+) \times .01 = 1.56 \times 10^{-10}$$

$$(Ag^+) = \frac{1.56 \times 10^{-10}}{.01} = 1.56 \times 10^{-8} \text{ mole/liter}$$

(2) Calculate (Ag^+) necessary to precipitate Ag_2CrO_4.

$$(Ag^+)^2(CrO_4^{--}) = (Ag^+)^2 \times .001 = 9 \times 10^{-12}$$

$$(Ag^+)^2 = \frac{9 \times 10^{-12}}{10^{-3}} = 9 \times 10^{-9} = 90 \times 10^{-10}$$

$$(Ag^+) = 9.5 \times 10^{-5} \text{ mole/liter.}$$

A greater concentration of Ag^+ is necessary to cause precipitation of Ag_2CrO_4 than AgCl, so AgCl will precipitate first.

(b) What will be the concentration of the Cl^- in this solution when the Ag_2CrO_4 begins to precipitate by the continued addition of Ag^+? Bear in mind that as the AgCl is precipitated by the addition of Ag^+ the Cl^- concentration is reduced.

The Ag^+ ion concentration necessary to precipitate the Ag_2CrO_4 is 9.5×10^{-5} mole/liter. For this concentration of Ag^+ the Cl^- concentration will be

$$(Cl^-) = \frac{1.56 \times 10^{-10}}{(Ag^+)} = \frac{1.56 \times 10^{-10}}{9.5 \times 10^{-5}} = 0.164 \times 10^{-5}$$
$$= 1.64 \times 10^{-6} \text{ mole/liter}$$

(c) What fraction of the amount of Cl^- originally present remains in solution when Ag_2CrO_4 begins to precipitate?

$$(Cl^-)\text{original} = .01 \text{ mole per liter}$$

(Cl^-) when pptn. of Ag_2CrO_4 begins $= 1.64 \times 10^{-6}$ mole per liter

$$\frac{1.64 \times 10^{-6}}{.01} = 1.64 \times 10^{-4} = .000164$$
$$= .0164\% \text{ of original } Cl^- \text{ present.}$$

Calculations Involving Both the Ionization Constant and Solubility Product Constant

Example 7.

How many moles of NH_4Cl must be added to 100 ml. of 0.1 M NH_4OH solution to prevent precipitation of $Mn(OH)_2$ when this solution is added to 100 ml. of a .02 M solution of $MnCl_2$?

$$K_{S.P.}[Mn(OH)_2] = 4.5 \times 10^{-14}$$
$$K_1(NH_4OH) = 1.8 \times 10^{-5}$$

In working this problem consider the concentrations of all substances in the final solution after the two original solutions are mixed. The concentration of the Mn^{++} ion will be .01 M and the OH^- just necessary to begin the precipitation of the $Mn(OH)_2$ can be calculated from its solubility product.

$$(Mn^{++}) \times (OH^-)^2 = .01 \times (OH^-)^2 = 4.5 \times 10^{-14}$$
$$(OH^-)^2 = 4.5 \times 10^{-12}$$
$$(OH^-) = 2.1 \times 10^{-6} \text{ mole/liter}$$

If the (OH^-) exceeds this value calculated, $Mn(OH)_2$ will be precipitated. To prevent precipitation, the (OH^-) must be less than this value. The (OH^-) can be diminished by the addition of

NH_4^+, in the form of NH_4Cl. The concentration of the NH_4^+ ion in equilibrium with this low concentration of OH^- can be calculated from the K_1 for NH_4OH.

$$\frac{(NH_4^+)(OH^-)}{(NH_4OH)} = 1.8 \times 10^{-5}$$

The (NH_4OH) is practically .05 mole per liter.

$$\frac{(NH_4^+) \times 2.1 \times 10^{-6}}{.05} = 1.8 \times 10^{-5}$$

$$(NH_4^+) = \frac{1.8 \times 10^{-5} \times .05}{2.1 \times 10^{-6}}$$

$$= 0.43 \text{ mole/liter}$$

$$= .086 \text{ mole/200 ml.}$$

Since this is the total amount of NH_4^+ which must be added in the form of NH_4Cl, it is this amount which must be added to the original 100 ml. of NH_4OH. The amount of NH_4^+ ion formed by the dissociation of NH_4OH is negligibly small and has been neglected.

QUESTIONS AND PROBLEMS

1. What is a heterogeneous equilibrium?

2. If solid barium sulfate is in equilibrium with its ions, Ba^{++} and SO_4^{--}, in solution, will this equilibrium be affected by the addition of more solid barium sulfate?

3. If in a saturated solution of silver chloride, the concentrations of the Ag^+ and Cl^- are each $1.25 \times 10^{-5} M$, what will be the final concentration of the Ag^+ if sufficient sodium chloride is added to the solution to increase the Cl^- concentration 100-fold?

4. What are the conditions necessary for the precipitation of a relatively insoluble salt?

5. If the product of the concentrations of the ions exceeds the solubility product will precipitation always result? Explain.

6. Is the solubility product for very small crystals the same as that for large crystals?

7. Explain why small crystals would be expected to be more soluble than large crystals.

8. What is the order of magnitude of the concentration of the ions necessary to produce a precipitate visible to the naked eye?

9. If a cube 1 cm. on the side is divided into one million cubes each of the same size, how much is the total surface increased?

10. Why do the surfaces of imperfect crystals adsorb substances to a greater extent than those of perfect crystals?

11. How may colloids be coagulated?

12. Explain the use of aluminon in qualitative analysis.

13. Why are catalysts more active when prepared at low temperatures?

14. The solubility of each of the following salts is given below in terms of grams per 100 ml. of solution. Calculate the solubility product constant for each substance.

Substance	Solubility in grams per 100 ml.
(a) $AgCl$	1.79×10^{-4}
(b) $AgBr$	1.65×10^{-5}
(c) AgI	2.88×10^{-7}
(d) $BaSO_4$	2.43×10^{-4}
(e) Ag_2CrO_4	4.32×10^{-3}
(f) $CaCO_3$	0.943×10^{-3}
(g) SrF_2	1.22×10^{-2}

15. The solubility product constants are given below for a few difficultly soluble substances. Calculate the solubility of each in terms of grams of solute per 100 ml. of solution.

Substance	Solubility Product Constant
(a) $Mg(OH)_2$	1.5×10^{-11}
(b) $BaCO_3$	8.1×10^{-9}
(c) Ag_2CrO_4	9.0×10^{-12}
(d) $Fe(OH)_3$	1.5×10^{-36}
(e) MgC_2O_4	8.8×10^{-5}
(f) $SrSO_4$	2.9×10^{-7}
(g) CuI	5.1×10^{-12}
(h) $AgCN$	2.2×10^{-12}

16. The solubility product constant for $BaCrO_4$ is 2.4×10^{-10}. If the concentration of the barium ion in a solution is .04 M, calculate the minimum concentration of the chromate ion, in terms of moles per liter, that will be required to begin the precipitation of barium chromate, assuming that a supersaturated solution is not formed. How many grams of sodium chromate must be added to 200 ml. of water to produce this amount of chromate ion?

17. How many grams of silver chromate will dissolve in 100 ml. of 0.1 M potassium chromate solution?

18. (a) Calculate the number of grams of PbS that would precipitate from 1 liter of saturated solution of PbI_2, if the solution is saturated with H_2S, assuming that the concentration of the sulfide ion is kept at 1.2×10^{-15} mole per liter.

(b) How many moles of Pb^{++} are left in solution?

19. Calculate the number of moles of AgCl that will dissolve (a) in 1 liter of 0.1 M KCl solution.

(b) in 1 liter of 0.1 M $CaCl_2$ solution.

20. If $AgNO_3$ is added slowly to each of the following solutions, calculate the concentration of the Ag^+ ion in the resulting solution just after the first trace of precipitate appears.

(a) 0.1 M KBr solution.　　　(b) 0.1 M K_2CrO_4 solution.

(c) A solution containing 1 mole HCl and .001 mole KI per liter.

21. The solubility of PbI_2 is .0701 g. per 100 ml. at room temperature.

(a) What is the concentration of Pb^{++}? Of I^-?

(b) Write the solubility product expression for PbI_2.

(c) Calculate the solubility product constant for PbI_2.

22. The solubility product constant for calcium oxalate at room temperature is 2.6×10^{-9}.

(a) What is the concentration of Ca^{++} and of $C_2O_4^{--}$ in a saturated solution of calcium oxalate?

(b) Calculate the number of grams of calcium oxalate dissolved in a liter of saturated solution.

23. The solubility product constant for lead iodate at room temperature is 2.6×10^{-13}. How many grams of lead iodate are required to make 200 ml. of a saturated solution?

24. Calculate the concentration of the OH^- in a saturated solution of silver hydroxide.

25. How many grams of NaOH are required to start the precipitation of $Mg(OH)_2$ in 100 ml. of a solution which contains 0.1 g. of $MgCl_2$?

26. If to a liter of solution containing 0.1 mole of Ag^+ enough Cl^- is added to make the final concentration of the Cl^- ion remaining in solution 1×10^{-4} mole per liter, what fraction of Ag^+ is left in solution?   (Assume no volume change.)

27. $AgNO_3$ is added to a solution containing .001 mole Cl^- and .001 mole Br^- per liter.   What are the concentrations of Cl^- and of Br^- remaining when the AgCl just begins to precipitate?

28. How many grams of Ag^+ are present in (a) 5 ml. of a saturated solution of AgBr?

(b) 5 ml. of a saturated solution of AgCl?

29. How many moles of AgCl would dissolve in 1 liter of the following solutions:

(a) 0.1 M NaCl   (d) 0.1 M $AgNO_3$

(b) 0.1 M KNO_3 (e) 1×10^{-5} M HCl

(c) Pure water

30. Solid AgCl is added to a 0.1 M KBr solution.   What is the ratio of the (Cl^-) to the (Br^-) in the solution when equilibrium is attained?

31. The solubility of the AgI is 2.88×10^{-7} g. per 100 ml. in water, and that of AgCl is 1.79×10^{-4} g. per 100 ml.   Assuming that there is no volume change when pulverized solid $AgNO_3$ is added little by little to 1 liter of a solution containing 0.1 mole of KCl and 0.1 mole of KI:

(a) At what concentration of Ag^+ will AgI first precipitate?

(b) At what concentration of Ag^+ will AgCl begin to precipitate?

(c) Which precipitates first, AgI or AgCl?

(d) What will be the concentration of I^- when AgCl starts to precipitate?

(e) What percentage of the I^- initially present will remain in solution when AgCl begins to precipitate?

(f) What will be the ratio of the concentration of Cl^- to that of I^- in the solution when AgCl begins to precipitate?   (Use result of (d) to obtain answer.)

(g) When half of the Cl^- initially present has been precipitated as AgCl, what will be the concentration of (1) Ag^+ and (2) I^- in the supernatant liquid?

(h) What is the ratio of the concentration of Cl^- to that of I^- in the supernatant liquid of part (g)?

32. The solubility of PbI_2 is 1.52×10^{-3} mole per liter and that of AgI 1.23×10^{-8} mole per liter at room temperature. Assuming that there is no volume change when solid NaI is added slowly to 1 liter of a solution which is .01 M in Pb^{++} and .01 M in Ag^+:

(a) At what concentration of I^- will AgI first precipitate?

(b) At what concentration of I^- will PbI_2 first precipitate?

(c) Which will precipitate first, AgI or PbI_2?

(d) What will be the concentration of Ag^+ in the solution when PbI_2 first starts to precipitate?

(e) What is, therefore, the ratio of the concentration of Pb^{++} to that of Ag^+ at this point?

(f) When the concentration of Pb^{++} has been reduced to half of its original value, what will be the concentration of I^-?

(g) Then what will the concentration of Ag^+ be at this concentration of Pb^{++}?

(h) What is then the ratio of the concentration of Pb^{++} to that of Ag^+ at the point described in parts (f) and (g)? Compare with the answer to part (e).

(i) When AgI and PbI_2 precipitate together, show from the solubility product constants that the concentration of the Ag^+ is always proportional to the square root of the concentration of the Pb^{++} under these conditions.

(j) Why are the ratios found in parts (c) and (h) not the same, whereas similar ratios in Problem 31 were found equal?

33. How many moles of $AgAc$ will dissolve in a liter of a 0.1 M HNO_3 solution? (The $K_{S.P.}$ for $AgAc$ is 4×10^{-3}.) (Note that in the resulting solution the concentration of HAc (unionized) is approximately 0.1 M.)

34. A solution contains .01 M Mg^{++} and .05 M NH_4Cl. How much NH_4OH must be added to 1 liter of this solution to begin the precipitation of $Mg(OH)_2$?

35. How many grams of NH_4Cl must be added to 50 ml. of 0.2 M NH_4OH to prevent the precipitation of $Mn(OH)_2$ when this solution is added to 50 ml. of .02 M $MnCl_2$ solution?

36. If 50 g. of $MgCl_2$ and 50 ml. of 6 M NH_4OH are added to enough water to make 1 liter of solution, how much NH_4Cl in grams must be added to this same solution to prevent precipitation of $Mg(OH)_2$? (Assume no volume change.)

37. A solution is .01 M in hydrogen ion and 0.1 M with respect to acetic acid. Calculate the concentration of the silver ion, in moles per liter, that will be required to just start precipitation of silver acetate.

CHAPTER VII

Polybasic Acids — Precipitation with Hydrogen Sulfide

Polybasic acids are those acids the molecules of which have more than one replaceable hydrogen atom and therefore dissociate to produce hydrogen ions in more than one step. Dibasic acids and tribasic acids, which are special classes of polybasic acids, have two and three replaceable hydrogen atoms respectively. Phosphoric acid, an example of a tribasic acid, dissociates to produce hydrogen ion in three steps, which are represented by the equations:

$$H_3PO_4 = H_2PO_4^- + H^+ \qquad (1)$$

$$H_2PO_4^- = HPO_4^{--} + H^+ \qquad (2)$$

$$HPO_4^{--} = PO_4^{---} + H^+ \qquad (3)$$

The process represented by equation (1) takes place to a greater extent than either (2) or (3), and (2) to a greater extent than (3). The ions, $H_2PO_4^-$ and HPO_4^{--}, resulting from the dissociation of phosphoric acid, are likewise acids and the relative strengths of H_3PO_4 and these ions as acids can be readily determined by a consideration of the three dissociation constants for phosphoric acid. The dissociation constant for the process represented by equation (1) is 7.5×10^{-3}; for the process represented by equation (2), 6.3×10^{-8}; and for (3), 3.6×10^{-13}. A 0.1 molar solution of phosphoric acid dissociates according to equation (1) to the extent of about 25%, while the concentration of PO_4^{---} in this same solution produced by step (3) is only about 10^{-18} molar. This small concentration of PO_4^{---} ion is the reason that most insoluble phosphates cannot be precipitated from phosphoric acid solution.

Sulfuric acid, the commonest example of a dibasic acid, is

100% dissociated into H^+ and HSO_4^- ions. The bisulfate ion, which dissociates according to the equation

$$HSO_4^- = H^+ + SO_4^{--} \tag{4}$$

behaves like a weak acid. Its dissociation constant is very nearly 1×10^{-2} and in a 0.1 molar H_2SO_4 solution the concentration of the SO_4^{--} is approximately .01 molar; i.e., about 10% of the HSO_4^- dissociates in sulfuric acid of this concentration. The bisulfate ion in a 0.1 molar solution of $NaHSO_4$, on the other hand, dissociates to the extent of about 30%. The dissociation of the HSO_4^- in sulfuric acid solution is less than that in a solution of $NaHSO_4$ of the same concentration because the excess H^+ has a common ion effect in the H_2SO_4 solution and represses the ionization of the HSO_4^-. There are no polybasic acids which are 100% dissociated in every step of the ionization.

Two common examples of dibasic acids which are weak in both stages of ionization are hydrogen sulfide, H_2S, and carbonic acid, H_2CO_3.

The first stage in the dissociation of hydrogen sulfide produces hydrogen and bisulfide ions.

$$H_2S = H^+ + HS^- \tag{5}$$

The HS^- formed in this reaction in turn dissociates to form hydrogen ion and sulfide ion.

$$HS^- = H^+ + S^{--} \tag{6}$$

The equilibrium expression for the first stage (equation 5) is

$$\frac{(H^+)(HS^-)}{(H_2S)} = K_1 = 9 \times 10^{-8} \tag{7}$$

and for the second stage,

$$\frac{(H^+)(S^{--})}{(HS^-)} = K_2 = 1.2 \times 10^{-15} \tag{8}$$

It will be observed that the constant for the second stage of ionization is almost 10^8 times smaller than that for the first stage; the HS⁻ ion is a very much weaker acid than is H_2S. The bisulfide ion is such a weak acid that of the amount formed by the dissociation of hydrogen sulfide only a very small fraction dissociates. For this reason, the concentrations of the H⁺ and HS⁻ ions are practically equal to each other in a solution of pure hydrogen sulfide. The concentration of hydrogen sulfide in a solution saturated with the gas at 1 atmosphere pressure is very nearly 0.1 molar at room temperature, 25° C. With this information it is not difficult to calculate the concentration of both the hydrogen ion and the bisulfide ion in a solution saturated with hydrogen sulfide. Since only a very small fraction of the hydrogen sulfide dissociates we may consider the concentration of the undissociated portion of the hydrogen sulfide to be 0.1 molar (the amount which dissociates is negligible compared with 0.1). If we let X be the concentration of the hydrogen ion at equilibrium, X will also be the concentration of the bisulfide ion. We then have:

$$\frac{(H^+)(HS^-)}{(H_2S)} = \frac{X^2}{0.1} = 9 \times 10^{-8} \tag{9}$$

$$X^2 = 9 \times 10^{-9} = 90 \times 10^{-10}$$

$$X = 9.5 \times 10^{-5} \text{ molar} = (H^+) = (HS^-)$$

If hydrogen ion is added to a saturated solution of hydrogen sulfide, the concentration of the undissociated hydrogen sulfide molecules will not be changed appreciably but the concentration of the bisulfide ion will be decreased and its concentration will be inversely proportional to the concentration of the hydrogen ion. The greater the concentration of the hydrogen ion, the smaller will be the concentration of the bisulfide ion.

A calculation of the concentration of the sulfide ion involves the second stage of ionization. For a saturated solution of hydrogen sulfide, we have just calculated the concentration of the hydrogen ion and of the bisulfide ion to be 9.5×10^{-5} molar. Since the dissociation constant for the second stage is so small, only a very small amount of the bisulfide ion dissociates; that is, the second dissociation (equation 6) does not lower the concentration of the bisulfide ion appreciably. Its concentration may then be considered to be 9.5×10^{-5} molar even after the second stage of dissociation has been taken into account. Likewise, the amount of hydrogen ion produced by the second stage of ionization does not add appreciably to the hydrogen ion concentration produced by the dissociation of the H_2S. Hence we may take the final equilibrium value of the hydrogen ion concentration to be the same as that calculated for the first stage of ionization, namely 9.5×10^{-5} mole per liter. In other words, even after the second stage of ionization has been considered, the hydrogen ion and bisulfide ion concentrations are practically the same. We may then calculate the sulfide ion concentration:

$$\frac{(H^+)(S^{--})}{(HS^-)} = K_2 = 1.2 \times 10^{-15}$$

$$\frac{9.5 \times 10^{-5}(S^{--})}{9.5 \times 10^{-5}} = 1.2 \times 10^{-15}$$

$$(S^{--}) = 1.2 \times 10^{-15} \text{ mole per liter}$$

Since the concentration of the hydrogen ion of the numerator in this expression cancels the bisulfide ion concentration of the denominator, the concentration of the sulfide ion is 1.2×10^{-15} molar. It will be noted that this value will be the approximate concentration of the sulfide ion even though the solution may not be saturated with hydrogen sulfide, for even under these conditions the concentration of the hydrogen ion and the concentration of the bisulfide ion will be practically equal to each other and will cancel in the equilibrium expression, leaving the sulfide ion concentration still 1.2×10^{-15} molar. In fact, for any weak dibasic acid the concentration of the doubly charged anion is practically equal to the second ionization constant.

The product of the equilibrium expressions for stages one and two of ionization (equations 7 and 8) is

$$\frac{(H^+)(HS^-)}{(H_2S)} \times \frac{(H^+)(S^{--})}{(HS^-)} = \frac{(H^+)^2(S^{--})}{(H_2S)} = K_1 \times K_2 = K_{12} \qquad (10)$$

$$K_1 \times K_2 = 9 \times 10^{-8} \times 1.2 \times 10^{-15} = 1.1 \times 10^{-22} = K_{12}$$

or

$$\frac{(H^+)^2(S^{--})}{(H_2S)} = 1.1 \times 10^{-22} \qquad (11)$$

This last expression cannot be used by itself to calculate both the concentration of the hydrogen ion and the sulfide ion in a solution which contains only hydrogen sulfide because both the concentration of the hydrogen ion and the concentration of the sulfide ion are unknown quantities and two equations are necessary to solve for two unknowns. The other equation necessary would involve K_1 alone. If the hydrogen ion concentration is determined from K_1 alone, then the sulfide ion concentration may be determined from equations (8) or (11).

Since a saturated solution of hydrogen sulfide in water is 0.1 molar with respect to the gas, we may write

$$\frac{(H^+)^2(S^{--})}{0.1} = 1.1 \times 10^{-22}$$

or

$$(H^+)^2(S^{--}) = 1.1 \times 10^{-23} = K_{12}(sat.) \qquad (12)$$

Equation (12) may be used when the hydrogen ion concentration of the saturated solution of H_2S is known or calculated from equation (7).

When the hydrogen ion is added to the solution in the form of a strong acid then the sulfide ion concentration may be determined from equation (12), since the hydrogen ion concentration is now known from the amount of strong acid added; the amount produced by the dissociation of hydrogen sulfide is negligible. For example, suppose we wish to calculate the sulfide ion concentration in a saturated solution of hydrogen sulfide to which hydrochloric acid has been added to make the hydrogen ion concentration 0.1 molar. Applying equation (12), we have

$$(H^+)^2(S^{--}) = (0.1)^2(S^{--}) = 1.1 \times 10^{-23}$$

$$(S^{--}) = \frac{1.1 \times 10^{-23}}{.01} = 1.1 \times 10^{-21}$$

In the same way we may calculate the sulfide ion concentration for solutions of any hydrogen ion concentration. The concentration of the sulfide ion is thus inversely proportional to the square of the hydrogen ion concentration. If the hydrogen ion concentration is increased tenfold over that in any given case, the sulfide ion concentration will accordingly be decreased one hundredfold. The following table gives the sulfide ion concentration for different solutions containing hydrogen sulfide. For the sake of completeness the table includes solutions of the sulfides for which calculations of the sulfide ion concentrations are considered in the next chapter on hydrolysis.

TABLE 16

CONCENTRATION OF THE SULFIDE ION IN
DIFFERENT SOLUTIONS

Solution	(S^{--}) (Molar Concentrations)
0.1 molar H_2S	1×10^{-15}
0.1 molar H_2S and 0.001 molar H^+ ion	1×10^{-17}
0.1 molar H_2S and 0.01 molar H^+ ion	1×10^{-19}
0.1 molar H_2S and 0.1 molar H^+ ion	1×10^{-21}
0.1 molar H_2S and 1.0 molar H^+ ion	1×10^{-23}
0.1 molar $(NH_4)_2S$	2×10^{-7}
0.1 molar Na_2S	1×10^{-3}

Precipitation of the Sulfides. The concentration of the sulfide ion, in a solution saturated with hydrogen sulfide and which contains hydrogen ion in 1 molar concentration, has the exceedingly low value of about 1×10^{-23} mole per liter. Since there are 6×10^{23} molecules in one mole, 1×10^{-23} mole per liter corresponds to about 6 sulfide ions

per liter. Yet when this solution is added to one containing
.001 mole of copper ion, Cu^{++}, per liter, a black precipitate
is formed immediately. It might seem inconceivable that
such a small concentration of sulfide ions could cause this
rapid precipitation of cupric sulfide, CuS, if the reaction
mechanism were the simple combination between sulfide
and cupric ions as represented by the equation,

$$Cu^{++} + S^{--} = CuS(solid) \qquad (13)$$

The concentration of the bisulfide ion in such a solution
is very much larger than the concentration of the sulfide
ion, and conceivably the bisulfide ion, HS^-, could combine
with the cupric ions, and hydrogen sulfide would be liberated
in such a way that the final result would be

$$2HS^- + Cu^{++} = CuS(solid) + H_2S \qquad (14)$$

In fact, it is not out of the question that an unstable intermediate compound, $Cu(HS)_2$, could be formed which immediately breaks down to form CuS and H_2S. Such processes
are known in the formation of oxides by precipitation. For
example, when a solution of silver nitrate is added to one of
sodium hydroxide, there results a dark brown precipitate of
silver oxide, Ag_2O. If the solutions used are dilute, a yellow-
brown precipitate is first observed, very probably AgOH,
and this changes to the brown precipitate of silver oxide
with the loss of water,

$$2AgOH = Ag_2O + H_2O \qquad (15)$$

Likewise, cupric hydroxide, $Cu(OH)_2$, a blue precipitate
formed by the addition of a sodium hydroxide solution to
one containing cupric ion, such as a copper sulfate solution,
slowly changes to black cupric oxide, CuO, when the precipitate is heated to 100° C.

$$Cu(OH)_2 = CuO + H_2O \qquad (16)$$

Sulfur and oxygen are in the same group in the periodic
system, and hydrogen sulfide is therefore the analogue of
water. Since hydrogen sulfide dissociates in two steps to

give sulfide ions, so water undoubtedly does the same to give the oxide ion, O^{--} ion, but since we have no means of measuring the oxide ion concentration, we have neglected it entirely. The oxide ion must be present at extremely low concentration, much lower than that of the sulfide ion in water solution. In view of these considerations it would not be surprising if we found that in the case of the precipitation of a sulfide the unstable hydrosulfide first formed and the breakdown of this to the sulfide and hydrogen sulfide then occurred.

The mechanism of the formation of a sulfide precipitate, or any precipitate for that matter, is immaterial in our calculations or reasoning involving the solubility product principle. We always assume that equilibrium is maintained, and when such is the case, the concentrations of the substances left in solution are those calculated by this principle, provided of course that the data upon which the calculations are based (solubility product constants) are correct. The precipitation of a given sulfide will take place for a given sulfide ion concentration even though this sulfide precipitate is not formed directly from its ions. The equilibrium involving a relatively insoluble salt in solution behaves as though the reaction takes place directly between its ions, regardless of what intermediate compounds may be formed. **Equilibrium has to do only with the final result and not with the means by which the result is obtained.**

The Separation of Sulfides into Groups. If the concentration of the sulfide ion in a solution containing some metal ion, Me^{++}, is so small that the product, $(Me^{++})(S^{--})$, does not exceed the solubility product constant for the metallic sulfide, then no precipitate will be formed. On the other hand, if the sulfide ion concentration is such that this product exceeds the solubility product constant, then a precipitate will appear providing (1) that a supersaturated solution is not formed and (2) that the amount of the metallic ion in the solution is sufficiently great to give a visible effect. The lower limit of the concentration of the metallic ion necessary to give a visible amount of precipitate is about 10^{-4} molar. The largest concentration of hydrogen ion which can be used conveniently in analysis is about 1 molar. This concentration of hydrogen ion in a saturated solution of hydrogen sulfide, as we have seen (see Table 10), provides a sulfide ion concentration of about 10^{-23} molar. Any sulfide of a bivalent metallic ion for which the solubility product constant is smaller than the product ($10^{-4} \times 10^{-23}$ = 10^{-27}) should be precipitated in barely detectable amounts in a solution which is 1 molar in hydrogen ion. By referring to the table of solubility product constants for some of the sulfides given in the Appendix, it will be observed that the sulfides of cadmium, copper, lead and mercury are included in this group. Other sulfides with greater solubility product constants require a greater sulfide ion concentration, hence a smaller hydrogen ion concentration, to bring about precipitation. The sulfides are then divided into two groups, (1) those which precipitate in acid solution and (2) those which precipitate in solutions of low hydrogen ion concentration. In practice one group is often precipitated in acid solution and filtered, the other group is precipitated by hydrogen sulfide after neutralizing the solution and making it alkaline. This last procedure then increases the sulfide ion concentration sufficiently to precipitate all sulfides that were not precipitated in the acid solution.

In practically all cases the precipitation of a metallic sulfide requires a much smaller H^+ ion concentration (larger S^{--} concentration) than is necessary to dissolve the already precipitated sulfide. This may be explained on the basis that the solubility of very small or incipient crystals is greater than that for large crystals. When precipitation sets in, the very small crystals must be formed first and the solubility product for these is greater than for the fully grown crystals. Therefore to effect precipitation the sulfide ion concentration must be somewhat greater than that calculated from the constants given in the Appendix, since these constants apply to the stable large crystals.

The Precipitation of Ferrous and Zinc Sulfides. If to a solution which is 0.1 molar with respect to both ferrous, Fe^{++}, and zinc, Zn^{++}, ions, acetic acid is added until its concentration is approximately 0.1 molar, and then hydrogen sulfide is passed into this solution, a white precipitate of zinc sulfide will be formed. Under these conditions ferrous sulfide, FeS, which is black, is not precipitated. The hydrogen ion concentration of a 0.1 molar acetic acid solution is approximately 10^{-3} molar. From equation (12) we calculate the sulfide ion concentration to be about 10^{-17} molar. Since precipitation occurs we may now conclude that the solubility product constant for zinc sulfide, ZnS, is less than $10^{-1} \times 10^{-17}$ or 10^{-18}. Since the ferrous sulfide does not precipitate under these conditions we might conclude that the solubility product constant for ferrous sulfide is greater than 10^{-18}. However, we should not be entirely justified in this conclusion for (1) a supersaturated solution may form and (2) the solubility product is different for the first formed small crystals. The value given in the tables is usually determined for large crystals. As a matter of fact, the solubility product constant given in the tables (see the Appendix) for ferrous sulfide (4×10^{-19}) is slightly smaller than 10^{-18}. The data from which we made our calculation may be in error by this small amount (a factor of about 2) or the effects of supersaturation and small crystals may play a significant rôle here.

If sodium acetate is added to the solution considered above, a black precipitate of the ferrous sulfide is obtained. The effect of the addition of sodium acetate is to lower the concentration of the hydrogen ion through the formation of the weak acetic acid.

$$H^+ + Ac^- = HAc$$

Lowering the hydrogen ion concentration raises the sulfide ion concentration to a point sufficient to cause the precipitation of ferrous sulfide. The same result could have been achieved by the addition of either sodium hydroxide or ammonium hydroxide. The hydroxide ion is even more effective than the acetate ion in reducing the hydrogen ion concentration.

When any metallic sulfide is precipitated with hydrogen sulfide the hydrogen ion concentration in the solution is increased during the course of the reaction.

$$H_2S + Me^{++} = MeS_{(s)} + 2H^+ \qquad (17)$$

This increase in hydrogen ion concentration may become great enough to render the precipitation incomplete. However, if hydroxide ion, acetate ion, ammonium hydroxide, or any ion or molecule which combines with hydrogen ion, is present in the solution the reaction proceeds readily with the formation of the sulfide, MeS.

While a 10^{-4} molar solution of the metallic ion is the approximate limit of visibility of a precipitate, yet this is not the lower limit of concentration which will discolor some other precipitate which might be formed. For example, if zinc sulfide, which when pure is white, is precipitated from a solution which contains only a slight trace of ferrous ion, the resulting precipitate will be gray. In fact, zinc sulfide seldom appears pure white when other ions are also in the solution. The small amount of ferrous sulfide which gives rise to the gray color may be prevented from precipitating by dissolving the gray precipitate in acetic acid and diluting to about 0.1 molar and again adding hydrogen sulfide. The presence of the hydrogen ions from the acetic acid lowers the sulfide ion concentration to a value which will prevent the formation of ferrous sulfide and the zinc sulfide will now appear white.

The precipitation of zinc sulfide and ferrous sulfide have been discussed here in order to show the important rôle that the hydrogen ion concentration plays in the precipitation of sulfides. The solubility product constants of copper and mercuric sulfides are so small that the hydrogen ion concentration cannot be increased sufficiently to prevent precipitation. Any sulfide which precipitates from acid solutions will of course precipitate from alkaline solutions for which the hydrogen ion concentration has a smaller, and the sulfide ion concentration a larger value.

Carbonic Acid and the Precipitation of the Carbonates. The ionization of carbonic acid in two steps is entirely analogous to the ionization of hydrogen sulfide. These two steps are represented by the equations:

$$H_2CO_3 = H^+ + HCO_3^- \tag{18}$$

and

$$HCO_3^- = H^+ + CO_3^{--} \tag{19}$$

The bicarbonate ion, like the bisulfide ion, is a very much weaker acid than the acid from which it is derived. The dissociation constants for carbonic acid, however, are somewhat larger than the similar constants for hydrogen sulfide.

$$\frac{(H^+)(HCO_3^-)}{(H_2CO_3)} = 3.5 \times 10^{-7} \tag{20}$$

and

$$\frac{(H^+)(CO_3^{--})}{(HCO_3^-)} = 7.0 \times 10^{-11} \tag{21}$$

By multiplying equation (20) by equation (21), we obtain

$$\frac{(H^+)(HCO_3^-)}{(H_2CO_3)} \times \frac{(H^+)(CO_3^{--})}{(HCO_3^-)} = \frac{(H^+)^2(CO_3^{--})}{(H_2CO_3)}$$

$$= 3.5 \times 10^{-7} \times 7.0 \times 10^{-11}$$

Therefore,

$$\frac{(H^+)^2(CO_3^{--})}{(H_2CO_3)} = 2.5 \times 10^{-17} \tag{22}$$

A saturated solution of carbon dioxide in water at 1 atmosphere pressure and at 25° C contains about .034 mole per liter. Since in this solution such a small fraction of the acid dissociates, the undissociated portion is present at very nearly the same concentration, i.e., .034 molar. Since the second stage of ionization occurs to an extremely small extent, it may be neglected in calculating the concentration of the hydrogen ion or the concentration of the bicarbonate ion. If X is the concentration of each of these ions then, according to equation (20),

$$\frac{(H^+)(HCO_3{}^-)}{(H_2CO_3)} = \frac{X^2}{.034} = 3.5 \times 10^{-7}$$

$$X^2 = 11.9 \times 10^{-9} = 1.19 \times 10^{-8}$$

$$X = 1.1 \times 10^{-4} \text{ mole per liter} = (H^+) = (HCO_3{}^-)$$

In calculating the carbonate ion concentration in such a solution from equation (21), we observe that since the hydrogen ion and bicarbonate ion concentrations are very nearly the same, they cancel in this expression and the carbonate ion concentration is equal in value to the second ionization constant, namely, 7×10^{-11} mole per liter.

The insoluble carbonates differ markedly from the sulfides in the magnitude of their solubility product constants; the solubility product constants for the most soluble of the so-called insoluble sulfides are considerably smaller in magnitude than those for the least soluble of the carbonates. Whereas most of the sulfides can be precipitated by the addition of hydrogen sulfide to solutions of their salts, this is not the case for any of the carbonates. They cannot be precipitated by the direct addition of carbon dioxide gas to solutions containing the appropriate metal ions. The product of the concentrations of the carbonate ion and the metal ion in such solutions is not as large as the solubility product constants of the respective carbonates. From an inspection of the values of the solubility product constant of lead carbonate it might appear that it could be precipitated from a solution containing lead ions by the direct addition of carbon dioxide gas, but the salts of this metal hydrolyze (subject to be considered in the next chapter) sufficiently to give an appreciable hydrogen ion concentration, which in turn lowers the carbonate ion concentration. Just as in the case of hydrogen sulfide where an increase in the hydrogen ion concentration is accompanied by a decrease in the sulfide ion concentration, so in this case increasing the hydrogen ion concentration decreases the carbonate ion concentration.

The insoluble carbonates can then be precipitated only

when the carbonate ion concentration is increased. This may be easily brought about by lowering the hydrogen ion concentration through the addition of a base. As a matter of fact, carbonic acid is not used for the precipitation of the carbonates but rather solutions of soluble carbonates such as sodium carbonate or ammonium carbonate, in which the concentration of the carbonate ion is relatively high. In qualitative analytical procedures these soluble carbonates are used to precipitate $CaCO_3$, $SrCO_3$ and $BaCO_3$.

EXAMPLES OF PROBLEMS INVOLVING POLYBASIC ACIDS AND SULFIDE PRECIPITATION

Example 1.

Calculate the CO_3^{--} concentration in a solution which is 0.1 molar in HCl and saturated with CO_2 at 1 atmosphere. In this solution the solubility is practically the same as that in water, namely .034 molar.

Since HCl is a strong acid the H^+ concentration is 0.1 M. The increase in this concentration because of the dissociation of H_2CO_3 is negligibly small and may be left out of consideration.

$$\frac{(H^+)^2(CO_3^{--})}{(H_2CO_3)} = 2.5 \times 10^{-17}$$

$$\frac{(0.1)^2(CO_3^{--})}{.034} = 2.5 \times 10^{-17}$$

$$(CO_3^{--}) = \frac{.034 \times 2.5 \times 10^{-17}}{10^{-2}} = 8.5 \times 10^{-17} M$$

Example 2.

Calculate the (H^+) necessary to give a (S^{--}) of 1×10^{-18} molar in a saturated solution of hydrogen sulfide. H_2S is soluble to the extent of 0.1 M.

$$\frac{(H^+)^2(S^{--})}{(H_2S)} = 1.1 \times 10^{-22}$$

$$\frac{(H^+)^2 \times 1 \times 10^{-18}}{0.1} = 1.1 \times 10^{-22}$$

$$(H^+)^2 = 1.1 \times 10^{-5} = 11 \times 10^{-6}$$

$$(H^+) = 3.3 \times 10^{-3} M$$

Example 3.

Calculate the minimum (H^+) necessary to prevent precipitation of ZnS when a .01 M ZnCl$_2$ solution is saturated with H$_2$S. The $K_{S.P.}$ for ZnS $= 1.2 \times 10^{-23}$.

The (S^{--}) below which no precipitation of ZnS takes place can be calculated from the solubility product constant.

$$(Zn^{++})(S^{--}) = .01 \times (S^{--}) = 1.2 \times 10^{-23}$$
$$(S^{--}) = 1.2 \times 10^{-21} \, M$$

The (H^+) which will be in equilibrium with this (S^{--}) may be obtained from the expression

$$\frac{(H^+)^2(S^{--})}{(H_2S)} = \frac{(H^+)^2 \times 1.2 \times 10^{-21}}{0.1} = 1.1 \times 10^{-22}$$

$$(H^+)^2 = \frac{1.1 \times 10^{-23}}{1.2 \times 10^{-21}} = 0.92 \times 10^{-2}$$

$$(H^+) = 0.96 \times 10^{-1} = .096 \text{ mole/liter, or about } 0.1 \, M$$

Example 4.

A solution contains .02 mole of Cd^{++} ion, .02 mole of Zn^{++} ion, and 1 mole of HCl per liter, and is saturated with H$_2$S at room temperature.

(a) What is the concentration of the S^{--} ion in this solution?

(b) Will CdS precipitate?

(c) Will ZnS precipitate?

Since the solubility of H$_2$S in the solution is 0.1 M then we may write

$$\frac{(H^+)^2(S^{--})}{(H_2S)} = \frac{(H^+)^2(S^{--})}{0.1} = 1.1 \times 10^{-22}$$

or $$(H^+)^2(S^{--}) = 1.1 \times 10^{-23}$$

If the (H^+) is 1 M, then

$$(1)^2(S^{--}) = 1.1 \times 10^{-23} \text{ and } (S^{--}) = 1.1 \times 10^{-23} \, M$$

If precipitation of both sulfides takes place, then at equilibrium the reactions are

$$CdS_{(s)} = Cd^{++} + S^{--}$$
$$ZnS_{(s)} = Zn^{++} + S^{--}$$

The solubility product expressions are respectively

$$(Cd^{++})(S^{--}) = 1 \times 10^{-28}$$
$$(Zn^{++})(S^{--}) = 1.2 \times 10^{-23}$$

In the case of CdS, the ion product, $(.02)(1.1 \times 10^{-23}) = 2.2 \times 10^{-25}$, is greater than the solubility product constant, so CdS precipitates. On the other hand, the ion product for ZnS, 2.2×10^{-25}, is less than the solubility product constant, so ZnS does not precipitate.

Example 5.

Calculate the concentration of the PO_4^{---} ion in a 0.1 M solution of H_3PO_4.

The H_3PO_4 ionizes in three stages, as follows:

$$H_3PO_4 = H^+ + H_2PO_4^- \qquad (1)$$
$$H_2PO_4^- = H^+ + HPO_4^{--} \qquad (2)$$
$$HPO_4^{--} = H^+ + PO_4^{---} \qquad (3)$$

The equilibrium expressions for the three stages of ionization are respectively

$$\frac{(H^+)(H_2PO_4^-)}{(H_3PO_4)} = K_{I_1} = 7.5 \times 10^{-3}$$

$$\frac{(H^+)(HPO_4^{--})}{(H_2PO_4^-)} = K_{I_2} = 6.3 \times 10^{-8}$$

$$\frac{(H^+)(PO_4^{---})}{(HPO_4^{--})} = K_{I_3} = 3.6 \times 10^{-13}$$

First calculate (H^+) and $H_2PO_4^-)$ from the first stage of ionization.

$$H_3PO_4 = H^+ + H_2PO_4^-$$

Concentrations: $0.1 - X$ X X

Therefore $\dfrac{(H^+)(H_2PO_4^-)}{(H_3PO_4)} = \dfrac{X^2}{0.1 - X} = 7.5 \times 10^{-3}$

Since the ionization constant is relatively large, X cannot be neglected in the denominator. Therefore

$$X^2 = 7.5 \times 10^{-3} (0.1 - X) = 7.5 \times 10^{-4} - 7.5 \times 10^{-3} X$$

or $\qquad X^2 + 7.5 \times 10^{-3} X - 7.5 \times 10^{-4} = 0$

Solution of the quadratic equation gives $X = 2.4 \times 10^{-2} M$ $= (H^+) = (H_2PO_4^-)$

Now calculate the (HPO_4^{--}) from the second stage of ionization.

$$H_2PO_4^- = H^+ + HPO_4^{--}$$

Concentrations: $(2.4 \times 10^{-2} - X)$ $(2.4 \times 10^{-2} + X)$ X

Therefore

$$\frac{(H^+)(HPO_4^{--})}{(H_2PO_4^-)} = \frac{(2.4 \times 10^{-2} + X)(X)}{(2.4 \times 10^{-2} - X)} = 6.3 \times 10^{-8}$$

Since the ionization constant is small, the value of X is negligible as compared with 2.4×10^{-2}; consequently, X may be neglected when it is subtracted from or added to this number. Then

$$X = (HPO_4^{--}) = 6.3 \times 10^{-8} M$$

Finally calculate (PO_4^{---}) from the third stage of ionization.

$$HPO_4^{--} \quad = \quad H^+ \quad + \quad PO_4^{---}$$

Concentrations: $(6.3 \times 10^{-8} - X)$ $(2.4 \times 10^{-2} + X)$ X

Therefore

$$\frac{(H^+)(PO_4^{---})}{(HPO_4^{--})} = \frac{(2.4 \times 10^{-2} + X)(X)}{(6.3 \times 10^{-8} - X)} = 3.6 \times 10^{-13}$$

Again neglecting X in comparison with 2.4×10^{-2} and with 6.3×10^{-8} on the basis of the extremely small value of the ionization constant (3.6×10^{-13}), the expression becomes

$$\frac{(2.4 \times 10^{-2})(X)}{(6.3 \times 10^{-8})} = 3.6 \times 10^{-13}$$

$$X = \frac{(3.6 \times 10^{-13})(6.3 \times 10^{-8})}{(2.4 \times 10^{-2})} = 9.5 \times 10^{-19}$$

Therefore $X = (PO_4^{---}) \approx 1 \times 10^{-18} M$. The concentration of the PO_4^{---} ion in a $0.1 M$ solution of H_3PO_4 is approximately $1 \times 10^{-18} M$.

Example 6.

To 50 ml. of $0.11 M$ $CdSO_4$ solution is added 5 ml. of $3 M$ HCl solution. The mixture is then saturated with H_2S at room temperature and CdS is found to precipitate. What is the concentration of the Cd^{++} ion left in solution? (Do not neglect the (H^+) produced by the reaction.)

Before precipitation the (Cd^{++}) has a value of $\frac{50}{55} \times 0.11$ or $0.1 M$. The (H^+) is $\frac{5}{55} \times 3$ or $0.28 M$. The reaction which takes place as the CdS precipitates is

$$Cd^{++} \quad + \quad H_2S \quad = \quad CdS_{(s)} \quad + \quad 2H^+$$

Since the reaction proceeds practically to completion, the increase in the (H^+) during the course of the reaction is $0.2\ M$. Thus, the total (H^+) in the solution when equilibrium is reached is $0.28\ M + 0.2\ M$ or $0.48\ M$. In a solution of this (H^+), saturated with H_2S, the (S^{--}) is

$$(H^+)^2(S^{--}) = 1.1 \times 10^{-23}$$
$$(0.48)^2(S^{--}) = 1.1 \times 10^{-23}$$
$$(S^{--}) = 4.8 \times 10^{-23}\ M$$

Since the Cd^{++} ion is in equilibrium with the S^{--} ion,

$$(Cd^{++})(S^{--}) = K_{S.P.} = 1 \times 10^{-28}$$
$$(Cd^{++})(4.8 \times 10^{-23}) = 1 \times 10^{-28}$$
$$(Cd^{++}) = 2.1 \times 10^{-6}\ M$$

Therefore, the (Cd^{++}) left in solution is 2.1×10^{-6} mole/liter.

QUESTIONS AND PROBLEMS

1. In what respect is sulfuric acid to be regarded as a strong acid and in what respect as a weak acid?

2. Explain without calculation why zinc sulfide cannot be precipitated from a solution which is 1 molar with respect to H^+ while copper sulfide can.

3. Is it necessary that we know the mechanism or steps by which a given reaction takes place in order to apply the Law of Mass Action to an equilibrium involving this reaction?

4. How could you precipitate ZnS from a solution containing Zn^{++} and Fe^{++} without precipitating FeS?

5. Why cannot insoluble carbonates be precipitated from solution by CO_2 or H_2CO_3 in a way that is analogous to the precipitation of the sulfides by H_2S?

6. Explain why it is not possible to precipitate slightly soluble phosphates from solution with phosphoric acid.

7. Explain why $BaCO_3$ dissolves in dilute HCl solution while $BaSO_4$ does not.

8. What is the concentration of the $C_2O_4^{--}$ ion in a $0.1\ M$ $H_2C_2O_4$ solution? Will such a solution precipitate MgC_2O_4 if $MgCl_2$ is added to make the solution $0.1\ M$ with respect to Mg^{++} ion? (Note: in the $H_2C_2O_4$ solution the concentration of the H^+ ion is practically the same as that for the $HC_2O_4^-$ ion.)

9. What is the concentration of the S^{--} ion in a solution saturated with H_2S at one-half atmosphere pressure and room temperature? What is the concentration of the H^+ ion in this solution? (The solubility of a gas is proportional to the saturation pressure — Henry's Law.)

10. What is the H^+ concentration in a water solution of H_2CO_3 saturated with CO_2 at a pressure of 500 pounds per square inch (34 atmospheres)? (A solution saturated with CO_2 at 1 atmosphere pressure at the same temperature contains .034 mole CO_2 per liter. Assume Henry's Law applies.)

11. Calculate the concentration of the H^+ ion in the following solutions. Neglect all but the first step of ionization.

(a) 0.1 M H_2CO_3

(b) 0.01 M H_2CO_3

(c) 0.01 M H_2S

(d) 0.04 M H_3BO_3

(e) 0.02 M H_3AsO_3

(f) 0.03 M H_2TeO_4

(g) 0.2 M $ClCH_2COOH$

(h) 0.1 M H_3PO_4

(i) 0.1 M $H_2C_2O_4$

(Use quadratic equation for problems (h) and (i). See the section on mathematical operations in the Appendix.)

12. Solutions of HCl are saturated with H_2S. From the total H^+ ion concentrations given below, calculate the corresponding S^{--} ion concentrations.

H^+ concentration

(a) 1×10^{-4} M

(b) 1×10^{-3} M

(c) 1×10^{-2} M

(d) 1×10^{-1} M

(e) 1 M

13. Plot the results of problem 12 using (H^+) as ordinates and (S^{--}) as abscissae. It may be convenient to save this plot for future reference.

14. Five ml. of 6 M HCl is added to 100 ml. of a solution containing 1 g. $ZnSO_4$ and 1 g. $CdSO_4$, and the solution is saturated with H_2S at room temperature.

(a) What is the concentration of the H^+ ion before H_2S is introduced?

(b) What is the concentration of the S^{--} ion after the solution becomes saturated with H_2S?

(c) Will CdS precipitate?

(d) Will ZnS precipitate?

(e) Explain your conclusions in detail.

15. Ammonium sulfide is gradually added to a solution which is 0.1 M in Cd^{++} ion and 0.1 M in Zn^{++} ion. Calculate the concentration of the Cd^{++} ion when ZnS begins to precipitate.

16. To 100 ml. of a hot .03 M solution of $PbCl_2$ is added 5 ml. of 6 M HCl solution. When the resulting solution is saturated with H_2S, PbS precipitates. How many moles of Pb^{++} ion are left in solution after it has cooled to room temperature? (Do not neglect the H^+ ion produced by the reaction.)

17. Hydrogen sulfide is added to separate solutions containing 50 mg. each of the following positive ions in 1 liter of solution. What is the S^{--} ion concentration when precipitation begins?

(a) Cu^{++} (b) Pb^{++} (c) Zn^{++} (d) Hg^{++} (e) Cd^{++}

18. A quantitative determination of zinc as ZnS is to be made. What must be the maximum concentration of the H^+ ion in the solution if no more than 0.3 mg. of Zn^{++} ion is to be left in a 100 ml. sample of the solution when saturated with H_2S?

19. Calculate the S^{--} ion concentration in a 0.1 M acetic acid solution which is saturated with H_2S.

20. Calculate the approximate concentrations of the following ions in a .05 M solution of phosphoric acid.

(a) H^+ (b) $H_2PO_4^-$ (c) HPO_4^{--} (d) PO_4^{---}

21. Ten ml. of 3 M HCl is added to 200 ml. of a solution containing .05 mole of $CuSO_4$ and .05 mole of $CdSO_4$, and the solution is saturated with H_2S at room temperature. Both CuS and CdS precipitate. How many moles of Cu^{++} ion and of Cd^{++} ion are left in solution? (Do not neglect the H^+ ion produced by the reactions.)

22. Calculate the concentration of the Hg^{++} ion in a saturated solution of HgS. How many Hg^{++} ions per 100 liters of the saturated solution does your answer represent? (Use Avogadro's number in making this calculation.)

23. What must be the concentration of a HCl solution to dissolve .01 mole of ZnS in a liter of the solution?

24. What must be the concentration of a HCl solution to dissolve .01 mole of CuS in a liter of the solution? Would it be possible to dissolve the CuS under these conditions?

25. One-tenth mole of Na_2SO_4 and 0.1 mole $NaHSO_4$ are added to enough water to make 100 ml. of solution. What is the H^+ ion concentration in this solution? HSO_4^- ion is a weak acid with a dissociation constant equal to .01.

This solution is then made .02 M with respect to each of the ions, Zn^{++}, Co^{++}, and Ni^{++}. It is then saturated with H_2S. Show by calculation that all three sulfides should precipitate. In practice only ZnS precipitates under these conditions. This is due to the fact that the rate of precipitation of ZnS is rapid whereas the rate of precipitation of CoS and of NiS is slow.

CHAPTER VIII

The Ionization of Water — Hydrolysis

The Equilibrium between Water and Its Ions. Water is often regarded as a non-conductor of electricity. When the instruments used in measuring conductance are not exceedingly sensitive and when the voltage used is not exceedingly high, pure water shows no appreciable conductance. Very sensitive instruments, however, show that pure water actually does conduct electricity to a very small extent. This conductance is due to the dissociation of a very small fraction of the water molecules into hydrogen and hydroxide ions, and in pure water the concentrations of these ions must be identical. Therefore, water may be regarded both as an acid and as a base.

Since water is the medium in which all electrolytes are dissociated and since water solutions are by far the most commonly occurring solutions in chemistry, the equilibrium between water and its ions is one of the greatest importance in all phases of chemistry that deal with solutions, not only in qualitative analysis but particularly in the chemistry of all plant and animal systems.

The reaction representing the equilibrium between water and its ions is

$$H_2O = H^+ + OH^- \tag{1}$$

If we followed the previously discussed rule regarding equilibrium constants, we would write the equilibrium expression for the reaction

$$\frac{(H^+)(OH^-)}{(H_2O)} = K$$

But the concentration of the hydrogen and hydroxide ions is so small in comparison with the large concentration of undissociated molecules that, for all practical purposes, the concentration of the undissociated molecules (denominator of above expression) may be regarded as a constant. One liter of water contains 55.5, i.e., $\frac{1000}{18}$, moles of water, and if this concentration should vary as much as 0.1 of a mole in any given reaction, the change in the concentration of the water molecules, (H_2O), would be negligible. Suppose, for example, that 0.1 mole of water was used up by some reaction which also involved this equilibrium. The amount of water left in the original 1 liter of solution, after the reaction was completed, would now be 55.4 moles instead of 55.5 moles. The difference between these two values is less than 0.2% and for all practical purposes we may regard the concentration of the undissociated water molecules as not having changed, i.e., (H_2O) is constant.

We may, therefore, write

$$(H^+)(OH^-) = K(H_2O)$$
$$(H^+)(OH^-) = K \times \text{constant}$$
$$(H^+)(OH^-) = K_w \tag{2}$$

where $K_w = K \times \text{constant} = K(H_2O)$. K_w is known as the dissociation constant of water. It has a value of 1×10^{-14} at room temperature. This means that for pure water

$$(H^+)(OH^-) = 1 \times 10^{-14}$$

and
$$(H^+) = (OH^-) = 1 \times 10^{-7} \text{ mole per liter}$$

The equilibrium existing between water and its ions (not the value of the equilibrium constant) can be shifted or changed

(1) by the addition of hydroxide ions in the form of a base or by the addition of hydrogen ions in the form of an acid, or

(2) by the removal of hydrogen ions or hydroxide ions through the addition of some other substance.

Let us consider the equilibrium between water and its ions (equation 1) and reiterate what is meant by shifting an equilibrium. By increasing the concentration of any of the substances on the right side of the equation, hydrogen ion or hydroxide ion, the equilibrium is shifted to the left. The equilibrium cannot be shifted to the right by increasing the concentration of the substance on the left for there is no way in which we can increase the concentration of water. The water molecules are already as close together as it is possible for them to be. By decreasing the concentration of either the hydrogen ion or the hydroxide ion, however, the equilibrium is shifted to the right.

Suppose some sodium hydroxide is added to pure water. This increases the concentration of the hydroxide ion with the final result that the hydrogen and hydroxide ions are still in equilibrium with each other, but the conditions of equilibrium are not the same as those existing in pure water. Strictly speaking, we should not say that the equilibrium is changed, for in the end condition there is still an equilibrium involving the same substances and the value of the equilibrium constant remains the same, but the *conditions* of equilibrium are changed. During the change in the conditions of equilibrium it is necessary that the concentration of the hydrogen ion decrease because the concentration of the hydroxide ion increases. The only way that the concentration of the hydrogen ion can decrease is by the combination of the hydrogen ions with some of the hydroxide ions to form water. In other words, the equilibrium under these conditions shifts from right to left to establish the new conditions. The original concentrations of the hydrogen and hydroxide ions were each 10^{-7} molar before the extra hydroxide ions were introduced. If the final concentration of the hydroxide ions, after equilibrium was reëstablished, was 10^{-5} molar, i.e., 100 times larger, then the final concentration of the hydrogen ion must be 10^{-9} molar or 100 times smaller than originally. Thus, under these new conditions,

$$(H^+)(OH^-) = 10^{-9} \times 10^{-5} = 10^{-14}$$

The concentration of the hydrogen ion is always inversely proportional to the concentration of the hydroxide ion. If one is increased tenfold, the other *must* be decreased tenfold; if one is increased fiftyfold, the other *must* be decreased fiftyfold of the original concentration. In no case does the concentration of either the hydroxide ion or the hydrogen ion become zero, because the Law of Mass Action would then require the concentration of the other ion to be infinite. The concentration of the hydrogen ion in a 1 molar solution of sodium hydroxide is about 10^{-14} molar. Likewise, the concentration of the hydroxide ion in a .01 molar solution of hydrochloric acid is 10^{-12} molar.

In the process of removing one of the ions of water by the addition of some other substance, new conditions of equilibrium are established by the dissociation of water to produce more ions and the equilibrium is shifted to the right (equation 1). It is with this process of partial removal of one of the ions of water that we are concerned in the problem of *hydrolysis*.

Hydrolysis. To understand better the process of hydrolysis let us consider this same equilibrium from a kinetic standpoint. In the equilibrium

$$H_2O = H^+ + OH^-$$

we may regard the reaction proceeding from left to right, as taking place through collisions of water molecules with each other. In the reverse reaction it is necessary that hydrogen ions and hydroxide ions collide with each other to react and form water molecules. At equilibrium both processes are proceeding at the same rate; as much water forms as dissociates. Now if it were possible to capture and remove a large part of the hydrogen ions as fast as they are formed, how would this equilibrium be affected? Water molecules would continue to dissociate at the same rate as they did previously, and since under these conditions the hydroxide ions could find fewer hydrogen ions, the reverse reaction would be blocked and the hydroxide ions would increase in concentration.

There are substances which capture hydrogen ions and

thereby cause an increase in the hydroxide ion concentration. The negative ion of any weak acid is a captor of hydrogen ions since a weak acid is formed. This process of capture does not go on indefinitely, for evidently the weak acid will itself dissociate to some extent to give hydrogen ions and a negative ion, eventually feeding hydrogen ions back into the medium at the same rate at which they are removed. The net result is that some hydrogen ions are removed and the number of hydroxide ions is increased.

This is the process taking place in hydrolysis. Let us consider a specific case, that of adding sodium acetate to water. The acetate ions, Ac^-, from sodium acetate capture some of the hydrogen ions from water to form weak acetic acid molecules.

$$H_2O \rightleftharpoons \boxed{ \begin{array}{c} H^+ \\ + \\ Ac^- \\ \updownarrow \\ HAc \end{array} } + OH^-$$

The acetic acid molecules dissociate to give back hydrogen ions, but a great number have been effectively removed from the medium and as a consequence the concentration of the hydroxide ion is increased. Another way of expressing this is: when acetate ions are added to the solution both acetate and hydroxide ions are competing for the hydrogen ions and therefore the concentration of the hydrogen ion is lowered. Reasoning on the basis of the equilibrium expression for water, the hydroxide ion concentration must be increased if the hydrogen ion concentration is decreased.

Similarly, the hydroxide ion may be captured, thereby increasing the concentration of the hydrogen ion. Ammonium ion, NH_4^+, is a captor of hydroxide ions. Any salt of ammonium hydroxide, such as ammonium chloride, ammonium sulfate, or ammonium nitrate, when added to water, will hydrolyze to produce a small amount of NH_4OH and give an acid solution. It follows then that salts of weak acids and strong bases give alkaline solutions (OH⁻ ions in excess) and salts of strong acids and weak bases give acid solutions (H⁺ ions in excess).

Salts of strong acids and strong bases do not hydrolyze. The ions of these salts do not have the ability to capture either hydrogen ions or hydroxide ions. To illustrate this point let us consider a solution of sodium chloride which is a salt of a strong acid (HCl) and a strong base (NaOH). In this solution neither the sodium ion nor the chloride ion has any tendency to capture either the hydrogen ion or the hydroxide ion, for both HCl and NaOH in solution are 100% ionized. The salts of weak acids and weak bases hydrolyze to a relatively large extent, capturing both the hydrogen ion and the hydroxide ion, and their solutions will be either basic or acidic depending upon which is the weaker, the acid or the base formed in the hydrolysis process. For example, a solution of ammonium cyanide, NH₄CN, will give an alkaline reaction because hydrocyanic acid, HCN, is weaker as an acid than is ammonium hydroxide as a base; that is, HCN tends to hold the hydrogen ions more tightly than NH₄OH holds the hydroxide ions.

We may write the reaction occurring during the hydrolysis of sodium acetate as follows:

$$Ac^- + H_2O = HAc + OH^- \tag{3}$$

The reaction proceeding from left to right is that which represents the capture of hydrogen ions by acetate ions. It is to be noted that this equation represents the over-all reaction. By this we mean that it tells us only what disappears and what is formed regardless of the intermediate steps. The reaction for hydrolysis is *not*, as one might expect,

$$H^+ + Ac^- = HAc$$

even though the water might first dissociate to give hydrogen ion. It is only one step of the hydrolysis reaction. In the over-all process water molecules and acetate ions ultimately disappear while hydroxide ions and acetic acid molecules are formed.

The equilibrium expression for reaction (3) is

$$\frac{(HAc)(OH^-)}{(Ac^-)} = K_H \tag{4}$$

As in the case of the equilibrium expression for water, the concentration of the water molecules, (H_2O), does not vary appreciably and is therefore omitted from the denominator of this expression. We may obtain the value of K_H from the values for the ionization constants of water and of acetic acid, the only two weak substances involved in the equilibrium. In every aqueous solution the H^+ and OH^- ions are in equilibrium with each other and

$$(H^+)(OH^-) = K_W \quad \text{or} \quad (OH^-) = \frac{K_W}{(H^+)}$$

Substituting $\frac{K_W}{(H^+)}$ for (OH^-) in equation (4), we obtain

$$\frac{(HAc)K_W}{(Ac^-)(H^+)} = K_H$$

But $\frac{(HAc)}{(Ac^-)(H^+)}$ is equal to $\frac{1}{K_A}$. Therefore

$$\frac{K_W}{K_A} = K_H = \frac{1 \times 10^{-14}}{1.85 \times 10^{-5}} = 5.4 \times 10^{-10} \tag{5}$$

We may verify this relationship in the following way

$$\frac{K_W}{K_A} = \frac{(H^+)(OH^-)}{\dfrac{(H^+)(Ac^-)}{(HAc)}} = \frac{(HAc)(H^+)(OH^-)}{(H^+)(Ac^-)} = \frac{(HAc)(OH^-)}{(Ac^-)}$$

Similarly, the equilibrium expression for the hydrolysis of an ammonium salt,

$$NH_4^+ + H_2O = NH_4OH + H^+ \tag{6}$$

becomes

$$\frac{(H^+)(NH_4OH)}{(NH_4^+)} = K_H \tag{7}$$

Substituting $\frac{K_W}{(OH^-)}$ for (H^+) in equation (7) we obtain

$$K_H = \frac{K_W}{K_I \text{ (for the base)}} \tag{8}$$

A salt of a weak acid and a weak base hydrolyzes to a large extent. This is to be expected since both H^+ and OH^- ions are captured by the negative and positive ions of the salt. Ammonium cyanide is a salt derived from ammonium hydroxide and hydrocyanic acid. In water ammonium cyanide hydrolyzes in accordance with the equation,

$$NH_4^+ + CN^- + H_2O = NH_4OH + HCN \tag{9}$$

The equilibrium expression for this reaction is

$$\frac{(NH_4OH)(HCN)}{(NH_4^+)(CN^-)} = K_H$$

By multiplying both numerator and denominator by $(H^+)(OH^-)$, it can easily be shown that

$$K_H = \frac{K_W}{K_I \text{ (acid)} \times K_I \text{ (base)}} \tag{10}$$

The salts of polybasic acids hydrolyze in two or more steps. For example, sodium sulfide, Na_2S, a salt of a dibasic acid, hydrolyzes as follows:

$$S^{--} + H_2O = HS^- + OH^- \tag{11}$$

and

$$HS^- + H_2O = H_2S + OH^- \tag{12}$$

The hydrolysis constant for reaction (11) is

$$\frac{(HS^-)(OH^-)}{(S^{--})} = \frac{K_W}{K_2} = \frac{1 \times 10^{-14}}{1.2 \times 10^{-15}} = 8.3$$

and that for reaction (12) is

$$\frac{(H_2S)(OH^-)}{(HS^-)} = \frac{K_W}{K_1} = \frac{1 \times 10^{-14}}{9 \times 10^{-8}} = 1.1 \times 10^{-7}$$

It will be observed that the hydrolysis constant for reaction (11) is very much larger than that for reaction (12). This fact is very significant, for it means that the hydrolysis produced by the second step is negligible as compared with that for the first step, and in calculating the hydroxide ion concentration or the sulfide ion concentration in solutions of soluble sulfides only the first step of hydrolysis need be considered.

Note that in equation (11) for the hydrolysis of the sulfide ion (**first** step) an equilibrium exists between the sulfide ion and the bisulfide ion. The same ions are also involved in the equilibrium for the **second** step of ionization of hydrogen sulfide ($HS^- = H^+ + S^{--}$). Therefore in calculating the hydrolysis constant for the **first** step of hydrolysis, K_W and the ionization constant for the **second** step of ionization are involved. Conversely, the **second** step of hydrolysis (equation 12) is concerned with the **first** step of ionization of hydrogen sulfide, ($H_2S = HS^- + H^+$).

The concentration of the hydrogen ion produced in solutions of salts of weak acids and strong bases, besides varying with the concentration of the salt, varies considerably from salt to salt, depending upon the relative weakness of the acid which is formed in the hydrolysis process. The larger the hydrolysis constant for such a salt, the greater will be the degree or extent of hydrolysis, and therefore the greater the hydroxide ion concentration. *The degree of hydrolysis is the fractional amount of the ions which hydrolyze,* i.e., the fractional part of the ions of the weak acid or base that have reacted with water. Equation (5) tells us that the hydrolysis constant will be larger the smaller the dissociation constant for the acid, i.e., the weaker the acid. The hydroxide ion concentration in a 0.1 molar solution of sodium acetate is about 10^{-5} molar; in a 0.1 molar solution of sodium cyanide, about 10^{-3} molar; in a 0.1 molar solution of sodium carbonate, approximately 4×10^{-3} molar, while that in a 0.1 molar solution of sodium sulfide is almost 0.1 molar. In the last case more than 99% of the sulfide ion hydrolyzes to produce the hydroxide ion. These examples are summarized in Table 17 on page 182. Note that as the constant for the acid decreases the constant for hydrolysis and the hydroxide ion concentration increases.

TABLE 17

HYDROLYSIS OF SALTS OF WEAK ACIDS

Solution	Weak acid formed	K_I	K_H	(OH^-) in. 0.1 M soln (approx.)
Sodium nitrite	Nitrous	4.5×10^{-4}	2.2×10^{-11}	1.5×10^{-6}
Sodium acetate	Acetic	1.85×10^{-5}	5.4×10^{-10}	7×10^{-6}
Sodium carbonate	Bicarbonate ion	7.0×10^{-11}	1.4×10^{-4}	4×10^{-3}
Sodium sulfide	Bisulfide ion	1.2×10^{-15}	8.0	10^{-1}

Examples of Hydrolysis. When a solution of ferric chloride is added to one containing sodium carbonate, a dark red precipitate of ferric hydroxide is formed and carbon dioxide is liberated from the solution. The hydroxide ion concentration in the sodium carbonate solution, formed by hydrolysis, is sufficient to precipitate the ferric hydroxide. Even though the carbonate ion concentration in the solution may be more than 100 times as great as the hydroxide ion concentration, the ferric hydroxide will still precipitate in preference to ferric carbonate. If ferric carbonate were very insoluble as compared with ferric hydroxide, this would not be the case. Then the carbonate would precipitate in preference to the hydroxide. If a soluble silver salt is added to a solution containing sodium carbonate, the carbonate and not the hydroxide (or oxide) will precipitate.

The over-all reaction taking place when ferric hydroxide is precipitated by a solution of sodium carbonate is

$$Fe^{+++} + 3CO_3^{--} + 3H_2O = 3HCO_3^- + Fe(OH)_3(solid) \quad (13)$$

This is followed by the reaction,

$$Fe^{+++} + 3HCO_3^- + 3H_2O = 3H_2CO_3 + Fe(OH)_3(solid) \quad (14)$$

The carbonic acid formed in the last reaction breaks down into water and carbon dioxide. It is to be noted that it is only by virtue of the hydrolysis of the carbonate and bicarbonate ions that the precipitation of ferric hydroxide takes place. These reactions may be written:

$$CO_3^{--} + H_2O = HCO_3^- + OH^- \qquad (15)$$
$$HCO_3^- + H_2O = H_2CO_3 + OH^- \qquad (16)$$

The ferric ion may then be considered to combine with the hydroxide ion produced by equations (15) and (16) to form ferric hydroxide:

$$Fe^{+++} + 3OH^- = Fe(OH)_3(\text{solid}) \qquad (17)$$

However, the over-all reaction includes only those substances which ultimately disappear and those which are formed and is expressed by the summation of equations (13) and (14).

$$2Fe^{+++} + 3CO_3^{--} + 6H_2O = 3H_2CO_3 + 2Fe(OH)_3(\text{solid}) \quad (18)$$

The soluble aluminum and chromium salts behave in an entirely analogous manner; aluminum hydroxide, $Al(OH)_3$, and chromium hydroxide, $Cr(OH)_3$, are formed in these cases. The same argument that has been given for the precipitation of ferric hydroxide by the carbonate solution may be applied, part for part, to the precipitation of the hydroxides of these two metals.

Ferric hydroxide is so insoluble that it may be precipitated from a solution containing a ferric salt by the addition of the relatively insoluble barium carbonate. The small amount of carbonate ion which enters the solution ($K_{\text{s.p.}}BaCO_3 = 8.1 \times 10^{-9}$) is sufficient to produce enough hydroxide ion to precipitate ferric hydroxide, but (CO_3^{--}) is not great enough to precipitate the carbonates of the zinc group. Therefore, since the hydroxides of the aluminum group are precipitated by this solution, $BaCO_3$ is sometimes used as a means for the separation of the zinc and the aluminum groups.

Ferrous hydroxide, $Fe(OH)_2$, is not precipitated by solutions of soluble carbonates. The basic ferrous carbonate, $Fe_2(OH)_2CO_3$, is sufficiently insoluble so that it precipitates in preference to the normal carbonate when a solution of sodium carbonate is added to one containing ferrous ion. If, however, ammonium carbonate is used in place of the sodium carbonate solution, ferrous carbonate rather than the basic ferrous carbonate will be precipitated. The presence of the ammonium ion in the ammonium carbonate solution lowers the hydroxide ion concentration (ammonium hydroxide is formed) to such an extent that the precipitation of ferrous carbonate is favored. As would be expected, the hydroxide ion concentration in a solution of ammonium carbonate, due to the hydrolysis of the ammonium ion, is smaller than the hydroxide ion concentration in a solution of sodium carbonate of the same concentration. The hydrolysis of the ammonium ion furnishes hydrogen ions which in turn use up available hydroxide ions in the solution.

When salts are said to be unstable in solution, these substances usually are decomposed in solution through hydrolysis with the formation of a precipitate or with the evolution of a gas. Aluminum sulfide, for example, when dissolved in water will form the insoluble aluminum hydroxide and hydrogen sulfide gas will be evolved. The aluminum ion, Al^{+++}, first formed reacts with the hydroxide ion of water, and the sulfide ion with the hydrogen ion of water. The net result of this double hydrolysis is

$$2Al^{+++} + 3S^{--} + 6H_2O = 2Al(OH)_3(solid) + 3H_2S(gas) \qquad (19)$$

There are many examples of salts of this kind that cannot be dissolved in water and recovered again by crystallization. In fact, many salts hydrolyze to such an extent that they are decomposed by the water vapor in air.

When a relatively insoluble carbonate such as barium carbonate, $BaCO_3$, is dissolved in water an appreciable amount of the carbonate ion hydrolyzes to form the bicarbonate ion. The concentration of the barium ion accordingly is not the same as the concentration of the carbonate ion under these conditions. The concentration of the barium ion is practically equal to the sum of the concentrations of the carbonate and bicarbonate ions. Through this process of hydrolysis the solution becomes very slightly alkaline. This equilibrium is represented in the following equation:

$$BaCO_3(solid) = Ba^{++} + CO_3^{--}$$
$$+$$
$$H_2O = HCO_3^- + OH^- \qquad (20)$$

The hydrolysis of the bicarbonate ion to form carbonic acid and hydroxide ion is negligible.

The relatively insoluble sulfides behave in exactly the same way; the sulfide ion hydrolyzes to give bisulfide and hydroxide ions. In calculating the solubility of either a relatively insoluble sulfide or carbonate from the solubility product constant, account must be taken of this hydrolysis process which involves the sulfide or the carbonate ion, as the case may be.

The concentrations of the different ions in equilibrium in a solution of a soluble bicarbonate such as sodium bicarbonate, $NaHCO_3$, cannot be accounted for by a simple process of hydrolysis. The equilibrium in this case is somewhat more complicated. The bicarbonate ion hydrolyzes to produce carbonic acid and the hydroxide ion,

$$HCO_3^- + H_2O = H_2CO_3 + OH^- \tag{21}$$

but the bicarbonate ion produces hydrogen ion through dissociation.

$$HCO_3^- = H^+ + CO_3^{--} \tag{22}$$

The hydrogen ion and the hydroxide ion produced according to equations (22) and (21) respectively, will combine to form water. If processes (21) and (22) were to occur to the same extent, then a solution of sodium bicarbonate would be neutral. By experiment we find that a sodium bicarbonate solution is very slightly alkaline, a fact which indicates that process (21) occurs to a slightly greater extent than process (22). By summing up the reactions considered above, we obtain the over-all reaction,

$$2HCO_3^- = H_2CO_3 + CO_3^{--} \tag{23}$$

The H_2CO_3 and the CO_3^{--} ion concentrations in a solution of sodium bicarbonate are very nearly the same.

Hydrolysis must also be taken into account to explain the properties of some of the common substances that are encountered in everyday life. Lye (sodium hydroxide) and ammonium hydroxide are two well known cleansing agents. The cleansing property of these substances is attributed in part to the hydroxide ion which reacts with fats and oils to produce soaps. Since the hydroxide ions can be produced by the hydroiysis of salts of weak acids, these substances also have the same property as that of the two hydroxides just mentioned. The common salts used for this purpose are washing soda, Na_2CO_3, borax, $Na_2B_4O_7$, water glass, Na_2SiO_3, and tri-sodium phosphate, Na_3PO_4. The weaker the acid which is produced by hydrolysis, the greater will be the concentration of the hydroxide ions. Of the four substances just considered, tri-sodium phosphate produces the greatest hydroxide ion concentration, since the ion, HPO_4^{--}, is the weakest acid involved.

$$PO_4^{---} + H_2O = HPO_4^{--} + OH^- \qquad (24)$$

Sodium silicate is one of the constituents of laundry soap and through its hydrolysis action increases the concentration of the hydroxide ion of the soap solution. All washing powders contain some hydrolyzable salt.

The common constituent of all baking powders is sodium bicarbonate. The other chief constituent is a substance which in solution furnishes the hydrogen ion which reacts with the bicarbonate ion to produce carbon dioxide gas. In some brands of baking powders the hydrogen ion is produced by a weak acid such as tartaric acid or an acid salt, while in others aluminum sulfate is used, which through the process of hydrolysis produces the hydrogen ion and aluminum hydroxide.

The Neutralization of Weak Acids and Weak Bases. When 0.1 mole of hydrochloric acid is neutralized in solution by 0.1 mole of sodium hydroxide, the solution produced could be exactly reproduced by the addition of 0.1 mole of sodium chloride to the same amount of water. When the acid and the base have just neutralized each other, the solution is neither acidic nor alkaline, for sodium chloride does not hydrolyze. If, on the other hand, 0.1 mole of acetic acid is neutralized in solution by exactly 0.1 mole of sodium hydroxide, the sodium acetate solution does not contain the same number of hydrogen ions as hydroxide ions. When a weak acid is neutralized by a strong base the end point of the neutralization does not occur when the concentrations of the hydrogen and hydroxide ions are the same, but rather when the solution is slightly alkaline. The concentration of the hydrogen ion or of the hydroxide ion at the neutralization point will depend upon the concentrations of the substances involved and upon the ionization constant of the acid formed in the hydrolysis process.

The process of neutralization of weak acids by strong bases may be illustrated by a specific example. Suppose 50 ml. of a 0.1 molar solution of hydrocyanic acid, HCN, is to be neutralized by 50 ml. of a 0.1 molar solution of sodium hydroxide. What will be the hydrogen and hydroxide ion concentrations at the point of neutralization? The final solution, through the addition of the two equal volumes, will be .05 molar with respect to sodium cyanide. The problem is then to calculate the hydrogen ion and the hydroxide ion concentrations in this solution. The equation representing the hydrolysis equilibrium is

$$CN^- + H_2O = HCN + OH^- \tag{25}$$

Let X be the concentration of the hydroxide ion. Then X must also be the concentration of the HCN, and $.05 - X$ is the concentration of the cyanide ion at equilibrium. Since we might expect the amount of cyanide ion hydrolyzed to be small as compared with the total amount of cyanide ion present, we may simplify this and let the concentration of the cyanide ion be practically equal to .05 molar rather than $.05 - X$. Then,

$$\frac{(HCN)(OH^-)}{(CN^-)} = \frac{X^2}{.05} = \frac{K_W}{K_A} = \frac{10^{-14}}{2.1 \times 10^{-9}} = 4.8 \times 10^{-6}$$

$$X^2 = 24 \times 10^{-8}$$

$$X = 5 \times 10^{-4} \text{ mole per liter} = (OH^-)$$

The concentration of the hydrogen ion is $\dfrac{10^{-14}}{5 \times 10^{-4}} = 2 \times 10^{-11}$ mole per liter. The hydrogen ion concentration in this solution is 5000 times smaller than that for pure water (10^{-7} molar), and the hydroxide ion concentration is 5000 times larger.

In selecting an indicator for this reaction under the conditions stipulated above, we should choose one that changes color as near as possible to the calculated hydrogen ion concentration. By referring to the table on page 108, we find that thymol phthalein would be the most suitable indicator. If methyl orange were used, the final solution obtained would still contain a large excess of the acid at the end point and would not be neutralized.

Buffer Solutions. Buffer solutions are solutions containing weak acids or weak bases together with the salts of weak acids or bases and have the property of maintaining a hydrogen ion concentration which is affected only slightly by the addition of appreciable amounts of either acid or base.

A solution containing 0.1 mole of acetic acid and 0.1 mole of sodium acetate per liter is such a buffer solution. Its hydrogen ion concentration is about 1.85×10^{-5} molar. A solution containing 1.85×10^{-5} mole of hydrochloric acid per liter would also have the same hydrogen ion concentration as the buffer solution described above, but its action toward acids and bases would be entirely different from that of the buffer solution. If 1.85×10^{-5} mole of sodium hydroxide is added to 1 liter of the above hydrochloric acid solution, the resulting solution would be neutral to the hydrogen ion, i.e., the hydrogen ion concentration would be 10^{-7} molar. Upon the addition of 1.85×10^{-5} mole of sodium hydroxide to 1 liter of the buffer solution, the hydrogen ion concentration would not be appreciably affected.

To understand better the action of the buffer solution, let us consider the equilibrium between the acid and its ions:

$$HAc = H^+ + Ac^-$$

$$\frac{(H^+)(Ac^-)}{(HAc)} = 1.85 \times 10^{-5}$$

$$(H^+) = \frac{(HAc)}{(Ac^-)} \times 1.85 \times 10^{-5} \qquad (26)$$

When the concentrations of the acetic acid molecules and of the acetate ions are made equal as they were in the example above, the concentration of the hydrogen ion has the same value as the dissociation constant. If as much as .05 mole of sodium hydroxide is added to 1 liter of the buffer solution (0.1 mole acetic acid and 0.1 mole of sodium acetate per liter), the hydrogen ion concentration will be affected relatively little. Under these conditions, .05 mole of the acetic acid has been neutralized by the added sodium hydroxide, and the solution now consists of .05 mole acetic acid and 0.15 mole of sodium acetate. Now the hydrogen ion concentration is

$$(H^+) = \frac{(HAc)}{(Ac^-)} \times 1.85 \times 10^{-5} = \frac{.05}{0.15} \times 1.85 \times 10^{-5} = 0.6 \times 10^{-5}$$

The hydrogen ion concentration has been lowered only three-fold by the addition of the sodium hydroxide. In a like manner, the addition of .05 mole of hydrochloric acid to the original buffer solution will increase the hydrogen ion concentration only threefold. In this case, the hydrogen ions produced by the hydrochloric acid combine with the acetate ions and are removed in the form of acetic acid molecules. After the hydrochloric acid has been added, the final solution will contain 0.15 mole of acetic acid and .05 mole of acetate ion and

$$(H^+) = \frac{0.15}{.05} \times 1.85 \times 10^{-5} = 5.5 \times 10^{-5} \text{ mole per liter}$$

The table on page 190 illustrates the buffer action of an acetic acid–sodium acetate solution in its ability to absorb either a strong acid, such as hydrochloric acid, or a strong base, such as sodium hydroxide, with but little change in the concentration of the hydrogen ion.

TABLE 18

BUFFER ACTION OF A SOLUTION CONTAINING 0.1 MOLE OF
ACETIC ACID AND 0.1 MOLE OF SODIUM ACETATE
PER LITER

ml. of 0.1 molar NaOH added to 1 liter of buffer solution	(H^+) of final solution	ml. of 0.1 molar HCl added to 1 liter of buffer solution	(H^+) of final solution
0	0.0000185	0	0.0000185
5	0.0000183	5	0.0000187
10	0.0000181	10	0.0000189
25	0.0000175	25	0.0000195
50	0.0000167	50	0.0000204
75	0.0000159	75	0.0000215
100	0.0000151	100	0.0000226

By adding as much as 100 ml. of either 0.1 molar hydrochloric acid solution or 0.1 molar sodium hydroxide solution to 1 liter of the buffer solution, the hydrogen ion concentration remains within the limits 1.51×10^{-5} and 2.26×10^{-5} mole per liter. By this treatment the hydrogen ion concentration of the original solution does not vary more than 25%. In contrast to this, if 100 ml. of 0.1 molar hydrochloric acid were added to pure water, the hydrogen ion concentration would increase 100,000-fold.

The above solution was such as to maintain the hydrogen ion concentration in the neighborhood of 10^{-5} molar. If it is desired to maintain the hydrogen ion concentration at a different value, a different acid and salt should be chosen. If it is desired to maintain the hydrogen ion concentration at about 10^{-9} molar (OH^- ion concentration of 10^{-5} molar), then hydrocyanic acid and potassium cyanide might be used, for this acid has an ionization constant equal to 2.1×10^{-9}. However, for most work this acid would be unsuitable because of its toxic nature.

Ions and salts of polybasic acids also form buffer solutions. For example, a solution of sodium bicarbonate is a buffer solution. The bicarbonate ion, HCO_3^-, is an ion of a salt of a weak acid; $NaHCO_3$ is the salt and H_2CO_3 the acid from which it is derived. Furthermore, the bicarbonate ion is itself a weak acid, dissociating to form hydrogen ions and carbonate ions. When hydrochloric acid is added to a solution of sodium bicarbonate, carbonic acid is formed and the hydrogen ion concentration of the solution is changed very little. If sodium hydroxide is added to this same solution, the carbonate ion is formed,

$$HCO_3^- + OH^- = H_2O + CO_3^{--} \qquad (27)$$

and again the hydrogen ion concentration is little affected.

Blood is a good example of a buffer solution. The principal ion and acid responsible for the buffer action of blood are the HCO_3^- ion and H_2CO_3. When excess hydrogen ion enters the blood stream it is absorbed principally by the reaction

$$H^+ + HCO_3^- = H_2CO_3 \qquad (28)$$

and when excess hydroxide ion is formed it disappears through the reaction

$$OH^- + H_2CO_3 = H_2O + HCO_3^- \qquad (29)$$

By this mechanism the hydrogen ion concentration in the blood stream remains remarkably constant — very slightly alkaline. Besides the HCO_3^- and H_2CO_3, there are other buffering substances, such as HPO_4^{--}, $H_2PO_4^-$, and hemoglobin, which also help control the H^+ ion concentration.

When carbon dioxide is produced in the tissues by metabolic processes, carbonic acid is formed, which in turn dissociates to produce hydrogen and bicarbonate ions. The hydrogen ion produced by this reaction is absorbed by the buffer action of the blood. When oxygen is breathed into the lungs it reacts with the hemoglobin and as a result of this reaction a large excess of hydrogen ions results. These hydrogen ions, which locally cannot be completely absorbed by the buffer action of the blood, now combine with the bicarbonate ions to form excess carbonic acid (CO_2 and H_2O). The carbon dioxide is then exhaled from the lungs.

The Hydrolysis of Metal Ions. A large number of metal ions hydrolyze to give acid solutions. We therefore conclude that the corresponding bases of these ions are weak. Many of these metal ions form polyacid bases, i.e., more than one ionizable OH radical is associated with the metal ion. Before considering the problem of the hydrolysis of these ions let us first examine the properties of these polyacid bases. Most of the polyacid bases are very insoluble, e.g., $Al(OH)_3$, $Pb(OH)_2$ and $Fe(OH)_3$. Without doubt these hydroxides ionize in two or more stages just as polybasic acids ionize in more than one stage. The equilibrium reactions between $Fe(OH)_3$, for example, and its ions, when it is dissolved in water, can be expressed by the following equations.

$$Fe(OH)_{3(s)} = Fe(OH)_{3\text{ (soln.)}} \tag{30}$$

$$Fe(OH)_{3\text{ (soln.)}} = Fe(OH)_2{}^+ + OH^- \tag{31}$$

$$Fe(OH)_2{}^+ = Fe(OH)^{++} + OH^- \tag{32}$$

$$Fe(OH)^{++} = Fe^{+++} + OH^- \tag{33}$$

Just as there are no polybasic acids which in moderate concentration ionize to the extent of 100% in any but the first stage of ionization so we may assume that polyacid bases behave similarly. But it must be borne in mind that most of the polyacid bases are very insoluble and therefore the concentrations of the ions in equilibrium with them must be very small. Because of the small concentration — which is equivalent to a very high dilution in solutions of soluble bases — all stages can nevertheless be practically completely dissociated.

Zinc hydroxide, for example, is very insoluble. Therefore the amount of undissociated and dissolved $Zn(OH)_2$ in equilibrium with the solid must be very small.

$$Zn(OH)_{2(s)} = Zn(OH)_{2\text{ (soln.)}} \tag{34}$$

The undissociated $Zn(OH)_2$ will ionize first as

$$Zn(OH)_{2\text{ (soln.)}} = Zn(OH)^+ + OH^- \tag{35}$$

and then will be further ionized in the following manner:

$$Zn(OH)^+ = Zn^{++} + OH^- \tag{36}$$

Just as a 1×10^{-5} M solution of HAc is ionized to the extent of 70%, while a 1 M solution is ionized to the extent of only 0.4% so, because of the low concentration, we might expect these insoluble bases to be highly ionized in spite of the fact that the ionization constants may be small. We lack data on the ionization constants for the various steps involved in the dissociation of most polyacid bases and therefore we group all stages of dissociation into a single reaction. For example, reactions (34), (35), and (36) may be grouped into the one reaction

$$Zn(OH)_{2\ (s)} = Zn^{++} + 2OH^- \qquad (37)$$

In view of the extreme insolubility of many polyacid bases this procedure will often be satisfactory. But when we consider the hydrolysis of the metal ions the problem is quite different since the concentration of these ions is usually not small.

If 0.1 mole of $ZnCl_2$ is dissolved in one liter of water the solution is found to be decidedly acidic. The reason for this is that the Zn^{++} ion undergoes hydrolysis, the first stage of which may be represented by the equation

$$Zn^{++} + H_2O = Zn(OH)^+ + H^+ \qquad (38)$$

The concentration of the Zn^{++} ion is high (approximately 0.1 M) but since the amount of hydrolysis is relatively small the concentrations of the $Zn(OH)^+$ and of the H^+ ions are small. The second stage of hydrolysis is much smaller than that of the first stage and may be neglected, since the concentration of the $Zn(OH)^+$ ion is itself very small. However, the reaction for the second stage of hydrolysis is

$$Zn(OH)^+ + H_2O = Zn(OH)_{2\ (soln.)} + H^+ \qquad (39)$$

To calculate the hydrolysis constant for equation (38) it is necessary that we know the value of the ionization constant for equation (36). It cannot be calculated by using the ionization constant for equation (37). The ionization constant for (36) is known and has a value of 4×10^{-5}.

The hydrolysis constant for the reaction represented by equation (38) is therefore equal to

$$\frac{(Zn(OH)^+)(H^+)}{(Zn^{++})} = \frac{K_W}{K_{I(base)}} = \frac{1 \times 10^{-14}}{4 \times 10^{-5}} = 2.5 \times 10^{-10} = K_H$$

If we let X equal the number of moles of Zn^{++} ion undergoing hydrolysis, then at equilibrium $(Zn(OH)^+)$ will be X, (H^+) will also equal X, and (Zn^{++}) will have a value of $(0.1 - X)$. Neglecting X as compared with 0.1 we have

$$\frac{X^2}{0.1} = 2.5 \times 10^{-10} \quad \text{or} \quad X^2 = 25 \times 10^{-12}$$

$$X = 5 \times 10^{-6} \text{ mole/liter} = (H^+)$$

Therefore the degree of hydrolysis is $\dfrac{5 \times 10^{-6}}{0.1}$ or 5×10^{-5}.

On a percentage basis the extent of hydrolysis is therefore .005%. The solution is found to be decidedly acidic, according to the calculation we have just carried out.

The constants for the different stages of ionization are not known for most hydroxides. Therefore we cannot calculate the hydrolysis constants for most positive metal ions which we know are hydrolyzed in solution.

If the hydroxide of a metal ion is insoluble we may conclude that the metal ion will hydrolyze to give an acidic solution. We base this conclusion on the assumption that the insolubility of the hydroxide is in part due to a firm binding between the metal ion and the OH^- ions. We may also assume that if all of the OH^- ions are held firmly, for example by the Al^{+++} ion in forming $Al(OH)_3$, then there should also be a firm binding between the Al^{+++} ion and the first OH^- ion to form $Al(OH)^{++}$. If such is the case, Al^{+++} ion in water should hydrolyze. This reasoning can be applied to any ion which forms an insoluble hydroxide; the facts are in accord with this postulate. Practically all metal ions other than those of the alkali or alkaline earth groups hydrolyze to give acidic solutions.

It has been our custom to write the symbol for a multivalent positive ion in its simplest form. For example, if $SnCl_4$ is dissolved in water we often write the formula for the resulting stannic ion as Sn^{++++}. Certainly this cannot be correct. Very probably most of the ions in such a solution are present as $SnCl^{+++}$ and $SnCl_2^{++}$ ions and very few of them are in the form of Sn^{++++} ion. However, we have no definite information relative to the composition of many ions of this type and therefore we use the simplest symbols or formulae possible. The same situation undoubtedly exists with Fe^{+++}, Al^{+++} and other trivalent and higher valent ion salts.

Hydrolysis and the Brønsted Definitions.* If the Brønsted definitions of acids and bases are to be adopted consistently, then the term hydrolysis becomes superfluous. What the older established definitions called hydrolysis becomes merely an acid-base reaction. But the terms hydrolysis and salt have become so firmly entrenched in chemical thought and in chemical literature that hydrolysis cannot be brushed aside without consideration. The introduction of this term into the Brønsted definitions, however, is apt to lead to some confusion if hydrolysis is not already understood in the light of the older definitions..

According to the older established definitions ions which hydrolyze in water solution can be divided into two classes; those which produce acidic and those which produce basic solutions. Let us consider these two types of hydrolysis separately and as an example of the first kind let us consider the hydrolysis of the ammonium ion. According to the older definitions the equation for the hydrolysis reaction is

$$NH_4^+ + H_2O = NH_4OH + H^+ \tag{40}$$

The mental picture for the process is that of competition between the H^+ ion and the NH_4^+ ion for the OH^- ion.

* Before reading this section the student is advised to review the section on the Brønsted Definitions of Acids and Bases on pages 110–117.

As the result of this competition, some H^+ ions are left in excess of OH^- ions and the solution is acidic.

According to the Brønsted definitions this same hydrolysis reaction is expressed as follows.

$$NH_4^+ \ + \ H_2O \ = \ NH_3 \ + \ H_3O^+ \qquad (41)$$
$$\text{Acid}_1 \qquad \text{Base}_2 \qquad \text{Base}_1 \qquad \text{Acid}_2$$

Examining equations (40) and (41) formally we see that the difference between them is that in equation (40) the water molecule is associated with the NH_3 molecule to form NH_4OH (a formula which emphasizes the basic nature of ammonia in water solution), and in equation (41) the water is associated with the H^+ ion, which is written as H_3O^+. According to the Brønsted definitions equation (41) represents merely an acid-base reaction and the NH_4^+ ion is regarded as a weak acid. The NH_3 and the H_2O molecules are competing for the proton. Equation (40) does not represent the actual process taking place any more than does equation (41); these details of the reaction are not known. Whether one uses equation (41) or equation (40), i.e., Brønsted or the older established definitions, is merely a question of convenience and ease of acquiring an understanding of the acid-base reaction in solution.

According to the older definitions hydrolysis is the reverse of neutralization, i.e., equation (40) reading from right to left represents a process of neutralization while from left to right, it represents hydrolysis. With the Brønsted definitions the reactions represented by both directions of equation (41) are acid-base reactions. Only if we borrow the concepts of hydrolysis and of neutralization from the older definitions may we define the process from left to right in equation (41) as hydrolysis and the process from right to left as neutralization. In general, on the basis of the newer definitions, hydrolysis is defined as a proton transfer reaction between a cation-acid or an anion-base and water, to produce the hydronium ion or the hydroxide ion respectively. But again it must be emphasized that if the

Brønsted definitions had been common usage for many years the term hydrolysis in inorganic chemistry would not be necessary.

Let us consider the equilibrium expression for reaction (41) and show the relationship between the constant for this expression and the constants for other reactions from which the value of the former may be calculated. As has been previously pointed out, reaction (41) is to be regarded as one of dissociation of a weak acid, and its constant may then be designated as $K_{I(acid)}^B$.*

$$K_{I(acid)}^B = \frac{(NH_3)(H_3O^+)}{(NH_4^+)} \tag{42}$$

The concentration of the water molecules is omitted from the expression since its value remains constant for all practical purposes. Consider next the two reactions

$$H_2O + H_2O = H_3O^+ + OH^- \tag{43}$$

and

$$NH_3 + H_2O = NH_4^+ + OH^- \tag{44}$$

The equilibrium expressions for (43), (44) are $(H_3O^+)(OH^-)$ and $\dfrac{(NH_4^+)(OH^-)}{(NH_3)}$ respectively. The first of these is equal to the equilibrium constant for water and is denoted by K_W^B, the second we shall denote merely by K_{eq}^B.

$$K_W^B = (H_3O^+)(OH^-) \tag{45}$$

$$K_{eq}^B = \frac{(NH_4^+)(OH^-)}{(NH_3)} \tag{46}$$

From equation (45) $(H_3O^+) = \dfrac{K_W^B}{(OH^-)}$

Substituting $\dfrac{K_W^B}{(OH^-)}$ for (H_3O^+) in equation (42), we obtain

$$K_{I(acid)}^B = \frac{(NH_3)K_W^B}{(NH_4^+)(OH^-)} = \frac{K_W^B}{\dfrac{(NH_4^+)(OH^-)}{(NH_3)}} \tag{47}$$

* Constants referring to the Brønsted definitions are distinguished from those of the older definitions by the superscript B.

But the demonimator in the last expression in equation (47) is equal to $K_{eq}{}^B$ (equation 46). Therefore

$$K_{I(acid)}^{B} = \frac{K_W^B}{K_{eq}^B} \tag{48}$$

Let us now return to the older definitions with which we previously showed that

$$K_H = \frac{K_W}{K_{I(base)}} \tag{49}$$

What was previously called the hydrolysis constant is now the acid constant ($K_{I(acid)}^{B}$ is equivalent to K_H), and what was previously known as the dissociation constant for the base is designated merely as an equilibrium constant, ($K_{eq}{}^B$ is equivalent to $K_{I(base)}$). Obviously $K_W{}^B$ is the same as K_W. Again we see only different names for the same phenomena; the relationships are the same.

Let us next consider the hydrolysis of an anion to produce an alkaline solution, and as an example we shall again use the acetate ion.

$$\underset{\text{Acid}_1}{H_2O} + \underset{\text{Base}_2}{Ac^-} = \underset{\text{Acid}_2}{HAc} + \underset{\text{Base}_1}{OH^-} \tag{50}$$

The hydrolysis reaction is expressed by the same equation (50) whether the Brønsted or the older definitions are used; the terminology only is different. The equilibrium expression for the reaction is $\dfrac{(HAc)(OH^-)}{(Ac^-)}$.

By the older terminology this expression is equal to the hydrolysis constant. By the Brønsted definitions it would more properly be called an acid-base equilibrium constant. Thus,

$$\frac{(HAc)(OH^-)}{(Ac^-)} = K_{eq}{}^B \tag{51}$$

It can be shown that

$$K_{eq}{}^B = \frac{K_W^B}{K_{I(acid)}^{B}} \tag{52}$$

where $K_{I(acid)}^{B}$ is the constant for the reaction

$$HAc + H_2O = H_3O^+ + Ac^- \qquad (53)$$

Using the older definitions, we previously showed that

$$K_H = \frac{K_W}{K_{I(acid)}} \qquad (54)$$

In this case the older K_H is equivalent to the newer K_{eq}^{B}.

The Ac^- ion is known as a strong base; it has a great tendency to take up protons. The strongly basic character of the Ac^- ion may be visualized in terms of the older concepts if we consider it in its hydrated form. Suppose that instead of representing the acetate ion by the symbol Ac^- we used $AcHOH^-$ ($Ac^- + H_2O$); i.e., included in its formula one molecule of water. Then it is easy to see that if the OH^- ion dissociated from this complex the HAc molecule would be formed and the stronger the base, the greater the concentration of OH^- ions produced. The tendency to acquire protons is equivalent to a tendency to produce OH^- ions.

$$AcHOH^- = HAc + OH^- \qquad (55)$$

This reaction is effectively the same as that represented by equation (50). This procedure, however, is not conventional. The hydrolysis of positive metal ions, according to the Brønsted definitions, will be considered in the next chapter.

EXAMPLES OF HYDROLYSIS PROBLEMS

Example 1.

(a) Calculate the concentration of the OH^- ion in a 0.1 M NaAc solution.

(b) What is the value of the concentration of the H^+ ion in this same solution?

(c) What is the degree of hydrolysis?

Sodium acetate is the salt of a strong base and a weak acid and therefore its solution will show an alkaline reaction. The equation representing the hydrolysis reaction is

$$Ac^- + H_2O = HAc + OH^-$$

Concentrations: $(0.1 - X)$ X X

Therefore

$$\frac{(HAc)(OH^-)}{(Ac^-)} = \frac{X^2}{0.1 - X} = \frac{K_W}{K_I} = \frac{1 \times 10^{-14}}{1.85 \times 10^{-5}} = 0.54 \times 10^{-9}$$

Neglecting X as compared with 0.1 in the denominator of the second expression, we have

$$\frac{X^2}{0.1} = 0.54 \times 10^{-9}$$

$$X^2 = 0.54 \times 10^{-10}$$

$$X = 0.75 \times 10^{-5} \text{ mole/liter} = (OH^-) = (HAc)$$

To calculate (H^+) we use the dissociation constant for water.

$$(H^+) = \frac{K_W}{(OH^-)} = \frac{1 \times 10^{-14}}{0.75 \times 10^{-5}} = 1.3 \times 10^{-9} \text{ mole/liter}$$

It is also possible to calculate the (H^+) in the following way. The HAc in solution is in equilibrium with its two ions, H^+ and Ac^-. The concentration of the undissociated HAc in this solution is the same as that of the OH^- ion and was found to be $0.75 \times 10^{-5} M$. The value for (Ac^-) is practically 0.1. We may therefore use the ionization constant for HAc to determine the (H^+).

$$\frac{(H^+)(Ac^-)}{(HAc)} = \frac{(H^+) \times 0.1}{0.75 \times 10^{-5}} = 1.85 \times 10^{-5}$$

$$(H^+) = \frac{1.85 \times 10^{-5} \times 0.75 \times 10^{-5}}{0.1}$$

$$(H^+) = 1.3 \times 10^{-9} \text{ mole/liter}$$

The degree of hydrolysis is the fractional amount of the Ac^- ion hydrolyzed. The amount of Ac^- ion which hydrolyzed was X or $0.75 \times 10^{-5} M$. Therefore the degree of hydrolysis is X divided by the total amount of Ac^- ion.

$$\text{Degree of hydrolysis} = \frac{X}{0.1} = \frac{0.75 \times 10^{-5}}{0.1} = 7.5 \times 10^{-5}$$

The per cent hydrolysis is equal to the degree of hydrolysis multiplied by 100.

$$\text{Per cent hydrolysis} = 7.5 \times 10^{-5} \times 100 = .0075\%$$

Example 2.

To 250 ml. of a 0.4 *M* HCN solution is added 250 ml. of a 0.4 *M* NaOH solution to give 500 ml. of the mixture. What will be the value of the (H$^+$) when the acid and base exactly neutralize each other? K_I(HCN) $= 2.1 \times 10^{-9}$.

Due to the fact that both the HCN and the NaOH solutions have been diluted to 500 ml., the resulting solution would contain these two substances each at a concentration of 0.2 *M* assuming no reaction to take place. After the reaction takes place and when equilibrium is reached a solution is obtained which would be the same as that produced by adding 0.2 mole of NaCN to a liter of water, or 0.1 mole NaCN to 500 ml. of water. Therefore, the concentration of the CN$^-$ ion in this solution is approximately 0.2 *M*, but it will be slightly less than this value due to the hydrolysis, as the following equation indicates.

$$CN^- + H_2O = HCN + OH^-$$

Concentrations: $(0.2 - X)$ X X

Then

$$\frac{(HCN)(OH^-)}{(CN^-)} = \frac{X^2}{0.2 - X} = \frac{K_W}{K_{I(acid)}} = \frac{1 \times 10^{-14}}{2.1 \times 10^{-9}} = 4.8 \times 10^{-6}$$

Neglecting X in comparison with 0.2

$$\frac{X^2}{0.2 - X} \simeq \frac{X^2}{0.2} = 4.8 \times 10^{-6}$$

$$X^2 = 0.96 \times 10^{-6}$$

$$X = 0.98 \times 10^{-3} \simeq 1 \times 10^{-3} \, \text{mole/liter} = (OH^-)$$

Since

$$(H^+)(OH^-) = 1 \times 10^{-14}$$

$$(H^+) = \frac{1 \times 10^{-14}}{(OH^-)} = \frac{1 \times 10^{-14}}{1 \times 10^{-3}}$$

$$(H^+) = 1 \times 10^{-11} \, \text{mole/liter}$$

Example 3.

(a) Calculate the concentration of the S^{--} ion in a 0.1 *M* Na$_2$S solution.

(b) Calculate the degree of hydrolysis of the S^{--} ion.

The hydrolysis of the HS$^-$ ion (second step) is negligible as compared with the hydrolysis of the S^{--} ion (first step).

The reaction is

$$S^{--} + H_2O = HS^- + OH^-$$

Let X be the number of moles of S^{--} ion undergoing hydrolysis. Then, at equilibrium, $(HS^-) = X$, $(OH^-) = X$, and $(S^{--}) = (0.1 - X)$. We then have

$$\frac{(HS^-)(OH^-)}{(S^{--})} = \frac{X^2}{0.1 - X} = K_H = \frac{K_W}{K_{I_2}} = \frac{1 \times 10^{-14}}{1.2 \times 10^{-15}} = 8.3$$

Since the value of K_H is large, X will be large as compared with 0.1 and we cannot neglect X in the expression $(0.1 - X)$. Accordingly, we must solve this equation by the use of the quadratic solution. Clearing of fractions, we have

$$X^2 = 0.83 - 8.3X$$

Transposing,

$$X^2 + 8.3X - 0.83 = 0$$

$$X = .099 \text{ mole/liter} = (HS^-) = (OH^-)$$

$$(0.1 - X) = (S^{--}) = .001 \text{ mole/liter}$$

(See the Appendix for the solution of the quadratic equation.)

This calculation may be made in a much more convenient way. From the large value for the hydrolysis constant it is apparent that most of the S^{--} ion will be hydrolyzed. Let us temporarily assume that the hydrolysis is complete. Then (HS^-) and (OH^-) will each have a value of 0.1 M. Now we shall allow these two ions to react to produce S^{--} ion and water until equilibrium is reached. Let X be the number of moles of HS^- ion and also of OH^- ion which disappear in attaining equilibrium. Then, at equilibrium, $(HS^-) = (0.1 - X)$, $(OH^-) = (0.1 - X)$, and $(S^{--}) = X$. Substituting these values in the equilibrium expression, we have

$$\frac{(0.1 - X)(0.1 - X)}{X} = 8.3$$

But since the equilibrium point is very far to the right, i.e., the hydrolysis is very nearly complete, X is now small as compared with 0.1 and may be neglected. Then the expression becomes

$$\frac{(0.1)^2}{X} = 8.3$$

and $X = \dfrac{.01}{8.3} = .0012$ mole/liter $= (S^{--})$ (compare with above).

The degree of hydrolysis is the amount of S^{--} ion hydrolyzed divided by the total amount of S^{--} ion originally present. Therefore

$$\text{Degree of hydrolysis} = \frac{.099}{0.1} = 0.99$$

The per cent hydrolysis is 0.99×100 or 99%.

Example 4.

What is the pH of a solution which contains 0.535 g. of NH_4Cl in 250 ml. of solution?

0.535 g. NH_4Cl is equal to $\dfrac{0.535}{53.5}$ or .01 mole. .01 mole of NH_4Cl in 250 ml. of solution is equivalent to .04 mole of NH_4Cl per liter. Thus, the concentration of the NH_4^+ ion is .04 M. The NH_4^+ ion undergoes hydrolysis to produce the H^+ ion according to the following equation.

$$NH_4^+ + H_2O = NH_4OH + H^+$$

Let X be the number of moles of NH_4^+ ion undergoing hydrolysis; then, at equilibrium, $(NH_4^+) = (.04 - X)$, $(NH_4OH) = X$, and $(H^+) = X$. Then we have

$$\frac{(NH_4OH)(H^+)}{(NH_4^+)} = \frac{X^2}{.04 - X} = K_H = \frac{K_W}{K_{I(base)}} = \frac{1 \times 10^{-14}}{1.8 \times 10^{-5}}$$

and $\quad \dfrac{X^2}{.04 - X} = 5.6 \times 10^{-10}$

Neglecting X as compared with .04 we have

$$\frac{X^2}{.04} = 5.6 \times 10^{-10}$$

$$X^2 = 22.4 \times 10^{-12}$$

$$X = 4.7 \times 10^{-6} \text{ mole/liter} = (H^+) = (NH_4OH)$$

$$p\text{H} = \log \frac{1}{(H^+)} = -\log (H^+)$$

$$\log (H^+) = \log (4.7 \times 10^{-6}) = \log 4.7 + \log 10^{-6}$$
$$= 0.67 + (-6) = -5.33$$

Therefore
$$p\text{H} = -\log (H^+) = -(-5.33) = 5.33$$

Example 5.

How many grams of NaAc must be added to 500 ml. of water to give a solution having a pH of 8.52? (Neglect the volume change due to the addition of the salt.)

The reaction is

$$Ac^- + H_2O = HAc + OH^-$$

From the value given for the pH of the solution, the (H^+) may be calculated. Then (OH^-) may be obtained from $K_W = (H^+)(OH^-) = 1 \times 10^{-14}$. In the NaAc solution $(HAc) = (OH^-)$. Having this information, the (Ac^-) in equilibrium with HAc and OH$^-$ ion may be determined from the hydrolysis equilibrium.

$$pH = - \log (H^+) = 8.52$$
$$\log (H^+) = - 8.52 = - 9.00 + 0.48$$

antilog $(- 9) = 10^{-9}$ and antilog $0.48 = 3.1$

Therefore $(H^+) = 3.1 \times 10^{-9} \ M$

$$(H^+)(OH^-) = 1 \times 10^{-14}$$

$$(OH^-) = \frac{1 \times 10^{-14}}{(H^+)} = \frac{1 \times 10^{-14}}{3.1 \times 10^{-9}} = 3.2 \times 10^{-6} \ M$$

If $(OH^-) = 3.2 \times 10^{-6} \ M$, then (HAc) has the same value. The equilibrium expression for the hydrolysis reaction is

$$\frac{(HAc)(OH^-)}{(Ac^-)} = K_H = \frac{K_W}{K_I} = \frac{1 \times 10^{-14}}{1.85 \times 10^{-5}} = 5.4 \times 10^{-10}$$

Then

$$\frac{(HAc)(OH^-)}{(Ac^-)} = \frac{(3.2 \times 10^{-6})(3.2 \times 10^{-6})}{(Ac^-)} = 5.4 \times 10^{-10}$$

$$(Ac^-) = \frac{(3.2 \times 10^{-6})^2}{5.4 \times 10^{-10}} = \frac{10.2 \times 10^{-12}}{5.4 \times 10^{-10}} = 1.9 \times 10^{-2} \ \text{mole/liter}$$

$$.019 \ \text{mole/liter} = \frac{.019}{2} \ \text{mole/500 ml.} = .0095 \ \text{mole/500 ml.}$$

The molecular weight of NaAc is 82. Therefore, .0095 mole/500 ml. is equivalent to .0095 × 82 or 0.78 g. NaAc/500 ml.

Example 6.

(a) What is the concentration of the H^+ ion and of the OH^- ion in a solution which is .05 M with respect to NH_4CN?

(b) What is the degree of hydrolysis of the NH_4CN?

Ammonium cyanide is a salt of a weak acid and of a weak base. Both ions undergo hydrolysis in accordance with the equation

$$NH_4^+ + CN^- + H_2O = NH_4OH + HCN$$

The equilibrium expression is

$$\frac{(NH_4OH)(HCN)}{(NH_4^+)(CN^-)} = K_H = \frac{K_W}{K_{I(base)} K_{I(acid)}} = \frac{1 \times 10^{-14}}{1.8 \times 10^{-5} \times 2.1 \times 10^{-9}}$$

$$K_H = \frac{1 \times 10^{-14}}{3.78 \times 10^{-14}} = 0.264$$

We shall assume that for every NH_4^+ ion which hydrolyzes, a CN^- ion also hydrolyzes. It can be shown readily that this assumption is a justifiable one provided the concentration of the NH_4CN is not exceedingly low. Let X be the number of moles of NH_4^+ ion undergoing hydrolysis; then X is also the number of moles of CN^- ion hydrolyzed. Since the initial concentration of the NH_4CN is .05 M and since the salt is completely ionized, the initial concentration of NH_4^+ ion and of CN^- ion is each .05 M. But at equilibrium, $(NH_4^+) = (.05 - X)$, and $(CN^-) = (.05 - X)$. Then

$$\frac{(NH_4OH)(HCN)}{(NH_4^+)(CN^-)} = \frac{X \times X}{(.05 - X)(.05 - X)} = \frac{X^2}{(.05 - X)^2} = 0.264$$

Taking the square root of both sides of the equation, we have

$$\frac{X}{.05 - X} = 0.514$$

$$X = .0257 - 0.514X$$

$$1.514X = .0257$$

$$X = .017 \text{ mole/liter} = (NH_4OH) = (HCN)$$

The value for the (H^+) may be calculated from the known amount of HCN produced and from the amount of CN^- ion remaining unhydrolyzed. The (HCN) was found to be .017 M; while the value for (CN^-) is $(.05 - X)$ or $(.05 - .017)$ or .033 M. The equation for the ionization of HCN is

$$HCN = H^+ + CN^-$$

while the equilibrium expression is

$$\frac{(H^+)(CN^-)}{(HCN)} = K_I = 2.1 \times 10^{-9}$$

Substituting in this expression the known values of (HCN) and (CN⁻), we have

$$\frac{(H^+)(.033)}{.017} = 2.1 \times 10^{-9}$$

$$(H^+) = \frac{.017 \times 2.1 \times 10^{-9}}{.033}$$

$$(H^+) = 1.08 \times 10^{-9} \text{ mole/liter}$$

The (OH⁻) then must be

$$(OH^-) = \frac{1 \times 10^{-14}}{1.08 \times 10^{-9}} = 0.93 \times 10^{-5} \text{ mole/liter}$$

The value for (OH⁻) could have been calculated from the known amounts of NH_4OH and NH_4^+ ion present in the solution.

$$NH_4OH = NH_4^+ + OH^-$$

and

$$\frac{(NH_4^+)(OH^-)}{(NH_4OH)} = K_I = 1.8 \times 10^{-5}$$

Since (NH_4OH) has a value of .017 M and the (NH_4^+) a value of .033 M, then

$$\frac{.033(OH^-)}{.017} = 1.8 \times 10^{-5}$$

$$(OH^-) = \frac{.017 \times 1.8 \times 10^{-5}}{.033} = 0.93 \times 10^{-5} \text{ mole/liter}$$

This value is the same as that obtained in the first calculation.

The degree of hydrolysis is the number of moles of NH_4CN hydrolyzed divided by the total amount of NH_4CN originally present.

$$\text{Degree of hydrolysis} = \frac{X}{.05} = \frac{.017}{.05} = 0.34$$

The per cent hydrolysis = $0.34 \times 100 = 34\%$

Experiments show that the concentration of the H^+ ion in a solution of NH_4CN is the same for all concentrations of the salt, provided the concentration is not too high, in which case the Law of Mass Action fails to hold, and provided that the concentration of the salt is not excessively low, in which case the degree of hydrolysis of the NH_4^+ ion cannot be regarded as the same as that of the CN^- ion. At intermediate concentrations of NH_4CN the (H^+) is independent of the salt concentration and has a value which is determined by the values of the three equilibrium constants, namely, K_W, $K_{I(base)}$, and $K_{I(acid)}$. This relationship is

$$(H^+) = \sqrt{\frac{K_W \cdot K_{I(acid)}}{K_{I(base)}}}$$

We may arrive at this conclusion in the following manner. From the equilibrium expression for the ionization of HCN

$$\frac{(H^+)}{K_{I(acid)}} = \frac{(HCN)}{(CN^-)}$$

From the hydrolysis equilibrium we have

$$\frac{(NH_4OH)(HCN)}{(NH_4^+)(CN^-)} = \frac{K_W}{K_{I(base)} K_{I(acid)}}$$

But since $\dfrac{(NH_4OH)}{(NH_4^+)} = \dfrac{(HCN)}{(CN^-)}$, and since the latter expression $= \dfrac{(H^+)}{K_{I(acid)}}$,

we have

$$\left(\frac{HCN}{CN^-}\right)^2 = \left(\frac{H^+}{K_{I(acid)}}\right)^2 = \frac{K_W}{K_{I(base)} K_{I(acid)}}$$

Then

$$(H^+)^2 = \frac{K_W (K_{I(acid)})^2}{K_{I(base)} K_{I(acid)}}$$

$$(H^+)^2 = \frac{K_W K_{I(acid)}}{K_{I(base)}}$$

and

$$(H^+) = \sqrt{\frac{K_W K_{I(acid)}}{K_{I(base)}}}$$

Substituting into this expression the values for the constants, we have

$$(H^+) = \sqrt{\frac{1 \times 10^{-14} \times 2.1 \times 10^{-9}}{1.8 \times 10^{-5}}} = 1.08 \times 10^{-9} \text{ mole/liter}$$

This value for the (H^+) is the same as that originally obtained directly from the hydrolysis equilibrium. It may be advantageous, as the occasion arises, to make use of this expression for calculating the concentration of the H^+ ion in a solution containing the salt of a weak acid and of a weak base.

Example 7.

Calculate the solubility of PbS in water:
(a) Neglecting the hydrolysis of the S^{--} ion.
(b) Considering the hydrolysis of the S^{--} ion.

The hydrolysis of the S^{--} ion becomes a very important factor in calculating the solubilities of sulfides from their solubility product constants and, conversely, in calculating the solubility product constants from solubility data. When hydrolysis is taken into account the solubility of any slightly soluble sulfide is about ten thousand times greater than that calculated by neglecting hydrolysis.

(a) First calculate the solubility of PbS neglecting hydrolysis. ($K_{S.P.}$ for PbS $= 7 \times 10^{-30}$.)

$$PbS_{(s)} = Pb^{++} + S^{--}$$

Let X equal the number of moles of PbS dissolved in 1 liter of solution. Then X will be equal to (S^{--}) and (Pb^{++}).

$$(Pb^{++})(S^{--}) = X^2 = 7 \times 10^{-30}$$
$$X = 2.6 \times 10^{-15} \text{ mole/liter}$$

Therefore, the solubility of PbS in water is 2.6×10^{-15} M, if the hydrolysis of the S^{--} ion is neglected.

(b) In considering the hydrolysis of the S^{--} ion we can assume that only the first step of hydrolysis is important, since the second step is negligibly small.

$$S^{--} + H_2O = HS^- + OH^-$$

The value for K_H for this reaction as calculated previously in *Example 3* is 8.3, and we found the S^{--} ion to be hydrolyzed to the extent of 99% in 0.1 M Na_2S solution. At lower concentrations the hydrolysis of the S^{--} ion is even greater than this. If the concentration of the S^{--} ion were extremely small, of the order of magnitude of the concentration of the OH^- ion in water, then the hydrolysis would be reduced somewhat due to the common ion effect of the OH^- ion. Nevertheless, the S^{--} ion at a concentration of 1×10^{-15} M would be practically completely hydrolyzed. In such an event the concentration of the OH^- ion produced by the hydrolysis would be only 1×10^{-15} M. This value is small compared with the concentration of the OH^- ion already present in water, namely, 1×10^{-7} M. Therefore, though the hydrolysis of the S^{--} ion in a saturated solution of PbS may be complete, the (OH^-) in the solution will still have a value of 1×10^{-7} M. Accordingly,

$$\frac{(HS^-)(OH^-)}{(S^{--})} = \frac{(HS^-) \times 1 \times 10^{-7}}{(S^{--})} = K_H = 8.3$$

$$\frac{(HS^-)}{(S^{--})} = 8.3 \times 10^7 \quad \text{or} \quad (S^{--}) = \frac{(HS^-)}{8.3 \times 10^7}$$

From this ratio we see that there are more than 80 million times as many HS^- ions as S^{--} ions in solution and that the hydrolysis is almost complete. From the two equilibria involved here

$$PbS_{(s)} = Pb^{++} + S^{--}$$
$$S^{--} + H_2O = HS^- + OH^-$$

it is evident that for every S^{--} ion which is removed by hydrolysis, one Pb^{++} ion and one HS^- ion are produced. Therefore, the concentration of the Pb^{++} ion will be practically the same as the concentration of the HS^- ion in solution.

Substituting the value for the S^{--} ion concentration in the solubility product expression, we have

$$(Pb^{++})(S^{--}) = (Pb^{++}) \frac{(HS^-)}{8.3 \times 10^7} = K_{S.P.} = 7 \times 10^{-30}$$

Since $\quad (Pb^{++}) = (HS^-)$,

$$\frac{(Pb^{++})^2}{8.3 \times 10^7} = 7 \times 10^{-30}$$

$$(Pb^{++})^2 = 5.8 \times 10^{-22}$$

$$(Pb^{++}) = 2.4 \times 10^{-11} \text{ mole/liter}$$

Therefore, the solubility of PbS in 1 liter of solution is also 2.4×10^{-11} mole per liter, which value is approximately ten thousand times greater than that obtained (2.6×10^{-15} M) when hydrolysis is neglected.

If we were to consider the second step of hydrolysis,

$$HS^- + H_2O = H_2S + OH^-$$

the calculated solubility would be further increased but the order of magnitude of the solubility would not be appreciably changed. In addition, the Pb^{++} ion undoubtedly hydrolyzes to give $Pb(OH)^+$ ion and $Pb(OH)_2$, and these effects would also increase the solubility of PbS.

Example 8.

Calculate the concentration of (a) the H^+ ion, (b) the OH^- ion, (c) the HCO_3^- ion, and (d) the CO_3^{--} ion in a solution which contains 0.1 mole of $NaHCO_3$ per liter.

Since $NaHCO_3$ is a salt it is completely ionized to give Na^+ and HCO_3^- ions. The HCO_3^- ion is not only a weak acid itself but it is also an ion of another weak acid, H_2CO_3. Therefore, the HCO_3^- ion takes part in two reactions in water solution,

$$HCO_3^- + H_2O = H_2CO_3 + OH^- \qquad (1)$$

and

$$HCO_3^- = CO_3^{--} + H^+ \qquad (2)$$

Reaction (1), the hydrolysis of the HCO_3^- ion, produces OH^- ion, while reaction (2), the ionization of the HCO_3^- ion, produces H^+ ion. As both reactions proceed, the H^+ and OH^- ions formed are practically all used up in the formation of water,

$$H^+ + OH^- = H_2O \qquad (3)$$

Adding equations (1), (2), and (3), we have

$$2HCO_3^- = H_2CO_3 + CO_3^{--} \qquad (4)$$

The equilibrium expression for (4) is

$$\frac{(H_2CO_3)(CO_3^{--})}{(HCO_3^-)^2} = K_{(4)}$$

When equations are added, the corresponding equilibrium expressions are multiplied. Therefore the numerical value for $K_{(4)}$ is

$$\frac{(H_2CO_3)(OH^-)}{(HCO_3^-)} \times \frac{(CO_3^{--})(H^+)}{(HCO_3^-)} \times \frac{1}{(H^+)(OH^-)} = K_{(1)} \times K_{(2)} \times K_{(3)}$$

Cancelling (H^+) and (OH^-) in the numerator and denominator,

$$\frac{(H_2CO_3)(CO_3^{--})}{(HCO_3^-)^2} = K_{(1)} \times K_{(2)} \times K_{(3)} = K_{(4)}$$

$K_{(1)}$ is the hydrolysis constant for the HCO_3^- ion and has a value of $\frac{1 \times 10^{-14}}{3.5 \times 10^{-7}}$; $K_{(2)}$ is the ionization constant for the second stage of ionization of carbonic acid and is equal to 7×10^{-11}; and $K_{(3)}$

equals $\dfrac{1}{K_W}$ or $\dfrac{1}{1 \times 10^{-14}}$. Substituting these values in the above expression, we have

$$\frac{(H_2CO_3)(CO_3^{--})}{(HCO_3^{-})^2} = \frac{1 \times 10^{-14}}{3.5 \times 10^{-7}} \times \frac{7 \times 10^{-11}}{1} \times \frac{1}{1 \times 10^{-14}}$$

$$= 2 \times 10^{-4} = K_{(4)} \tag{5}$$

Referring to equations (1), (2), and (3), it is seen that for every OH^- ion which reacts with H^+ ion to form water, one H_2CO_3 molecule and one CO_3^{--} ion are produced. Therefore, for practical purposes we are justified in making the assumption that at equilibrium the (H_2CO_3) will be the same as the (CO_3^{--}). We can also assume that since reactions (1) and (2) predominate to the left, the (HCO_3^{-}) remains practically unchanged; therefore, in this case the value for (HCO_3^{-}) will be for all practical purposes 0.1 M.

Making use of equation (5) and letting (H_2CO_3) and (CO_3^{--}) each be X, we have

$$\frac{X^2}{(0.1)^2} = 2 \times 10^{-4}$$

$$X^2 = 2 \times 10^{-6}$$

$$X = 1.42 \times 10^{-3} \text{ mole/liter} = (H_2CO_3) = (CO_3^{--})$$

Having obtained the values for (H_2CO_3) and (CO_3^{--}), (H^+) and (OH^-) may then be calculated from the equilibrium expressions of (1) and (2). Taking reaction (2), we have

$$\frac{(H^+)(CO_3^{--})}{(HCO_3^{-})} = \frac{(H^+) \times 1.42 \times 10^{-3}}{0.1} = K_{(2)} = 7 \times 10^{-11}$$

$$(H^+) = \frac{0.1 \times 7 \times 10^{-11}}{1.42 \times 10^{-3}} = 4.95 \times 10^{-9} \text{ mole/liter}$$

The value for (OH^-) may then be obtained from the water equilibrium as follows.

$$(OH^-) = \frac{1 \times 10^{-14}}{4.95 \times 10^{-9}} = 2.1 \times 10^{-6} \text{ mole/liter}$$

The $NaHCO_3$ solution is found to be basic.

The value for the concentration of the hydrogen ion in this solution may be obtained more conveniently by making use of a general rule which can readily be shown to hold for acid salts of the type $NaHCO_3$. The rule states that the (H^+) is equal to the square root of the product of the two ionization constants for the dibasic acid. Thus, in the present case,

$$(H^+) = \sqrt{K_{I_1} \times K_{I_2}}$$
$$(H^+) = \sqrt{3.5 \times 10^{-7} \times 7 \times 10^{-11}}$$
$$(H^+) = \sqrt{24.5 \times 10^{-18}}$$
$$(H^+) = 4.95 \times 10^{-9} \text{ mole/liter}$$

This value is the same as that obtained in the previous calculation. Since the latter calculation does not involve the concentration of the dissolved $NaHCO_3$, the value obtained for (H^+) must be the same for all concentrations of the salt.

The rule, in this case, may be derived from the first and second ionizaton constants for carbonic acid.

$$\frac{(H^+)^2 \, (CO_3^{--})}{(H_2CO_3)} = K_1 \times K_2$$

Remembering that for all practical purposes (CO_3^{--}) and (H_2CO_3) are practically the same, we therefore cancel them out in the above expression, and

$$(H^+) = \sqrt{K_1 \times K_2}$$

At intermediate concentrations, this relationship applies to such ions of weak acids as $HC_2O_4^-$, $H_2PO_4^-$, $H_2PO_3^-$, HSO_3^-, and HS^-.

QUESTIONS AND PROBLEMS

1. Write the equation representing the dissociation of water into H^+ and OH^- ions. Explain why the addition of more water will not shift this equilibrium. How may it be shifted?

2. Why is the equilibrium expression for the dissociation of water written $(H^+) \times (OH^-)$ and not $\dfrac{(H^+) \times (OH^-)}{(H_2O)}$?

3. When solid sodium acetate is added to water why do not all of the Ac^- ions combine with H^+ ions to form acetic acid?

4. Does (a) the salt of a weak acid and a strong base, (b) the salt of a strong acid and a weak base, (c) the salt of a strong acid and a strong base, produce an acidic, basic or neutral solution?

5. Show that the hydrolysis constant for a salt of a strong base and a weak acid is equal to the ionization constant for water divided by the dissociation constant for the acid.

6. Show that the hydrolysis constant for the **first** step of hydrolysis for the salt of a strong base and a weak dibasic acid is equal to the ionization constant for water divided by the **second** dissociation constant for the acid.

7. Explain why aluminum hydroxide and not aluminum carbonate is precipitated from solution when a solution of sodium carbonate is added to one of aluminum sulfate.

8. Why is BaS not stable when added to water?

9. Why is the carbonate ion concentration in a solution of ammonium carbonate less than it is in a sodium carbonate solution of the same molarity?

10. Explain by the Rule of Le Chatelier why the degree of hydrolysis of sodium acetate increases as the solution is diluted.

11. Write equations for the hydrolysis reactions occurring when sodium carbonate is dissolved in water.

12. If a 0.1 molar solution of HCN is neutralized by a 0.1 molar solution of NaOH the two solutions do not neutralize each other when the H^+ ion concentration is 10^{-7} molar but rather when the H^+ concentration is about 10^{-11} molar. Explain.

13. What is a buffer solution? Explain its action.

14. Write the ionic equations for the reaction representing the hydrolysis of each of the following salts:

(a) Ammonium chloride — NH_4Cl
(b) Sodium acetate — $NaC_2H_3O_2$
(c) Methyl ammonium chloride — CH_3NH_3Cl
(d) Sodium benzoate — $NaC_6H_5CO_2$
(e) Potassium cyanide — KCN
(f) Sodium phenolate — NaC_6H_5O
(g) Barium nitrite — $Ba(NO_2)_2$
(h) Lithium formate — $LiCHO_2$
(i) Dimethyl ammonium chloride — $(CH_3)_2NH_2Cl$
(j) Potassium propionate — $KC_3H_5O_2$

15. Calculate the hydrolysis constant for each of the salts listed in problem 14. (K_I for the corresponding acids or bases are given in tables in the Appendix.)

16. Calculate the (H^+) for (a) a 0.1 molar, (b) a .01 molar solution of each of the salts listed in problem 14.

17. What is the pH value for each of the solutions in problem 16?

18. What is the degree of hydrolysis for each salt in problem 16?

19. How many grams of sodium acetate must be added to 1 liter of water to give an OH^- ion concentration of 1×10^{-5} mole/liter?

20. How many grams of NH_4Cl must be added to 1 liter of water to give an OH^- ion concentration of 10^{-9} mole/liter?

21. How many moles of NH_4Cl must be added to 1 liter of water to give the same pH value as a 0.1 molar solution of HCN?

22. (a) Using only $K_I(HAc)$, calculate the H^+ concentration in a solution containing 0.1 mole sodium acetate and 0.1 mole acetic acid.   (b) Repeat the calculation using K_H.

23. What is the concentration of the undissociated HAc in a solution containing 1 mole NaAc per liter?

24. A .01 molar solution of NaCN is found to be hydrolyzed to the extent of 2.2%. What is the value of the ionization constant for HCN?

25. Show by calculation whether it is possible to make a solution of sodium formate concentrated enough to produce the same OH^- concentration as that of a .001 molar solution of KCN. (In this case assume the Law of Mass Action to hold for concentrated solutions.)

26. Calculate (a) the hydrolysis constant, (b) the H^+ ion concentration, and (c) the degree of hydrolysis for a 0.1 M Na_2CO_3 solution. (Neglect the second hydrolysis step.)

27. What will be the minimum concentration of a NaAc solution necessary to begin the precipitation of $Mg(OH)_2$ if equal quantities of this solution and one containing 0.2 mole Mg^{++} ion per liter are mixed?

28. Solid Na_2S is added slowly to a .01 M $FeSO_4$ solution. Which will be precipitated first, $Fe(OH)_2$ or FeS?

29. Calculate the H^+ ion concentration in the resulting solution when equal amounts of the following are mixed:
  (a) 0.1 M HCl and 0.1 M NH_4OH
  (b) 0.1 M HCl and 0.1 M NaOH
  (c) 0.1 M H_2SO_4 and 0.1 M NaOH (see p. 130)
  (d) .02 M HAc and .02 M NaOH
  (e) 0.1 M H_2S and 0.2 M NaOH

30. Calculate the CO_3^{--} ion concentration and the OH^- ion concentration in a .01 M solution of $NaHCO_3$. (See *Example 8*, page 210.)

31. If $MgCl_2$ is added slowly to a solution which is 0.1 M with respect to $NaHCO_3$, which will begin to precipitate first, $Mg(OH)_2$ or $MgCO_3$? (See *Example 8*, page 210.)

32. Calculate the solubility in moles per liter of the following sulfides in water, (1) neglecting the hydrolysis of the S^{--} ion, (2) considering the hydrolysis of the S^{--} ion.

    (a) CdS   (b) CuS   (c) PbS   (d) Ag_2S (e) CoS

33. What must be the ratio of (Ac^-) to (HAc) in a buffer solution made up of acetic acid and sodium acetate if the H^+ ion concentration is to be maintained at 10^{-5} M?

34. What is the concentration of the H^+ ion in a solution which is .01 M with respect to $ZnCl_2$? ($K_I(Zn(OH)^+$ has a value of 4×10^{-5}.)

35. Calculate the ratio of the (HPO_4^{--}) to $(H_2PO_4^-)$ in a solution in which these two ions are used as a buffer, if the pH of the solution is to be maintained at (a) 6.0, (b) 7.0, and (c) 8.0. Assume that the H^+ ion concentration is controlled entirely by the reaction $H_2PO_4^- = H^+ + HPO_4^{--}$.

CHAPTER IX

Complex Ions

For the sake of simplicity and because of a lack of definite information we designate an ion in solution merely by the symbol of the element or radical and by the charge which the ion carries. Thus, hydrogen ion is written as H^+; sodium ion, Na^+; chloride ion, Cl^-; sulfate ion, SO_4^{--}, etc. There is sufficient evidence for the argument that no ion exists in solution as a simple charged atom or group as its chemical symbol might imply. It has been shown by experiments designed to determine the relative amounts of electricity carried by various ions in solution that ions carry with them relatively large quantities of water. Although it is not possible as yet to determine the absolute amount of water carried by each, these experiments do allow calculations to be made concerning the amount of water carried by an ion of one element or group, relative to that transported by an ion of another element or group. For example, if we arbitrarily assume that the fastest moving ion, the hydrogen ion, carries a minimum amount of water, one molecule, then the potassium ion carries on the average about five; the sodium ion, eight; the lithium ion, fourteen; while the chloride ion carries about four molecules of water. These numbers are known as the *hydration numbers* of the ions. These hydration numbers vary with the concentration of the solution. They are related to the speeds of the ions, in that an ion carrying a large amount of water moves slowly in comparison with an ion which carries a relatively small amount of water.

From what has been said in earlier chapters regarding the attractive forces between ions of opposite charge, it would seem reasonable to expect that these attractive forces also

216

exist between ions and water molecules to give rise to hydrated ions, since the water molecule is a dipole having separated positive and negative centralizations of charge. Polar molecules tend to attract each other to form aggregates of molecules and, similarly, we might conclude that polar water molecules are attracted to charged ions in solution. Accordingly, we may look upon all ions as solvated in solution, i.e., having molecules of solvent attached to them.

The union between most ions and water molecules is not a very firm one and the law of definite proportions does not apply in this case, since the amount of water held by each ion is very probably indefinite. In the case of the cobalt ion, however, a compound is formed, i.e., a very definite number of water molecules attach themselves firmly to each cobalt ion. Other substances besides water react with some ions in solution in a definite way and form complex ions.

The Hydronium Ion. Since the hydrogen ion moves much faster than any other ion in solution when subjected to an electric field, we believe that it has associated with it less water than other ions. If we assume that it combines with one molecule of water, we may write its formula as $H^+(H_2O)$ or H_3O^+.

$$H^+ + H_2O = H_3O^+ \tag{1}$$

The latter ion is known as the **hydronium ion** and is believed by many to represent the condition of the hydrogen ion in water. The evidence for the existence of such a combination is somewhat indirect.

When two substances react with each other to form a third substance, an energy change takes place which usually manifests itself in the form of heat; heat is either liberated or absorbed. The former is the more usual case. This heat effect is usually large when the substance formed possesses great stability. In general, the smaller the heat effect the less stable is the product. When one substance dissolves in another, an energy change likewise results. Heat is usually, not always, absorbed in the process of solution, but the magnitude of the energy change is usually very small compared to that involved in a chemical reaction. When HCl, H_2SO_4, HBr, HNO_3, and similar substances are placed in water a very large amount of heat is liberated, much more than one would expect from the simple process of solution. On the contrary, when sodium chloride is placed in water, a small amount of heat is absorbed. Many other salts behave similarly. Where the hydrogen ion is involved in the process of solution, the amount of heat liberated is comparable with that of many chemical reactions. This behavior may be ascribed to the formation of the hydronium ion.

If we assume that one molecule of water is associated with the hydrogen ion, the resulting hydronium ion may be represented structurally as being similar to the ammonium ion. The hydronium ion is a complex ion and is the fundamental particle used in the Brønsted definitions for the explanation of acid-base reactions.

The Ammonium Ion. Pure liquid ammonia, boiling point − 33.5° C, is a poorer conductor of electricity than is pure water; the conductivity of water is at least 10,000 times greater than that of ammonia. When hydrogen chloride is placed in pure ammonia the resulting solution is found to be an excellent conductor of electricity; the value of its conductivity is of the same order of magnitude as that of hydrogen chloride in water. In this case a reaction takes place which involves the formation of a new ion. The ion produced is quite familiar to us, the ammonium ion, and its formation may be expressed by the equation,

$$H^+ + NH_3 = NH_4^+ \qquad (2)$$

The ammonium ion is a complex ion and may be looked upon as an analogue of the hydronium ion. It differs from the hydronium ion in that it forms salts with negative ions which possess considerable stability. When the excess ammonia from the solution just considered is allowed to evaporate, a solid remains which upon examination is found to be ammonium chloride. It is known that solid ammonium chloride may be heated to several hundred degrees before it noticeably dissociates to give ammonia and hydrogen chloride. Ammonia reacts in a similar manner with many other hydrogen compounds; thus HBr, HI, H_2SO_4, and HNO_3 form ammonium salts with ammonia, all of which are highly stable in that they may be crystallized from solution.

Pure ammonia ionizes very slightly in accordance with the equation,

$$NH_3 = H^+ + NH_2^- \tag{3}$$

The hydrogen ion formed in this process combines with ammonia, as expressed in equation (2). The NH_2^- (amide) ion in liquid ammonia corresponds to the OH^- ion in water, and metal ions in combination with the NH_2^- ion behave as bases.

Like hydrogen chloride in water (hydronium chloride), ammonium chloride behaves as an acid in liquid ammonia. It will react with ammono bases such as potassium amide, KNH_2, sodium amide, $NaNH_2$, etc., to form salts and ammonia. These reactions are analogous to those between hydrochloric acid and hydroxides in water. Typical reactions in the two solvents may be written:

$$H_3O^+ + OH^- = 2H_2O \tag{4}$$
$$NH_4^+ + NH_2^- = 2NH_3 \tag{5}$$

One of the characteristic properties of an acid in an aqueous medium is its ability to react with certain metals with the displacement of hydrogen. Thus,

$$Zn + 2H^+ = Zn^{++} + H_2 \tag{6}$$

or, using hydronium chloride,

$$Zn + 2H_3O^+ = Zn^{++} + H_2 + 2H_2O \tag{7}$$

Ammonium chloride in liquid ammonia behaves in a similar manner,

$$Zn + 2NH_4^+ = Zn^{++} + H_2 + 2NH_3 \tag{8}$$

Like the hydronium ion in water, the ammonium ion in ammonia is an acid. The only essential difference between the two is that the ammonium ion possesses a far greater stability at ordinary temperatures than does the hydronium ion. The similarity of water to ammonia leads to the assumption of the hydronium ion as the analogue of the ammonium ion. However, for most purposes it is immaterial which formula we use. Simplicity recommends the use of the symbol H^+ rather than H_3O^+ for the hydrogen ion in water solution.

Solid Hydrates and Ammonates. The ability of ions to combine with water and ammonia molecules is not limited to the hydrogen ion. As we previously stated, attractive forces exist between ions and polar water molecules, and all ions are more or less associated with water in this medium. In most cases the resulting combination, which is not a definite one, is capable of existence only in solution. Sometimes a crystalline product containing water may be obtained from solution. The number of such compounds is relatively large; only a few familiar examples may be mentioned here, such as $CuSO_4 \cdot 5H_2O$, $CaCl_2 \cdot 6H_2O$, $Na_2SO_4 \cdot 10H_2O$ and $CrCl_3 \cdot 6H_2O$. These addition compounds, made up of salts and water molecules, are commonly called **hydrates**. The fact that these solids contain water in definite proportions is no assurance that definite proportions hold true in solution. The crystal lattice, i.e., the space distribution in the crystal, allows a definite number of water molecules to be associated with each particle (ion or atom) in the crystal. Such restrictions do not prevail in solution.

Ammonia shows an even greater tendency to combine with ions both in water and in liquid ammonia to form analogous solid compounds, called **ammonates**. Characteristic examples of such combinations are $CuSO_4 \cdot 4NH_3$, $CaCl_2 \cdot 8NH_3$, $CrCl_3 \cdot 6NH_3$ and $CoCl_3 \cdot 6NH_3$. All of these ammonates may be crystallized from solution and upon analysis they have been shown to be definite compounds. In general, the ammonates are more stable, both in solution and in the solid state, than are the analogous combinations containing water molecules. This property of ions or molecules to combine with solvent molecules is not confined entirely to water and ammonia. Molecules of many other solvents show the same tendency to a greater or lesser degree. This fact is demonstrated clearly when one considers that there are known in well-crystallized form several thousand combinations similar to those mentioned above, in which water, ammonia, alcohols, amines and many other solvent molecules assume a definite part in the crystalline solid complex.

Valence and Complex Molecules. An examination of complex molecules reveals that the valence relationships among their atoms cannot be explained by the ordinary concepts which apply fairly well to other types of molecules. It appears that in each instance the ion in the complex molecule exhibits a combining capacity which exceeds the primary or ordinary valence. Thus in $[Cu(NH_3)_4]^{++}$ the copper ion displays the ability to acquire four additional molecules of ammonia. On the other hand, the cobalt ion takes on six molecules of water or ammonia. A similar situation exists in many other known compounds. This additional combining capacity is usually spoken of as the **auxiliary valence,** which for the copper ion is four and for the cobalt ion, six. What is the nature of this auxiliary valence and what explanation can be offered to account for it?

In an earlier chapter we considered the electronic structures of atoms and molecules and on this basis explained the difference between the main and sub-groups of the periodic system. It is the elements of the sub-groups, with their shells of 18 rather than 8 electrons in the next to their outermost shells, that we shall now consider with respect to the formation of complex ions and molecules.

When the periodic table is followed into the third series of elements (beginning with argon), scandium appears in the third group. This element is not very closely related to the preceding elements in the same group. Since it is in the first long series, between argon and krypton, which series is composed of 18 elements, a shell of 18 electrons must be taken into consideration. In the case of scandium one electron falls back into a shell which already possesses a stable grouping of eight electrons; this shell then contains nine electrons. This is the first step in the formation of an inner shell of 18 electrons. The same shell for the element titanium (atomic number 22, one greater than that of scandium) contains 10 electrons, for vanadium it contains 11 electrons, etc., until zinc (atomic number 30) is reached, which has 18 electrons. This number persists in this shell as far as the next rare gas, krypton (atomic number 36). The fourth series of the periodic table is likewise a long series and contains 18 elements, while the fifth series contains 32 elements, due to the 14 rare earth elements which occupy a single position in the table. The elements in these long series have more than 8 electrons in the next to the outermost shell. The outermost shell contains the normal valence electrons. In the long series we find the elements which make up the sub-groups of the table and, in addition, the transition elements, such as iron, cobalt and nickel.

Ions which show no auxiliary valence have a completed group of eight electrons in the outermost shell. Those displaying auxiliary valence have in their outermost shells either a completed or partially completed group of 18 electrons. Thus, the magnesium ion (magnesium atom minus 2 electrons) has an outer group of 8 electrons while the zinc ion has an outer group of 18.

The auxiliary valence which is displayed in the formation of complex molecules is undoubtedly due to forces which result from the electrons of that shell immediately within the one containing the valence electrons of the atoms, i.e., the outermost shell of the ions. The binding between metal ion and the solvent molecules is probably of the nonpolar type. This fact is strongly suggested when one considers the properties of these complexes.

The Coordination Theory of Werner. About the beginning of the century, Alfred Werner, a German chemist, made a thorough study of complex molecules and proposed a theory which fits their observed properties in a remarkable manner. He first introduced the concept of auxiliary valence, thus explaining the behavior of these compounds. Let us examine this theory in order to explain the properties of a typical complex molecule such as $CoCl_3 \cdot 6NH_3$. This molecule is a salt, a good conductor of electricity in water solution, and its anion may readily be identified as the chloride ion by the precipitation of silver chloride when silver nitrate is added to its solution. All the chlorine is found in the anion form, and sulfuric acid converts the complex into the corresponding sulfate salt. Contrary to what might be expected, sulfuric acid fails to remove any ammonia molecules from the complex, even though ammonia and hydrogen ion have a great tendency to combine with each other to form the ammonium ion, NH_4^+. It is therefore evident that the ammonia is associated in a very firm manner with the cobalt ion. On the basis of these properties and according to the theory of Werner the molecule is represented as $[Co(NH_3)_6]Cl_3$, or

$$\left[\begin{array}{ccc} & NH_3 & \\ NH_3 & | & NH_3 \\ & \diagdown | \diagup & \\ & Co & \\ & \diagup | \diagdown & \\ NH_3 & | & NH_3 \\ & NH_3 & \end{array} \right] Cl_3$$

It is assumed that the addition of the six molecules of ammonia takes place through the auxiliary valencies. The complex grouping contains only a cobalt atom and ammonia molecules, and as a unit it does not possess properties characteristic of either constituent. The chlorine atoms, however, retain their characteristic properties, in that all three are readily removed by silver ions with the formation of silver chloride. Consequently, all three chlorine atoms must exist in solution as chloride ions. The conductivity of this complex in water solution has a value similar to that of a typical tri-univalent electrolyte such as ferric chloride,

$FeCl_3$; hence the complex must produce four ions. Accordingly, we may indicate its structure in solution as

$$\left[\begin{array}{c} NH_3 \\ NH_3 \quad | \quad NH_3 \\ \diagdown \quad \diagup \\ Co \\ \diagup \quad | \quad \diagdown \\ NH_3 \quad | \quad NH_3 \\ NH_3 \end{array} \right]^{+++} \quad + \; 3Cl^-$$

One molecule of ammonia may be easily removed from the cobalt complex discussed above by heating the solid to 250°C. This procedure produces the compound $CoCl_3 \cdot 5NH_3$. When this molecule is treated with silver ion in water solution, only two chlorine atoms are removed through the precipitation of silver chloride. In addition, the conductivity of this salt shows it to be a bi-univalent electrolyte, producing only three ions. Its structure may be represented as

$$\left[\begin{array}{c} Cl \\ NH_3 \quad | \quad NH_3 \\ \diagdown \quad \diagup \\ Co \\ \diagup \quad | \quad \diagdown \\ NH_3 \quad | \quad NH_3 \\ NH_3 \end{array} \right]^{++} \quad + \; 2Cl^-$$

In like manner $[Co(NH_3)_4Cl_2]Cl$ is found to be a uni-univalent electrolyte, because of its conductivity and because silver ion reacts with only one chloride ion per molecule. $[Co(NH_3)_3Cl_3]$ is quite insoluble in water and is a non-conductor of the electric current. Silver ion fails to precipitate silver chloride when added to a solution of this compound. Continued removal of ammonia and the addition of potassium nitrite produces $K[Co(NH_3)_2(NO_2)_4]$, which is found to be a uni-univalent electrolyte and to ionize as

$$K[Co(NH_3)_2(NO_2)_4] = K^+ + [Co(NH_3)_2(NO_2)_4]^- \quad (9)$$

Here the cobalt atom is contained in the complex anion. The resulting charge on the complex ion is negative because the nitrite ions replacing the ammonia molecules in the complex are themselves negatively charged. The resulting charge on any complex ion can easily be determined by taking the algebraic sum of the charges on the constituent parts of the complex ion. Thus, in this case,

$$Co^{+++} \text{ contributes } 3 +$$
$$2NH_3 \text{ contribute } 0$$
$$\underline{4NO_2^- \text{ contribute } 4 -}$$
$$\text{resultant charge } 1 -$$

The next member of the series is not known, but its formula would be $K_2[Co(NH_3)(NO_2)_5]$, a uni-bivalent electrolyte. The last member of the series is well known as potassium cobaltinitrite which is only slightly soluble in water. In one of the analytical tests for potassium ion, the sodium salt, $Na_3[Co(NO_2)_6]$, is added to a solution of the unknown. In dilute solution $NaK_2[Co(NO_2)_6]$ is precipitated if potassium ion is present; in concentrated solution $K_3[Co(NO_2)_6]$ may be formed. The latter is a uni-trivalent electrolyte, as shown by the magnitude of its conductivity, and ionizes in solution to produce four ions,

$$K_3[Co(NO_2)_6] = 3K^+ + [Co(NO_2)_6]^{---} \tag{10}$$

The following series of platinum compounds is also well established: $[Pt(NH_3)_6]Cl_4$, $[Pt(NH_3)_5Cl]Cl_3$, $[Pt(NH_3)_4Cl_2]Cl_2$, $[Pt(NH_3)_3Cl_3]Cl$, $[Pt(NH_3)_2Cl_4]$, $[Pt(NH_3)Cl_5]K$, and $[PtCl_6]K_2$. It will be observed that the number of single constituents associated with the central atom in the complex cation or anion, as the case may be, in both the cobalt and platinum series, is always six. This number is known as the **coordination number,** which for most ions is usually 4 or 6. In the case of the well-known copper-ammonia complex ion, $[Cu(NH_3)_4]^{++}$, the coordination number of the copper is 4.

The coordination number of an ion in many instances is equal to twice the charge on the ion. Thus the coordination number of Cu^{++} is 4; that of Zn^{++}, 4; that of Ag^+, 2; that of Cu^+, 2; and that of Co^{+++}, 6. This rule is not a rigid one; the most common exception is the coordination number of 6 for Fe^{++} in the ferrocyanides.

The complex anion or cation or molecule is sometimes designated as the **coordination sphere.** Thus the coordination sphere of the compound $[Co(NH_3)_5Cl]Cl_2$ contains one cobalt atom, five molecules of ammonia and one chlorine atom. Polyvalent acid radicals, such as SO_4^{--}, CO_3^{--}, $C_2O_4^{--}$ (oxalate) ions, may be taken up by the central atom and occupy two positions in the coordination sphere; for example, in the complex $[Co(NH_3)_4SO_4]Cl$, the coordination number of the cobalt ion remains as 6. Although the examples given above for the cobalt and platinum series contain only ammonia molecules, it must be remembered that water and other solvent molecules can occupy positions within the coordination sphere. The ammonia complexes are chosen here since they are well defined and relatively simple. Examples of complexes which contain other kinds of molecules are: $[Cr(H_2O)_6]Cl_3$, $[Cr(H_2O)_4Cl_2]Cl$, $[Cu(H_2O)_4]SO_4$, $K_4[Fe(CN)_6]$, $K_2[Ni(CN)_4]$, $K[Ag(CN)_2]$, and $[Co(NH_3)_5(H_2O)]Cl_3$.*

Complex Anions. Most of our attention thus far, in relation to complex molecules, has been directed toward the properties of complex cations. However, the complex anions are not only commonly encountered in analytical procedures but are of the greatest importance in the separation of groups of elements and of the individual elements and their ions.

A complex anion frequently encountered in analytical procedures is the argenti-cyanide ion, $Ag(CN)_2^-$. Silver cyanide is one of the slightly soluble salts of the silver ion; its solubility product constant is 2.2×10^{-12}. However, when potassium cyanide is added to a suspension of the solid silver cyanide in water, it is found to dissolve readily.

---

* For a more detailed account of the nomenclature and general properties of complex molecules, see Robert Schwarz, *Chemistry of the Inorganic Complex Compounds,* tr. by L. W. Bass, John Wiley and Son, New York, 1923.

Since potassium chloride, which furnishes a high concentration of potassium ion in water, does not affect the solubility of the silver cyanide appreciably, it may be concluded that the cyanide ion is the constituent responsible for the reaction, which we may express in the form of an equation,

$$AgCN(solid) + CN^- = Ag(CN)_2^- \qquad (11)$$
$$\updownarrow$$
$$Ag^+ + CN^-$$

Here the silver cyanide combines with the negative cyanide ion to form a complex anion. This reaction is typical of the reactions of the ions of the copper group, zinc group, and of the transition elements of the periodic table, which are in accord with the views presented earlier in this chapter. Other examples of cyanide complexes are: $Fe(CN)_6^{----}$, $Fe(CN)_6^{---}$, $Au(CN)_2^-$, $Cd(CN)_4^{--}$, $Cu(CN)_3^{--}$, and $Hg(CN)_4^{--}$ ions. The halogens, thiocyanate group, thiosulfate group and other constituents may take the place of the cyanide group in many of these compounds to give complex anions. Many of these substances are not only of importance in analytical chemistry but also in applied chemistry. The extraction of gold from its ores and the electrorefining of silver and of copper are well-known cases of the application of the chemistry of complex anions to industrial processes.

Auxiliary Valence and Molecular Structure. Although the theory of auxiliary valence from the standpoint of electronic structure is not as clear-cut as the simple valence theory heretofore discussed, yet several important correlations present themselves.

Let us consider the structure of the zinc ammonia complex ion, $Zn(NH_3)_4^{++}$, as a basis for our discussion. The K, L and M shells of the Zn^{++} ion contain 2, 8 and 18 electrons, respectively. Let us assume that each of the four ammonia molecules share 2 electrons with the central Zn^{++} ion. The zinc ammonia complex ion structure would then be that illustrated in Figure 23, on page 228. The configuration of

electrons about the zinc nucleus in the complex ion would be:
2, 8, 18 and 8, the same structure as that of krypton.

Although it is difficult to find many complex ions the structure of which fall into as clear a picture as this, a rather
large number exist for which the total outside electrons contributed as a sharing process by both the central ion and

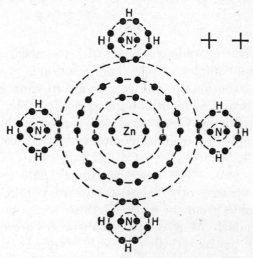

Figure 23.   Zinc-Ammonia Complex Ion

the complementary groups, equals 26 (18 + 8). All the
complexes of the Co^{+++} ion fit this scheme. As an example
consider the $Co(NH_3)_6^{+++}$ complex ion. The outermost
shell of the Co^{+++} ion contains 14 electrons (see table in
appendix) and the six NH_3 groups contribute 12 electrons.
The same is true for the $Co(NH_3)_5Cl^{++}$ ion and the
$Co(NO_2)_6^{---}$ ion. Some of the other ions and molecules
which fall into this category are the platinum ion complexes
previously listed, $Fe(CN)_6^{---}$, $CdCl_4^{--}$, $HgBr_4^{--}$ and
$Ni(CO)_4$. Many other examples of this kind can be found.
The assumption usually made in these cases is that when
the electrons assume the 18- and 8-electron outer structure
there is little distinction between the electrons in the 18 and
the 8 groups.

There are many cases also known for complex ions having less than 26 in the outer shells. The $Cu(NH_3)_4^{++}$ ion, for example, has only 25. Apparently, the 18 shell need not be completely filled to obtain a stable structure. Very seldom, however, do complex ions display more than 26 electrons in the outer two shells. Complexes of the cobaltous ion, Co^{++}, such as $Co(CN)_6^{----}$, are examples of the latter type, but these complex ions are very good reducing agents, i.e., they have a strong tendency to lose this extra electron.

Homoatomic Anions. Many complex anions are known which are formed by the combination of negative ions with neutral atoms or molecules. When the neutral atom or molecule and the negative ion of such a complex involve only a single element, then the complex anion is known as a **homoatomic** anion. Potassium iodide is a salt which in water solution ionizes completely to give potassium and iodide ions. Although iodine displays a very low solubility in pure water, when added to an aqueous solution of potassium iodide it dissolves readily. Properties of the solution, such as the lowering of the freezing point and the conductivity, indicate the presence of only two ions. This and other evidence points to the conclusion that a tri-iodide ion is formed through the reaction,

$$I^- + I_2 = I_3^- \qquad (12)$$

The combining weights are also in agreement with this equation. Thus it appears that the negative iodide ion takes up a molecule of iodine, I_2, to form a complex anion, the type which has already been designated as a homoatomic anion. Although this reaction proceeds only as far as the tri-iodide stage in water solution, in the solid condition iodide ions of greater complexity are easily produced. Thus, the iodide ion under suitable conditions will take up molecules of iodine to form complex anions, I_5^-, I_7^-, and I_9^-. As might be expected, an odd number of iodine atoms is always present in the complex anion. Ions having an even number of iodine atoms are not known.

Many other negative ions show properties conforming to those of the iodide ion, one of which we shall consider in relation to analytical procedures and problems of analysis, namely, the sulfide ion, S^{--}. This ion in water solution reacts with sulfur to produce complex anions which contain only sulfur atoms and bear a charge of -2; the first stage of the reaction is represented by the equation,

$$S^{--} + S = S_2^{--} \qquad (13)$$

Evidence points to further reaction to form S_3^{--}, S_4^{--}, S_5^{--} ions, and perhaps anions containing a larger number of sulfur atoms. It will be observed that each ion carries a charge of -2, regardless of the number of sulfur atoms it contains.

In the separation of the arsenic from the copper group, yellow ammonium sulfide is used, since this reagent dissolves the sulfides of the arsenic group but not those of the copper group. The exact composition of the ammonium polysulfide is not known; the solution undoubtedly consists of a mixture of several of the complex sulfide ions mentioned before. For simplicity we shall regard it as containing chiefly S_2^{--} ions. Taking arsenous sulfide as typical of the arsenic group, we may illustrate the action of the ammonium polysulfide (yellow ammonium sulfide) by the equation,

$$As_2S_3(solid) + 3S_2^{--} = 2AsS_4^{---} + S \qquad (14)$$

The arsenous sulfide is oxidized by the polysulfide solution to the thioarsenate ion, AsS_4^{---}, which is an example of another type of complex anion. The sulfur formed in reaction (14) is of course again dissolved by the sulfide solution. Ammonium or sodium sulfide will dissolve As_2S_5 readily but will not dissolve As_2S_3 to any appreciable extent. We may regard the process of solution of As_2S_3 by the polysulfide as one of oxidation by the dissolved sulfur with subsequent solution of the As_2S_5, as illustrated by the equations,

$$As_2S_3 + 2S(dissolved) = As_2S_5 \qquad (15)$$

$$As_2S_5 + 3S^{--} = 2AsS_4^{---} \qquad (16)$$

The rôle played by complex anions and cations in procedures of qualitative analysis will be described in Part II of this text, when we consider the properties of individual ions, the properties of analytical groups and the methods used for their separation.

Equilibria Involving Complex Ions. Experiments were previously described in which silver ion and hydrogen ion failed to remove chlorine and ammonia respectively from the coordination sphere of $[Co(NH_3)_5Cl]Cl_2$. Although this indicates that these constituents are held very firmly in the complex ion, it does not mean that there is complete absence of dissociation of the ion. It does mean, however, that this complex ion does not dissociate sufficiently to give a high enough Cl^- ion concentration for the precipitation of silver chloride, and that the NH_3 concentration in equilibrium with the complex ion is too small for the formation of an appreciable amount of the ammonium ion.

When ammonium hydroxide is slowly added to a solution of silver nitrate, there is first observed a brown precipitate of silver hydroxide (or silver oxide). In the presence of a large number of silver ions, there are sufficient hydroxide ions from the ionization of the ammonium hydroxide to exceed the solubility product constant of silver hydroxide. However, the continued addition of ammonium hydroxide to this same solution is found to dissolve the silver hydroxide with the formation of the complex silver ion.

Experiments show that the ammonia molecule is responsible for the dissolving of the silver hydroxide. The original solution of silver nitrate contains only silver and nitrate ions, while the ammonium hydroxide solution introduces four new constituents, ammonium ions, hydroxide ions, free ammonia and ammonium hydroxide molecules, all of which are in equilibrium with each other:

$$NH_3 + H_2O = NH_4OH = NH_4^+ + OH^- \qquad (17)$$

Neither the ammonium ion nor the hydroxide ion is responsible for the dissolving of silver hydroxide by an excess of ammonium hydroxide. The only two constituents left are free ammonia and ammonium hydroxide molecules. We are not able to distinguish between the two, the equilibrium between them never having been determined. We may consider ammonia in water as consisting entirely of free ammonia, NH_3, or of ammonium hydroxide, NH_4OH, molecules, whichever is more convenient. For our purposes it matters little which we choose. The silver-ammonia complex ion, $Ag(NH_3)_2{}^+$, is the substance formed. (It is to be noted that the names of these complexes are **ammonia** complexes and not **ammonium** complexes. Ammonia refers to the molecule NH_3; ammonium to the radical NH_4.) The co-ordination number of the silver ion in the silver-ammonia complex is 2. The original experiment may now be expressed in the form of two equations,

$$Ag^+ + NH_4OH = AgOH(solid) + NH_4{}^+ \tag{18}$$

$$AgOH(solid) + 2NH_3 = Ag(NH_3)_2{}^+ + OH^- \tag{19}$$

Since silver ion and ammonia combine to form the silver-ammonia ion, we would also expect this ion to dissociate somewhat into its constituents,

$$Ag(NH_3)_2{}^+ = Ag^+ + 2NH_3 \tag{20}$$

The dissociation process is in a general way like the dissociation of weak acids and bases. Lacking sufficient information, the dissociation is expressed by the over-all reaction (equation 20), rather than by steps. According to the equation three kinds of particles are in equilibrium with each other, the silver-ammonia complex ion, silver ion, and ammonia molecules. If an additional amount of silver ions were added to this system, the equilibrium would shift to the left, with the formation of more silver-ammonia ions. The addition of ammonia molecules would have the same effect. Dilution with water would favor the dissociation of the complex to produce more ions. We may write an equilibrium constant for this reaction in the usual way, with the products appearing in the numerator and the reactants in the denominator as follows:

$$\frac{(Ag^+)(NH_3)^2}{(Ag(NH_3)_2{}^+)} = K = 6.8 \times 10^{-8} \qquad (21)$$

The dissociation constant has a value of 6.8×10^{-8} which is sufficiently low to signify that the dissociation of the complex ion is slight. What then is the amount of dissociation of this complex ion in a solution in which it is present at moderate concentration?

Let us take, for example, a solution which is 0.1 molar with respect to silver-ammonia and nitrate ions, $Ag(NH_3)_2{}^+$ and $NO_3{}^-$. The concentration of the silver-ammonia ion would be very nearly 0.1 molar provided it were not appreciably dissociated. Since we know from the small value of the equilibrium constant that its dissociation must be very low, we can assume that the concentration of the silver-ammonia ion is practically 0.1 molar at equilibrium. Let X be the number of moles of the complex which dissociate, then the concentration of the silver ion at equilibrium will be X and the concentration of the ammonia molecules, $2X$. Therefore,

$$\frac{(Ag^+)(NH_3)^2}{(Ag(NH_3)_2{}^+)} = \frac{X(2X)^2}{0.1} = \frac{4X^3}{0.1} = 6.8 \times 10^{-8}$$

$$4X^3 = 6.8 \times 10^{-9} \quad \text{and} \quad X^3 = 1.7 \times 10^{-9}$$

$$X = 1.2 \times 10^{-3} \quad \text{and} \quad 2X = 2.4 \times 10^{-3} \text{ mole per liter}$$

In a 0.1 molar solution of the silver-ammonia nitrate, the concentration of the silver ion is then 1.2×10^{-3} mole per liter and the concentration of the free ammonia is twice as great. These values appear to be quite large, larger than one would expect for a highly stable complex. As a matter of fact the silver-ammonia complex is about the least stable of the known ammonia complexes. It will be recalled that in the case of the cobalt-ammonia complexes the addition of sulfuric acid merely converted the original salt to the sulfate and failed to remove any ammonia from the complex ion. However, in the case of the silver-ammonia complex the situation is entirely different. When a strong acid is added to a solution of the latter the complex is destroyed due to the combination of the ammonia with hydrogen ion. In this process the equilibrium (equation 20) shifts to the right. Addition of sulfide ion, iodide ion and other ions which form very insoluble salts with silver ion will also destroy the complex.

But now consider the situation in the presence of the chloride ion. Suppose we attempted to make a solution 0.1 molar with respect to silver-ammonia and chloride ions. What would the concentration of the silver ion be in this solution? It is obvious that the concentration of the silver ion could not be 1.2×10^{-3} mole per liter as it was in the case of the silver-ammonia complex nitrate solution, for with a concentration of chloride ion in the solution as high as 0.1 mole per liter, the solubility product constant would be exceeded for silver chloride ($K_{S.P.} = 1.56 \times 10^{-10}$) by more than one million-fold. Hence, silver chloride would precipitate from solution and the concentration of the silver ion would be greatly reduced. It is apparent that in such a case the silver ion concentration must satisfy both equilibria, the complex ion equilibrium and the solubility product equilibrium of silver chloride. In order to prevent the precipitation of silver chloride in this solution, it is evident that the concentration of the Ag^+ ion must be less than 1.56×10^{-9}, for

$$(Ag^+)(Cl^-) = (Ag^+)(0.1) = 1.56 \times 10^{-10}$$

or $\qquad (Ag^+) = 1.56 \times 10^{-9}\ M$

This amount of silver ion must likewise be in equilibrium with the silver-ammonia complex ion, which in turn requires a fairly high concentration of ammonia in solution to prevent the dissociation of the complex ion. In other words, a relatively high concentration of ammonia is required to dissolve silver chloride, the quantitative calculation of which is to be found in the following examples and problems.

The Hydrolysis of Metal Ions According to the Brønsted Definitions. According to the Brønsted definitions the process of hydrolysis is merely an acid-base reaction, and if a metal ion reacts with water to produce an acidic solution it must be regarded as a weak acid or a proton donor. The aluminum ion, for example, is a weak acid but in representing its acid properties the formula or symbol cannot be written as Al^{+++} since as such it does not indicate that aluminum ion contains protons which can be donated. Therefore, for the purposes of hydrolysis, the metal ions must be written in their hydrated forms; the water molecules associated with the metal ions contain the protons to be donated.

From what has already been said about the coordination number of metal ions we may assume that in water solution the aluminum ion has six molecules of water associated with it. With this assumption the formula for the aluminum ion in solution may be written $Al(H_2O)_6^{+++}$. When this ion undergoes hydrolysis the reaction for the process can be expressed by the equation

$$Al(H_2O)_6^{+++} + H_2O = Al(H_2O)_5(OH)^{++} + H_3O^+ \quad (22)$$
$$\text{Acid}_1 \qquad\qquad \text{Base}_2 \qquad\qquad \text{Base}_1 \qquad\qquad \text{Acid}_2$$

Likewise the hydrolysis of the zinc ion can be expressed by the equation

$$Zn(H_2O)_4^{++} + H_2O = Zn(H_2O)_3(OH)^+ + H_3O^+ \quad (23)$$
$$\text{Acid}_1 \qquad\qquad \text{Base}_2 \qquad\qquad \text{Base}_1 \qquad\qquad \text{Acid}_2$$

In the latter case the coordination number of the zinc ion is four.

The equilibrium expression for the reaction expressed by equation (23) is

$$\frac{(Zn(H_2O)_3(OH)^+)(H_3O^+)}{(Zn(H_2O)_4^{++})} = \frac{K_W^B}{K_{I(base)}^B} = K_A^B = \frac{1 \times 10^{-14}}{4 \times 10^{-5}}$$

$$= 2.5 \times 10^{-10} \quad (24)$$

The ionization constant for the base, $Zn(H_2O)_3(OH)^+$, has a value of 4×10^{-5}. The value for the equilibrium constant, $K_A{}^B$, is the same as that previously calculated as the hydrolysis constant (see page 194). Obviously, the value for this constant must be the same in both cases since the difference lies merely in the fact that in the latter case four molecules of water have been added arbitrarily to both sides of the equation. The equilibrium constant, $K_A{}^B$, for the hydrolysis of the $Zn(H_2O)_4{}^{++}$ ion, on the basis of the Brønsted definitions may be regarded as being equivalent to the acid ionization constant for this ion (see page 196 for the hydrolysis of the $NH_4{}^+$ ion). Except in relatively few cases experimental data are lacking on the ionization of hydrated metal ions as acids in water solution, so it is not possible to treat their equilibria quantitatively.

Both of the ions discussed above, $Al(H_2O)_6{}^{+++}$ and $Zn(H_2O)_4{}^{++}$, are to be regarded as complex ions. Not only are they capable of losing protons, according to equations (22) and (23), but they also can dissociate in other ways to produce a number of different types of ions. Taking $Al(H_2O)_6{}^{+++}$ ion as an example, a stepwise dissociation process would produce $Al(H_2O)_5{}^{+++}$, $Al(H_2O)_4{}^{+++}$, $Al(H_2O)_3{}^{+++}$, $Al(H_2O)_2{}^{+++}$, $Al(H_2O)^{+++}$ and Al^{+++} ions. The overall process is represented by the equation

$$Al(H_2O)_6{}^{+++} = Al^{+++} + 6H_2O \qquad (25)$$

In addition, ions even more complex than $Al(H_2O)_6{}^{+++}$ ion are undoubtedly present in water solutions of aluminum salts. For lack of any definite information concerning the composition of such ions, simplicity recommends the use of $Al(H_2O)_6{}^{+++}$ as a symbol for the hydrated form. The same reasoning may be applied to all metallic ions present in a solvent. With the older established definitions the use of the "hydrated" symbols is not necessary.

To be consistent in the use of the hydrated formulae for the metal ions, all of their reactions should include these formulae unless other more stable complexes are known to be formed. For example, the reaction between zinc ion and hydrogen sulfide to produce the slightly soluble zinc sulfide should be written as

$$Zn(H_2O)_4^{++} + H_2S = ZnS_{(s)} + 2H_2O + 2H_3O^+ \quad (26)$$

But this procedure becomes very cumbersome and for such reactions as represented by equation (26) it is much more convenient to write them with the metal ions in the non-hydrated form.   The above reaction would then be written

$$Zn^{++} + H_2S + 2H_2O = ZnS_{(s)} + 2H_3O^+ \quad (27)$$

Both the hydrated and non-hydrated forms for the metal ions are used, depending upon whether or not one wishes to emphasize the acid properties of such ions.

EXAMPLES OF PROBLEMS INVOLVING COMPLEX IONS

Example 1.

How many moles of NH_3 must be added to 1 liter of water to enable this solution to dissolve .001 mole of solid silver bromide? The solubility product constant for AgBr has a value of 7.7×10^{-13}, and the value for the dissociation constant for the silver-ammonia complex ion is 6.8×10^{-8}.

The reaction which takes place when the solid AgBr dissolves is

$$AgBr_{(s)} + 2NH_3 = Ag(NH_3)_2^+ + Br^- \quad (1)$$

Two equilibria are involved in this process,

$$AgBr_{(s)} = Ag^+ + Br^- \quad (2)$$

and

$$Ag(NH_3)_2^+ = Ag^+ + 2NH_3 \quad (3)$$

The concentration of the Ag^+ ion must be the same for both equilibria as long as solid AgBr and $Ag(NH_3)_2^+$ ion are present. From the equation for the reaction we see that .001 mole of AgBr, when it has just dissolved, produces .001 mole of $Ag(NH_3)_2^+$ ion and .001 mole of Br^- ion: From equation (2) we have

$$(Ag^+)(Br^-) = 7.7 \times 10^{-13}$$

When (Br^-) becomes .001 M, then

$$(Ag^+) = \frac{7.7 \times 10^{-13}}{.001} = 7.7 \times 10^{-10} \text{ mole/liter}$$

This latter value will also be the concentration of the Ag^+ ion which is in equilibrium with the complex ion when the AgBr has just dissolved, since both equilibria are confined to the same solution. Practically all of the silver in the solution is in the form of $Ag(NH_3)_2^+$ ion. Therefore, we may assume that the concentration of the $Ag(NH_3)_2^+$ ion is .001 M. Then, from the equilibrium expression for reaction (3), we have

$$\frac{(Ag^+)(NH_3)^2}{(Ag(NH_3)_2^+)} = \frac{7.7 \times 10^{-10} \times (NH_3)^2}{.001} = 6.8 \times 10^{-8}$$

$$(NH_3)^2 = \frac{6.8 \times 10^{-8} \times 10^{-3}}{7.7 \times 10^{-10}} = 8.8 \times 10^{-2}$$

$$(NH_3) = 2.97 \times 10^{-1} = 0.3 \ M \ \text{(approximately)}$$

In this calculation the amount of ammonia consumed in forming the complex ion is .002 mole, which is negligible compared with 0.3 mole. However, it should be emphasized that the total amount of ammonia required to dissolve the AgBr is the sum of the combined and free amounts; in other words, it is 0.297 + .002 or 0.299 mole. Since the application of the Law of Mass Action is not valid when the solutions become too concentrated, the value of 0.3 M is sufficient, though approximate.

Example 2.

What is the concentration of the Zn^{++} ion in a solution made by adding 0.1 mole of $ZnCl_2$ and 0.4 mole of NH_3 to water to make 1 liter of solution?

Since the formula for the zinc-ammonia complex ion is $Zn(NH_3)_4^{++}$, the amounts of Zn^{++} ion and NH_3 given here are just sufficient to form 0.1 mole of the complex ion. Let us assume that this amount of the complex ion is formed and that it dissociates until equilibrium is reached, in accordance with the equation

$$Zn(NH_3)_4^{++} = Zn^{++} + 4NH_3$$

The dissociation constant for this complex ion has a value of 2.6×10^{-10}. If X moles of the complex ion dissociate, then, at equilibrium, $(Zn^{++}) = X$, $(NH_3) = 4X$, and $(Zn(NH_3)_4^{++}) = 0.1 - X$. We then have

$$\frac{(Zn^{++})(NH_3)^4}{(Zn(NH_3)_4^{++})} = \frac{X(4X)^4}{0.1 - X} = \frac{(4)^4 X^5}{0.1 - X} = \frac{256 X^5}{0.1 - X} = 2.6 \times 10^{-10}$$

Neglecting X as compared with 0.1, the expression becomes

$$\frac{256X^5}{0.1} = 2.6 \times 10^{-10}$$

$$X^5 = \frac{2.6 \times 10^{-10} \times 0.1}{2.56 \times 10^2}$$

$$= \frac{2.6 \times 10^{-11}}{2.6 \times 10^2} = 1 \times 10^{-13}$$

$$= 100 \times 10^{-15}$$

$$X = 2.5 \times 10^{-3} = .0025 \text{ mole/liter} = (Zn^{++})$$

$$(NH_3) = 4X = .01 \text{ mole/liter}$$

In extracting the fifth root of 100×10^{-15} the student might encounter some difficulty in finding the fifth root of 100. All that is necessary to do in this case is to obtain the logarithm of 100 which is 2.00. Dividing this by 5 we have 0.4 and the antilog of 0.4 is very nearly 2.5.

Example 3.

(a) How many moles of AgI will dissolve in 1 liter of 1 M NH$_4$OH solution?

Silver iodide is very slightly soluble in pure water ($K_{\text{S.P.}} = 1.5 \times 10^{-16}$), but in NH$_4$OH solution there is some tendency for the Ag$^+$ ion to combine with the NH$_3$ to form the Ag(NH$_3$)$_2^+$ ion, according to the equation

$$AgI_{(s)} + 2NH_3 = Ag(NH_3)_2^+ + I^- \tag{1}$$

However, the amount of complex ion formed will be very small since AgI is so insoluble. From the equilibrium expression for the complex ion we have

$$\frac{(Ag^+)(NH_3)^2}{(Ag(NH_3)_2^+)} = 6.8 \times 10^{-8} \tag{2}$$

Since such a small amount of the complex ion is formed it may be assumed that practically all of the ammonia exists in the free condition in solution and has a value of 1 M. Then

$$(Ag^+) = 6.8 \times 10^{-8}(Ag(NH_3)_2^+)$$

From this expression it is seen that the concentration of the Ag(NH$_3$)$_2^+$ ion is very much larger than the concentration of the free Ag$^+$ ion. This means that practically all of the silver in solution is in the form of the complex ion. Also the concentration of the I^- ion in solution must be practically the same as the concentration of the complex ion.

$$(I^-) = (Ag(NH_3)_2{}^+)$$

From the solubility product expression, we have

$$(Ag^+)(I^-) = (Ag^+)(Ag(NH_3)_2{}^+) = 1.5 \times 10^{-16}$$

Substituting in the second expression the value for the $(Ag(NH_3)_2{}^+)$ above,

$$(Ag^+) \frac{(Ag^+)}{6.8 \times 10^{-8}} = 1.5 \times 10^{-16}$$

$$(Ag^+)^2 = 1.5 \times 10^{-16} \times 6.8 \times 10^{-8} = 10.2 \times 10^{-24}$$

$$(Ag^+) = 3.2 \times 10^{-12}$$

$$(Ag(NH_3)_2{}^+) = (I^-) = \frac{3.2 \times 10^{-12}}{6.8 \times 10^{-8}} = 4.7 \times 10^{-5} \text{ mole/liter}$$

Thus the concentration of the I^- ion is $4.7 \times 10^{-5}\ M$; this value is also the solubility of the AgI in the $1\ M$ NH_4OH solution.

The same result could have been obtained in the following manner. Since two equilibria are involved in this system, let us divide one equilibrium expression by the other. Then

$$\frac{(Ag^+)(I^-)}{\dfrac{(Ag^+)(NH_3)^2}{(Ag(NH_3)_2{}^+)}} = \frac{(Ag(NH_3)_2{}^+)(I^-)}{(NH_3)^2} = \frac{1.5 \times 10^{-16}}{6.8 \times 10^{-8}} = 22 \times 10^{-10}$$

This is the equilibrium constant for reaction (1). But since (NH_3) has a value of $1\ M$ and $(Ag(NH_3)_2{}^+)$ equals (I^-),

$$(Ag(NH_3)_2{}^+) \times (I^-) = (I^-)^2 = 22 \times 10^{-10}$$

$$(I^-) = 4.7 \times 10^{-5}\ M = (Ag(NH_3)_2{}^+)$$

$$= \text{Solubility of AgI}$$

(b) What concentration of NH_4OH would be necessary to dissolve $.01\ M$ of AgI in 1 liter of solution?

Using the value obtained in (a) we have

$$\frac{(Ag(NH_3)_2{}^+)(I^-)}{(NH_3)^2} = 22 \times 10^{-10}$$

If $.01$ mole of AgI were to dissolve, (I^-) and $(Ag(NH_3)_2{}^+)$ would each have a value of $.01\ M$. Then

$$\frac{(.01)(.01)}{(NH_3)^2} = 22 \times 10^{-10}$$

$$(NH_3)^2 = \frac{1 \times 10^{-4}}{22 \times 10^{-10}} = 4.5 \times 10^4$$

$$(NH_3) = 2.1 \times 10^2 = 210\ M\ \text{(impossible)}$$

This value of 210 M is obtained on the assumption that the Law of Mass Action holds in very concentrated solutions. Evidently, the AgI will not completely dissolve, since it is not possible to obtain at room temperature a solution of ammonia in water of higher concentration than about 18 M.

The method used in (b) could also have been applied in *Example 1*.

Example 4.

A given solution contains .01 mole of Cl^- ion and .07 mole of NH_3 per liter. If .01 mole of solid $AgNO_3$ is added to 1 liter of this solution will AgCl precipitate? The solution of this problem involves two equilibria,

$$AgCl_{(s)} = Ag^+ + Cl^-$$

and $\qquad Ag(NH_3)_2^+ = Ag^+ + 2NH_3$

The equilibrium expressions are

$$(Ag^+)(Cl^-) = 1.56 \times 10^{-10}$$

and $\qquad \dfrac{(Ag^+)(NH_3)^2}{(Ag(NH_3)_2^+)} = 6.8 \times 10^{-8}$

Due to the great stability of the complex ion we shall first assume that .01 mole of this ion is formed from .01 mole of Ag^+ ion. This process would consume .02 mole of NH_3; then .05 mole of NH_3 would be left in solution. Under these conditions, we can calculate the concentration of the free Ag^+ ion in solution.

$$\frac{(Ag^+)(.05)^2}{.01} = 6.8 \times 10^{-8}$$

$$(Ag^+) = \frac{6.8 \times 10^{-8} \times .01}{2.5 \times 10^{-3}} = 2.72 \times 10^{-7}\ \text{mole/liter}$$

Since .01 mole of Cl^- ion is present per liter of solution, the product of the ion concentrations is $(2.72 \times 10^{-7})(.01)$ or 2.72×10^{-9}. This value is greater than the solubility product constant; therefore, AgCl precipitates.

This problem could be solved in another manner. Let us

calculate the amount of Ag^+ ion necessary to start the precipitation of AgCl when .01 M Cl^- ion is present. This would be

$$(Ag^+) = \frac{1.56 \times 10^{-10}}{.01} = 1.56 \times 10^{-8} M$$

With this amount of free Ag^+ ion in solution and making the assumption that .01 mole of $Ag(NH_3)_2^+$ is formed, we can then calculate the amount of free NH_3 which would be required to maintain these conditions. Then

$$\frac{(1.56 \times 10^{-8})(NH_3)^2}{.01} = 6.8 \times 10^{-8}$$

$$(NH_3)^2 = \frac{6.8 \times 10^{-8} \times .01}{1.56 \times 10^{-8}} = 4.36 \times 10^{-2}$$

$$(NH_3) = 2.1 \times 10^{-1} = 0.21 \ M.$$

This value for the amount of free ammonia necessary to maintain .01 mole of the complex in solution is much larger than the available ammonia; therefore, AgCl precipitates.

Example 5.

What is the concentration of the Cu^+ ion and of the CN^- ion in a .01 M solution of $K_2Cu(CN)_3$?

$K_2Cu(CN)_3$ is a salt which is ionized completely as follows

$$K_2Cu(CN)_3 = 2K^+ + Cu(CN)_3^{--}$$

On the other hand, the complex ion dissociates slightly

$$Cu(CN)_3^{--} = Cu^+ + 3CN^-$$

The equilibrium expression for the dissociation of the complex ion is

$$\frac{(Cu^+)(CN^-)^3}{(Cu(CN)_3^{--})} = 5 \times 10^{-28}$$

If we let X moles of the complex ion dissociate then at equilibrium, $(Cu^+) = X$, $(CN^-) = 3X$, and $(Cu(CN)_3^{--}) = .01 - X$.   Then we have

$$\frac{(X)(3X)^3}{.01 - X} = \frac{27X^4}{.01 - X} \cong \frac{27X^4}{.01} = 5 \times 10^{-28}$$

$$27X^4 = 5 \times 10^{-30} = 500 \times 10^{-32}$$

$$X^4 = 18.5 \times 10^{-32}$$

$$X = 2.07 \times 10^{-8} \text{ mole/liter} = (Cu^+)$$

$$3X = 6.2 \times 10^{-8} \text{ mole/liter} = (CN^-)$$

QUESTIONS AND PROBLEMS

1. Is there any definite experimental evidence for the existence of the hydronium ion?

2. Compare the properties of water and ammonia. What is the water analogue of the ammonium ion?

3. What is the ammonia analogue of the hydroxide ion?

4. What are hydrates and ammonates?

5. How does the electronic structure of ions which form complex ions differ from those which do not?

6. On the basis of the coordination theory of Werner, give the structures (not electronic) of the respective complex ions formed when the following salts are dissolved in water: $CoCl_3 \cdot 4NH_3$, $CoCl_3 \cdot 6NH_3$, $Cu(NO_3)_2 \cdot 4NH_3$, $K_3Fe(CN)_6$ and $PtCl_4 \cdot 5NH_3$.

7. Give examples of four complex anions.

8. What is a homoatomic anion? Give two examples.

9. Why does ammonium polysulfide dissolve SnS readily while ammonium sulfide will not?

10. What experiments could be designed to show that the ammonia molecule and not the NH_4^+ nor the OH^- ions are responsible for the solution of silver oxide by excess ammonium hydroxide?

11. If 0.1 mole $AgNO_3$, 0.1 mole $NaCl$ and 0.2 mole NH_3 were added to 1 liter of water, show by calculation whether $AgCl$ would precipitate.

12. If it were possible to prepare solid $Ag(NH_3)_2Cl$ and if 0.1 mole of this were added to 1 liter of water, would $AgCl$ precipitate? Explain.

13. What is the Zn^{++} concentration in a solution that has been made by adding 0.1 mole $ZnCl_2$ and 1 mole of NH_3 to enough water to give 1 liter of solution?

14. Which gives the greater concentration of Ag^+; a solution made by adding 1 mole $AgNO_3$ and 2 moles KCN to 1 liter of water or a solution made by adding 0.1 mole $AgNO_3$ and 1 mole NH_3? (Note: In the first solution neglect hydrolysis of CN^- ion. In the second solution 0.2 mole NH_3 is used in making $Ag(NH_3)_2^+$. Assume the Law of Mass Action for these more concentrated solutions.)

15. Will 0.1 g. AgBr dissolve in 100 ml. of 1 M NH_4OH solution?

16. Will 0.1 g. AgI dissolve in 100 ml. of 1 M NH$_4$OH solution?

17. How much ammonia (expressed in grams) is necessary to dissolve 1 g. AgCl in 100 ml. of water?

18. Calculate the concentration of Ag$^+$ ion in a solution which is .05 M with respect to Ag(NH$_3$)$_2$NO$_3$.

19. Calculate the Cu$^+$ ion concentration in a solution which contains .02 mole K$_2$Cu(CN)$_3$ per liter.

20. What is the CN$^-$ ion concentration in a solution 0.1 M with respect to K$_2$Cd(CN)$_4$?

21. What is the concentration of NH$_3$ in a solution which contains .04 mole Ag(NH$_3$)$_2$NO$_3$ per liter?

22. (a) Which solution furnishes the higher concentration of Cd^{++} ion, a 0.1 M solution of Cd(NH$_3$)$_4$Cl$_2$ or a 0.1 M solution of K$_2$Cd(CN)$_4$?

(b) Give the ratio of the Cd^{++} ion concentrations in these two solutions.

23. If to a liter of a solution, which is .06 M with respect to K$_2$Cu(CN)$_3$ and .06 M with respect to K$_2$Cd(CN)$_4$, CN$^-$ ion is added to increase its concentration to .005 M, what will be the concentration of (a) the Cu$^+$ ion, and (b) the Cd^{++} ion?

24. One liter of a solution contains 0.1 mole of Cl$^-$ ion and 0.1 mole of CN$^-$ ion. To this solution solid silver nitrate is added little by little.

(a) What happens?

(b) How many moles of AgNO$_3$ must be added before a precipitate begins to appear?

(c) When a precipitate first appears, what will be the concentration of the Cl$^-$ ion, of the CN$^-$ ion, and of the Ag$^+$ ion?

(Note: AgCN does not precipitate in this solution.)

25. Give the electronic structure for the CdCl$_4^{--}$ ion, as was done for the Zn(NH$_3$)$_4^{++}$ ion in Figure 23.

CHAPTER X

Amphoteric Substances

The metals of the alkali and alkaline earth groups of the periodic table are often classified as highly electropositive elements. They exhibit a pronounced tendency to lose electrons and thereby form positive ions. Sodium in its reactions with other elements loses one electron readily to give sodium ion, Na^+, while calcium of the alkaline earth group loses two electrons with the formation of a positive calcium ion, Ca^{++}. These elements are among the first few of the electromotive force (E.M.F.) series of the elements, since this series is one in which the elements are arranged according to the decreasing tendency to lose electrons and form positive ions. In contrast to the alkali metals, sulfur and chlorine of the sixth and seventh groups respectively show a decided tendency to acquire electrons in their reactions with other elements and thereby form negative ions. The latter elements are accordingly termed electronegative; e.g., chlorine can acquire one electron and sulfur two electrons to give ions bearing one and two negative charges respectively.

Sodium and calcium on the one hand, and sulfur and chlorine on the other, represent extreme types in the classification of the elements according to their tendencies to lose or gain electrons. A large proportion of the elements of the periodic table show dual properties which are characteristic of both sodium and chlorine. They may react with some elements to lose electrons and with other elements to gain them. Hydrogen under favorable conditions reacts with chlorine to form hydrogen chloride. In this reaction we regard the hydrogen atom as partially giving up an electron to the chlorine atom, and we may regard the hydrogen chloride molecule as one containing hydrogen in the more electropositive condition and chlorine in the more electronegative condition. Likewise, hydrogen reacts directly with sodium to form sodium hydride, NaH. This substance is an excellent conductor of electricity in the fused state in which it must be ionized as positive sodium ions and negative hydrogen or hydride ions, H^-, since upon electrolysis hydrogen is liberated at the anode. In this reaction the hydrogen atom acquires an extra electron to form a negative hydrogen ion. Apparently the hydrogen atom has a greater tendency to acquire an electron and a smaller tendency to lose an electron than has the sodium atom. So far as chemical evidence goes, the sodium atom shows no tendency to form negative ions. Thus hydrogen may behave in a dual manner, it may gain or lose electrons depending upon its environment. If it is in the presence of a strongly electronegative element such as chlorine it will behave electropositively, while in the presence of a strongly electropositive element, for example sodium, it will behave electronegatively. Such elements lie in an intermediate position in the E.M.F. series and are sometimes spoken of as **amphoteric** elements, a designation which implies this dual character.

Many other elements show amphoteric properties in their reactions. Thus, sulfur, selenium and tellurium of the sixth group of the periodic table react with chlorine and oxygen to form chlorides and oxides. They likewise react with sodium, potassium and other electropositive elements to form sulfides, selenides and tellurides which are salts. Examples of such compounds are: Na_2S, Na_2Se, Na_2Te, K_2S, K_2Se and K_2Te. Phosphorus, arsenic, antimony and bismuth of the fifth group of the periodic table behave in a similar manner, while germanium, tin and lead may be mentioned as typical examples of the fourth-group elements. Even elements in the second and third groups such as zinc, cadmium, mercury, gallium, indium and thallium will combine with sodium and other strongly electropositive elements to form definite compounds. This dual behavior is the general case rather than the exceptional one.

Amphoteric Hydroxides. Many of the elements which show this dual behavior in the ability to acquire and to lose electrons in their reactions show another, but somewhat different, type of duality in the reactions of their hydroxides. It is well known that the oxides of strongly electropositive elements such as Na_2O, K_2O, CaO and MgO form strong bases in water solution, NaOH, KOH, $Ca(OH)_2$ and $Mg(OH)_2$ respectively. However, oxides of strongly electronegative elements such as SO_3, N_2O_5 and Cl_2O_7 in water solution are decidedly acidic in character; they are the anhydrides of the acids, H_2SO_4, HNO_3 and $HClO_4$ respectively.

Oxides of most of the elements which lie in an intermediate position in the E.M.F. series of elements, which are neither strongly electropositive nor strongly electronegative, show both acidic and basic properties in water. As would be predicted, such acids and bases are extremely weak. Thus lead oxide, PbO; aluminum oxide, Al_2O_3; chromic oxide, Cr_2O_3; zinc oxide, ZnO; stannous oxide, SnO; and antimonous oxide, Sb_2O_3, are the anhydrides of the very weak hydroxides, $Pb(OH)_2$, $Al(OH)_3$, $Cr(OH)_3$, $Zn(OH)_2$, $Sn(OH)_2$ and $Sb(OH)_3$ respectively, which hydroxides may also be regarded as very weak acids. To emphasize the acidic properties of these hydroxides their formulae could be written H_2PbO_2, H_3AlO_3 (or $HAlO_2 + H_2O$), H_3CrO_3 (or $HCrO_2 + H_2O$), H_2ZnO_2, H_2SnO_2 and H_3SbO_3 (or $HSbO_2 + H_2O$). In the cases of H_3AlO_3, H_3CrO_3 and H_3SbO_3 only one hydrogen is replaceable in water solution, the simpler and more informative formulae $HAlO_2$, $HCrO_2$ and $HSbO_2$ respectively are usually used. In each of these cases the same substance may be represented by two differently arranged formulae; by convention, one emphasizes the basic properties and the other, the acidic properties.

All of these hydroxides are very slightly soluble in water but dissolve readily when either a strong acid such as hydrochloric acid or a strong base such as sodium hydroxide is present. Taking $Al(OH)_3$ as an example, we may write,

$Al(OH)_3 + 3HCl$ (in solution)

$$= AlCl_3 \text{(in solution)} + 3H_2O \qquad (1)$$

and

$Al(OH)_3 + NaOH$ (in solution)

$$= NaAlO_2 \text{(in solution)} + 2H_2O \qquad (2)$$

Both of these reactions appear familiar in that the products in each case are a salt and the solvent, water; in other words, they are neutralization reactions. Since both HCl, an acid, and NaOH, a base, are used, it must necessarily follow that the aluminum hydroxide is functioning in equation (1) as a base and in equation (2) as an acid. Hydroxides which show properties characteristic of both acids and bases are known as **amphoteric hydroxides.**

The ionization of aluminum hydroxide when acting both as a weak acid and a weak base is expressed in the following equation:

$$Al^{+++} + 3OH^- = \left\{ \begin{array}{l} Al(OH)_3 \\ H_3AlO_3 \end{array} \right\} \begin{array}{l} = AlO_2^- + H^+ + H_2O \qquad (3) \\ \text{(solid)} \end{array}$$

For lack of definite information regarding the ionization of aluminum hydroxide as a base we have expressed the reaction as one producing $3OH^-$ ions. It is a weak polyacid base and undoubtedly would not be expected to ionize highly even in the first stage, let alone in the two successive stages. However, at present it is not experimentally feasible to determine the exact extent of ionization of aluminum hydroxide for each of the three steps. Equation (3) also shows the aluminate ion, AlO_2^-, a product of the ionization of aluminum hydroxide as an acid.

We may now predict, with the aid of Le Chatelier's Rule, the effect of strong acids and of strong bases upon the equilibrium. If a strong acid, such as hydrochloric acid, is added to a suspension of aluminum hydroxide in water, the hydrogen ions which are in excess combine with some of the hydroxide ions to form water. According to the Rule of Le Chatelier, we would predict a shift in the equilibrium to the left. The tendency is for the equilibrium to shift in such a way as to attempt to retrieve the loss of hydroxide ions. This can be done only by the further dissociation of aluminum hydroxide from the solid phase. As fast as hydroxide ions are produced by this process, they are removed by hydrogen ions. Finally, all the solid dissolves and the concentration of the hydroxide ions in solution still remains at a very small value due to the continued removal of the hydroxide by hydrogen ions. Although the hydroxide ions are depleted as fast as they are produced by the ionization of the aluminum hydroxide, the latter reaction also yields large amounts of aluminum ions which remain as such in solution. Therefore, when hydrochloric acid is used as a source of hydrogen ions, the final result is that the solid aluminum hydroxide dissolves and the solution contains aluminum and chloride ions. Hydrogen and hydroxide ions will also be present in concentrations which must satisfy the water equilibrium, $(H^+)(OH^-) = 1 \times 10^{-14}$.

The addition of a strong base such as sodium hydroxide furnishes a large concentration of hydroxide ions. According to Le Chatelier's Rule the equilibrium should shift in such a direction as to use up hydroxide ions; that is, it should shift to the right as equation (3) is written. Naturally, hydrogen ions will be removed from the reaction medium by their combination with hydroxide ions to form water. When this happens more aluminum hydroxide will dissolve to give hydrogen ions and aluminate ions in an attempt to retrieve the loss of hydrogen ions. The hydrogen ions are removed as fast as they are produced and finally, when all of the solid aluminum hydroxide has dissolved, sodium ions and aluminate ions will be left in solution in large quantities, and the hydrogen ion and hydroxide ion concentrations will be in accord with that demanded by the water equilibrium.

Aluminum hydroxide has been taken here as a typical example of an amphoteric hydroxide. Others previously mentioned, $Pb(OH)_2$, $Cr(OH)_3$, $Zn(OH)_2$, $Sn(OH)_2$ and

$Sb(OH)_3$ behave similarly in that they dissolve and function as bases in the presence of a strong acid, and also dissolve and function as acids in the presence of a strong base. The latter reaction is the more unfamiliar one and in the presence of sodium hydroxide the following ions are produced: $HPbO_2^-$, CrO_2^-, ZnO_2^{--}, $HSnO_2^-$, and SbO_2^-, namely plumbite, chromite, zincate, stannite and antimonite ions.

As was previously stated the amphoteric hydroxides are derived from elements occupying an intermediate position in the E.M.F. series. They must necessarily occupy a similar intermediate position in a given series of the periodic table since the elements of the main groups to the left are strongly electropositive, while those of the main groups to the right are strongly electronegative. Those elements which show both properties lie in between these two extremes. As one passes from one extreme position of the table to the other, the change in properties is not an abrupt one; on the contrary, it is very gradual. As an example, let us choose the series of the table beginning with the inert gas argon, atomic number 18 (see back cover); the next element, potassium, forms a very strong base, potassium hydroxide. Under ordinary conditions of temperature it acts only as a base in water solution. Calcium hydroxide, representative of the second group, likewise possesses only basic properties in water. Scandium hydroxide is also a strong base, but titanium hydroxide, vanadium hydroxide and chromium hydroxide, hydroxides of the fourth, fifth and sixth groups respectively in the series under consideration, show amphoteric properties in that they form titanates, vanadites and chromites with strong bases. Vanadates and chromates are also known, being derived from the higher valence hydroxides, which, however, are distinctly more acidic than basic in nature. In the seventh group manganous hydroxide, $Mn(OH)_2$, is a moderately strong base and possesses very little acid properties; while H_2MnO_4, manganic acid, is a weak acid and $HMnO_4$, permanganic acid, is a very strong acid. In general, the higher the valence of the metal in any two or more similarly derived acids the more acidic properties it will display. Thus, stannic acid is a stronger acid than stannous acid, arsenic is stronger than arsenous, chromic stronger than chromous, etc. Ferric, ferrous, cobaltous, nickelous, and cuprous hydroxides are distinctly basic in aqueous solutions and acid properties are entirely lacking. The next element of the series, zinc, atomic number 30, forms a hydroxide, $Zn(OH)_2$, which is well known for its amphoteric properties. Following zinc hydroxide are $Ga(OH)_3$, $Ge(OH)_4$ and $AsO(OH)_3$, all of which dissolve in sodium hydroxide solution to produce gallate, germanate and arsenate ions. H_2SeO_4, selenic acid, and $HBrO_3$, bromic acid, are decidedly acidic in water. Thus, in this series of eighteen elements, many of their hydroxides are amphoteric.

Within a given group, occupying an intermediate position in the periodic table, the amphoteric properties change as one proceeds from the element of lower to one of higher atomic weight. Thus HNO_2 shows only acid properties; H_3PO_3 likewise is acidic; H_3AsO_3 or $As(OH)_3$ and H_3SbO_3 or $Sb(OH)_3$ are amphoteric, while $Bi(OH)_3$ is basic in its reactions. Thus, in passing from nitrogen to bismuth in the main fifth group, the hydroxides change from strong acids to weak acids and moderately strong bases, but the change is a gradual one.

Amphoteric Sulfides. Sulfur occupies a position in the sixth group of the periodic table just below oxygen. Hence, many of the compounds of sulfur contain the sulfur atom in a position similar to that occupied by oxygen in the more familiar oxygen compounds. In qualitative analysis we are particularly interested in the amphoteric nature of analogous sulfides and oxides. Since hydrogen sulfide is the analogue of water, the bisulfide ion of the hydrogen sulfide system corresponds to the hydroxide ion of the water system, as the following equations readily demonstrate:

$$H_2O = H^+ + OH^- \tag{4}$$
$$H_2S = H^+ + SH^- \tag{5}$$

Likewise, the metal sulfides are analogues of the metal oxides; K_2S, CaS, As_2S_5 and Sb_2S_3 in the hydrogen sulfide system correspond to K_2O, CaO, As_2O_5 and Sb_2O_3 respectively in the water or oxygen system. On the basis of these analogies, one might expect sulfides to dissolve in the presence of bisulfide ions in the same way that oxides or hydroxides, in an aqueous medium, dissolve in the presence of hydroxide ions. When the sulfides behave in this manner, they are exhibiting acid properties. A few examples will serve to illustrate this type of reaction.

$$As_2S_5 + 6HS^- = 2AsS_4^{---} + 3H_2S \qquad (6)$$

or $\qquad As_2S_5 + 2HS^- = 2AsS_3^- + H_2S \qquad (7)$

$$Sb_2S_5 + 6HS^- = 2SbS_4^{---} + 3H_2S \qquad (8)$$

Actually the H_2S produced in the above equations reacts with the OH^- ions to produce HS^- ions and water. Therefore the equation for the process of the solution of As_2S_5 by HS^- ions in alkaline solution is

$$As_2S_5 + 3HS^- + 3OH^- = 2AsS_4^{---} + 3H_2O \qquad (9)$$

rather than that given by equation (6). The same would be true for the reactions represented by equations (7) and (8).

Another explanation may be given for the fact that arsenic and antimony sulfides dissolve in alkaline sulfide solution. In such a solution, the concentration of the sulfide ion is certainly appreciable and much larger than the concentration of the oxide ion, O^{--}, in solutions containing alkali hydroxides, since the bisulfide ion is dissociated to a much greater extent to give hydrogen and sulfide ions than is the hydroxide ion to give hydrogen and oxide ions. As a matter of fact, it has not been possible through experiment to determine the concentration of the oxide ion. Due to the presence of sulfide ions in alkaline sulfide solutions, it is possible, however, to explain the solubility of arsenic and antimony sulfides as follows:

$$As_2S_5 + 3S^{--} = 2AsS_4^{---} \qquad (10)$$

$$As_2S_3 + 3S^{--} = 2AsS_3^{---} \tag{11}$$

$$As_2S_5 + S^{--} = 2AsS_3^- \tag{12}$$

$$Sb_2S_5 + 3S^{--} = 2SbS_4^{---} \tag{13}$$

Antimony and tin in the lower valence states are much more strongly basic or more weakly acidic than in the higher valence states. Accordingly, antimonous sulfide dissolves with difficulty in ammonium sulfide solution and stannous sulfide is practically insoluble in this medium. However, antimonic and stannic sulfides are readily soluble in this same solvent.

Just as oxygen can oxidize a lower valence oxide to a higher valence one, so sulfur can oxidize a lower to a higher valence sulfide. Ammonium polysulfide is ammonium sulfide containing dissolved sulfur (chemically combined with the sulfide ion). When the lower sulfides are treated with ammonium polysulfide they are oxidized to the higher valence state in which they are readily soluble. This process of solution has already been discussed in the previous chapter, as an illustration of complex ion formation. The process of solution of the amphoteric sulfides may be explained on the basis of the amphoteric properties of the sulfides and on the basis of sulfur in sulfide solution acting as an oxidizing agent.

Application of Amphoteric Substances to Analysis. Suppose we consider a solution which has been obtained as a hydrochloric acid extraction of an ore known to contain iron, zinc and aluminum. We wish to separate these elements from each other in solution by methods which will reduce the difficulties to a minimum. The solution contains all three elements in the form of their chlorides and is slightly acidic. We might first add sodium hydroxide to the solution to the point of neutralization and obtain a precipitate containing all three substances in the form of hydroxides, $Fe(OH)_3$, $Al(OH)_3$ and $Zn(OH)_2$. Knowing that both zinc and aluminum hydroxides are decidedly amphoteric in nature, let us continue the addition of the sodium hydroxide solution. Both $Al(OH)_3$ and $Zn(OH)_2$ dissolve immediately with the formation of aluminate and zincate ions respectively; however, ferric hydroxide is not amphoteric and does not dissolve in the presence of excess hydroxide ion. Accordingly, the ferric hydroxide can be separated at this point by filtration. Ammonium hydroxide would not behave in the same way as the sodium hydroxide since the former does not furnish sufficient hydroxide ions to dissolve aluminum and zinc hydroxides.

If it should appear desirable to separate the aluminum from the zinc, the filtrate could be treated with hydrochloric acid until the zinc and aluminum hydroxides dissolve, and to this solution could be added excess ammonium hydroxide. Under these conditions the aluminum hydroxide would precipitate and the zinc would stay in solution in the form of the zinc-ammonia ion, $Zn(NH_3)_4^{++}$.

Thus, through the application of the amphoteric properties of the aluminum and zinc hydroxides and the subsequent use of the ability of the zinc ion to form complex ions, it is possible to readily separate these three elements from each other. The hydroxides, $Fe(OH)_3$, $Al(OH)_3$ and $Cr(OH)_3$ may also be separated from each other by the same general procedure; $Al(OH)_3$ and $Cr(OH)_3$ are amphoteric while $Fe(OH)_3$ is not. Chromium and aluminum may be subsequently separated from each other by the oxidation of the chromite ion, CrO_2^-, to the chromate ion, CrO_4^{--}. Chromium ion combining with other elements displays two principal valences of $+3$ and $+6$, while aluminum in compound form has only the one valence of $+3$. Other examples to illustrate the behavior of amphoteric hydroxides and sulfides in the separation and identification of ions are too numerous to mention here. However, several illustrations will be given in Part II of this text relating to the separation of the analytical groups and the properties of individual ions.

Amphoteric Hydroxides as Coordinated Complexes. To illustrate the application of the Brønsted definitions to problems involving amphoteric hydroxides, let us choose aluminum hydroxide as the example for consideration. This hydroxide was also used as an example (page 248) in the discussion of this same subject with the older established definitions.

Many hydroxides do not have a constant and definite composition. Nevertheless we use definite formulae to designate them. In our previous discussions, for the sake of convenience we designated aluminum hydroxide by the formula $Al(OH)_3$. According to this formula this substance should consist of 34.58% aluminum, 61.55% oxygen, and 3.87% hydrogen. Under most circumstances an analysis of aluminum hydroxide would not give these percentages but other rather widely different values. The reason for this discrepancy is that aluminum hydroxide when freshly precipitated contains additional water not indicated in the formula, $Al(OH)_3$. This additional water may be chemically bound to the aluminum atom or it may merely be adsorbed. When the aluminum hydroxide is dried it loses water, and upon continued drying the loss of water does not stop when the composition corresponds to the formula $Al(OH)_3$, but rather when its composition is such as to correspond more nearly to the formula $AlO(OH)$ or $Al_2O_3 \cdot H_2O$. Upon excessive drying (by heating) all the water is lost and only the oxide Al_2O_3 remains. The formula for aluminum hydroxide is therefore often written as $Al_2O_3 \cdot XH_2O$. But for convenience, most chemists have adopted the formula $Al(OH)_3$ for this substance.

To explain the hydrolysis of the aluminum ion by the Brønsted definitions we wrote its formula as $Al(H_2O)_6^{+++}$ (p. 235), assuming a coordination number of six for the aluminum ion. In keeping with this same concept we can also write an analogous formula for aluminum hydroxide in the hydrated form, again using the coordination number of six. Its formula would then be $Al(H_2O)_3(OH)_3$. Using this formula let us explain the amphoteric nature of aluminum hydroxide as we have done with the older definitions. As an amphoteric hydroxide this substance is both a proton donor and a proton acceptor. When dissolved in water it may be regarded as accepting protons from and donating them to water molecules.

$$\overset{\text{Acid}_1}{\text{Al(H}_2\text{O)}_3\text{(OH)}_{3(s)}} + \overset{\text{Base}_2}{\text{H}_2\text{O}} = \overset{\text{Base}_1}{\text{Al(H}_2\text{O)}_2\text{(OH)}_4^-} + \overset{\text{Acid}_2}{\text{H}_3\text{O}^+} \quad (14)$$

$$\underset{\text{Base}_2}{3\text{H}_2\text{O}} + \underset{\text{Acid}_1}{\text{Al(H}_2\text{O)}_6^{+++}} = \underset{\text{Acid}_2}{3\text{H}_3\text{O}^+} + \underset{\text{Base}_1}{\text{Al(H}_2\text{O)}_3\text{(OH)}_{3(s)}} \quad (15)$$

In the first equilibrium (14) aluminum hydroxide is represented as a weak acid, i.e., as a proton donor. In equation (15) reading right to left, it is represented as a proton acceptor or as a base. This latter process could be expressed in three stages, i.e., aluminum hydroxide is a tri-acid base, but for convenience we have combined all three steps in this single equation. Both reactions (14) and (15) are acid-base reactions. If aluminum hydroxide is treated with a strong acid the equilibrium (15) is shifted to the left; the solid is dissolved and the aluminum ion, $\text{Al(H}_2\text{O)}_6^{+++}$ is formed. If a sodium hydroxide solution is added to a suspension of aluminum hydroxide the OH^- ion of the solution combines with the H_3O^+ ion, shifting the equilibrium reaction (14) to the right, and aluminate ion $\text{Al(H}_2\text{O)}_2\text{(OH)}_4^-$ is formed. The over-all reaction for this latter process is

$$\text{Al(H}_2\text{O)}_3\text{(OH)}_3 + \text{OH}^- = \text{Al(H}_2\text{O)}_2\text{(OH)}_4^- + \text{H}_2\text{O} \quad (16)$$

The amphoteric nature of zinc hydroxide can be explained in an analogous way. In this case the formula of zinc hydroxide can be written as $\text{Zn(H}_2\text{O)}_2\text{(OH)}_2$; the coordination number of zinc is assumed to be four. Then the equilibrium reactions representing the amphoteric nature of zinc hydroxide are

$$\overset{\text{Acid}_1}{\text{Zn(H}_2\text{O)}_2\text{(OH)}_{2(s)}} + \overset{\text{Base}_2}{2\text{H}_2\text{O}} = \overset{\text{Base}_1}{\text{Zn(OH)}_4^{--}} + \overset{\text{Acid}_2}{2\text{H}_3\text{O}^+} \quad (17)$$

$$\underset{\text{Acid}_1}{\text{Zn(H}_2\text{O)}_4^{++}} + \underset{\text{Base}_2}{2\text{H}_2\text{O}} = \underset{\text{Acid}_2}{2\text{H}_3\text{O}^+} + \underset{\text{Base}_1}{\text{Zn(H}_2\text{O)}_2\text{(OH)}_{2(s)}} \quad (18)$$

In acid solution the equilibrium of the lower equation is shifted to the left; $Zn(H_2O)_2(OH)_{2(s)}$ dissolves and $Zn(H_2O)_4^{++}$ is formed. In alkaline solution the OH^- ion combines with the H_3O^+ ion and the equilibrium of reaction (17) is shifted to the right. The over-all reaction for the dissolving of solid zinc hydroxide by a solution of sodium hydroxide is then

$$Zn(H_2O)_2(OH)_{2(s)} + 2OH^- = Zn(OH)_4^{--} + 2H_2O \quad (19)$$

All amphoteric hydroxides may be treated in the same way. In each case the accepted coordination number of the metal ion should be used.

The structural form of zinc hydroxide in solution is similar to that given for zinc ammonia complex (see Fig. 23) except that two of the NH_3 groups are replaced by OH^- ions and two by water molecules. Structurally, equation (19) may be represented by the equation

$$
\begin{array}{cc}
\text{H} & \text{H}\\
\text{H :O: H} & :\!\ddot{\text{O}}:\\
:\!\ddot{\text{O}}:\!\overset{..}{\text{Zn}}:\!\ddot{\text{O}}: + 2:\!\ddot{\text{O}}:\!\text{H} = \text{H}:\!\ddot{\text{O}}:\!\overset{..}{\text{Zn}}:\!\ddot{\text{O}}:\!\text{H} + 2\text{H}:\!\ddot{\text{O}}:\!\text{H} & (20)\\
\text{H :O: H} & :\!\ddot{\text{O}}:\\
\text{H} & \text{H}
\end{array}
$$

In this reaction each of the two water molecules in the complex may be thought of as losing a hydrogen ion, which combines with the OH^- ion to produce water. As a result $Zn_4 (OH)_4]^{--}$ complex ion is formed. The latter ion is essentially hydrated zincate ion.

EXAMPLES OF PROBLEMS INVOLVING AMPHOTERIC SUBSTANCES

Example 1.

How many moles of NaOH must be added to 1 liter of water to dissolve completely .001 mole of zinc hydroxide?

The reaction is expressed by the equation

$$Zn(OH)_{2(s)} + 2OH_{(s)}^- = ZnO_2^{--} + 2H_2O$$

Zinc hydroxide is a weak acid and ionizes to give H^+ and ZnO_2^{--} ions.

$$Zn(OH)_{2(s)} = ZnO_2^{--} + 2H^+$$

The equilibrium expression for the ionization of $Zn(OH)_2$ as an acid is

$$(ZnO_2^{--})(H^+)^2 = 1 \times 10^{-29}$$

If .001 mole of $Zn(OH)_2$ dissolves, then .001 mole of ZnO_2^{--} ion will be produced.

$$(ZnO_2^{--})(H^+)^2 = (.001)(H^+)^2 = 1 \times 10^{-29}$$
$$(H^+)^2 = 1 \times 10^{-26}$$
$$(H^+) = 1 \times 10^{-13} \text{ mole/liter}$$

From the water equilibrium (OH^-) may be calculated.

$$(OH^-) = \frac{1 \times 10^{-14}}{(H^+)} = \frac{1 \times 10^{-14}}{1 \times 10^{-13}} = 0.1 \text{ mole/liter}$$

This value for (OH^-) is the amount in solution at equilibrium after the .001 mole of $Zn(OH)_2$ has dissolved. But to dissolve the $Zn(OH)_2$ an additional amount (.002 mole) of OH^- ion was required. Therefore the total amount of OH^- ion needed to dissolve .001 mole of $Zn(OH)_2$ and to maintain it in solution as ZnO_2^{--} ion is 0.1 + .002 or 0.102 mole.

(The constant used in this calculation is not accurate enough nor is the Law of Mass Action sufficiently valid to warrant taking into account the amount of OH^- ion consumed in the reaction. Therefore the answer 0.1 mole, instead of 0.102 mole, is more appropriate.)

Example 2.

A solution is .05 M with respect to OH^- ion and is in equilibrium with solid $Pb(OH)_2$. What is the concentration of (a) the Pb^{++} ion, (b) the $HPbO_2^-$ ion, and (c) the H^+ ion in the solution? (Disregard the second step of ionization of $Pb(OH)_2$ as an acid.)

In this solution the following equilibria are present.

$$Pb(OH)_{2(s)} = Pb^{++} + 2OH^- \qquad (1)$$
$$Pb(OH)_{2(s)} = HPbO_2^- + H^+ \qquad (2)$$

Since (OH^-) has a value of .05 M and the value for the solubility product constant for $Pb(OH)_2$ is 2.5×10^{-16}, we have from equation (1)

$$(Pb^{++})(OH^-)^2 = (Pb^{++})(.05)^2 = 2.5 \times 10^{-16}$$

Therefore
$$(Pb^{++}) = \frac{2.5 \times 10^{-16}}{2.5 \times 10^{-3}} = 1 \times 10^{-13} \; M$$

From equation (2) we may write
$$(HPbO_2^-)(H^+) = 2.1 \times 10^{-16}$$

Since the value for (OH^-) is .05 M, (H^+) must be
$$\frac{1 \times 10^{-14}}{(OH^-)} = \frac{1 \times 10^{-14}}{5 \times 10^{-2}} = 2 \times 10^{-13} \; M$$

Then
$$(HPbO_2^-)(2 \times 10^{-13}) = 2.1 \times 10^{-16}$$
$$(HPbO_2^-) = \frac{2.1 \times 10^{-16}}{2 \times 10^{-13}} = 1.05 \times 10^{-3} \; M \cong 1 \times 10^{-3} \; M$$

Example 3.

How many moles of $Cr(OH)_3$ will dissolve in 1 liter of 0.2 M NaOH solution? The equation for the reaction is
$$Cr(OH)_{3(s)} + OH^- = CrO_2^- + 2H_2O$$

According to this equation the number of moles of $Cr(OH)_3$ which dissolves will be equivalent to the number of moles of CrO_2^- ion in solution.

As an acid $Cr(OH)_3$ ionizes as follows:
$$Cr(OH)_{3(s)} = CrO_2^- + H^+ + H_2O$$

The ionization constant has a value of 9×10^{-17}; therefore
$$(CrO_2^-)(H^+) = 9 \times 10^{-17}$$

Since (OH^-) has a value of 0.2 M, (H^+) is $\dfrac{1 \times 10^{-14}}{0.2}$ or $5 \times 10^{-14} \; M$.

Then
$$(CrO_2^-)(5 \times 10^{-14}) = 9 \times 10^{-17}$$
$$(CrO_2^-) = \frac{9 \times 10^{-17}}{5 \times 10^{-14}} = 1.8 \times 10^{-3} \; mole/liter$$

Therefore .0018 mole of $Cr(OH)_3$ dissolves in 1 liter of 0.2 M NaOH solution.

QUESTIONS AND PROBLEMS

1. What are the anhydrides of the following substances: (a) HNO_3, (b) $Ca(OH)_2$, (c) NaOH, (d) H_2SO_4, (e) $Mg(OH)_2$ and (f) $HClO_4$?

2. Give the formulae of the hydroxides of which the following are the anhydrides: ZnO, Cr_2O_3, PbO, Al_2O_3 and Sb_2O_3.

3. Rearrange the formulae of the hydroxides given in question 2 in such a way as to emphasize their acidic properties.

4. Write the equations for the equilibrium involved when aluminum hydroxide acts both as an acid and as a base.

5. How may the equilibrium in problem 4 be shifted so as to produce (a) a large concentration of Al^{+++} ions, (b) a large concentration of AlO_2^- ions?

6. Are the elements in the first main group of the periodic system more electronegative than those of the fourth group or vice versa?

7. In the series of eighteen elements of the periodic table beginning with argon, name those the hydroxides of which are not amphoteric.

8. Which hydroxide acts as a stronger acid, $Sn(OH)_2$ or $Sn(OH)_4$?

9. Predict which hydroxide would act as the stronger acid, $Ge(OH)_2$ or $Ge(OH)_4$. Explain the basis of your prediction.

10. Write the formula for the sulfur analogue of each one of the following oxygen compounds: (a) H_2O, (b) SnO, (c) K_2O, (d) CO_2, (e) OH^-.

11. Give equations for the reactions involved when As_2O_5 is dissolved by a solution containing OH^- and when As_2S_5 is dissolved by a solution containing HS^- ions.

12. Why will SnS dissolve readily in ammonium polysulfide while in ammonium sulfide it is soluble only to a very small extent?

13. Making use of the amphoteric properties of $Zn(OH)_2$ and $Al(OH)_3$ and the complex-forming properties of Zn^{++} show how $Zn(OH)_2$, $Al(OH)_3$ and $Fe(OH)_3$ may be separated from each other.

14. How many moles of $NaOH$ must be added to 100 ml. of water to dissolve completely .001 mole of $Zn(OH)_2$?

15. A saturated solution of $Zn(OH)_2$ in water contains the following ions in equilibrium with each other: Zn^{++}, ZnO_2^{--}, H^+, and OH^-. Calculate the concentration of each ion in such a solution. (Note: from the solubility product constant for $Zn(OH)_2$

calculate (Zn^{++}) and (OH$^-$), then obtain (H$^+$) from the water equilibrium, and finally calculate (ZnO$_2$$^{--}$) from the equilibrium for the ionization of Zn(OH)$_2$ as an acid.)

16. What is the concentration of the Zn^{++} ion and of the ZnO$_2$$^{--}$ ion in a solution which is .01 molar with respect to OH$^-$ ion and which is in equilibrium with solid Zn(OH)$_2$?

17. A solution is 0.1 molar with respect to OH$^-$ ion and is in equilibrium with solid Pb(OH)$_2$. What is the concentration of (a) the Pb^{++} ion, (b) the HPbO$_2$$^-$ ion, and (c) the H$^+$ ion in this solution?

18. Will .002 mole of Cr(OH)$_3$ dissolve in 1 liter of 0.1 molar NaOH solution?

19. Excess Al(OH)$_3$ is added to 1 liter of a solution of NaOH. After equilibrium is reached .01 mole of Al(OH)$_3$ is dissolved. What is the final concentration of the OH$^-$ ion?

20. Write equations (17) and (18) in structural form, similar to equation (20).

CHAPTER XI

Oxidation-Reduction Equilibria

In Chapter III we considered oxidation and reduction only from the standpoint of the balancing of equations, and we learned that any equation can be balanced just as easily when reversed — i.e., from right to left as well as from left to right. Therefore, the fact that an equation can be balanced does not mean that it necessarily proceeds as indicated. This question can be determined only by experiment. Experiments to determine the course of a reaction are made in a variety of ways. The commonest of these involves the use of electrical cells, but the detailed method by which such experiments are carried out is too involved for this course. It is possible to correlate all such equilibrium experiments in such a way that one hundred experiments will serve to determine the course of thousands of other reactions. In this chapter we shall see how this is done.

Relative Strengths of Oxidizing and Reducing Agents. The metals are regarded as good reducing agents since they all exhibit a tendency to lose electrons and form positive ions. This tendency varies considerably from metal to metal. The alkali and alkaline earth metals show a great tendency to lose electrons while this tendency is much less pronounced in the case of the noble metals such as platinum and gold. The so-called electromotive series of the elements is an arrangement based upon the tendency of elements to lose electrons and is accordingly also an arrangement of the elements as reducing agents. The alkali and alkaline earth metals are found at the beginning while platinum and gold are at the end of the series of metals. Hydrogen occupies an intermediate position.

It is possible to determine the order of the metals in this series by displacement reactions, since the elements which show a great tendency to lose electrons and form positive ions will displace elements from solution which show this same tendency to a lesser degree. The following are a few familiar examples of displacement reactions:

$$Ca + Zn^{++} = Zn + Ca^{++} \tag{1}$$
$$Zn + Fe^{++} = Fe + Zn^{++} \tag{2}$$
$$Fe + Sn^{++} = Sn + Fe^{++} \tag{3}$$
$$Sn + Cu^{++} = Cu + Sn^{++} \tag{4}$$
$$Cu + 2Ag^{+} = 2Ag + Cu^{++} \tag{5}$$

The order of the decreasing tendency of these elements to lose electrons is Ca, Zn, Fe, Sn, Cu and Ag, which is also the decreasing order of these elements as reducing agents. Since every reducing agent must react with an oxidizing agent in an oxidation-reduction reaction, the ions of these particular elements are therefore the oxidizing agents. The ion of the best reducing agent is itself the poorest oxidizing agent, for if a metal has a great tendency to lose electrons its ion must have a small tendency to acquire them. When both the metal and its ion are listed as an oxidation-reduction couple we obtain a table of oxidizing and reducing agents as follows:

$$
\begin{array}{ccc}
& Ca & Ca^{++} \\
& Zn & Zn^{++} \\
& Fe & Fe^{++} \\
& Sn & Sn^{++} \\
& Cu & Cu^{++} \\
& Ag & Ag^{+}
\end{array}
$$

Reducing Agents ↑ — Oxidizing Agents ↓

Most of the non-metals have a pronounced tendency to gain electrons, that is, to behave as oxidizing agents. Those elements which show a greater tendency to acquire electrons and form negative ions will displace elements from solution which show this same tendency to a lesser degree. For example,

$$Cl_2 + 2Br^{-} = 2Cl^{-} + Br_2 \tag{6}$$
$$Br_2 + 2I^{-} = 2Br^{-} + I_2 \tag{7}$$
$$I_2 + H_2S = 2I^{-} + S + 2H^{+} \tag{8}$$

As far as the ability to gain electrons is concerned these substances fall in the decreasing order of Cl_2, Br_2, I_2 and S. Sulfur is the weakest and chlorine the strongest oxidizing agent of this group. The ions of these elements may be regarded as reducing agents. On the basis of reactions which are known to take place between these non-metals and the metals, both may be included in a single table.

TABLE 19

OXIDATION-REDUCTION COUPLES

Reducing Agents		Oxidizing Agents
	Ca —— Ca^{++}	
	Zn —— Zn^{++}	
	Fe —— Fe^{++}	
	Sn —— Sn^{++}	
	H$_2$S —— S + 2H$^+$	
	Cu —— Cu^{++}	
	I$^-$ —— I$_2$	
	Ag —— Ag$^+$	
	Br$^-$ —— Br$_2$	
	Cl$^-$ —— Cl$_2$	

Any substance on the right side of the table (oxidizing agent) will react with any substance on the left (reducing agent) provided that the reducing agent lies *above* the oxidizing agent. For example, iodine will react with zinc to produce iodide ion and zinc ion in solution.

$$I_2 + Zn = Zn^{++} + 2I^- \tag{9}$$

It has already been shown that oxidizing and reducing agents are not limited to the elements alone. Many ions of the elements and groups of elements (radicals) may take the part of reducing and oxidizing agents. Thus MnO_4^- ion, in the presence of H^+ ion, will oxidize Fe^{++}, I^-, Cl^- and Br^- ions; $Cr_2O_7^{--}$ ion, in the presence of H^+ ion, will oxidize Br^-, I^- and many other ions; Sn^{++} ion will reduce NO_3^-, ClO^-, AsO_4^{---}, Bi^{+++}, Fe^{+++} and other ions.

Oxidation-Reduction Equilibria. Table 20, which is an extension of Table 19, includes all of the principal oxidizing and reducing agents commonly used in inorganic chemistry.

By the use of this table, in conjunction with the tables which list the solubility product constants of difficultly soluble substances and the ionization constants for weak acids, it is possible to predict the course of more than 10,000 reactions. Such predictions may be made on a quantitative as well as a qualitative basis. In other words, it is possible to calculate the equilibrium constants for all of these oxidation-reduction reactions. To obtain some idea of the significance of Table 20, the meaning of the symbols involved, and the manner in which it was constructed, it is necessary to consider some specific oxidation-reduction equilibria.

Suppose, for example, that we consider the equilibrium between Fe^{++} ion, Fe^{+++} ion, H^+ ion and H_2, which is represented by the equation

$$2H^+ + 2Fe^{++} = H_2 + 2Fe^{+++} \tag{10}$$

This oxidation-reduction reaction, as written in equation (10), involves an increase and decrease of two charges or two electrons. Dividing this equation by two in order to obtain an oxidation-reduction change of only one charge or one electron, we have

$$H^+ + Fe^{++} = \tfrac{1}{2}H_2 + Fe^{+++} * \tag{11}$$

This equation represents an equilibrium which in every respect is like the equilibria discussed in previous chapters. Likewise, the expression for the equilibrium constant will contain the concentrations of the products of the reaction in the numerator and the concentrations of the reactants in the denominator.

$$\frac{(H_2)^{\frac{1}{2}}(Fe^{+++})}{(H^+)(Fe^{++})} = K_{eq} = 10^{-12.5} \dagger \tag{12}$$

* In equation (11) the coefficient of H_2 is $\tfrac{1}{2}$. When considering any equation from the standpoint of molecules and single ions we eliminate all fractional coefficients. However, if the equation is interpreted in terms of moles it is quite permissible to use fractions. In this latter sense equation (11) is interpreted; one mole of hydrogen ion when reacting with one mole of ferrous ion produces one-half mole hydrogen gas and one mole ferric ion.

† $10^{-12.5}$ is a pure exponential number and is equal to $10^{+0.5} \times 10^{-13}$ which in turn is equal to 3.16×10^{-13}. For the present purpose it is very much

The value of the constant, $10^{-12.5}$, has been determined experimentally by measuring the pressure of the hydrogen gas (expressed in atmospheres) and the concentrations of the Fe^{++}, Fe^{+++} and H^+ ions (in terms of moles per liter of solution). In many oxidation-reduction reactions the equilibrium is displaced so far in one direction that the small concentrations of the reactants cannot be determined by ordinary analytical methods. However, in many cases the voltage delivered by an E.M.F. cell, consisting of the ions and molecules of an oxidation-reduction system in equilibrium, can be measured. This voltage depends upon the concentrations of the constituents of the oxidation-reduction equilibrium and serves as a means of determining the equilibrium constants for the reactions. Such cells are similar to the familiar Daniell cell. For our present purpose we shall omit any discussion of the analytical method of determining the concentrations of substances involved in equilibria of this kind.

In equation (12) there are two oxidation-reduction couples involved, namely, $\frac{1}{2}H_2$ —— H^+ and Fe^{++} —— Fe^{+++}. For convenience these couples are to be regarded as half-reactions, the equilibrium expressions for which are

$$\frac{(H_2)^{\frac{1}{2}}}{(H^+)} = K_1 \quad \text{and} \quad \frac{(Fe^{+++})}{(Fe^{++})} = K_2 \tag{13}$$

It is impossible to obtain absolute values for the equilibrium constants for the half-reactions since oxidation can proceed only when accompanied by a reduction reaction and vice versa. In this particular case Fe^{++} ion can be converted to Fe^{+++} ion only in the presence of an oxidizing agent which in equation (11) is the H^+ ion. The identical argument applies for the reduction process. However, if we could obtain **relative** values for the half-reactions it would then be possible to use combinations of these relative values to

more convenient to use these fractional exponents rather than mixed numbers. For a complete discussion of exponential numbers see the Appendix.

calculate equilibrium constants for oxidation-reduction reactions involving any two or more of the half-reactions. *Such a procedure is possible.*

To illustrate the significance of the half-reaction constants given in Table 20, let us consider the equilibrium expressions of equation (12). It is not possible to obtain a definite numerical value for either of the half-reaction constants, yet we can obtain **relative** values of these ratios by assuming some arbitrary value for one of them. For convenience, allow the ratio $\dfrac{(H_2)^{\frac{1}{2}}}{(H^+)}$ to be equal to $\dfrac{1}{\alpha}$, i.e., the inverse of this ratio $\dfrac{(H^+)}{(H_2)^{\frac{1}{2}}}$, to be equal to α. Substituting this value in equation (12) we obtain $10^{-12.5}\alpha$ for the value of the ratio $\dfrac{(Fe^{+++})}{(Fe^{++})}$ since

$$\frac{(H_2)^{\frac{1}{2}}}{(H^+)} \times \frac{(Fe^{+++})}{(Fe^{++})} = \frac{1}{\alpha} \times \frac{(Fe^{+++})}{(Fe^{++})} = 10^{-12.5}$$

and
$$\frac{(Fe^{+++})}{(Fe^{++})} = 10^{-12.5}\alpha$$

Now consider another reaction involving Fe^{++} and Fe^{+++} ions.

$$MnO_4^- + 5Fe^{++} + 8H^+ = Mn^{++} + 5Fe^{+++} + 4H_2O \quad (14)$$

This equation involves an oxidation-reduction change of five units of charge or five electrons. Changing equation (14) so that only one unit of charge is involved, we have

$$\tfrac{1}{5}MnO_4^- + Fe^{++} + \tfrac{8}{5}H^+ = \tfrac{1}{5}Mn^{++} + Fe^{+++} + \tfrac{4}{5}H_2O \quad (15)$$

The equilibrium constant for this reaction is

$$\frac{(Fe^{+++})(Mn^{++})^{\frac{1}{5}}H_2O^{\frac{4}{5}}}{(Fe^{++})(MnO_4^-)^{\frac{1}{5}}(H^+)^{\frac{8}{5}}} = K_{eq} = 10^{13.3} \text{ (experimental)} \quad (16)$$

In this expression we have included the term $H_2O^{\frac{4}{5}}$ where normally it would be omitted, as in past examples, for the concentration of the water molecules does not change appreciably in such reactions and for all practical purposes may be regarded as remaining constant. Although the term can be omitted from equation (16) we shall see later that its inclusion will be very convenient in the selection of the proper half-reactions required for the calculation of the oxidation-reduction equilibrium constants in question. All such terms which can be omitted appear in *italics*. Formally each of these *italicized* terms may be regarded as being equal to unity. Substances which do not change appreciably in concentration during the course of a reaction, such as water, and all substances existing in a separate phase (not in solution), such as relatively insoluble solids, come under this classification.

The value of the term $\dfrac{(\text{Fe}^{+++})}{(\text{Fe}^{++})}$ was previously found to be equal to $10^{-12.5}\alpha$ (maintaining the value $\dfrac{(\text{H}^{+})}{(\text{H}_2)^{\frac{1}{2}}}$ as α). Thus,

$$\frac{(\text{Fe}^{+++})}{(\text{Fe}^{++})} \times \frac{(\text{Mn}^{++})^{\frac{1}{5}} H_2 O^{\frac{4}{5}}}{(\text{MnO}_4^{-})^{\frac{1}{5}}(\text{H}^{+})^{\frac{8}{5}}} = 10^{-12.5}\alpha \times \frac{(\text{Mn}^{++})^{\frac{1}{5}} H_2 O^{\frac{4}{5}}}{(\text{MnO}_4^{-})^{\frac{1}{5}}(\text{H}^{+})^{\frac{8}{5}}} = 10^{13.3}$$

and therefore

$$\frac{(\text{Mn}^{++})^{\frac{1}{5}} H_2 O^{\frac{4}{5}}}{(\text{MnO}_4^{-})^{\frac{1}{5}}(\text{H}^{+})^{\frac{8}{5}}} = \frac{10^{13.3}}{10^{-12.5}\alpha} = \frac{10^{25.8}}{\alpha}$$

The inverse of this value is $10^{-25.8}\alpha$, as given in Table 20.

We shall next consider the reaction represented by the equation

$$3\text{Fe}^{++} + \text{NO}_3^{-} + 4\text{H}^{+} = 3\text{Fe}^{+++} + \text{NO} + 2\text{H}_2\text{O} \quad (17)$$

Reducing this equation to represent one electron change, we have

$$\text{Fe}^{++} + \tfrac{1}{3}\text{NO}_3^{-} + \tfrac{4}{3}\text{H}^{+} = \text{Fe}^{+++} + \tfrac{1}{3}\text{NO} + \tfrac{2}{3}\text{H}_2\text{O} \quad (18)$$

the value for the equilibrium constant of which is

$$\frac{(\text{Fe}^{+++})(\text{NO})^{\frac{1}{3}} H_2 O^{\frac{2}{3}}}{(\text{Fe}^{++})(\text{NO}_3^{-})^{\frac{1}{3}}(\text{H}^{+})^{\frac{4}{3}}} = 10^{3.5} \text{ (experimental)} \quad (19)$$

Since $\dfrac{(\text{Fe}^{+++})}{(\text{Fe}^{++})}$ equals $10^{-12.5}\alpha$, the value for $\dfrac{(\text{NO}_3^{-})^{\frac{1}{3}}(\text{H}^{+})^{\frac{4}{3}}}{(\text{NO})^{\frac{1}{3}} H_2 O^{\frac{2}{3}}}$ is accordingly $10^{-16}\alpha$, as given in Table 20.

In this way it is possible to build up values for the half-reaction constants for all oxidation-reduction couples. It will be observed that for every completed reaction the alphas (α's) always cancel. The reason for reducing every half-reaction to one which involves a change of only one unit of charge or one electron is to allow for this cancellation. Since the alpha term always cancels it can be omitted. The values of the half-reaction constants in Table 20 therefore include only the coefficients of alpha.

TABLE 20

OXIDATION-REDUCTION HALF-REACTIONS

For convenience in locating the half-reaction in the table, each equation is given in terms of whole number coefficients. The equilibrium expression for the half-reaction, however, is for a one electron loss, or a gain of one unit of valence number. The exponent of the half-reaction constant is given to the first place following the decimal point. In some cases the experimental data for the determination of this value do not warrant a significant figure of this magnitude, while in other cases they do. Therefore the figure following the decimal point is not always significant; it represents an estimated value of the average accuracy. For convenience, the solid phases such as Li and the practically non-varying components such as H_2O are included in the equilibrium expressions for the half-reactions and appear in *italics*. These will either cancel in the calculated equilibrium expression for a complete reaction or they are to be omitted after the equilibrium expression has been finally set up. They are included here for convenience in manipulating the half-reaction expressions. The exponents for the solid and non-varying components have no significance. These are also included for convenience. The concentrations of gases, for example (H_2), are to be expressed in terms of pressures (atmospheres).

As in Table 19 the right-hand member of each half-reaction is an oxidizing agent, and the left-hand member a reducing agent.

* Compiled from data obtained from *Reference Book of Inorganic Chemistry*, Latimer and Hildebrand (Macmillan), and from *International Critical Tables*, (McGraw-Hill).

The best reducing agents are at the beginning of the table and the best oxidizing agents at the end. Any given oxidizing agent will oxidize any reducing agent lying above it in this table.

It is possible to predict qualitatively whether or not some of the simpler reactions will proceed merely by inspecting the relative positions of the appropriate half-reactions in the table. In many cases, however, the complete reaction in question will involve more than two half-reactions. Under such conditions a quantitative calculation of the equilibrium constant is necessary. In any event the extent to which a given reaction will proceed can only be determined by making a quantitative calculation involving the half-reaction constants.

HALF-REACTION	EQUILIBRIUM EXPRESSION	VALUE OF CONSTANT
1. $Li \longrightarrow Li^+$	$\dfrac{(Li^+)}{Li}$	$10^{50.0}$
2. $Rb \longrightarrow Rb^+$	$\dfrac{(Rb^+)}{Rb}$	$10^{49.6}$
3. $K \longrightarrow K^+$	$\dfrac{(K^+)}{K}$	$10^{49.5}$
4. $Sr \longrightarrow Sr^{++}$	$\dfrac{(Sr^{++})^{\frac{1}{2}}}{Sr^{\frac{1}{2}}}$	$10^{49.5}$
5. $Ba \longrightarrow Ba^{++}$	$\dfrac{(Ba^{++})^{\frac{1}{2}}}{Ba^{\frac{1}{2}}}$	$10^{49.1}$
6. $Ca \longrightarrow Ca^{++}$	$\dfrac{(Ca^{++})^{\frac{1}{2}}}{Ca^{\frac{1}{2}}}$	$10^{48.7}$
7. $Na \longrightarrow Na^+$	$\dfrac{(Na^+)}{Na}$	$10^{46.0}$
8. $Mg \longrightarrow Mg^{++}$	$\dfrac{(Mg^{++})^{\frac{1}{2}}}{Mg^{\frac{1}{2}}}$	$10^{40.6}$
9. $Al \longrightarrow Al^{+++}$	$\dfrac{(Al^{+++})^{\frac{1}{3}}}{Al^{\frac{1}{3}}}$	$10^{28.8}$
10. $Mn \longrightarrow Mn^{++}$	$\dfrac{(Mn^{++})^{\frac{1}{2}}}{Mn^{\frac{1}{2}}}$	$10^{18.6}$
11. $CN^- + 2OH^- \longrightarrow CNO^- + H_2O$	$\dfrac{(CNO^-)^{\frac{1}{2}} H_2O^{\frac{1}{2}}}{(CN^-)^{\frac{1}{2}}(OH^-)}$	$10^{16.4}$

HALF-REACTION	EQUILIBRIUM EXPRESSION	VALUE OF CONSTANT
12. Zn —— Zn^{++}	$\dfrac{(Zn^{++})^{\frac{1}{2}}}{Zn^{\frac{1}{2}}}$	$10^{12.8}$
13. H_2Te —— $Te + 2H^+$	$\dfrac{Te^{\frac{1}{2}}(H^+)}{(H_2Te)^{\frac{1}{2}}}$	$10^{11.8}$
14. Cr —— Cr^{++}	$\dfrac{(Cr^{++})^{\frac{1}{2}}}{Cr^{\frac{1}{2}}}$	$10^{10.2}$
15. S^{--} —— S	$\dfrac{S^{\frac{1}{2}}}{(S^{--})^{\frac{1}{2}}}$	$10^{8.6}$
16. H_2Se —— $Se + 2H^+$	$\dfrac{Se^{\frac{1}{2}}(H^+)}{(H_2Se)^{\frac{1}{2}}}$	$10^{8.5}$
17. Ga —— Ga^{+++}	$\dfrac{(Ga^{+++})^{\frac{1}{3}}}{Ga^{\frac{1}{3}}}$	$10^{8.5}$
18. Fe —— Fe^{++}	$\dfrac{(Fe^{++})^{\frac{1}{2}}}{Fe^{\frac{1}{2}}}$	$10^{7.4}$
19. Cr^{++} —— Cr^{+++}	$\dfrac{(Cr^{+++})}{(Cr^{++})}$	$10^{6.8}$
20. Cd —— Cd^{++}	$\dfrac{(Cd^{++})^{\frac{1}{2}}}{Cd^{\frac{1}{2}}}$	$10^{6.7}$
21. In —— In^{+++}	$\dfrac{(In^{+++})^{\frac{1}{3}}}{In^{\frac{1}{3}}}$	$10^{6.4}$
22. Ti^{++} —— Ti^{+++}	$\dfrac{(Ti^{+++})}{(Ti^{++})}$	$10^{6.3}$
23. Tl —— Tl^+	$\dfrac{(Tl^+)}{Tl}$	$10^{5.7}$
24. $P + 4H_2O$ —— $H_3PO_4 + 5H^+$	$\dfrac{(H_3PO_4)^{\frac{1}{5}}(H^+)}{P^{\frac{1}{5}}H_2O^{\frac{4}{5}}}$	$10^{5.1}$
25. $Co(CN)_6^{----}$ —— $Co(CN)_6^{---}$	$\dfrac{(Co(CN)_6^{---})}{(Co(CN)_6^{----})}$	$10^{5.1}$
26. Co —— Co^{++}	$\dfrac{(Co^{++})^{\frac{1}{2}}}{Co^{\frac{1}{2}}}$	$10^{4.9}$

HALF-REACTION	EQUILIBRIUM EXPRESSION	VALUE OF CONSTANT
27. $Ni \longrightarrow Ni^{++}$	$\dfrac{(Ni^{++})^{\frac{1}{2}}}{Ni^{\frac{1}{2}}}$	$10^{3.7}$
28. $V^{++} \longrightarrow V^{+++}$	$\dfrac{(V^{+++})}{(V^{++})}$	$10^{3.4}$
29. $Cu_2O + 2OH^- \longrightarrow 2CuO + H_2O$	$\dfrac{CuO \, H_2O^{\frac{1}{2}}}{Cu_2O^{\frac{1}{2}}(OH^-)}$	$10^{2.5}$
30. $Sn \longrightarrow Sn^{++}$	$\dfrac{(Sn^{++})^{\frac{1}{2}}}{Sn^{\frac{1}{2}}}$	$10^{2.2}$
31. $Pb \longrightarrow Pb^{++}$	$\dfrac{(Pb^{++})^{\frac{1}{2}}}{Pb^{\frac{1}{2}}}$	$10^{2.0}$
32. $9OH^- + \cdot NH_3 \longrightarrow NO_3^- + 6H_2O$	$\dfrac{(NO_3^-)^{\frac{1}{8}} H_2O^{\frac{6}{8}}}{(OH^-)^{\frac{9}{8}}(NH_3)^{\frac{1}{8}}}$	$10^{2.0}$
33. $2Hg + 2I^- \longrightarrow Hg_2I_2$	$\dfrac{Hg_2I_2^{\frac{1}{2}}}{Hg(I^-)}$	$10^{0.7}$
34. $H_2 \longrightarrow 2H^+$	$\dfrac{(H^+)}{(H_2)^{\frac{1}{2}}}$	10^0
35. $2OH^- + NO_2^- \longrightarrow NO_3^- + H_2O$	$\dfrac{(NO_3^-)^{\frac{1}{2}} H_2O^{\frac{1}{2}}}{(NO_2^-)^{\frac{1}{2}}(OH^-)}$	10^0
36. $HCN + H_2O \longrightarrow HCNO + 2H^+$	$\dfrac{(HCNO)^{\frac{1}{2}}(H^+)}{(HCN)^{\frac{1}{2}} H_2O^{\frac{1}{2}}}$	10^0
37. $Sb + 3H_2O \longrightarrow H_3SbO_3 + 3H^+$	$\dfrac{H_3SbO_3^{\frac{1}{3}}(H^+)}{Sb^{\frac{1}{3}} H_2O}$	10^0
38. $W + 3H_2O \longrightarrow WO_3 + 6H^+$	$\dfrac{WO_3^{\frac{1}{6}}(H^+)}{W^{\frac{1}{6}} H_2O^{\frac{1}{2}}}$	10^0
39. $WO^{+++} + 2H_2O \longrightarrow WO_3 + 4H^+$	$\dfrac{WO_3(H^+)^4}{(WO^{+++})H_2O^2}$	10^0
40. $Ti^{+++} + H_2O \longrightarrow TiO^{++} + 2H^+$	$\dfrac{(TiO^{++})(H^+)^2}{(Ti^{+++})H_2O}$	$10^{-0.7}$
41. $2Hg + 2Br^- \longrightarrow Hg_2Br_2$	$\dfrac{Hg_2Br_2^{\frac{1}{2}}}{Hg(Br^-)}$	$10^{-2.2}$

	HALF-REACTION	EQUILIBRIUM EXPRESSION	VALUE OF CONSTANT
42.	$Sn^{++} \longrightarrow Sn^{++++}$	$\dfrac{(Sn^{++++})^{\frac{1}{2}}}{(Sn^{++})^{\frac{1}{2}}}$	$10^{-2.2}$
43.	$H_2O + H_2SO_3 \longrightarrow SO_4^{--} + 4H^+$	$\dfrac{(SO_4^{--})^{\frac{1}{2}}(H^+)^2}{H_2O^{\frac{1}{2}}(H_2SO_3)^{\frac{1}{2}}}$	$10^{-2.4}$
44.	$Cu^+ \longrightarrow Cu^{++}$	$\dfrac{(Cu^{++})}{(Cu^+)}$	$10^{-2.9}$
45.	$H_2S \longrightarrow S + 2H^+$	$\dfrac{S^{\frac{1}{2}}(H^+)}{(H_2S)^{\frac{1}{2}}}$	$10^{-2.9}$
46.	$Bi \longrightarrow Bi^{+++}$	$\dfrac{(Bi^{+++})^{\frac{1}{3}}}{Bi^{\frac{1}{3}}}$	$10^{-3.4}$
47.	$2Ta + 5H_2O \longrightarrow Ta_2O_5 + 10H^+$	$\dfrac{Ta_2O_5^{\frac{1}{10}}(H^+)}{Ta^{\frac{1}{5}}H_2O^{\frac{1}{2}}}$	$10^{-3.4}$
48.	$As + 3H_2O \longrightarrow H_3AsO_3 + 3H^+$	$\dfrac{H_3AsO_3^{\frac{1}{3}}(H^+)}{As^{\frac{1}{3}}H_2O}$	$10^{-4.1}$
49.	$Mo + 3H_2O \longrightarrow MoO_3 + 6H^+$	$\dfrac{MoO_3^{\frac{1}{6}}(H^+)}{Mo^{\frac{1}{6}}H_2O^{\frac{1}{2}}}$	$10^{-4.2}$
50.	$2Hg + 2Cl^- \longrightarrow Hg_2Cl_2$	$\dfrac{Hg_2Cl_2^{\frac{1}{2}}}{Hg(Cl^-)}$	$10^{-4.6}$
51.	$V + H_2O \longrightarrow VO^{++} + 2H^+$	$\dfrac{(VO^{++})^{\frac{1}{4}}(H^+)^{\frac{1}{2}}}{V^{\frac{1}{4}}H_2O^{\frac{1}{4}}}$	$10^{-5.1}$
52.	$Cu \longrightarrow Cu^{++}$	$\dfrac{(Cu^{++})^{\frac{1}{2}}}{Cu^{\frac{1}{2}}}$	$10^{-5.8}$
53.	$V^{+++} + H_2O \longrightarrow VO^{++} + 2H^+$	$\dfrac{(VO^{++})(H^+)^2}{(V^{+++})H_2O}$	$10^{-6.8}$
54.	$4OH^- \longrightarrow O_2 + 2H_2O$	$\dfrac{(O_2)^{\frac{1}{4}}H_2O^{\frac{1}{2}}}{(OH^-)}$	$10^{-6.8}$
55.	$U^{++++} + 2H_2O \longrightarrow UO_2^{++} + 4H^+$	$\dfrac{(UO_2^{++})^{\frac{1}{2}}(H^+)^2}{(U^{++++})^{\frac{1}{2}}H_2O}$	$10^{-6.9}$
56.	$S + 3H_2O \longrightarrow H_2SO_3 + 4H^+$	$\dfrac{(H_2SO_3)^{\frac{1}{4}}(H^+)}{S^{\frac{1}{4}}H_2O^{\frac{3}{4}}}$	$10^{-8.0}$

HALF-REACTION	EQUILIBRIUM EXPRESSION	VALUE OF CONSTANT
57. $Fe(CN)_6^{----} \longrightarrow Fe(CN)_6^{---}$	$\dfrac{(Fe(CN)_6^{---})}{(Fe(CN)_6^{----})}$	$10^{-8.3}$
58. $H_3AsO_3 + H_2O \longrightarrow H_3AsO_4 + 2H^+$	$\dfrac{H_3AsO_4^{\frac{1}{2}}(H^+)}{H_3AsO_3^{\frac{1}{2}}H_2O^{\frac{1}{2}}}$	$10^{-8.3}$
59. $Ni(OH)_2 + 2OH^- \longrightarrow NiO_2 \cdot 2H_2O$	$\dfrac{NiO_2 \cdot 2H_2O^{\frac{1}{2}}}{Ni(OH)_2^{\frac{1}{2}}(OH^-)}$	$10^{-8.3}$
60. $MoO^{+++} + 2H_2O \longrightarrow MoO_3 + 4H^+$	$\dfrac{MoO_3(H^+)^4}{(MoO^{+++})H_2O^2}$	$10^{-8.5}$
61. $Cu \longrightarrow Cu^+$	$\dfrac{(Cu^+)}{Cu}$	$10^{-8.6}$
62. $2I^- \longrightarrow I_2$	$\dfrac{I_2^{\frac{1}{2}}}{(I^-)}$	$10^{-9.1}$
63. $3I^- \longrightarrow I_3^-$	$\dfrac{(I_3^-)^{\frac{1}{2}}}{(I^-)^{\frac{3}{2}}}$	$10^{-9.1}$
64. $Hg_2Cl_2 + 2Cl^- \longrightarrow 2HgCl_2$	$\dfrac{(HgCl_2)}{Hg_2Cl_2^{\frac{1}{2}}(Cl^-)}$	$10^{-10.7}$
65. $MnO_4^{--} \longrightarrow MnO_4^-$	$\dfrac{(MnO_4^-)}{(MnO_4^{--})}$	$10^{-11.2}$
66. $H_2O_2 \longrightarrow O_2 + 2H^+$	$\dfrac{(O_2)^{\frac{1}{2}}(H^+)}{(H_2O_2)^{\frac{1}{2}}}$	$10^{-11.5}$
67. $MnO_2 + 4OH^- \longrightarrow MnO_4^{--} + 2H_2O$	$\dfrac{(MnO_4^{--})^{\frac{1}{2}}H_2O}{MnO_2^{\frac{1}{2}}(OH^-)^2}$	$10^{-12.0}$
68. $Fe^{++} \longrightarrow Fe^{+++}$	$\dfrac{(Fe^{+++})}{(Fe^{++})}$	$10^{-12.5}$
69. $Se + 3H_2O \longrightarrow H_2SeO_3 + 4H^+$	$\dfrac{(H_2SeO_3)^{\frac{1}{4}}(H^+)}{Se^{\frac{1}{4}}H_2O^{\frac{3}{4}}}$	$10^{-12.7}$
70. $2Hg \longrightarrow Hg_2^{++}$	$\dfrac{(Hg_2^{++})^{\frac{1}{2}}}{Hg}$	$10^{-13.5}$
71. $Ag \longrightarrow Ag^+$	$\dfrac{(Ag^+)}{Ag}$	$10^{-13.6}$
72. $Hg \longrightarrow Hg^{++}$	$\dfrac{(Hg^{++})^{\frac{1}{2}}}{Hg^{\frac{1}{2}}}$	$10^{-14.6}$

HALF-REACTION	EQUILIBRIUM EXPRESSION	VALUE OF CONSTANT
73. $3OH^- \longrightarrow HO_2^- + H_2O$	$\dfrac{(HO_2^-)^{\frac{1}{2}} H_2O^{\frac{1}{2}}}{(OH^-)^{\frac{3}{2}}}$	$10^{-14.7}$
74. $2H_2O + NH_4^+ \longrightarrow HNO_2 + 7H^+$	$\dfrac{(HNO_2)^{\frac{1}{6}}(H^+)^{\frac{7}{6}}}{(NH_4^+)^{\frac{1}{6}} H_2O^{\frac{1}{3}}}$	$10^{-14.6}$
75. $CoO + 2OH^- \longrightarrow CoO_2 + H_2O$	$\dfrac{CoO_2^{\frac{1}{2}} H_2O^{\frac{1}{2}}}{CoO^{\frac{1}{2}}(OH^-)}$	$10^{-15.2}$
76. $3H_2O + NH_4^+ \longrightarrow NO_3^- + 10H^+$	$\dfrac{(NO_3^-)^{\frac{1}{8}}(H^+)^{\frac{10}{8}}}{(NH_4^+)^{\frac{1}{8}} H_2O^{\frac{3}{8}}}$	$10^{-15.3}$
77. $Hg_2^{++} \longrightarrow 2Hg^{++}$	$\dfrac{(Hg^{++})}{(Hg_2^{++})^{\frac{1}{2}}}$	$10^{-15.6}$
78. $Cl^- + 2OH^- \longrightarrow ClO^- + H_2O$	$\dfrac{(ClO^-)^{\frac{1}{2}} H_2O^{\frac{1}{2}}}{(Cl^-)^{\frac{1}{2}}(OH^-)}$	$10^{-15.9}$
79. $NO + 2H_2O \longrightarrow NO_3^- + 4H^+$	$\dfrac{(NO_3^-)^{\frac{1}{3}}(H^+)^{\frac{4}{3}}}{(NO)^{\frac{1}{3}} H_2O^{\frac{2}{3}}}$	$10^{-16.0}$
80. $HNO_2 + H_2O \longrightarrow NO_3^- + 3H^+$	$\dfrac{(NO_3^-)^{\frac{1}{2}}(H^+)^{\frac{3}{2}}}{(HNO_2)^{\frac{1}{2}} H_2O^{\frac{1}{2}}}$	$10^{-16.1}$
81. $NO + H_2O \longrightarrow HNO_2 + H^+$	$\dfrac{(HNO_2)(H^+)}{(NO) H_2O}$	$10^{-16.6}$
82. $I^- + H_2O \longrightarrow HIO + H^+$	$\dfrac{(HIO)^{\frac{1}{2}}(H^+)^{\frac{1}{2}}}{(I^-)^{\frac{1}{2}} H_2O^{\frac{1}{2}}}$	$10^{-16.8}$
83. $2Br^- \longrightarrow Br_2$	$\dfrac{(Br_2)^{\frac{1}{2}}}{(Br^-)}$	$10^{-18.1}$
84. $I^- + 3H_2O \longrightarrow IO_3^- + 6H^+$	$\dfrac{(IO_3^-)^{\frac{1}{6}}(H^+)}{(I^-)^{\frac{1}{6}} H_2O^{\frac{1}{2}}}$	$10^{-18.5}$
85. $VO^{++} + 2H_2O \longrightarrow HVO_3 + 3H^+$	$\dfrac{(HVO_3)(H^+)^3}{(VO^{++}) H_2O^2}$	$10^{-18.6}$
86. $Tl^+ \longrightarrow Tl^{+++}$	$\dfrac{(Tl^{+++})^{\frac{1}{2}}}{(Tl^+)^{\frac{1}{2}}}$	$10^{-20.4}$
87. $H_2SeO_3 + H_2O \longrightarrow H_2SeO_4 + 2H^+$	$\dfrac{(H_2SeO_4)^{\frac{1}{2}}(H^+)}{(H_2SeO_3)^{\frac{1}{2}} H_2O^{\frac{1}{2}}}$	$10^{-20.4}$

HALF-REACTION	EQUILIBRIUM EXPRESSION	VALUE OF CONSTANT
88. $2H_2O \longrightarrow O_2 + 4H^+$	$\dfrac{(O_2)^{\frac{1}{4}}(H^+)}{H_2O^{\frac{1}{2}}}$	$10^{-20.8}$
89. $Cr^{+++} + 4H_2O \longrightarrow HCrO_4^- + 7H^+$	$\dfrac{(HCrO_4^-)^{\frac{1}{3}}(H^+)^{\frac{7}{3}}}{(Cr^{+++})^{\frac{1}{3}} H_2O^{\frac{4}{3}}}$	$10^{-22.0}$
90. $2Cr^{+++} + 7H_2O \longrightarrow Cr_2O_7^{--} + 14H^+$	$\dfrac{(Cr_2O_7^{--})^{\frac{1}{6}}(H^+)^{\frac{14}{6}}}{(Cr^{+++})^{\frac{1}{3}} H_2O^{\frac{7}{6}}}$	$10^{-22.0}$
91. $Br^- + H_2O \longrightarrow HBrO + H^+$	$\dfrac{(HBrO)^{\frac{1}{2}}(H^+)^{\frac{1}{2}}}{(Br^-)^{\frac{1}{2}} H_2O^{\frac{1}{2}}}$	$10^{-22.6}$
92. $Mn^{++} + 2H_2O \longrightarrow MnO_2 + 4H^+$	$\dfrac{MnO_2^{\frac{1}{2}}(H^+)^2}{(Mn^{++})^{\frac{1}{2}} H_2O}$	$10^{-22.6}$
93. $Cl^- + 4H_2O \longrightarrow ClO_4^- + 8H^+$	$\dfrac{(ClO_4^-)^{\frac{1}{8}}(H^+)}{(Cl^-)^{\frac{1}{8}} H_2O^{\frac{1}{2}}}$	$10^{-22.9}$
94. $2Cl^- \longrightarrow Cl_2$	$\dfrac{(Cl_2)^{\frac{1}{2}}}{(Cl^-)}$	$10^{-23.0}$
95. $2Au + 3H_2O \longrightarrow Au_2O_3 + 6H^+$	$\dfrac{Au_2O_3^{\frac{1}{6}}(H^+)}{Au^{\frac{1}{3}} H_2O^{\frac{1}{2}}}$	$10^{-23.1}$
96. $I^- + 4H_2O \longrightarrow IO_4^- + 8H^+$	$\dfrac{(IO_4^-)^{\frac{1}{8}}(H^+)}{(I^-)^{\frac{1}{8}} H_2O^{\frac{1}{2}}}$	$10^{-23.7}$
97. $Br^- + 3H_2O \longrightarrow BrO_3^- + 6H^+$	$\dfrac{(BrO_3^-)^{\frac{1}{6}}(H^+)}{(Br^-)^{\frac{1}{6}} H_2O^{\frac{1}{2}}}$	$10^{-24.1}$
98. $Cl^- + 3H_2O \longrightarrow ClO_3^- + 6H^+$	$\dfrac{(ClO_3^-)^{\frac{1}{6}}(H^+)}{(Cl^-)^{\frac{1}{6}} H_2O^{\frac{1}{2}}}$	$10^{-24.6}$
99. $Cl^- + H_2O \longrightarrow HClO + H^+$	$\dfrac{(HClO)^{\frac{1}{2}}(H^+)^{\frac{1}{2}}}{(Cl^-)^{\frac{1}{2}} H_2O^{\frac{1}{2}}}$	$10^{-25.4}$
100. $Mn^{++} \longrightarrow Mn^{+++}$	$\dfrac{(Mn^{+++})}{(Mn^{++})}$	$10^{-25.4}$
101. $Au \longrightarrow Au^+$	$\dfrac{(Au^+)}{Au}$	$10^{-25.4}$
102. $2SO_4^{--} + 2H^+ \longrightarrow H_2S_2O_8$	$\dfrac{(H_2S_2O_8)^{\frac{1}{2}}}{(SO_4^{--})(H^+)}$	$10^{-25.4}$

HALF-REACTION	EQUILIBRIUM EXPRESSION	VALUE OF CONSTANT
103. $Mn^{++} + 4H_2O \longrightarrow MnO_4^- + 8H^+$	$\dfrac{(MnO_4^-)^{\frac{1}{5}}(H^+)^{\frac{8}{5}}}{(Mn^{++})^{\frac{1}{5}} H_2O^{\frac{4}{5}}}$	$10^{-25.8}$
104. $MnO_2 + 2H_2O \longrightarrow MnO_4^- + 4H^+$	$\dfrac{(MnO_4^-)^{\frac{1}{3}}(H^+)^{\frac{4}{3}}}{MnO_2^{\frac{1}{3}} H_2O^{\frac{2}{3}}}$	$10^{-27.6}$
105. $Fe^{+++} + 4H_2O \longrightarrow FeO_4^{--} + 8H^+$	$\dfrac{(FeO_4^{--})^{\frac{1}{3}}(H^+)^{\frac{8}{3}}}{(Fe^{+++})^{\frac{1}{3}} H_2O^{\frac{4}{3}}}$	$10^{-28.8}$
106. $Bi^{+++} + 6H_2O \longrightarrow HBiO_3 + 5H^+$	$\dfrac{HBiO_3^{\frac{1}{2}}(H^+)^{\frac{5}{2}}}{(Bi^{+++})^{\frac{1}{2}} H_2O^3}$	$10^{-28.8}$
107. $2H_2O \longrightarrow H_2O_2 + 2H^+$	$\dfrac{(H_2O_2)^{\frac{1}{2}}(H^+)}{H_2O}$	$10^{-30.2}$
108. $Co^{++} \longrightarrow Co^{+++}$	$\dfrac{(Co^{+++})}{(Co^{++})}$	$10^{-30.5}$
109. $Ni^{++} + 4H_2O \longrightarrow NiO_2 \cdot 2H_2O + 4H^+$	$\dfrac{NiO_2 \cdot 2H_2O^{\frac{1}{2}}(H^+)^2}{(Ni^{++})^{\frac{1}{2}} H_2O^2}$	$10^{-30.5}$
110. $O_2 + H_2O \longrightarrow O_3 + 2H^+$	$\dfrac{(O_3)^{\frac{1}{2}}(H^+)}{(O_2)^{\frac{1}{2}} H_2O^{\frac{1}{2}}}$	$10^{-32.2}$
111. $2F^- \longrightarrow F_2$	$\dfrac{(F_2)^{\frac{1}{2}}}{(F^-)}$	$10^{-47.5}$

EXAMPLES TO ILLUSTRATE USE OF TABLE 20

Example 1.

Is it possible for hydrochloric acid to dissolve copper to form hydrogen gas and cupric ion? We know from experience that it is not. While a qualitative examination of the relative positions of the couples in the table will give us this information, we may confirm this fact and observation by a calculation which uses the values given in the table for the equilibrium involved. The equation for this reaction is

$$Cu + 2H^+ = Cu^{++} + H_2 \qquad (1)$$

The corresponding equilibrium expression is

$$\frac{(Cu^{++})(H_2)}{Cu(H^+)^2} = K_{eq} \qquad (2)$$

From the table we find that $\dfrac{(Cu^{++})^{\frac{1}{2}}}{Cu^{\frac{1}{2}}}$ has a value of $10^{-5.8}$ and $\dfrac{(H_2)^{\frac{1}{2}}}{(H^+)}$ the value of 10^0 or 1. Combining these two half-reaction expressions, we obtain

$$\frac{(Cu^{++})^{\frac{1}{2}}}{Cu^{\frac{1}{2}}} \times \frac{(H_2)^{\frac{1}{2}}}{(H^+)} = 10^{-5.8} \times 10^0 = 10^{-5.8} \tag{3}$$

Squaring both sides of equation (44) we obtain equation (45) with a numerical value for the constant of $10^{-11.6}$. Then omitting Cu, since it is in the solid phase, we obtain

$$\frac{(Cu^{++})(H_2)}{(H^+)^2} = K_{eq} = 10^{-11.6} \tag{4}$$

The small value of this constant indicates that this reaction will not proceed from left to right to any appreciable extent. If the value of any equilibrium constant were 1, then the reaction would proceed about halfway toward completion before equilibrium would be reached. At this point the concentrations of the products would be of the same order of magnitude as the concentrations of the reactants. If the constant were greater than 1, the concentrations of the products must exceed those of the reactants at equilibrium and therefore the reaction would proceed to a greater extent to the right. When the value of the constant is less than 1, the concentrations of the reactants exceed those of the products at equilibrium. Any reaction proceeds to a lesser extent from left to right, the smaller the value of the constant. The small value of the constant ($10^{-11.6}$) for the equilibrium considered in *Example 1* indicates that the reaction proceeds to the right only to an inappreciable extent. We may then conclude that the reaction has a pronounced tendency to proceed from right to left. In other words, it should be possible to precipitate copper from solutions of its salts by merely passing hydrogen gas into the solution. However, this reaction does not take place at ordinary temperatures because its speed is too slow. It should be possible to affect this change by means of a catalyst. This is not feasible with a contact catalyst since its surface would immediately become covered with metallic copper, rendering it inactive. But by increasing the temperature to 150° C the velocity of the reaction is increased sufficiently to bring about the reduction of cupric ion to free copper by hydrogen.

Example 2.

Let us determine whether it is possible for metallic copper to dissolve in nitric acid solution to form cupric ion and nitric oxide. The equation for the reaction is

$$3Cu + 2NO_3^- + 8H^+ = 3Cu^{++} + 2NO + 4H_2O \qquad (5)$$

Consequently,

$$\frac{(Cu^{++})^3(NO)^2 H_2O^4}{Cu^3(NO_3^-)^2(H^+)^8} = \frac{(Cu^{++})^3(NO)^2}{(NO_3^-)^2(H^+)^8} = K_{eq} \qquad (6)$$

In equation (6) the equilibrium expression is written in two forms. In the first, solid Cu and H_2O are included but it is to be understood that they have no significance and are to be disregarded in that the concentration of H_2O does not change appreciably. They may be regarded as always being equal to 1 if they are not eliminated from the expression finally obtained.

The value for the half-reaction $\dfrac{(Cu^{++})^{\frac{1}{2}}}{Cu^{\frac{1}{2}}}$ is $10^{-5.8}$, for one electron change (see #52 of Table 20). For a change of two electrons the value is $10^{-11.6}$, which when raised to the third power becomes $10^{-34.8}$ or approximately 10^{-35}. The value for the half-reaction constant for $\dfrac{(NO)^2 H_2O^4}{(NO_3^-)^2(H^+)^8}$ is that for $\dfrac{(NO)^{\frac{1}{3}} H_2O^{\frac{2}{3}}}{(NO_3^-)^{\frac{1}{3}}(H^+)^{\frac{4}{3}}}$ (the inverse of #79 of the table) raised to the sixth power,

$$\frac{(NO)^2 H_2O^4}{(NO_3^-)^2(H^+)^8} = (10^{16})^6 = 10^{96}$$

Therefore

$$\frac{(Cu^{++})^3}{Cu^3} \times \frac{(NO)^2 H_2O^4}{(NO_3^-)^2(H^+)^8} = \frac{(Cu^{++})^3(NO)^2}{(NO_3^-)^2(H^+)^8} = 10^{-35} \times 10^{96} = 10^{61} \qquad (7)$$

With such a high positive value as 10^{61} it is evident that the reaction will take place. Experiment verifies this conclusion.

Example 3.

Is it possible for nitric acid to react with metallic zinc with the formation of zinc and ammonium ions? The balanced and completed equation for the reaction is

$$4Zn + NO_3^- + 10H^+ = 4Zn^{++} + NH_4^+ + 3H_2O \qquad (8)$$

The equilibrium expression is

$$\frac{(Zn^{++})^4}{Zn^4} \times \frac{(NH_4^+)H_2O^3}{(NO_3^-)(H^+)^{10}} = \frac{(Zn^{++})^4(NH_4^+)}{(NO_3^-)(H^+)^{10}} = K_{eq} \qquad (9)$$

The value for $\dfrac{(Zn^{++})^4}{Zn^4}$ for a two electron change taken to the fourth power is $(10^{12.8})^8$ or 10^{102} (see #12 of Table 20), while the value for the half-reaction, $\dfrac{(NH_4^+)H_2O^3}{(NO_3^-)(H^+)^{10}}$ is $(10^{15.3})^8$ which is equal to 10^{122} (#76 of Table 20). Therefore the value for the equilibrium constant of equation (8) is $10^{102} \times 10^{122} = 10^{224}$. This value is so much greater than unity that the reaction readily proceeds and the equilibrium position is practically completely to the right. This does not mean that the ammonium ion is the only possible product. Calculation would show that other compounds with different valence states of nitrogen, such as NO and NO_2 can be formed by the action of nitric acid on zinc. Which of the nitrogen compounds are formed to the largest extent will depend upon the relative speeds of the different reactions involved.

Making the same calculation but using copper instead of zinc we find that the reaction which produces cupric and ammonium ions is likewise possible but the tendency for the reaction to proceed is not as great. The fact that ammonium ion is not found to a large extent when copper reacts with nitric acid must be attributed to the slow speed of this reaction as compared with the speed of those reactions which produce nitric oxide and nitrogen dioxide.

Example 4.

Table **20** may also be used in conjunction with the solubility product constants and with the ionization constants of weak acids and weak bases. *Examples 4 and 5* are designed to illustrate the use of this application.

Is it possible for nitric acid to dissolve an appreciable amount of cupric sulfide with the formation of nitric oxide, cupric ion and free sulfur? The equation for the reaction is

$$3CuS + 2NO_3^- + 8H^+ = 3S + 3Cu^{++} + 2NO + 4H_2O \quad (10)$$

Therefore

$$\frac{(Cu^{++})^3(NO)^2 H_2O^4 S^3}{CuS^3(NO_3^-)^2(H^+)^8} = K_{eq} \quad (11)$$

Since solid CuS is involved we must use the solubility product expression for CuS which is $(Cu^{++})(S^{--})$ or $\dfrac{(Cu^{++})(S^{--})}{CuS}$. This demands that a $(S^{--})^3$ appear in the numerator. Likewise, it is necessary to use the half-reaction expression $\dfrac{S}{(S^{--})}$ which in turn demands a $(S^{--})^3$ in the denominator. To satisfy both these conditions multiply both numerator and denominator by $(S^{--})^3$.

$$\frac{(Cu^{++})^3(S^{--})^3}{CuS^3} \times \frac{S^3}{(S^{--})^3} \times \frac{(NO)^2H_2O^4}{(NO_3^-)^2(H^+)^8} = K_{eq} \qquad (12)$$

Equation (10) involves a six electron change and the expressions (11) and (12) are likewise for a six electron change. Therefore all half-reaction constants must be raised to the sixth power. The solubility product constant for CuS is $10^{-37.5}$ (see table of solubility product constants in the Appendix).

$$\frac{(Cu^{++})^3(S^{--})^3}{CuS^3} = (10^{-37.5})^3 = 10^{-113}$$

$$\frac{S^3}{(S^{--})^3} = (10^{8.6})^6 = 10^{52} \ (\#15 \text{ of Table } 20)$$

$$\frac{(NO)^2H_2O^4}{(NO_3^-)^2(H^+)^8} = (10^{16})^6 = 10^{96} \ (\#79 \text{ of Table } 20)$$

$$\frac{(Cu^{++})^3(S^{--})^3}{CuS^3} \cdot \frac{S^3}{(S^{--})^3} \cdot \frac{(NO)^2H_2O^4}{(NO_3^-)^2(H^+)^8} = 10^{-113} \times 10^{52} \times 10^{96} = 10^{35} \quad (13)$$

Omitting all solid phases and H_2O, we have

$$\frac{(NO)^2(Cu^{++})^3}{(NO_3^-)^2(H^+)^8} = 10^{35}$$

Consequently this reaction can proceed in accordance with equation (10). Experience in the laboratory verifies this conclusion.

Carrying out a similar calculation using mercuric sulfide instead of cupric sulfide we find that this substance has a relatively small tendency to be dissolved by nitric acid.

Example 5.

Is it possible for a solution containing 0.1 mole of acetic acid and 0.1 mole of sodium nitrate per liter to dissolve cadmium sulfide appreciably? The equation for the reaction is

$$3CdS + 2NO_3^- + 8HAc = 3Cd^{++} + 3S + 2NO + 8Ac^- + 4H_2O \quad (14)$$

and the corresponding equilibrium expression,

$$\frac{(Cd^{++})^3(NO)^2(Ac^-)^8 H_2O^4 S^3}{CdS^3(NO_3^-)^2(HAc)^8} = K_{eq} \qquad (15)$$

Multiplying the numerator and the denominator of this expression by $(S^{--})^3 \times (H^+)^8$, we obtain

$$\frac{(Cd^{++})^3(S^{--})^3}{CdS^3} \cdot \frac{S^3}{(S^{--})^3} \cdot \frac{(NO)^2 H_2 O^4}{(NO_3^-)^2(H^+)^8} \cdot \frac{(H^+)^8(Ac^-)^8}{(HAc)^8} = K_{eq} \quad (16)$$

$$\frac{(Cd^{++})^3(S^{--})^3}{CdS^3} = (10^{-28})^3 = 10^{-84} \text{ (from solubility product}$$
$$\text{constant)}$$

$$\frac{(NO)^2 H_2 O^4}{(NO_3^-)^2(H^+)^8} = (10^{16})^6 = 10^{96} \text{ (\#79 of Table 20)}$$

$$\frac{S^3}{(S^{--})^3} = (10^{8.6})^6 = 10^{52} \text{ (\#15 of Table 20)}$$

$$\frac{(H^+)^8(Ac^-)^8}{(HAc)^8} = (10^{-4.7})^8 = 10^{-37} \text{ (from the ionization con-}$$
$$\text{stant for acetic acid)}$$

The value of the above expression then becomes

$$10^{-84} \times 10^{96} \times 10^{52} \times 10^{-37} \text{ or } 10^{27}$$

Therefore $\dfrac{(Cd^{++})^3(NO)^2(Ac^-)^8}{(NO_3^-)^2(HAc)^8} = 10^{27}$. If the (NO_3^-) and (HAc) were each 0.1 mole (i.e., 10^{-1} mole) per liter, the denominator becomes 10^{-10} and the numerator then has a value of 10^{17}. If the (Ac^-) should reach a value of 0.1 mole per liter as a maximum and the (NO) a pressure of one atmosphere (since it is a gas), $(Cd^{++})^3$ would be $10^{17}/10^{-8}$ or 10^{25} at equilibrium. Therefore cadmium sulfide would readily dissolve in this solution to form free sulfur and cadmium ion provided, of course, that the rate of the reaction is sufficiently great. The values given above merely show that such a reaction is possible and that there is a pronounced tendency for it to take place, but they give no information concerning the speed of the reaction.

Carrying out a similar calculation using cupric sulfide instead of cadmium sulfide, we find that the above solution will not dissolve the cupric sulfide appreciably.

Restrictions in the Interpretation of Results of Calculations. The calculations made from the foregoing table only show what the equilibrium will be when it is attained, but they do not indicate in any way that the equilibrium will be attained in a reasonable period of time. The time necessary to reach equilibrium will depend upon the speed of the reaction. The velocity of a reaction is a factor which is independent of the equilibrium. If, however, calculation shows that a reaction cannot take place because of equilibrium restrictions, then the velocity of the reaction does not become a consideration, for no reaction can proceed beyond its equilibrium value. In other words, calculations from Table 20 show definitely when a reaction *does not take place* to any appreciable extent and show which reactions *will take place* only if the velocity is great enough.

Often several different products can be formed from the same reactants. For example, zinc reacting with nitric acid produces NO, NO_2 or NH_4^+ ion. The relative amounts of these substances formed will depend upon the relative velocities of the respective reactions involved.

Do Reactions Take Place Completely? If a reaction takes place completely its equilibrium constant must be equal to infinity. Strictly speaking, no reaction goes to completion but many reactions have such large values for their equilibrium constants that for all practical purposes we may regard them as complete. For example, the reaction

$$5H_2S + 2MnO_4^- + 6H^+ = 2Mn^{++} + 5S + 8H_2O \qquad (20)$$

has an equilibrium constant equal to 10^{234}. Such a large value of this constant is practically equivalent to complete reaction. Likewise, the equilibrium constant for the reaction

$$3H_2S + Cr_2O_7^{--} + 8H^+ = 2Cr^{+++} + 3S + 7H_2O \qquad (21)$$

is 10^{118}. It is not entirely meaningless to use such large numerical values. These two values show that MnO_4^- ion, in the presence of H^+ ion, is a better oxidizing agent than is $Cr_2O_7^{--}$ ion in the same medium, and that it is even possible for MnO_4^- ion with H^+ ion to oxidize Cr^{+++} ion to $Cr_2O_7^{--}$ ion.

PROBLEMS AND EXERCISES

1. Calculate the equilibrium constant for each of the following oxidation-reduction reactions. In each case determine whether it is possible for the reaction to proceed from left to right to any appreciable extent.

	Equation for Reaction	Ref. Nos. in Table 20*
(a)	$2Fe^{+++} + H_2SO_3 + H_2O = SO_4^{--} + 2Fe^{++} + 4H^+$	43, 68
(b)	$2H_2S + H_2SO_3 = 3S + 3H_2O$	45, 56
(c)	$3Cl^- + 2NO_3^- + 5H^+ = 3HClO + 2NO + H_2O$	79, 99
(d)	$3MnO_4^{--} + 2H_2O = MnO_2 + 2MnO_4^- + 4OH^-$	65, 67
(e)	$6Ag + ClO_3^- + 5Cl^- + 6H^+ = 6AgCl + 3H_2O$	71, 98
(f)	$2Cr^{+++} + 6Co^{+++} + 7H_2O = Cr_2O_7^{--} + 6Co^{++} + 14H^+$	90, 108
(g)	$3ZnS + 2NO_3^- + 8H^+ = 3Zn^{++} + 3S + 2NO + 4H_2O$	15, 79
(h)	$4ZnS + NO_3^- + 10H^+ = 4Zn^{++} + 4S + NH_4^+ + 3H_2O$	15, 76
(i)	$CdS + SO_4^{--} + 4H^+ = Cd^{++} + S + H_2SO_3 + H_2O$	15, 43
(j)	$Br^- + MnO_2 + 3H^+ = HBrO + Mn^{++} + H_2O$	91, 92
(k)	$CuS + SO_4^{--} + 4H^+ = Cu^{++} + S + H_2SO_3 + H_2O$	15, 43
(l)	$Cu + 2HNO_2 + 2H^+ = Cu^{++} + 2NO + 2H_2O$	52, 81
(m)	$PbS + 4H_2O_2 = PbSO_4 + 4H_2O$	15, 43, 56, 107

2. Is it possible for metallic tin to be dissolved appreciably by nitric acid to produce Sn^{++} ion and NH_4^+ ion?

3. Is it possible for mercuric sulfide to be dissolved appreciably by nitric acid with the production of Hg^{++} ion, NO and free sulfur?

4. A solution is 0.1 molar with respect to each of $Cr_2O_7^{--}$, H^+ and Cl^- ions. Can a reaction proceed to an appreciable extent in this solution to form free chlorine and Cr^{+++} ion?

5. Can silver sulfide be dissolved to any appreciable extent by concentrated nitric acid with the formation of Ag^+ ion, free sulfur and nitric oxide?

6. Can cupric sulfide be dissolved to any appreciable extent by a solution containing hydrogen peroxide and hydrochloric acid to form Cu^{++} ion, free sulfur and water?

7. From the half-reactions 78 and 99 in Table 20, calculate the dissociation constant for HClO.

8. From the half-reactions 15 and 45, and Kw calculate the value of the constant for the reaction $S^{--} + 2H_2O = S + 2OH^- + H_2$.

*In addition to the half-reaction constants, the solubility product constants for slightly soluble substances are also required for several of these calculations.

9. From half-reaction 45 and the first and second dissociation constants for H_2S, determine the value of the constant for half-reaction 15, and compare your answer with that given in the table. (There is not complete agreement, and one or more of these values should be changed).

10. From the half-reaction 56, the first and second dissociation constants for sulfurous acid and K_w determine the value for the half-reaction $S + 6OH^- \longrightarrow SO_3^{--} + 3H_2O$, i.e. for the expression

$$\frac{(SO_3^{--})^{\frac{1}{4}} (H_2O)^{\frac{3}{4}}}{(S)^{\frac{1}{4}} (OH^-)^{\frac{3}{2}}}$$

11. Using the result in 10, together with half-reaction 15 and the solubility products for $Fe(OH)_3$, $Fe(OH)_2$ and FeS, determine whether the following reaction can proceed from left to right:

$$7Fe(OH)_2 + SO_3^{--} + 3H_2O = FeS + 6Fe(OH)_3 + 2OH^-$$

PART II

PART II

CHAPTER XII

Laboratory Techniques

Before undertaking any work in the laboratory it will be necessary for the student to construct a few simple pieces of apparatus and to become acquainted with laboratory manipulations. This section deals with this introductory work. As his work in the course develops, the student will find it profitable to refer to this section for information when new problems of technique arise.

APPARATUS TO BE CONSTRUCTED AND ASSEMBLED

Wash-Bottle. Figure 24 shows a sketch of a wash-bottle. Obtain a 250 ml. flask of the type shown in the sketch and fit it with a two-hole rubber stopper. The pieces to be inserted into the stopper are constructed in the following way. The nozzle is made by drawing out a piece of 6 mm. glass tubing after it has been heated in the flame of a Bunsen burner to the softening point. After it has cooled scratch it with a file to allow the tube to be broken at the proper place. To bend a glass tube rotate it in a horizontal position in the flame of a burner equipped with a wing-top. Continue the heating with rotation of the tube until the glass is soft enough to bend without kinking. This procedure necessitates the heating of at least a two-inch portion of the glass tubing. Heat very slowly to allow a uniform distribution of the heat. The angles of bending of the two pieces should be such that the upper end of the exit tube, which connects with the nozzle, is parallel with the upper end of the delivery tube. The ends of all tubes should be heated just to the softening point (fire-polishing) to remove all sharp edges. After they have cooled they should be lubricated with water, saliva, or preferably alcohol, and then inserted in the rubber stopper. **Be careful!** Hold the tube in a towel to protect the hand in case the glass tube

should break. Grasp the tube near the end that is to be inserted into the stopper. Push the tube through the hole
until it protrudes about two inches. Then grasp the pro-

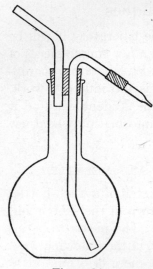

truding end of the tube and **pull**
it into position. The moistened
surface of glass allows this operation to be carried out with greater
ease and safety. Finally assemble
the apparatus and introduce about
100 ml. of water. Test the wash-
bottle for leaks by blowing into the
inlet tube, observing whether the
column of water maintains its position in the outlet tube when the
finger is placed over the end of the
mouthpiece. When full pressure is
applied the nozzle should deliver a
fine, even, unscattered stream of
water.

Figure 24.

Stirring Rods. It is convenient
to have at hand several glass stirring rods, each 4–6 mm.
in diameter and approximately 15 cm. in length. Obtain
glass rods from the storeroom and cut them to the proper
length. Fire-polish each end of rod in the flame.

Capillary Syringes. Two types of medicine droppers are
needed in the course; one for adding reagent solutions on a
small scale and a second type for washing small quantities of
precipitates (see Figure 25 on facing page). The first type is
the standard medicine dropper of approximately 1 ml. capacity (1 ml. capacity refers to that of the glass tube only) and
which delivers about twenty drops per ml. For the second
type ("capillary syringe") it is necessary to draw out the tip
of the ordinary dropper to a very small nozzle in a flame so as
to obtain a fine stream of water when the bulb is subjected
to pressure. To draw out the tip of the capillary, remove
the rubber bulb and weld the end of the medicine dropper
to a small piece of glass tubing or glass rod in the Bunsen

flame. This extra piece of tubing or rod acts as a handle in making the syringe. To pull out the end of the dropper, rotate it with both hands well above the luminous flame of the Bunsen burner. Allow it to just reach the softening point and then pull it out. Break the capillary at a point such that the orifice formed is very small. If it is too small the end may be broken off to obtain the desired opening. The tip should be so small that at least 15 seconds are required to fill the syringe. Each student should have 6 medicine droppers, two of which should be converted into syringes.

Apparatus for Saturation with H₂S. This apparatus is depicted in Figure 26. The wash-bottle B may be a permanent piece of apparatus which remains connected to the H₂S generator. In such a case the student need not construct it. If it is to be constructed use a bottle of about 200–300 ml. capacity. The flask D is a 25 ml. Erlenmeyer flask. The instructions for bending the glass tubing are given in the description of the assembly of the wash-bottle.

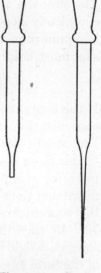

Figure 25. Dropper and Capillary Syringe

To saturate a solution contained in a test tube use the tube illustrated in Figure 27. The rubber stopper should fit a 10 ml. test tube and is meant to slide along the tube to the proper distance from the end. The stopper is provided to cap the test tube after the air has been displaced thus preventing excessive escape of the H₂S. This apparatus should be connected to the wash-bottle at C (Figure 26).

GENERAL MANIPULATIVE PROCEDURES

Precipitation. Whenever a reagent is added to a solution to bring about the precipitation of a desired compound conditions most favorable for its complete precipitation and subsequent separation should be employed. In the first place an excess of the reagent must be used to insure completeness of precipitation. Although in no instance may any given ion be completely removed from solution, nevertheless its concentration in the solution after precipitation may be reduced to a negligible value. For example, suppose we have a solution containing .01 mole of Ag^+ ion per liter and a solution of NaCl is added to it to precipitate AgCl. The problem is to remove the silver from the solution as completely as possible. When solid silver chloride is present in equilibrium with its ions in solution the following expression must hold.

$$(Ag^+)(Cl^-) = K_{S.P.} = 1.56 \times 10^{-10}$$

If the concentration of the Cl^- ion is made .01 M, then the concentration of the Ag^+ ion left in solution will be only 1.56×10^{-8} M, which value is so small as to be negligible. Under these conditions the precipitation is regarded as complete for the purpose of separation of Ag^+ ion from the remaining ions in the solution. On the other hand, if the concentration of the Cl^- ion in the solution were only 10^{-7} M, then the concentration of the Ag^+ ion remaining in solution would be 1.56×10^{-3} M, which value is about 16% of the total amount of Ag^+ ion originally present. Under the latter conditions the precipitation is far from complete. It is apparent from the equilibrium expression given above that as the concentration of the Cl^- ion in the solution is increased, the concentration of the Ag^+ ion is decreased by a corresponding amount. A reasonable amount of Cl^- ion must be maintained in the solution to remove from it all but a negligible quantity of Ag^+ ion. On the other hand a very large excess of Cl^- ion will bring about the formation of the complex, $AgCl_2^-$ ion, and thereby increase the solubility of AgCl. Many ions form complexes of this type. In most cases an estimation can be made as to what is an adequate but not an excessive amount of reagent to be added. For example, if a 0.1 M solution of any particular ion is ample, it is obviously undesirable to increase the concentration to 1 M. All precipitations should be carried out with this point in mind. The directions given in the procedures which follow in this text are based upon a consideration of the optimum conditions for precipitation and should be adhered to closely. Nevertheless, the student should check the completeness of precipitation by adding a drop of the reagent to the filtrate collected in the separation of the precipitate. If the filtrate shows precipitation is incomplete, more of the reagent should be added, the solution again filtered or centrifuged and the second filtrate tested with the reagent. This procedure should be continued until the filtrate fails to give a precipitate.

There are other factors to be considered in precipitation procedures. Precipitation should be carried out in such a manner as to favor the formation of large crystals, the coagulation of colloids, and the reduction of the adsorption of other ions. These conditions are favored by heating the solution and adding the reagent slowly with constant stirring. In certain cases, the hydrogen ion concentration must be adjusted so as to favor these conditions. In other cases, salts are added to the solution to prevent the formation of colloids. For this purpose the addition of solutions of ammonium salts or the addition of the solid salts themselves may be used conveniently.

Saturation of a Solution with a Gas. Precipitation with Hydrogen Sulfide. In the precipitation of insoluble sulfides by hydrogen sulfide either in acidic or basic solutions the apparatus shown in Figure 26 should be used. Hydrogen sulfide gas from a generator or from a gasometer (storage tank, if cylinders of liquid hydrogen sulfide are used) enters the apparatus at the point indicated in the sketch. A stopcock A controls the flow of the gas into the wash-bottle B which contains water. Wash-bottle B may be a permanent piece of apparatus which remains connected to the supply of hydrogen sulfide at all times. It serves to remove any hydrochloric acid that might be carried over from the generator in the gas stream. It is in turn connected by means of soft rubber tubing C (longer than shown in figure) to the flask D (25 ml. capacity) which contains the unknown solution to be saturated with hydrogen sulfide. The inlet tube to D projects below the rubber stopper to a point which is about 2 cm. above the liquid to be saturated. After the solution has been placed in D the inlet tube is attached to C. Be sure that the inlet tube is clean.

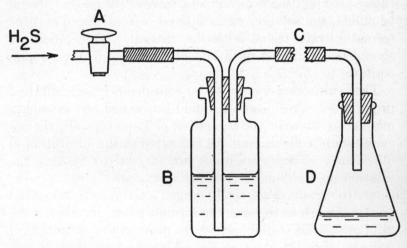

Figure 26.   Apparatus for Saturating a Solution with Hydrogen Sulfide

Insert the inlet tube into the Erlenmeyer flask but do not stopper it tightly. Partly open the stop-cock A and allow the H_2S to sweep out the air in D. This will require only a few seconds. With the gas flowing, stopper the flask D with the stopper of the inlet tube and shake or rotate D. Loosen the stopper in D to again sweep out the gas and stopper tightly. Again rotate or shake the flask.

As shaking continues, the solution in D absorbs the hydrogen sulfide, thereby causing the precipitation. Shaking should be continued until the bubbling of the gas through the water in B is almost completely retarded. At this point the solution in D should be saturated with hydrogen sulfide and the precipitation of the sulfides should be complete. Only 2 to 3 minutes is required for saturation of the unknown solution, provided the flask D contains the normal amount of solution, 3 ml. To insure complete precipitation this procedure should be repeated with the filtrate until hydrogen sulfide fails to produce a precipitate.

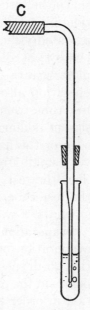

Figure 27.
Saturation Tube

If the solution to be saturated is contained in a 10 ml. test tube use the tube illustrated in Figure 27. This procedure should only be used for small quantities of solution. The inlet tube should be very clean and may be inserted below the surface of the liquid. If prolonged saturation is necessary stopper the test tube with the stopper and saturate in a manner similar to that described above.

Heating of Solutions. All solutions must be heated carefully to avoid bumping and spattering. Not only will bumping cause a serious loss of the test solution but it may often be dangerous. The spattering of hot solutions may give rise to painful burns. These burns may be serious if the solution contains strong acids or hydroxides.

All solutions contained in very small test tubes should be heated in a water bath or in a small beaker of boiling water. This procedure also applies to solutions contained in 10 ml. test tubes if these test tubes are more than one-third full. With the larger amounts of solution (more than 3 ml.) it is advisable to pour it into a casserole and to heat it in this container. The solution, reduced in volume, may be returned to the test tube if desired.

Solutions contained in a 10 ml. test tube and occupying less than one-third the capacity of the tube may be heated directly by the flame of the Bunsen burner. Use a test tube holder in all cases of strong acids and always point the mouth of the test tube away from yourself or any other person nearby. To carry out this operation bring the bottom of the test tube to the edge of the flame and after allowing it to remain there for about one second, withdraw it and gently shake the test tube. Continue this procedure until the solution is heated. This operation may also be carried out by repeatedly flicking the end of the test tube into the flame, i.e., by not allowing the test tube to remain in the flame for more than a fraction of a second at a time. The flicking operation also shakes the solution. Quickly withdraw the test tube from the flame completely as soon as there is any sign of boiling and then proceed very gently using only the edge of the flame. If the 10 ml. test tube contains only a very small amount of solution (not strongly acidic or alkaline) the test tube may be held with the fingers instead of the test tube holder. Practise this operation with varying amounts of water.

Evaporation. The analytical procedures may specify evaporation of a solution to a definite volume or evaporation to dryness. In addition, it may be advisable at some points in the procedure to concentrate a solution by evaporation in order to have a smaller volume with which to deal, thereby saving time in subsequent filtrations and other manipulations. A small casserole or porcelain evaporating dish is suitable for this operation. However, the container should be as small as possible for the amount of liquid prepared. For many purposes a water bath will suffice as a source of heat. When corrosive fumes are evolved during the process of evaporation, the hood should be used unless the quantity of material is very small. If evaporation does not take place rapidly on a water bath, an open flame may be used. For this purpose the liquid is placed in a small casserole which is then rotated horizontally in the flame. This motion allows the liquid to come in contact with the hot walls of the casserole, thereby facilitating evaporation. Too hot a flame must not be used, otherwise bumping and spattering will take place.

In heating to dryness remove the casserole or evaporating dish while there is still some liquid left. The heat capacity of the dish is sufficient to complete the operation without further heating.

Testing Acidity or Alkalinity of Solutions. To test the acidity or alkalinity of a solution place a piece of litmus (or test) paper on the towel or paper on the desk, or on a watch glass, and then dip the end of a stirring rod into the solution and apply it to the paper. In this way several tests may be made with a single strip of paper. Sometimes it is possible to tear off a small fragment of the test paper and place it in the solution, but the former method is preferable.

Cleaning Glassware. All reaction vessels should be thoroughly clean before they are to be used. Small traces of contaminants in any test solution may give rise to spurious results.

All apparatus should be cleaned as soon after use as possible. Test tubes should be cleaned with a test tube brush. Use ground pumice or some cleaning powder if necessary. If these agents fail it may be advisable to use a strong concentrated acid such as HNO_3. (Do not use the test tube brush with acids.) Test tubes containing sulfur and some sulfides can be easily cleaned with a few drops of commercial ammonium sulfide or yellow ammonium sulfide. The test tubes should be rinsed with distilled water. The same procedure applies to casseroles, evaporating dishes and beakers except that the test tube brush may be omitted.

When medicine droppers or capillary syringes are used for solutions, they should be rinsed several times in a beaker containing distilled water immediately after use. They should then be placed in another beaker containing distilled water for storage. The beaker containing the wash water should be refilled with distilled water at frequent intervals.

Flame Tests. Two wires should always be used for a flame test; one for the unknown solution and the other for a solution known to contain the ion in question at a concentration of about that to be expected in the unknown.

Prepare two pieces of Chromel wire, both looped at the end and each inserted into a cork as a handle as shown in Figure 28.

Never rely upon memory to judge the characteristics of the flame. Alternately apply the two wires to the flame; one for the unknown and the other for the comparison solution.

The nitrate and sulfate salts of the unknown do not give good flame tests. In the flame these break down into the corresponding oxides which do not volatilize readily. Therefore a drop or two of 6 M HCl should be added to the solution (comparison as well as unknown) or solid, on a watch glass, and the looped end of the wire should be dipped into it. The loop should be small enough to retain a drop of the liquid within it.

Do not use the hottest portion of the flame but rather bring the looped end containing the

Figure 28. Wire for Flame Tests

solution slowly up to its edge. Some flame colors last a relatively long time; some are very ephemeral, disappearing quickly. Do not lay the wires on the table top. Use the towel or paper spread on the desk for this purpose.

PROCEDURES WHEN CENTRIFUGATION OPERATIONS ARE USED

The Centrifuge and Its Operation. There are two general types of centrifuges used for analytical purposes — the hand-driven and the motor-driven types. The hand-driven are not recommended but may be used.

The motor-driven centrifuge consists of the driving motor, a shaft, and an attached head, which is known as the rotor, in which the test tubes that are to be spun are placed. When the rotor is spinning a centrifugal force is developed which like gravity brings about the settling of the precipitate. The difference in the time required for settling and centrifugation lies in the fact that the centrifugal force is much greater than the gravitational force at the earth's surface. There is a simple formula which relates the characteristics of the centrifuge to the force of gravity.

Centrifugal force (number of times greater than gravity) =
$$\frac{\text{diameter (in feet)} \times (\text{R.P.M.})^2}{6000}$$

R.P.M. refers to revolutions per minute. Thus if the centrifuge operates at 1600 R.P.M. and the effective diameter is 6 inches ($\frac{1}{2}$ foot) the centrifugal force is equal to

$$\frac{.5 \times (1600)^2}{6000} = 210 \text{ times that of gravity.}$$

The rate of sedimentation or settling depends upon (1) the centrifugal force; (2) the size of the particle; the larger the particle the quicker it settles; (3) the difference in density between the solid and that of the solution; the greater this difference the faster the settling, and (4) the viscosity of the solution; the greater the viscosity the slower the settling. With these factors in mind it is easy to understand the following considerations.

Figure 29. The Centrifuge
(Courtesy Wilkens-Anderson Company, Chicago)

(a) The greater the density of the salt, the greater is the sedimentation rate. $BaSO_4$ is very dense, as are the sulfides; hence, they settle quickly if the particles are not too small. Sulfur has a much smaller density than a sulfide and for this reason it should be possible to separate sulfur from sulfides by controlling the speed of the rotor or the time of centrifugation.

(b) The greater the concentration of the salts in the solution, the slower is the rate of sedimentation. The addition of salts to a solution increases its density and decreases the difference in density between the precipitate and the solution; hence, the slower rate.

(c) The smaller the amount of solution in a test tube the faster the sedimentation. With a larger amount of solution more of the precipitate is nearer the center of rotation and therefore this portion of it is subjected to a smaller centrifugal force.

(d) Colloids need much longer time for spinning. Due to the small size of the particles the sedimentation is slow.

In operating the centrifuge always balance it symmetrically. See to it that approximately equal amounts of liquid are in the two opposite test tubes. An unbalanced centrifuge vibrates and may become dangerous if it is subjected to this vibration continuously. The vibration wears the bearings supporting the rotor, usually identical with those of the motor.

Do not usurp the centrifuge by spinning it an undue length of time. Two minutes time is usually ample, except for the finer and lighter precipitates.

Before beginning a centrifugation see to it that particles are not floating on the surface of the liquid or are adhering to the side of the test tube. Surface tension effects prevent surface particles from settling. Agitate the surface with a stirring rod if necessary, and wash down the side of the test tube, using the capillary syringe and a very small amount of water or appropriate solution.

Under no circumstances use test tubes with broken or cracked lips. When spinning in the centrifuge these broken ends which protrude above the surface of the rotor may cause serious injury to the operators.

Do not attempt to retard the speed of the centrifuge with the hand until the electric current has been turned off and until the rotor has lost its full speed. Under no circumstances brake the rotor with the hand if it does not have a smooth outside surface.

If the centrifuge should become unduly hot, notify the instructor. Do not abuse the mechanism in any way. It should be well cared for at all times. Above all, do not let it come in direct contact with corrosive chemical reagents.

Test tubes should not be too full of liquid since spilling may corrode and produce an unbalanced rotor.

Washing of Precipitates. Before the precipitate which has already been centrifuged is washed, it should be separated as completely as possible from the supernatant liquid. In pouring off the supernatant liquid a few drops are often held behind by the surface tension of the liquid. To remove these last drops tip the test tube upside down and drain the test tube with the aid of a piece of filter paper. Making contact between the liquid and the stirring rod often suffices to accomplish this end. It is important that these last drops be removed in as much as they may contain more dissolved salt than is held in the precipitate.

Add the required amount of distilled water or wash solution to the test tube containing the centrifuged precipitate and then with the aid of the stirring rod agitate the precipitate until it is in suspension. Then centrifuge and pour off the wash water. In almost all cases this operation should be carried out at least twice.

It sometimes happens that the removal of the ions in the solution by washing causes the precipitate to become dispersed, i.e., to form a colloid, which then cannot be easily centrifuged. In such a case add some ammonium salt which will not interfere with subsequent tests.

Transferring Precipitates. In semi-micro procedure it is usually not necessary to transfer precipitates from one test tube to another. If the precipitate is to be treated with some reagent in a casserole or evaporating dish, the reagent is first added to the precipitate in the test tube. It is brought into suspension by agitation with the stirring rod and the suspension is then poured into the open receptacle. The test tube may be washed by tipping it into an almost vertical (upside down) position and while holding the mouth of the test tube over the receptacle, the sides of the test tube may be subjected to the very fine stream of solution from a capillary syringe.

The transferring of a part or the whole of the precipitate

to another test tube is accomplished by suspending the precipitate in distilled water (or a suitable reagent) and by withdrawing the suspension with a medicine dropper, from which it is ejected into the second container.

Precipitates can sometimes be transferred with a spatula but this operation is usually quite difficult, especially when the containers are test tubes.

PROCEDURES WHEN FILTRATION OPERATIONS ARE USED

Filtration.   Filtration is one of the most time-consuming operations of the laboratory work.   This operation is greatly expedited if the volume of liquid is maintained at a reason-

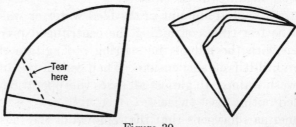

Figure 30.

able minimum and if the filtration procedures are carried out in an efficient manner.   For the purposes of this course, the procedures are so devised that at no time should the volume of liquid exceed 10 ml.

The funnel used for filtration should be about 4 cm. in diameter and should have a short stem.   The filter paper (55 mm. in diameter) should be folded in exact halves and then not quite into quarters as shown in Figure 30.   A small corner is torn off as indicated by the dotted line in the figure. This tear seals the paper against an inflow of air to the underside of the filter paper.   The folding angle here is greater than 90° and depends upon the shape of the particular funnel with which it is used.   This may readily be determined by making a few tests using different angles of fold and noting which gives the greatest rate of flow of water.   The filter prepared in this manner is then inserted into the funnel, moistened with distilled water and then pressed with the fingers against the top part of the funnel to make a tight fit. This particular technique is an important one in speeding up filtration, since it insures the support of a column of liquid in the stem of the funnel and thereby leads to a small but an appreciable suction on the filter paper.

The precipitate should be allowed to settle before filtration so that a greater portion of the supernatant liquid may be poured through the filter paper in the funnel before it becomes clogged. The precipitate is then washed in the test tube with a small quantity of distilled water which is likewise transferred to the filter paper. This procedure is repeated two or three times and then the bulk of the precipitate and the remaining liquid is introduced to the filter. For the latter operation it is essential that in the process of transfer a small stirring rod be placed across the mouth of the test tube so that the liquid will follow the rod to the funnel. A rubber "policeman" (a stirring rod with one end covered by a short piece of rubber tubing) may be used to detach the last traces of solid precipitate which adhere to the glass walls of the test tube or flask.

In many instances it is advisable to heat the tube or flask, containing the liquid and the precipitate, in a beaker of hot water before filtration is attempted. The hot liquid flows faster through the filter and heating also coagulates the precipitate with the production of larger particles, thereby facilitating filtration. It is evident that this procedure cannot be used if the precipitate is appreciably soluble at the higher temperatures.

The speed of filtration may also be increased by the application of suction. For this purpose a side-arm test tube or a side-arm 25 ml. filter flask may be conveniently used to catch the filtrate. The side-arm of the apparatus is connected through a safety-trap to the aspirator pump and the funnel is inserted through a rubber stopper which fits tightly in the mouth of the flask as shown in Figure 31 on this page. For this operation it is necessary to use a hardened filter paper or a retaining cone in the funnel to prevent rupture of the paper when suction is applied.

Washing of Precipitate on Filter Paper. To wash a precipitate on a filter paper use the fine capillary syringe and with it spray the distilled water or washing solution around the outer edge of the paper thus washing the precipitate down into the apex of the cone. If the capillary syringe

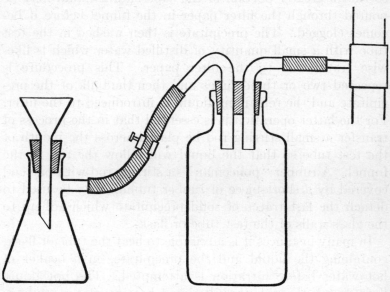

Figure 31.

delivers a fine stream of water, the precipitate is loosened from the paper and is suspended in the wash water. Allow the filter to drain thoroughly before adding more wash water or solution, and with each successive washing bring the precipitate more toward the apex of the cone.

Removing and Transferring the Precipitate from the Filter Paper. Several different procedures may be used to remove the precipitate from the filter paper. The selection of one of these methods depends upon the intended use of the precipitate and its subsequent treatment. A common procedure is that of punching a small hole through the apex of the filter paper with a small pointed glass rod and then washing the precipitate into the receiving vessel with a fine stream of water from the wash-bottle or capillary syringe. Another method is that of removing the filter paper and its contents from the funnel, unfolding the paper over a small evaporating dish or casserole and then washing the precipitate with water into the receiving dish while holding the paper in an inclined position. If the precipitate is sufficiently dry and present in an appreciable quantity, the bulk of it may be scraped with a spatula from the unfolded paper into the desired container. In this case the small amount retained by the paper may be removed by washing as previously described. Still another method for removing the precipitate is that of soaking the unfolded filter paper and its contents in a dish containing water. This latter method is applicable to precipitates which are held to the filter paper loosely and which are not too dry.

If the amount of precipitate is very small, it is advisable to place the entire filter paper and its contents in a dish containing water or solution to dissolve it. The filter paper may then be removed by filtration.

REAGENTS

Each student is provided with 12 small reagent bottles most of which are similar to the medicine bottles used by pharmacists; shown in Figure 32. These may be kept in a tray provided for this purpose or they may be stored each as a separate unit, and when used they are to be placed in a definite order in a row at the back of the laboratory desk. These bottles are for the following common reagents.

6 M Acetic Acid	18 M Sulfuric Acid
12 M Hydrochloric Acid	6 M Sulfuric Acid
6 M Hydrochloric Acid	15 M Ammonium Hydroxide
3 M Hydrochloric Acid	6 M Ammonium Hydroxide
15 M Nitric Acid	3 M Ammonium Hydroxide
6 M Nitric Acid	6 M Sodium Hydroxide

The stoppers for these bottles are usually made of a hard rubber or plastic composition, and this as well as the rubber cap of the dropper is attacked rapidly by concentrated HNO_3 and more slowly by concentrated H_2SO_4 and HCl. Therefore the bottle containing the 15 M HNO_3 must be glass stoppered. It is also desirable to use glass stoppered bottles for the 18 M H_2SO_4, the 12 M HCl, and the 15 M NH_4OH. However these latter reagents may be kept in the composition or rubber capped bottles provided the cap and the

Figure 32. Student
Reagent Bottle

Figure 33. Large
Reagent Bottle

rubber bulb of the medicine dropper are renewed periodically (every semester). These bottles are to be refilled from the larger supply bottles (500 ml.) kept on the general reagent shelf.

The other reagents which are used less frequently are kept in 250 ml. bottles on the reagent shelf. These bottles (Figure 33) are also provided with droppers. In using these be very careful that the tips of the droppers do not come in contact with the test solutions, thus contaminating the reagents. *Never dip the end of the droppers into any foreign solution.*

THE NOTEBOOK

The keeping of a good notebook for scientific work is an accomplishment that often requires much experience to learn. Most beginners either write too much or too little. This essential task should take up as little of the student's time as possible and yet the notebook should be sufficiently complete to contain all of the important information in an easily obtainable form. The student should obtain specific advice from his instructor on the notebook, its form and contents. However, some general suggestions on this subject might be made here.

Bear in mind that the instructor may want to review or inspect the notebook; therefore, do not be too verbose. Do not copy passages of instructions from the laboratory directions; refer to these by page, paragraph, or test number. Tabulate as many of the results as possible and record all observations in the form of short, concise statements. When an experiment or a significant part of an experiment is completed, record the results immediately.

In keeping notes on an analysis, make a list in a vertical column of all of the ions for which tests are to be made. This table can be used to advantage as a rough index to the specific tests which follow later. The conclusions reached regarding the presence or absence of ions can be inserted into this table after sufficient information has been obtained. Make certain to note all phenomena which seem to be irregular, since it is often possible for the instructor as well as the student to locate difficulties in an analysis by examining such notations. Record the date of the experiment.

GENERAL INSTRUCTIONS

The qualities which make for excellence in laboratory technique are orderliness, neatness, and cleanliness. These qualities are inherent in some people who naturally become good technicians. Others must develop them by making a special effort to overcome careless habits. Eventually their application becomes a habit and no further special effort is then required. Such a habit the laboratory worker in science should strive to acquire.

Orderliness is largely a state of mind. The orderly mind thinks ahead to the next operation when carrying out the operation at hand. What one does now very often depends upon what one is to do next. *Do not read only one step at a time in the laboratory directions.* Look ahead, to get the general picture of the procedure well in mind.

Neatness and cleanliness have more to do with the appearance of the student's desk and the condition of his apparatus and equipment with which he is to work. Do not allow dirty test tubes and flasks to accumulate. Place them in some definite place and wash them at the first opportunity. Replace the stoppers of the reagent bottles as soon as the reagent has been poured out, and then return the bottles to their specified places, either to the reagent racks or to the shelves. Always have those pieces of equipment at hand which are most often used.

The following suggestions should be adopted by the student when working in the laboratory.

(1) Upon beginning work spread a clean towel or paper on the top of the desk. The more common and frequently used apparatus should be arranged on the desk in an orderly fashion. All apparatus should have been cleaned during the previous laboratory period.

(2) Make certain that the reagent bottles at the desk are clean.

(3) Place several medicine droppers and capillary syringes in a beaker of distilled water. This water is to be used for diluting solutions and for washing precipitates. Never place a dropper on the bare desk; use the towel or paper, or a watch glass.

(4) Read the laboratory directions carefully and then plan a program of work for the day.

(5) During the course of the work place dirty test tubes and flasks in a definite place, preferably in a beaker, and

wash them at convenient intervals. This task can often be done while waiting for a solution to evaporate, to filter, or to be centrifuged.

(6) In pouring a reagent from a bottle hold the stopper between the third and fourth finger of the hand holding the bottle. The solution should be poured from the back side of the bottle, i.e., the bottle is to be held with the label side up.

(7) While the student is expected to adhere closely to directions, he should not work blindly. Some bit of information may show a certain test to be unnecessary. If, for example, he observes that an ammoniacal solution of his unknown is colorless he can be sure that Cu^{++} ion is absent. Specific tests for this ion may therefore be omitted.

(8) A blank test should always be made whenever an unknown test is doubtful. The blank test serves as a basis for comparison. In addition, if the test for a given ion is found to be negative, the student can determine whether the conditions for obtaining the test were satisfactory by adding to the final solution one drop of a solution containing the ion in question.

THE UNKNOWN

The analytical procedures described in this text have been devised so as to reduce to a minimum the time required for their successful operation. This is done in part by specifying the amount of unknown sample. The minimum amount of a given salt present in an unknown solution is from 1 to 8 mg. per ml., depending upon the atomic weight of the ion under consideration. This amount is sufficient for the success of all the tests to be applied. The volume of the solution containing the unknown ions is 3 ml. Accordingly each ion should be present at a concentration of about .02 M*. For solid unknowns the amounts used are of the same order of magnitude.

* Most of the tests in the procedures used in this text are sufficiently sensitive to allow detection at one-fifth the concentrations here specified or lower. However, a moderate "factor of safety" has been allowed the student.

INTRODUCTION TO THE POSITIVE IONS

The elements may be classified in two distinctly different ways: (1) according to their atomic numbers as in the familiar periodic classification and (2) according to the reactions and properties of their ions which lend themselves to analytical separation and detection. The latter classification includes, in addition to the simple ions, compound and complex ions such as the ammonium (NH_4^+) and sulfate (SO_4^{--}) ions, and the silver-ammonia $[Ag(NH_3)_2^+]$ and chloro-platinate ($PtCl_6^{--}$) ions. In this classification ions which form compounds having similar properties are placed in a single group. For example, only Ag^+, Hg_2^{++} and Pb^{++} ions react with Cl^- ion in solution to form relatively insoluble chlorides. These three elements then constitute one group in the analytical classification. Likewise, those sulfides which can be precipitated in acid solution of sufficient strength constitute another group. The latter includes the sulfides of Hg^{++}, Pb^{++}, Bi^{+++}, Cu^{++}, Cd^{++}, As^{+++}, Sb^{+++} and Sn^{++} ions. A third group is made up of positive ions, the hydroxides or sulfides of which are precipitated by a solution containing NH_4OH, NH_4Cl and $(NH_4)_2S$. It includes Al^{+++}, Cr^{+++}, Fe^{+++}, Ni^{++}, Co^{++}, Mn^{++} and Zn^{++} ions. A fourth group consists of Ca^{++}, Ba^{++}, Sr^{++} and Mg^{++} ions which, with the exception of the latter, form relatively insoluble carbonates, while a fifth group is made up of K^+, Na^+ and NH_4^+ ions, the chlorides, sulfides, hydroxides and carbonates of which are soluble. Such a grouping of the positive ions allows for the separation of most of the common elements.

This method of separating the different ions from each other is not a unique one. Small variations in procedure may shift one ion from one group to another but in the main the different methods of separation are very much alike.

310

Since the compounds of elements in a given main group of the periodic table have similar properties it is to be expected that these elements will also appear in the same analytical group. In some cases this expectation is realized. Thus Ca^{++}, Ba^{++} and Sr^{++} ions are precipitated together as carbonates, while Na^+, K^+ and NH_4^+ ions constitute another group. However, the compounds of elements in the sub-groups of the periodic system do not show the same close similarity in chemical and physical properties exhibited by the compounds of the main group elements, and since many of the more common elements belong to the sub-groups, this parellelism between the periodic table classification and the analytical classification is not very marked.

The five groups of positive ions in the analytical procedure are presented in the following order:

(1) The alkali group; Na^+, K^+, and NH_4^+.

(2) The silver group; Ag^+, Pb^{++}, and Hg_2^{++}.

(3) The copper-arsenic group; Hg^{++}, Pb^{++}, Bi^{+++}, Cu^{++}, Cd^{++}, As^{+++}, Sb^{+++}, Sn^{++}, and Sn^{++++}.

(4) The aluminum − zinc group; Al^{+++}, Cr^{+++}, Fe^{+++}, Co^{++}, Ni^{++}, Fe^{++}, Mn^{++}, and Zn^{++}.

(5) The alkaline earth group; Ba^{++}, Ca^{++}, Sr^{++}, and Mg^{++}.

In each chapter the general chemical properties of the group are discussed first. This is followed by the specific properties of the different ions within the group, the preliminary experiments, and finally by the analytical procedure.

CHAPTER XIII

The Alkali Metal Group of Ions

Na^+, K^+ and NH_4^+ Ions

The alkali metals resemble each other very closely in their physical and chemical properties. Lithium is somewhat different but since it is a less common element it will not be included in the procedures of this text. All the metals of this group are rapidly attacked by oxygen and moisture; hence, they cannot exist as such when exposed to the atmosphere. They are the most strongly electropositive elements known and accordingly react readily with elements or groups of elements which show a pronounced tendency to become electronegative. Their hydroxides form the strongest of bases in an aqueous medium and consequently the salts of strong acids are not hydrolyzed. The compounds of the alkali metals are characterized by their general solubility in water solution; only a very few insoluble salts are known. The ions bear a single positive charge which is representative of the only known valence state.

The ammonium ion is included with those of the alkali metals in the analytical procedures since it shows very similar properties. It carries a single positive charge, most of its salts are soluble in water and in its chemical properties it resembles the alkali metal ions. As a matter of fact, very good evidence has been presented to show that the free ammonium group, NH_4, is a highly electropositive metal which occupies a position in the E.M.F. series comparable to that of sodium and potassium. The ammonium ion, however, differs from the alkali metal ions in that it forms a relatively weak base, NH_4OH. This difference in behavior affords a means of identifying the ammonium ion in the presence of the alkali metal ions.

Since there are relatively few slightly soluble compounds of the ions of the alkali group, the analytical procedures

312

cannot be very satisfactory. Those compounds which are slightly soluble are not sufficiently insoluble to render them capable of identification. This point is made apparent in the following list of solubilities of the more insoluble compounds of these ions. If the ions of this group are present in the original unknown solution only to the extent of .02 M, it is evident that they cannot be very satisfactorily separated and identified by chemical means.

TABLE 21

Equilibria Involving Alkali Metal Ions

(s) denotes solid phase

Equilibria			Molar Solubility (Approximate)
$2Na^+$	$+ B_4O_7^{--}$	$= Na_2B_4O_{7(s)}$	0.2
$2Na^+$	$+ C_2O_4^{--}$	$= Na_2C_2O_{4(s)}$	0.24
$2Na^+$	$+ SiF_6^{--}$	$= Na_2SiF_{6(s)}$	0.035
$2Na^+$	$+ H_2Sb_2O_7^{--}$	$= Na_2H_2Sb_2O_{7(s)}$	0.008
K^+	$+ ClO_4^-$	$= KClO_{4(s)}$	0.15
$2K^+$	$+ PtCl_6^{--}$	$= K_2PtCl_{6(s)}$	0.03
K^+	$+ HC_4H_4O_6^-$	$= KHC_4H_4O_{6(s)}$	0.03
$2K^+$	$+ SiF_6^{--}$	$= K_2SiF_{6(s)}$	0.006
$3K^+$	$+ Co(NO_2)_6^{---}$	$= K_3Co(NO_2)_{6(s)}$	$\sim$ 0.001
NH_4^+	$+ HC_4H_4O_6^-$	$= NH_4HC_4H_4O_{6(s)}$	0.06
$2NH_4^+$	$+ PtCl_6^{--}$	$= (NH_4)_2PtCl_{6(s)}$	0.02
$3NH_4^+$	$+ Co(NO_2)_6^{---}$	$= (NH_4)_3Co(NO_2)_{6(s)}$	$\sim$ 0.001

From Table 21 it is seen that the most insoluble salt of Na^+ ion is the pyroantimonate, $Na_2H_2Sb_2O_7$, while that of the K^+ ion is $K_3Co(NO_2)_6$. In the case of Na^+ ion, potassium pyroantimonate may be used as the precipitating agent, while for the identification of the K^+ ion, sodium cobalti-nitrite may be used. Since neither is highly satisfactory, it is advisable to omit these tests, unless the ions in question are present in solution at relatively high concentrations, and instead rely entirely upon the flame tests. Sodium salts impart a yellow color to the flame while those of potassium give a violet color. In making these tests it is essential that a comparison be made with a known sample. In addition, for the identification of potassium by the flame test, it is advisable to use two thicknesses of cobalt glass in order to eliminate more completely the colors due to the presence of other ions, in particular Na^+ and Ca^{++} ions.

The presence of NH_4^+ ion in solution may be readily detected through the addition of a strong base, such as NaOH or $Ca(OH)_2$, with subsequent heating of the solution to liberate NH_3, and finally through the detection of NH_3 by moist red litmus paper. The odor of NH_3 may be sufficiently strong to be detected. An examination of the equilibria involved in a solution containing NH_3 and NH_4^+ ion explains this test.

$$NH_3 + H_2O = NH_4OH = NH_4^+ + OH^- \qquad (1)$$

The strong base furnishes a high concentration of OH^- ions which drives the reaction to the left with the production of free NH_3. At higher temperatures the solubility of NH_3 in water is considerably less than at room temperature. Consequently, when the solution is heated more NH_3 gas is liberated. When it comes in contact with moistened litmus paper, OH^- ion is produced according to equation (1) and a basic reaction is observed.

Ammonia can be detected in very small amounts by the use of Nessler's Reagent which contains the complex ion HgI_4^{--} in a concentration of about 0.5 M and is 3 M with respect to OH^- ion. It is made by dissolving HgI_2 in KI solution and then adding KOH. This reagent in combining with NH_3 produces a red-brown colloidal precipitate which has the formula $NH_2Hg_2I_3$ and in very small amounts this colloidal precipitate imparts a yellow color to the solution. The solution to be analyzed is made alkaline with NaOH and the NH_3 is distilled into the Nessler's Reagent. The reaction is

$$2HgI_4^{--} + NH_3 + OH^- = NH_2Hg_2I_3 + H_2O + 5I^-$$

This reagent is so sensitive that great care must.be used to exclude the contamination of the unknown solution by the NH_3 present in the air of the laboratory.

Preliminary Experiments

A–1. Test for NH_4^+ Ion. Add 10 drops (0.5 ml.) of 0.1 M NH_4NO_3 solution to 2.5 ml. of water in a small beaker or evaporating dish and determine the presence of the NH_4^+ ion in the following manner. Add 6 M NaOH solution dropwise until the solution is just alkaline (see directions page 297). Add 1 ml. of 6 M NaOH solution in excess. Have ready a moistened strip of red litmus paper adhering to the under side of a watch glass just large enough to cover the container. Place the watch glass over the container and heat the solution gently. The ammonia generated from the hot solution will react with the litmus paper turning it blue.[1] When NH_4^+ ion is present in sufficient concentration, the odor of ammonia can be easily detected. Try this same experiment using only 1 drop of 0.1 M NH_4NO_3 solution and 1 ml. of water.

NOTE 1. *If the heating is too vigorous, some of the boiling NaOH solution may spatter onto the litmus paper. Do not confuse scattered blue spots on the litmus paper caused by spattering with the even change to blue brought about by the NH_3.*

A–2. Test for Na^+ Ion. Prepare a .02 M solution of $NaNO_3$ by adding 0.5 ml. of the 0.1 M $NaNO_3$ solution to 2 ml. of water. Add 1 ml. of 6 M HCl.[2]

Bend one end of an iron, Nichrome, or Chromel wire into a very small loop so that it will retain a drop of the solution to be tested. The other end of the wire may be inserted into a cork for a handle (see page 298). Dip the loop end of the wire into the solution containing the Na^+ ion and insert it into the edge of the blue flame of the Bunsen burner. Note the intense yellow flame characteristic of sodium. To clean the wire heat it in the flame and while it is hot, dip it into a drop of 6 M HCl placed on a watch glass, and again heat. Now using a clean wire, test various reagents in the laboratory which are not supposed to contain Na^+ ion. Note that a weak sodium flame is obtained. This is to be distinguished from the very strong positive test.

Make a solution which is .002 M in Na^+ ion, i.e., take one part of the solution previously used and add to it 9 parts of water. Again note the strong sodium flame. With experience it is possible to distinguish between sodium present in small traces and that present as an essential constituent of the solution. Save the original solution containing the Na^+ ion as a comparison for later tests.

NOTE 2. *In making any flame test always add HCl to the solution. If nitrates alone are present, these upon heating will be converted to the oxides which are relatively non-volatile. Chlorides are not as easily converted to the oxides and are usually volatile at high temperatures.*

A–3. Test for K^+ Ion. Prepare 2.5 ml. of a .02 M KNO_3 solution. Add 1 ml. 6 M HCl and as previously described make a flame test for potassium. Note the light violet color of the flame. This color is easily obscured by the presence of other ions, particularly sodium. To distinguish the K^+ ion in the presence of other ions the light emitted by the other ions is filtered out by means of a cobalt glass. One thickness of the cobalt glass is not sufficient to extinguish all the extraneous light, therefore two are necessary. Now view the potassium flame through two thicknesses of cobalt glass. Note the deep red color. The flames of some other ions are visible through this filter yet none of them give this characteristic color of potassium.

Prepare a solution which is .002 M with respect to the K^+ ion by diluting one part of the former solution with 9 parts of water and again test for potassium. Save the original solution for later tests.

4. Test for K^+ and Na^+ Ions in the Presence of Each Other. Add 5 drops of 0.1 M $NaNO_3$ solution and 5 drops of 0.1 M KNO_3 solution to 1.5 ml. of water. Add 1 ml. of 6 M HCl. Test for both Na^+ and K^+ ions by the method outlined in the previous experiments.

5. Test for K^+ and Na^+ Ions in the Presence of Other Ions. Prepare a solution containing a number of ions selected *ad lib* from the reagent shelf. Divide the solution into two parts and make one of these .02 M with respect to both Na^+ and K^+ ions. Add 6 M HCl to each part, as directed before, and perform tests for the sodium and potassium ions on both these solutions.

Analysis of the Alkali Metal Group

Obtain from the laboratory instructor a sample of an unknown solution which is to be tested for the Na^+, K^+, and NH_4^+ ions. To 1 ml. of this solution in a casserole or evaporating dish add 6 M NaOH dropwise until alkaline and add 1 ml. of the NaOH solution in excess. Test for the NH_4^+ ion as directed in Preliminary Experiment **A-1**.

Make 10 drops of the original solution acidic with 6 M HCl, added dropwise, and add 10 drops of 6 M HCl in excess. If the original solution is already acidic, merely add 10 drops of 6 M HCl. Test for the K^+ and Na^+ ions as directed in the previous Preliminary Experiments. In each case do not rely upon your memory for the color and intensity of the flames from the Na^+ and K^+ ions but make a comparison test by using two wires, one for the unknown solution and one for the solution known to contain the ion in question.

CHAPTER XIV

The Silver Group

Ag$^+$, Pb^{++} and Hg$_2$$^{++}$ Ions

The reagent used for the separation of the silver group from the other groups in the analytical procedure is the chloride ion. This reagent is adopted here since the chlorides of the three ions under consideration are the only insoluble ones of all the cations which we shall study in this course. Lead chloride is by no means completely precipitated when Pb^{++} and Cl$^-$ ions are present. It is not very soluble in cold solutions but its solubility increases rapidly with increasing temperature. Consequently, considerable Pb^{++} ion is carried through to the next analytical group of cations; only a portion of it is precipitated along with silver and mercurous chlorides. However, the amount of Pb^{++} ion remaining in solution after the precipitation of the silver group may be reduced to a minimum by cooling and by using an excess of the precipitating reagent. Another difficulty which may arise in the precipitation of the chlorides of these ions is that the insoluble oxychloride of bismuth and of antimony may appear under some conditions. By controlling the concentrations of both the H$^+$ and the Cl$^-$ ions this difficulty may be avoided.

Silver Ion, Ag$^+$. Silver ion is characterized by its ability to form a large number of insoluble compounds with certain anions. In addition, it shows a marked tendency to form a relatively large number of stable complex ions. Much of the chemistry of the Ag$^+$ ion is expressed in the following table in which there are listed equilibria involving slightly soluble silver compounds and complex ions. In the case of any of the slightly soluble compounds the equilibrium is between the solid phase and its ions in solution; while for a complex ion the equilibrium is one which involves this ion and its products of dissociation. The order in the table is

318

made on the basis of decreasing concentration of Ag^+ ion at equilibrium. (s) denotes solid phase. For purposes of comparison the concentration of the complex ion in solution is taken as 1 M.

TABLE 22

EQUILIBRIA INVOLVING SILVER ION

$$\text{Decreasing Concentration of } Ag^+ \text{ Ion} \downarrow$$

$$Ag^+ + Ac^- = AgAc_{(s)}$$
$$2Ag^+ + SO_4^{--} = Ag_2SO_{4(s)}$$
$$2Ag^+ + CO_3^{--} = Ag_2CO_{3(s)}$$
$$Ag^+ + IO_3^- = AgIO_{3(s)}$$
$$2Ag^+ + C_2O_4^{--} = Ag_2C_2O_{4(s)}$$
$$2Ag^+ + CrO_4^{--} = Ag_2CrO_{4(s)}$$
$$Ag^+ + OH^- = AgOH_{(s)}(\tfrac{1}{2}Ag_2O_{(s)} + \tfrac{1}{2}H_2O)$$
$$Ag^+ + Cl^- = AgCl_{(s)}$$
$$Ag^+ + SCN^- = AgSCN_{(s)}$$
$$Ag^+ + CN^- = AgCN_{(s)}$$
$$Ag^+ + 2NH_3 = Ag(NH_3)_2^+$$
$$Ag^+ + Br^- = AgBr_{(s)}$$
$$Ag^+ + I^- = AgI_{(s)}$$
$$Ag^+ + 2CN^- = Ag(CN)_2^-$$
$$2Ag^+ + S^{--} = Ag_2S_{(s)}$$

Since the above equilibria are arranged according to decreasing concentration of Ag^+ ion, it is apparent that S^{--} ion will react with Ag^+ ion in equilibrium with any of the complex ions or with any of the solid silver compounds appearing above Ag_2S in this table. From this table we can predict the course of fourteen reactions involving the sulfide ion. In each case the equilibrium is displaced to the right as the equation is written.

$$S^{--} + 2Ag(CN)_2^- = Ag_2S_{(s)} + 4CN^-$$
$$S^{--} + 2AgI_{(s)} = Ag_2S_{(s)} + 2I^-$$
$$S^{--} + 2AgBr_{(s)} = Ag_2S_{(s)} + 2Br^-$$
$$S^{--} + 2Ag(NH_3)_2^+ = Ag_2S_{(s)} + 4NH_3$$
$$S^{--} + 2AgCN_{(s)} = Ag_2S_{(s)} + 2CN^-$$
$$S^{--} + 2AgSCN_{(s)} = Ag_2S_{(s)} + 2SCN^-$$
$$S^{--} + 2AgCl_{(s)} = Ag_2S_{(s)} + 2Cl^-$$
$$S^{--} + 2AgOH_{(s)} = Ag_2S_{(s)} + 2OH^-$$
$$S^{--} + Ag_2CrO_{4(s)} = Ag_2S_{(s)} + CrO_4^{--}$$

$$S^{--} + Ag_2C_2O_{4(s)} = Ag_2S_{(s)} + C_2O_4^{--}$$
$$S^{--} + 2AgIO_{3(s)} = Ag_2S_{(s)} + 2IO_3^{-}$$
$$S^{--} + Ag_2CO_{3(s)} = Ag_2S_{(s)} + CO_3^{--}$$
$$S^{--} + Ag_2SO_{4(s)} = Ag_2S_{(s)} + SO_4^{--}$$
$$S^{--} + 2AgAc_{(s)} = Ag_2S_{(s)} + 2Ac^{-}$$

In a like manner, thirteen equations may be written for the CN^- ion in the formation of the $Ag(CN)_2^-$ ion, twelve equations for the I^- ion, eleven equations for the Br^- ion, etc.; making a total of 105 equations which may be derived from Table 22. These equations represent the more important chemical properties of the Ag^+ ion in its reactions with other ions and compounds.

When two ions show about the same tendency to combine with silver ion, in other words when the concentration of the Ag^+ ion is very nearly the same for two equilibria, it is possible to reverse the order of reaction by changing the concentrations of the reactants. Thus, according to the table, Br^- ion will react with $Ag(NH_3)_2^+$ ion to form AgBr and NH_3.

$$Br^- + Ag(NH_3)_2^+ = AgBr_{(s)} + 2NH_3 \qquad (2)$$

But if an excess of NH_3 is introduced AgBr will dissolve. Thus, the reaction may be made to go from right to left or from left to right by changing the relative concentrations of the NH_3 and Br^- ion respectively. Such a situation is possible only when the concentration of the Ag^+ ion at equilibrium with the substances in question is of the same order of magnitude.

Although Table 22 gives a great deal of information concerning the chemistry of the Ag^+ ion, there are certain specific and characteristic properties of this ion and some of its compounds which should be emphasized.

In the presence of OH^- ion **silver hydroxide** is precipitated from solutions containing Ag^+ ion. The hydroxide is not very stable even at ordinary temperatures; it decomposes to give the **oxide,** Ag_2O. (Thus, when we speak of silver hydroxide we implicitly refer to silver oxide.) Silver hydroxide is not appreciably soluble in excess alkali hydroxide;

AgOH does not have pronounced amphoteric properties. On the other hand, AgOH is soluble in excess NH_4OH with the formation of the silver-ammonia complex ion, $Ag(NH_3)_2^+$. Consequently, it is apparent that the $Ag(NH_3)_2^+$ ion furnishes a smaller concentration of Ag^+ ion through dissociation than solid AgOH.

The halide ions, with the exception of the F^- ion, form relatively insoluble salts with Ag^+ ion. Of these salts, the iodide is the least soluble and the chloride the most soluble. (Table 22 also gives this information.) **Silver chloride** is somewhat soluble in solutions containing a high concentration of Cl^- ion with the formation of a complex ion, such as $AgCl_2^-$. This complex ion is relatively unstable and therefore a high concentration of Cl^- ion is required to dissolve AgCl. According to Table 22, AgCl is also soluble in NH_3 and in KCN solutions with the formation of a complex ion in each case. **Silver bromide** is less soluble than AgCl in water but its reactions are very similar to those of the chloride; the differences are due to the lower concentration of Ag^+ ion in the saturated solutions of the bromide. Thus, the formation of complex silver ions from AgBr requires a higher concentration of NH_3 and CN^- ions. **Silver iodide** is so insoluble that only the cyanide complex ion is formed in appreciable quantities.

Silver sulfide, Ag_2S, is the least soluble of all silver salts. It may be precipitated from solutions containing Ag^+ ion by H_2S and alkali sulfides. However, it is soluble in HNO_3 and in concentrated KCN solutions.

$$3Ag_2S_{(s)} + 2NO_3^- + 8H^+ = 6Ag^+ + 3S_{(s)} + 2NO + 4H_2O \quad (3)$$

$$Ag_2S_{(s)} + 4CN^- = 2Ag(CN)_2^- + S^{--} \quad (4)$$

Other relatively insoluble compounds of the silver ion are the carbonate, the cyanide, chromate, ferricyanide, phosphate, thiocyanate and all salts of organic acids. In fact, the fluoride and nitrate of silver are the only highly soluble compounds. The acetate and sulfate are moderately soluble.

Silver ion is a good oxidizing agent. It will oxidize Pb, Hg, As, Sn, Sn^{++} ion, Cd, Fe, and many other substances. Its strength as an oxidizing agent may be readily determined from its position (#71) in Table 20 of the half-reactions given in Chapter XI.

Since silver hydroxide in solution is a moderately strong base most silver salts are not appreciably hydrolyzed.

Lead Ion, Pb^{++}. Lead forms two kinds of positive ions, Pb^{++} and Pb^{++++}. Compounds of the latter type (plumbic) are exceedingly unstable and consequently are encountered only under unusual and carefully controlled conditions. Thus we shall have occasion to deal only with the plumbous ion and its compounds.

As the atomic weight of an element increases within a group of the periodic system, the hydroxides of the elements become more basic. In addition, it is well known that the

TABLE 23

EQUILIBRIA INVOLVING LEAD ION

Decreasing Concentration of Pb^{++} Ion ↓

$$Pb^{++} + 2Cl^- = PbCl_{2(s)}$$
$$Pb^{++} + 2Br^- = PbBr_{2(s)}$$
$$Pb^{++} + 2I^- = PbI_{2(s)}$$
$$Pb^{++} + S_2O_3^{--} = PbS_2O_{3(s)}$$
$$Pb^{++} + 2F^- = PbF_{2(s)}$$
$$Pb^{++} + SO_4^{--} = PbSO_{4(s)}$$
$$Pb^{++} + 2OH^- = Pb(OH)_{2(s)}$$
$$Pb^{++} + 2IO_3^- = Pb(IO_3)_{2(s)}$$
$$Pb^{++} + C_2O_4^{--} = PbC_2O_{4(s)}$$
$$Pb^{++} + CO_3^{--} = PbCO_{3(s)}$$
$$Pb^{++} + CrO_4^{--} = PbCrO_{4(s)}$$
$$3Pb^{++} + 2PO_4^{---} = Pb_3(PO_4)_{2(s)}$$
$$Pb^{++} + S^{--} = PbS_{(s)}$$

hydroxides of the elements in the lower valence states are decidedly more basic than those of higher valence. Thus plumbic hydroxide possesses more acidic than basic characteristics while the reverse is true for the **plumbous hydroxide,** Pb(OH)$_2$. However, Pb(OH)$_2$ shows amphoteric properties in that plumbites may readily be formed. Since $Pb(OH)_2$ in solution is a moderately strong base, salts of the Pb^{++} ion are not extensively hydrolyzed.

The nitrate, acetate, chlorate and persulfate of Pb^{++} ion are very soluble in water while the bromate is moderately soluble. Many of the other more common salts of this ion show a limited solubility. Table 23 gives a list of the less soluble compounds in the order of decreasing concentration of Pb^{++} ion in equilibrium with the solid salt.

On the basis of the thirteen equilibria listed in Table 23 it is possible to write seventy-eight equations expressing the more important chemical properties of the Pb^{++} ion. Since the solubilities (molar) of several salts given in this table are of the same order of magnitude, the direction of some of the predicted reactions may be reversed by making the concentration of the anion of the more soluble substance large as compared with that of the less soluble compound. Lead sulfide is exceedingly insoluble. It is always precipitated when Pb^{++} and S^{--} ions are present in the same solution. Thus, all of the solid salts above PbS in the table will be converted to PbS by S^{--} ion.

The **chloride** is the most soluble and the **fluoride** the least soluble of the halogen compounds of Pb^{++} ion. The **bromide** and **iodide** occupy intermediate positions in the order named. The solubility of the chloride changes very rapidly with temperature; at 100° its solubility is more than three times that at room temperature. Consequently, it is essential that the precipitation of $PbCl_2$ be confined to moderately low temperatures if Pb^{++} ion is to be detected in the silver group. It is accordingly impossible to remove $PbCl_2$ completely in this group. Lead ion will also be found in a later group where it is precipitated practically completely by H_2S through the formation of the highly insoluble PbS.

When NH_4OH is added to solutions containing Pb^{++} ion, white **basic salts** of indefinite composition are precipitated. One might represent the reaction with the chloride as follows:

$$PbCl_2 + NH_4OH = Pb(OH)Cl_{(s)} + NH_4^+ + Cl^- \quad (5)$$

These basic salts are not soluble in excess NH_4OH solution, which indicates that Pb^{++} ion does not form a complex ion with ammonia. This property of the Pb^{++} ion distinguishes it from Ag^+, Cu^{++} and Cd^{++} ions.

Alkali hydroxides precipitate **hydrated lead oxides** from solutions containing Pb^{++} ions. Undoubtedly there are stages of hydration of the oxides which correspond to the normal hydroxide, $Pb(OH)_2$. **Lead hydroxide** is found to be readily soluble in excess NaOH or KOH solutions with the formation of **plumbites.** This reaction clearly demonstrates the amphoteric nature of the hydroxide.

$$H^+ + HPbO_2^- = Pb(OH)_{2(s)} = Pb^{++} + 2OH^- \qquad (6)$$
$$\begin{array}{ccc} + & or & + \\ OH^- & H_2PbO_{2(s)} & 2H^+ \\ \updownarrow & & \updownarrow \\ H_2O & & 2H_2O \end{array}$$

The biplumbite ion, $HPbO_2^-$, is produced in dilute NaOH solution, while in concentrated solutions the plumbite ion, PbO_2^{--}, is probably present. The amphoteric nature of $Pb(OH)_2$ distinguishes Pb^{++} ion from Ag^+, Hg_2^{++}, Bi^{+++}, Cu^{++} and Cd^{++} ions.

Alkali carbonates and bicarbonates precipitate the normal **lead carbonate** from cold solutions containing Pb^{++} ion.

$$Pb^{++} + CO_3^{--} = PbCO_{3(s)} \qquad (7)$$

In hot solutions a **basic carbonate** is formed, the composition of which is variable and is dependent upon the concentrations of the constituents undergoing reaction.

Cyanides, ferrocyanides and thiocyanates precipitate the corresponding salts of lead from solutions containing Pb^{++} ions. The ferrocyanide is quite insoluble, the cyanide, slightly soluble and the thiocyanate, moderately soluble.

Lead sulfide is precipitated from solutions of Pb^{++} ions, in the presence of H^+ or OH^- ions or in neutral solution, by H_2S or soluble sulfides. PbS is not soluble in dilute acids, nor in the presence of excess OH^- ion. It does not dissolve in solutions of alkali sulfides. In the presence of dilute nitric acid oxidation of the S^{--} ion results with the formation of free sulfur.

$$3PbS_{(s)} + 2NO_3^- + 8H^+ = 3Pb^{++} + 3S_{(s)} + 2NO + 4H_2O \quad (8)$$

If precipitation of PbS is carried out in hydrochloric acid solution through the addition of H_2S, it is advisable to maintain the concentration of the hydrogen ion at a reasonable value, not in excess of 1.5 M. In the more concentrated solutions of HCl, PbS fails to precipitate. Not only is the concentration of the S^{--} ion lowered by the presence of a large amount of H^+ ion but, in addition, the concentration of the Pb^{++} ion is materially reduced by the Cl^- ion through the formation of the slightly ionized $PbCl_2$.

It was pointed out previously that lead salts show very little ionization in water solution. These salts, together with those of mercury and cadmium, behave exceptionally in this respect. Whereas one might expect lead chloride to ionize practically completely in aqueous solution, its ionization is only of the order of magnitude of a few per cent. In addition, in the presence of excess Cl^- ion, complex ions are formed which tend to reduce the concentration of the Pb^{++} cation.

$$PbCl_2 + 2Cl^- = PbCl_4^{--} \quad (9)$$

Mercurous Ion, Hg_2^{++} — Mercuric Ion, Hg^{++}. Although the silver group includes only the mercurous ion, it is desirable at this point to consider the chemistry of the mercuric ion as well. The chemistry of one ion often involves that of the other. In the analytical scheme the mercuric ion falls into the copper-arsenic group of ions.

Mercury forms two series of compounds, mercurous and mercuric, in which it displays valences of one and two respectively. Since mercury is a very weakly electropositive element, both **mercurous** and **mercuric hydroxides** are very weak bases. These hydroxides do not exist as such in the solid state, only the anhydrides (the oxides) are known. Thus, mercurous and mercuric salts are extensively hydrolyzed in water.

The mercurous ion is represented as a doubly charged ion consisting of two atoms of the element, Hg_2^{++}. The structure of the unassociated mercurous ion, Hg^+, is unique in that it has one remaining outside electron with all the interior electronic shells filled. The total electrons in this ion is an odd number, 79. In general, molecules or atoms having an odd number of electrons tend to couple with each other since the electrons themselves have a great tendency to form pairs. Thus, sodium atoms which have an odd number of electrons pair with each other in the vapor state to form Na_2 molecules. In the same way Hg^+ ions couple to produce Hg_2^{++}. In addition to the tendency of electrons to form stable groups of eight, they show a tendency to couple and form electronic pairs.

The **sulfate, acetate** and **nitrate** of Hg_2^{++} ion are somewhat soluble in water but on standing tend to hydrolyze with the precipitation of basic salts. To prevent hydrolysis it is necessary to add an acid to the solution. Most of the mercurous salts are relatively insoluble in water. The equilibria involving mercurous ion are listed in Table 24.

TABLE 24

EQUILIBRIA INVOLVING MERCUROUS ION

Decreasing Concentration of Hg_2^{++} Ion ↓

$$Hg_2^{++} + 2Cl^- = Hg_2Cl_{2(s)}$$
$$Hg_2^{++} + 2Br^- = Hg_2Br_{2(s)}$$
$$Hg_2^{++} + 2I^- = Hg_2I_{2(s)}$$
$$Hg_2^{++} + S^{--} = Hg_2S_{(s)}$$

The **carbonate, oxalate, phosphate, thiocyanate** and **chromate** of Hg_2^{++} ion are also very slightly soluble in water although they are all more soluble than the sulfide.

The **nitrate, acetate, chlorate, cyanide** and **chloride** of Hg^{++} ion are readily soluble in water. The **chromate, oxalate** and **phosphate** of this ion are very slightly soluble. Equilibria involving the Hg^{++} ion and solid salts, as well as some of the more common complex ions, are listed in Table 25 in the order of decreasing concentration of Hg^{++} ion. For the complex ions, a concentration of 1 mole per liter is taken in establishing their positions.

TABLE 25

EQUILIBRIA INVOLVING MERCURIC ION

Decreasing Concentration of Hg^{++} Ion		
$Hg^{++} + 2Br^-$	$=$	$HgBr_{2(s)}$
$Hg^{++} + 2SCN^-$	$=$	$Hg(SCN)_{2(s)}$
$Hg^{++} + SO_4^{--}$	$=$	$HgSO_{4(s)}$
$Hg^{++} + 2I^-$	$=$	$HgI_{2(s)}$
$Hg^{++} + 3Cl^-$	$=$	$HgCl_3^-$
$Hg^{++} + 4Br^-$	$=$	$HgBr_4^{--}$
$Hg^{++} + 4SCN^-$	$=$	$Hg(SCN)_4^{--}$
$Hg^{++} + 4I^-$	$=$	HgI_4^{--}
$Hg^{++} + 4CN^-$	$=$	$Hg(CN)_4^{--}$
$Hg^{++} + S^{--}$	$=$	$HgS_{(s)}$

Some of the reactions predicted from Table 25 may be reversed by changing the relative concentrations of the reacting ions. **Mercuric sulfide,** however, furnishes a very much lower concentration of Hg^{++} ions than do any of the other mercuric compounds and therefore HgS cannot be dissolved by any of the ions listed in the table. In fact it can only be dissolved by aqua regia.

Table 24 and 25 give the more important properties of the Hg_2^{++} and Hg^{++} ions. However, there are certain specific properties of these two ions which should be emphasized.

When metallic mercury is added to a solution of $Hg(NO_3)_2$ a solution of $Hg_2(NO_3)_2$ is eventually produced. An oxidation-reduction reaction is involved which may be represented by the equation

$$Hg^{++} + Hg = Hg_2^{++} \tag{10}$$

The above reaction proceeds until equilibrium is established which in the case of the nitrate solutions is such that about one hundred times as much Hg_2^{++} as Hg^{++} is present. This equilibrium can be shifted to the left by removing the Hg^{++} ion through the formation of some very insoluble mercuric compound. Thus, when H_2S is added to a solution containing Hg_2^{++} ion, HgS and Hg, and not Hg_2S, are formed. Mercuric sulfide is much less soluble than mercurous sulfide and for this reason the equilibrium as represented by equation (10) is shifted to the left and free mercury is produced.

When ammonia is added to a solution of $HgCl_2$ a very insoluble white **ammonobasic salt,** $Hg(NH_2)Cl$, is formed.

$$HgCl_2 + 2NH_3 = Hg(NH_2)Cl_{(s)} + NH_4^+ + Cl^- \quad (11)$$

In this equation mercuric chloride is written as $HgCl_2$ and not in its ionized form since it is a weak salt. The NH_2 radical is the ammonia analogue of the OH radical (see page 219), and the compound $Hg(NH_2)Cl$ is therefore **mercuric ammonobasic chloride.** The reaction is termed *ammonolysis*, analogous to *hydrolysis*, since ammonia rather than water is the reacting constituent. However, the ammonolysis involves only one of the chlorine atoms. If complete ammonolysis were to take place, the nitride of mercury would be formed. In the same manner, complete hydrolysis of a mercuric salt would produce the oxide of mercury since the hydroxide (base) is not stable.

When solid **mercurous chloride** is treated with NH_3 the equilibrium expressed in equation (10) is again shifted to the left and the very insoluble $Hg(NH_2)Cl$ and free mercury are formed. Since the free mercury is very finely divided it

$$
\begin{array}{ccc}
Hg^{++} + Hg_{(s)} = Hg_2^{++} & & (12) \\
+ & & + \\
2NH_3 & & 2Cl^- \\
+ & & \updownarrow \\
Cl^- & & Hg_2Cl_{2(s)} \\
\updownarrow & & \\
Hg(NH_2)Cl_{(s)} & & \\
+ & & \\
Hg_{(s)} & & \\
+ & & \\
NH_4^+ & &
\end{array}
$$

appears black and masks the white $Hg(NH_2)Cl$ formed at the same time. The reactions involved may be expressed by the equilibrium combinations given in scheme (12), page 328. The over-all equation, i.e., the reaction involving only what disappears and what is formed regardless of the intermediate steps, is

$$Hg_2Cl_{2(s)} + 2NH_3 = Hg(NH_2)Cl_{(s)} + Hg_{(s)} + NH_4^+ + Cl^- \quad (13)$$

It will be recalled that AgCl is soluble in NH_3 while $PbCl_2$ shows no reaction; thus, the above reaction is one characterized only by mercury salts of the silver group of ions.

Alkali hydroxides added to solutions containing Hg_2^{++} ion precipitate **mercurous oxide**, Hg_2O, which does not exhibit any amphoteric properties. NaOH or KOH precipitate HgO from solutions containing Hg^{++} ions. It likewise fails to show any amphoteric tendencies.

Hydrogen sulfide, alkali sulfides or ammonium sulfide precipitate **mercuric sulfide** from solutions containing the Hg_2^{++} ion. Mercurous sulfide may be formed here at lower temperatures but at room temperature internal oxidation and reduction produce HgS and Hg. At low temperatures the speed of the internal oxidation-reduction reaction is not great enough to produce HgS in accordance with equation (10). When any of the above mentioned sulfides are added to solutions of mercuric salts, HgS is precipitated. The reaction evidently proceeds through several stages as is indicated by the color changes during precipitation. There is first formed a white precipitate which changes to yellow, red, brown and finally black. These stages probably represent different products as well as different sizes of particles. Mercuric sulfide is relatively insoluble in dilute HNO_3 but slightly soluble in the hot concentrated acid. It is readily soluble in aqua regia and only very slightly soluble in $(NH_4)_2S$ or $(NH_4)_2S_x$.

When $SnCl_2$ is added to solutions of mercuric salts, Hg_2Cl_2 is precipitated. An excess of the reducing agent produces metallic Hg.

$$2HgCl_2 + Sn^{++} = Hg_2Cl_{2(s)} + Sn^{++++} + 2Cl^- \qquad (14)$$
$$Hg_2Cl_{2(s)} + Sn^{++} = 2Hg_{(s)} + Sn^{++++} + 2Cl^- \qquad (15)$$

This reaction is a useful as well as a characteristic one for the detection of mercury in the form of Hg^{++} ion.

Mercurous ion is readily distinguished from Hg^{++} ion in solution in that the former produces the highly insoluble Hg_2Cl_2 in the presence of Cl^- ion, while the chloride of the latter is highly soluble. Mercuric ion, on the other hand, is distinguished from the arsenic group of ions in that the latter in the form of sulfides are readily soluble in $(NH_4)_2S_x$ while HgS is not. Mercuric sulfide, however, is soluble in alkali sulfides and polysulfides.

Preliminary Experiments

1. To 2 ml. of water add 2 drops of 0.1 M $AgNO_3$ solution and 3 drops of 0.1 M KBr solution to produce a slight excess of Br^- ion. To this mixture add sufficient concentrated NH_4OH solution to just dissolve the precipitate. Again add enough KBr solution to reprecipitate the AgBr. Redissolve the AgBr again by adding NH_4OH. Repeat this procedure several times. Write equations for the reactions and explain the appearance and disappearance of the precipitate. On the basis of the results of this experiment what prediction can you make regarding the relative concentrations of Ag^+ ion furnished by AgBr (saturated solution) and the silver-ammonia complex ion respectively?

2. (a) To 2 ml. of 0.1 M $AgNO_3$ solution add a few drops of dilute NaOH (use medicine dropper). Write the formula of the precipitate formed. Write the equation for the reaction.

(b) To this mixture add dropwise 0.1 M NaCl solution until the first precipitate has been transformed completely into a white precipitate. What is the formula of the white precipitate? Write the equation for the reaction which has taken place.

(c) Now, add enough NH_4OH to dissolve this white precipitate. The substance formed in this last reaction is the complex ion, $Ag(NH_3)_2^+$, and the reaction is

$$AgCl_{(s)} + 2NH_3 = Ag(NH_3)_2^+ + Cl^-$$

(d) Finally, to the solution in (c) add a few drops of 0.1 M KI solution. Write the formula of the precipitate formed and give the equation for the reaction. (NH_3 is one of the products formed.)

(e) Explain how the reactions involved in (a), (b), (c) and (d) are consistent with the arrangement of the equilibria listed in Table 22.

(f) On the basis of the results of these experiments, devise an experiment to confirm the relative position of Ag_2S in Table 22.

3. To 2 ml. of water add 2 drops of 0.1 M $AgNO_3$ solution, and to this solution add 5 drops of 0.1 M NaCl. Now add 6 M NH_4OH dropwise and note that the precipitate dissolves.

(a) Devise an experiment to show that the NH_4^+ ion is not responsible for dissolving the AgCl.

(b) Devise an experiment to show that the OH^- ion is not responsible for this effect.

(c) What substance in NH_4OH is responsible for this effect?

4. Add 1 M NH_4OH dropwise to 1 ml. of 0.1 M $AgNO_3$ solution and note that the precipitate of Ag_2O first formed dissolves in excess of NH_4OH.

Now add a few crystals of NH_4NO_3 to 1 ml. of 0.1 M $AgNO_3$ solution and then add an excess of 1 M NH_4OH solution drop by drop. No precipitate of Ag_2O is produced in this experiment.

(a) How does the addition of NH_4^+ ion (NH_4NO_3) effect the concentration of the OH^- ion?

(b) Explain why Ag_2O is not precipitated, whereas it was when NH_4NO_3 had not been added.

5. (*NOTE. If desirable this experiment may be deferred until the chapter on complex ions has been considered.*)

To 20 drops of 0.1 M $AgNO_3$ solution in a test tube add 20 drops of 1 M NH_4OH and to the mixture add .02 M NaCl solution dropwise until a permanent precipitate of AgCl first appears. Record the number of drops of NaCl solution added.

(a) What is the final volume of the mixture?

(b) Assuming that practically all the Ag^+ ion is converted to $Ag(NH_3)_2^+$ ion, and that an inappreciable amount is removed by the Cl^- ion, what is the concentration of the $Ag(NH_3)_2^+$ ion in the final solution?

(c) Neglecting the amount of Cl^- ion that is removed as AgCl, what is the concentration of this ion in the final solution?

(d) If no NH_3 had combined with Ag^+ ion what would be the concentration of NH_3 in the final solution? (a 6 M NH_4OH solution is the same as a 6 M NH$_3$ solution). The actual concentration of uncombined NH$_3$ in the final solution is the value just calculated for the total NH$_3$ minus 2 times the concentration of the Ag(NH$_3$)$_2{}^+$ ion. Why?

(e) Knowing that (Ag$^+$) (Cl$^-$) must be equal to 1.56 $\times$ 10^{-10} (solubility product) and knowing the concentration of Cl$^-$ ion from (c) calculate the concentration of the uncombined Ag$^+$ ion in the final solution.

(f) The Ag(NH$_3$)$_2{}^+$ ion dissociates as follows:

$$Ag(NH_3)_2{}^+ = Ag^+ + 2NH_3$$

and the equilibrium expression is

$$\frac{(Ag^+)(NH_3)^2}{(Ag(NH_3)_2{}^+)} = K_{eq}$$

From the values of (Ag$^+$), (NH$_3$) and (Ag(NH$_3$)$_2{}^+$) determined in (e), (d) and (b) respectively, calculate the numerical value of K_{eq}. Compare your value with that given in Table 46 of the Appendix.

6. Devise an experiment to show that Pb(OH)$_2$ is amphoteric.

7. (a) Add 1 ml. 0.1 M Pb(NO$_3$)$_2$ solution to 2 ml. water and to this solution add 20 drops of 3 M HCl to precipitate PbCl$_2$. Filter the solution and by means of the capillary syringe wash the crystals with 1 ml. of boiling water. Collect the washings and cool by placing the test tube in cold water. Explain.

(b) To the latter mixture (crystals and solution) add 2 drops 1 M K$_2$CrO$_4$ solution. Write an equation for the reaction. Which is the more soluble, PbCl$_2$ or PbCrO$_4$? From Table 23 predict whether H$_2$S would convert the PbCrO$_4$ into PbS.

8. (a) To about 1 ml. of 0.1 M Hg$_2$(NO$_3$)$_2$ solution add 10 drops of 6 M HCl solution.

(b) To about 1 ml. of 0.1 M Hg(NO$_3$)$_2$ solution add 10 drops of 6 M HCl solution. Note the difference in the two experiments.

9. (a) Add 1 small drop of metallic mercury to 1 ml. of 0.1 M Hg(NO$_3$)$_2$ solution and heat.

(b) Add a few drops of HCl solution to solution (a). What is the evidence that a reaction took place between Hg and Hg^{++} in (a)?

(c) Filter solution obtained in (b) and to the filtrate add a few drops of $SnCl_2$ solution. What is the evidence that the reaction in (a) was not complete?

(d) Write equations to express the reactions of (a) and (b) and (c).

10. Add a few drops of 1 M NH_4OH to 1 ml. of 0.1 M $HgCl_2$ solution and observe the precipitate. Write an equation for the reaction.

11. Prepare a small quantity of freshly precipitated Hg_2Cl_2 and to its suspension in water add a few drops of 1 M NH_4OH solution. Observe any changes which take place. Give an equation for the reaction.

12. Add a large excess of 1 M NaOH solution to

(a) 1 ml. of 0.1 M $Hg_2(NO_3)_2$ solution

(b) 1 ml. of 0.1 M $Hg(NO_3)_2$ solution.

(c) Write equations to express the reactions which take place in (a) and (b).

(d) What important conclusion may be drawn from the results of these two experiments?

13. Construct a table similar to the following, listing the changes which take place when $AgCl$, $PbCl_2$ and Hg_2Cl_2 are subjected to the reagents:

(a) Hot water

(b) NH_4OH solution

(c) NaOH solution

(d) NaOH solution in excess

(The effect of the first reagent is given in the outline below as an example.)

Reagent	AgCl	$PbCl_2$	Hg_2Cl_2
Hot water	no effect	dissolves	no effect
NH_4OH			
NaOH			
NaOH in excess			

14. On the basis of the results of the above experiments and your knowledge of the chemical properties of Ag^+, Pb^{++} and Hg_2^{++} ions, outline two procedures for the precipitation, separation and identification of these ions.

The Analysis of the Silver Group
SCHEMATIC OUTLINE

Add 6 M HCl — Precipitate: $PbCl_2$, Hg_2Cl_2, AgCl (Filtrate may contain ions of subsequent groups) Treat with hot water **(B)**		
Solution: Pb^{++} Add 6 M HAc and 1 M K_2CrO_4	Residue: AgCl, Hg_2Cl_2 Pour 6 M NH_4OH through the filter	
Precipitate: $PbCrO_4$ (yellow) **(B–1)**	Black residue on filter: $Hg + Hg(NH_2)Cl$ **(B–2)**	Solution: $Ag(NH_3)_2^+$ Add 6 M HNO_3 Precipitate: AgCl **(B–3)**

NOTE 1. *In the analysis of the silver group it is not advisable to use the centrifuge. Filtering is more convenient for the required operations.*

B. Precipitation of the Silver Group. Obtain a sample of a solution of an unknown from the laboratory instructor and to 3 ml. of it add 10 drops of 6 M HCl from a medicine dropper, with constant shaking. If no precipitate appears, it is evident that Ag^+, Pb^{++}, and Hg_2^{++} ions are absent. (Small amounts of Pb^{++} ion may be present owing to the relatively high solubility of $PbCl_2$.) In the event of the formation of a precipitate, pour the contents on a filter supported by a 40 mm. funnel. Test the filtrate for completeness of precipitation by adding 1 drop of 6 M HCl. If a precipitate appears add 2 more drops of 6 M HCl[2] and pour through the filter containing the precipitates.[3]

NOTE 2. *A slight excess of HCl is added for the following reasons:*
(a) *the common ion effect insures more complete precipitation,*
(b) *the precipitation of BiOCl and SbOCl is prevented, and*
(c) *the possibility of colloidal suspensions of the chlorides is lessened.*

NOTE 3. *The addition of a very large excess of HCl is to be avoided. With a large excess or a high concentration of Cl^- ion, soluble complex chloride ions of silver and lead, namely, $PbCl_4^{--}$ and $AgCl_2^-$, will be formed.*

B–1. Test for Pb^{++} Ion. Place about 25 ml. of distilled water in a beaker and heat to boiling. Gently lift the filter paper cone which contains the precipitates out of the funnel. Slowly pour about one-half of the water through the funnel to heat it, discarding this water. Quickly place the filter paper back into the funnel. Place a test tube under the stem of the funnel and with the aid of the capillary syringe, add 2 ml. of hot water to the precipitate.

Add to the solution first 1 drop of 6 M acetic acid and then 1 drop of 1 M K_2CrO_4 solution. A yellow precipitate of $PbCrO_4$ shows the presence of Pb^{++} ion.

To confirm $PbCrO_4$, dissolve this precipitate by adding a few drops of 6 M NaOH solution to the suspended $PbCrO_4$. If necessary separate by filtration any undissolved residue and to the filtrate add acetic acid to reprecipitate $PbCrO_4$.[4]

The precipitate remaining on the filter may contain AgCl and Hg_2Cl_2, and if Pb^{++} ion has been found present, an additional quantity may be still left on the filter. To remove the greater part of Pb^{++} ion from the filter, add 2 more ml. of hot water and discard the washings.

NOTE 4. *The NaOH solution containing the plumbite ion is neutralized with HAc rather than HCl to prevent too high a H⁺ ion concentration which in turn would prevent the precipitation of lead chromate.*

B–2. Test for Hg_2^{++} Ion. Now treat the residue on the filter paper with 10 drops of 6 M NH_4OH solution and collect the liquid which passes through the filter in a small test tube. Label this **B–3** and reserve for Ag^+ ion test. If the residue on the filter becomes decidedly black, the presence of Hg_2^{++} ion is strongly indicated. The black residue is the result of the formation of the white ammono-basic salt, $Hg(NH_2)Cl$, and black metallic mercury.[5]

NOTE 5. *If there is any doubt about the presence of Hg_2^{++} ion, it may be confirmed in the following manner:*

Transfer the precipitate to a small evaporating dish or casserole. Treat with 10 drops of aqua regia and heat the mixture carefully over a free flame until the excess aqua regia is removed and the residue appears for the most part to be dissolved. Then add about 5 drops of water and finally 2 drops of SnCl₂ solution. A while or gray precipitate confirms the presence of Hg_2^{++} ion in the original solution.

B–3. Test for Ag^+ Ion. The filtrate **B–3** reserved for the detection of Ag^+ ion is treated with 6 M HNO_3 added drop by drop until the solution is acidic. A white precipitate of AgCl shows Ag^+ ion to be present.[6]

NOTE 6. *If the amount of silver ion present in the solution is very small, as compared with that of the mercurous ion, and if the filtration is slow, the $Ag(NH_3)_2^+$ ion may be reduced to free silver according to the equation,*

$$2Hg + 2Ag(NH_3)_2^+ + 2Cl^- = Hg_2Cl_2 + 2Ag + 4NH_3$$

and be retained on the filter. It is not very probable that all the silver would be retained in this way. If the final test for silver is very doubtful, then dissolve the black precipitate in 6 M HNO_3 and add a few drops of 1 M HCl. The silver will precipitate from the nitric acid solution as AgCl. The mercury will be in the form of $HgCl_2$ which is soluble.

Equations for Pertinent Reactions

$Ag^+ + Cl^- = AgCl_{(s)}$

$Hg_2^{++} + 2Cl^- = Hg_2Cl_{2(s)}$

$Pb^{++} + 2Cl^- = PbCl_{2(s)}$

$Pb^{++} + CrO_4^{--} = PbCrO_{4(s)}$

$PbCrO_{4(s)} + 3OH^- = HPbO_2^- + CrO_4^{--} + H_2O$

$HPbO_2^- + CrO_4^{--} + 3H^+ = PbCrO_{4(s)} + 2H_2O$

$Hg_2Cl_{2(s)} + 2NH_3 = Hg_{(s)}(black) + Hg(NH_2)Cl + NH_4^+ + Cl^-$

$AgCl_{(s)} + 2NH_3 = Ag(NH_3)_2^+ + Cl^-$

$Ag(NH_3)_2^+ + Cl^- + 2H^+ = AgCl_{(s)} + 2NH_4^+$

CHAPTER XV

The Copper–Arsenic Group

Hg^{++}, Pb^{++}, Bi^{+++}, Cu^{++} and Cd^{++}; H_3AsO_4, H_3AsO_3, H_3SbO_4, Sb^{+++}, Sn^{++} and Sn^{++++}

The copper-arsenic group of ions is precipitated by hydrogen sulfide in dilute (0.2–0.3 M) HCl solution. This procedure serves to separate these ions from those of subsequent groups. If the concentration of the hydrogen ion is too great, the sulfides of cadmium and lead will fail to precipitate, and some of the other more soluble sulfides may likewise fall into this category. On the other hand, if the concentration of the hydrogen ion is too small, considerably lower than 0.2 M, zinc, nickel and cobalt sulfides will precipitate if the corresponding ions are present.

The H^+ ion regulates the concentration of the S^{--} ion when H_2S is passed into the solution. The higher the concentration of the H^+ ion, the lower the concentration of the S^{--} ion, as may be readily seen by an examination of the following equilibrium for a saturated solution of H_2S.

$$(H^+)^2(S^{--}) = 1.1 \times 10^{-23}$$

If the concentration of the H^+ ion is maintained at 0.3 M, it follows from the above expression that the concentration of the S^{--} ion in such a solution is approximately 1.2×10^{-22} mole per liter. This condition is favorable for the precipitation of the sulfides of the copper-arsenic group.

After the sulfides have been precipitated they may be separated according to the differences in solubility they show with various reagents. These differences in solubility may be explained by a consideration of the equilibria between the sulfides and their respective ions. (MS represents any metal sulfide of the group.)

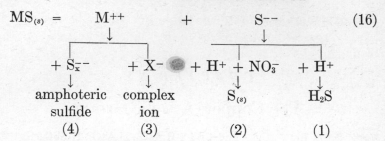

$$MS_{(s)} = \quad M^{++} \quad + \quad S^{--} \qquad (16)$$

$+ S_x^{--}$	$+ X^-$	$+ H^+ + NO_3^-$	$+ H^+$
amphoteric	complex	$S_{(s)}$	H_2S
sulfide	ion		
(4)	(3)	(2)	(1)

The above general equilibrium may be shifted to the right (MS dissolved) either by the removal of the M^{++} ion or the S^{--} ion. This may be accomplished in four different ways as indicated in equation (16).

(1) If MS is not too insoluble, H^+ ion alone suffices.

(2) If MS is very insoluble, H^+ and NO_3^- (or aqua regia) are necessary. Free sulfur is formed in this case.

(3) M^{++} may form a very stable complex ion with X^- (X^- may represent CN^-). This method is not generally applicable.

(4) If M^{++} forms an amphoteric sulfide, $(NH_4)_2S$ or $(NH_4)_2S_x$ will dissolve the MS. The sulfides of arsenic, antimony and tin behave in this way.

Bismuth Ion, Bi^{+++}. Bismuth forms two series of compounds in which the valence state of the bismuth atom is plus three and plus five respectively. Very little is known about compounds of bismuth in the plus five state since they are relatively unstable. Hence, our attention will be devoted entirely to the chemistry of the bismuth ion, Bi^{+++}. The salts of this ion are readily hydrolyzed in water, with the formation of basic salts or the **hydroxide** of bismuth. The latter is a moderately weak base. In addition to the hydroxide, the **oxalate, phosphate** and **iodate** of bismuth are very slightly soluble in water.

The **chloride, bromide, iodide, nitrate** and **sulfate** of bismuth hydrolyze forming the corresponding basic salts.

$$Bi^{+++} + Cl^- + H_2O = BiOCl_{(s)} + 2H^+ \qquad (17)$$

The oxychloride is quite insoluble but since the reaction is readily reversible an excess of H^+ ion serves to keep the bismuth chloride in solution. The other salts named above behave in a similar manner.

Although BiOCl is only slightly soluble in water, H_2S precipitates bismuth sulfide.

$$2BiOCl_{(s)} + 3H_2S = Bi_2S_{3(s)} + 2H^+ + 2Cl^- + 2H_2O \quad (18)$$

The equilibrium predominates to the right, indicating that a saturated solution of Bi_2S_3 furnishes fewer Bi^{+++} ions than a saturated solution of the oxychloride. All other normal salts as well as basic salts of the Bi^{+++} ion behave similarly, in the presence of H_2S or of solutions containing appreciable amounts of S^{--} ion.

Bismuth sulfide is insoluble in cold solutions of dilute acids but dissolves in boiling dilute HNO_3 as well as in hot concentrated HCl.

$$Bi_2S_{3(s)} + 2NO_3^- + 8H^+ = 2Bi^{+++} + 3S_{(s)} + 2NO + 4H_2O \quad (19)$$

The sulfide is practically insoluble in solutions of $(NH_4)_2S$ or of $(NH_4)_2S_x$. This property serves to distinguish bismuth from the ions of the arsenic group.

White **bismuth hydroxide,** $Bi(OH)_3$, is precipitated by alkali hydroxides from solutions containing Bi^{+++} ion. When the solution is heated a yellow dehydration product, $BiO(OH)$ is formed. Bismuth hydroxide is not appreciably soluble in excess alkali, thus it possesses no amphoteric properties and accordingly bismuthites are unknown. This property distinguishes bismuth from tin and antimony. Bismuth hydroxide also fails to dissolve in NH_4OH solution, which is evidence that the Bi^{+++} ion does not form a complex with NH_3, whereas Cu^{++} and Cd^{++} ions do. In fact, Bi^{+++} ion forms only a very few complex ions. One example worthy of mention is the BiI_4^- ion which is produced when BiI_3 is present with excess I^- ion in solutions not too strongly acid. The complex ion imparts a yellow color to the solution and acts as a delicate test for bismuth.

One of the best characteristic tests for the Bi^{+++} ion is its reduction to metallic bismuth by sodium stannite.

$$2Bi^{+++} + 3SnO_2^{--} + 6OH^- = 2Bi_{(s)} + 3SnO_3^{--} + 3H_2O \quad (20)$$

Copper Ion, Cu^{++}. Copper is not a very electropositive element; it occupies an intermediate position, below hydrogen, in the oxidation-reduction series of the elements. It forms two series of compounds, cuprous and cupric, in which the valence states of the copper atom are plus one and plus two respectively. In general, cuprous salts are found to be quite insoluble and show a marked tendency to change to the cupric condition. In the presence of air their solutions are readily oxidized to the cupric state. Consequently, cuprous salts are of relatively little importance in the identification of copper.

The Cu^{++} ion in water solution is characterized by its blue color, the character of which changes with the concentration of the Cu^{++} ion. This property is probably due to a change in the extent of hydration of the ion. Cupric salts are sufficiently hydrolyzed to produce excess H^+ ions in water solution; consequently, cupric hydroxide in solution must be a moderately weak base.

Cupric ion shows a distinct tendency to unite with certain other ions and molecules to form complex ions. In addition, many cupric salts show a limited solubility in water. The more important equilibria involving slightly soluble substances and complex ions are listed in Table 26 in order of decreasing concentration of cupric ion.

TABLE 26

EQUILIBRIA INVOLVING CUPRIC ION

$$Cu^{++} + 2IO_3^- = Cu(IO_3)_{2(s)}$$
$$Cu^{++} + C_2O_4^{--} = CuC_2O_{4(s)}$$
$$Cu^{++} + CrO_4^= = CuCrO_{4(s)}$$
$$Cu^{++} + 2OH^- = Cu(OH)_{2(s)}$$
$$Cu^{++} + 4NH_3 = Cu(NH_3)_4^{++}$$
$$Cu^{++} + S^{--} = CuS_{(s)}$$

Decreasing Concentration of Cu^+ Ion ↓

In addition to the above, other slightly soluble cupric salts are the **oxalate, carbonate, chromate, cyanide, ferrocyanide, ferricyanide** and **phosphate.** Their respective positions in Table 26 are not known, but it is certain that they would lie above CuS.

Alkali hydroxides precipitate **cupric hydroxide** from solutions containing Cu^{++} ion. The hydroxide is somewhat soluble in a large excess of a concentrated solution of the reagent, due to the formation of a cuprate ion, $HCuO_2^-$.

Ammonium hydroxide precipitates either basic salts or cupric hydroxide from solutions of Cu^{++} ion. Both are soluble in an excess of the reagent with the formation of the characteristic blue **cupric-ammonia complex ion,** $Cu(NH_3)_4^{++}$.

One of the most insoluble compounds of the Cu^{++} ion is the **sulfide.** It is readily precipitated from solutions containing Cu^{++} and S^{--} ions. The sulfide is insoluble in dilute acids and alkalies, not appreciably soluble in $(NH_4)_2S$, $(NH_4)_2S_x$ or Na_2S solutions, and only very slightly soluble in Na_2S_x solutions. This distinguishes the Cu^{++} ion from those of the arsenic group (As^{+++}, Sb^{+++} and Sn^{++}). CuS also is insoluble in $6\ M\ H_2SO_4$ solution, while CdS is readily soluble in this reagent. On the other hand, CuS dissolves in hot dilute HNO_3.

$$3CuS_{(s)} + 2NO_3^- + 8H^+ = 3Cu^{++} + 2NO + 3S_{(s)} + 4H_2O \quad (21)$$

Mercuric sulfide is not appreciably soluble in HNO_3; aqua regia is required to dissolve it. The Cl^- ion present in aqua regia combines with the Hg^{++} ion to form both the weak soluble salt, $HgCl_2$, and the complex ion, $HgCl_3^-$. This property distinguishes CuS from HgS. Cupric sulfide also is soluble in KCN solutions, whereas PbS, Bi_2S_3, CdS and HgS fail to dissolve in this reagent.

Cupric ion in the presence of CN^- ion yields **cuprous cyanide,** CuCN, although **cupric cyanide** is formed as an intermediate step.

$$Cu^{++} + 2CN^- = Cu(CN)_{2(s)} \quad (22)$$

Cupric cyanide is unstable and decomposes as follows:

$$2Cu(CN)_{2(s)} = Cu_2(CN)_{2(s)} + (CN)_2 \qquad (23)$$

If an excess of CN^- ion is used, the **cupro-cyanide complex ion** is formed.

$$Cu_2(CN)_{2(s)} + 4CN^- = 2Cu(CN)_3^{--} \qquad (24)$$

The over-all reaction may be written

$$2Cu^{++} + 8CN^- = 2Cu(CN)_3^{--} + (CN)_2 \qquad (25)$$

The cupro-cyanide complex ion is exceedingly stable and thereby furnishes fewer Cu^+ ions than any other cuprous compound.

Cupric ferrocyanide, reddish-brown in color, is a very insoluble salt which serves as a sensitive test for the Cu^{++} ion. Its formation may be represented by

$$2Cu^{++} + Fe(CN)_6^{----} = Cu_2Fe(CN)_{6(s)} \qquad (26)$$

This salt is insoluble in dilute acids but soluble in solutions of NH_4OH. The latter reaction indicates that the cupric-ammonia complex ion furnishes fewer Cu^{++} ions than does the saturated solution of $Cu_2Fe(CN)_6$.

Some of the more important equilibria involving the **cuprous** ion are given in Table 27, in which the order as expressed is that of decreasing concentration of cuprous ion.

TABLE 27

EQUILIBRIA INVOLVING CUPROUS ION

Decreasing Concentration of Cu^+ Ion ↓	Reaction
	$2Cu^+ + 2Cl^- = Cu_2Cl_{2(s)}$
	$2Cu^+ + 2Br^- = Cu_2Br_{2(s)}$
	$2Cu^+ + 2CNS^- = Cu_2(CNS)_{2(s)}$
	$2Cu^+ + 2I^- = Cu_2I_{2(s)}$
	$2Cu^+ + S^{--} = Cu_2S_{(s)}$
	$Cu^+ + 3CN^- = Cu(CN)_3^{--}$

Cadmium Ion, Cd^{++}. Although cadmium exhibits a valence of one as well as of two in its compounds, those of the former are extremely rare and we shall therefore confine our attention entirely to the chemistry of the Cd^{++} ion. Many cadmium salts are insoluble or very slightly soluble in water; the soluble salts of the ion are the nitrate, chlorate, nitrite, thiosulfate, acetate, chloride, bromide, iodide and sulfate. Cadmium ion shows a marked tendency to form complex ions with halide and other ions. Very little is known concerning the strength of cadmium hydroxide as a base. Cadmium salts are not extensively hydrolyzed, thus one might predict that in solution the hydroxide is a moderately strong base. However, since many of the salts exist in water solution in the form of complex ions, it is difficult to make any exact statements regarding this point. The halides of Cd^{++} ion like those of Hg^{++} are weakly ionized in solution.

The more important equilibria involving the Cd^{++} ion are given in Table 28.

TABLE 28

Equilibria Involving Cadmium Ion

Decreasing Concentration of Cd^{++} Ion ↓

$$Cd^{++} + 2CN^- = Cd(CN)_{2(s)}$$
$$Cd^{++} + 4NH_3 = Cd(NH_3)_4^{++}$$
$$Cd^{++} + C_2O_4^{--} = CdC_2O_{4(s)}$$
$$Cd^{++} + 4CN^- = Cd(CN)_4^{--}$$
$$Cd^{++} + S^{--} = CdS_{(s)}$$

Other slightly soluble compounds of Cd^{++} ion which might be included in the above table are the thiosulfate, thiocyanate, iodate, carbonate, chromate, phosphate and hydroxide. The relative positions of these compounds arc unknown but may be readily determined by experiments.

Alkali hydroxides precipitate **cadmium hydroxide** from solutions containing Cd^{++} ion; the precipitated hydroxide is not soluble in an excess of the alkali. Therefore $Cd(OH)_2$ does not exhibit any amphoteric properties and in this respect cadmium is distinguished from the arsenic group.

Ammonium hydroxide also precipitates $Cd(OH)_2$ which is found to be readily soluble in an excess of the reagent with the formation of the **cadmium-ammonia complex ion,**

$Cd(NH_3)_4{}^{++}$. This reaction distinguishes cadmium from lead and bismuth of the copper group.

$$Cd(OH)_{2(s)} + 4NH_3 = Cd(NH_3)_4{}^{++} + 2OH^- \quad (27)$$

Cadmium sulfide (yellow) is formed when H_2S is passed into solutions of Cd^{++} ion that are not too strongly acid. Alkali sulfides produce a similar effect. Since CdS furnishes fewer Cd^{++} ions than any other cadmium compound, as Table 28 demonstrates, it is evident that the sulfide is not soluble in NH_4OH, NaOH, KOH and KCN solutions. However, it is soluble in solutions of high H^+ ion concentration. Dilute, hot nitric acid accomplishes the same purpose by oxidizing the sulfide to free sulfur.

$$3CdS_{(s)} + 2NO_3{}^- + 8H^+ = 3Cd^{++} + 2NO + 3S_{(s)} + 4H_2O \quad (28)$$

Cyanide ion precipitates **cadmium cyanide,**

$$Cd^{++} + 2CN^- = Cd(CN)_{2(s)} \quad (29)$$

which is soluble in an excess of the reagent, due to the formation of **cadmium cyanide complex ion.**

$$Cd(CN)_{2(s)} + 2CN^- = Cd(CN)_4{}^{--} \quad (30)$$

Since $Cd(CN)_4{}^{--}$ ion falls above CdS in Table 22, H_2S passed into solutions containing this complex ion precipitates cadmium sulfide.

$$Cd(CN)_4{}^{--} + H_2S = CdS_{(s)} + 2CN^- + 2HCN \quad (31)$$

It will be recalled that this is not the case when H_2S is passed into solutions of the cupro-cyanide complex ion.

Arsenous Ion and Arsenic Ion. The element arsenic forms two series of compounds in which it exhibits valences of plus three and plus five respectively. The hydroxides of the element in both valence states are decidedly acidic in character and show very little basic properties. Both acids are comparatively weak, arsenous acid being much weaker than arsenic acid. (The ionization constant for the first stage of ionization of arsenous acid, H_3AsO_3, has a value of 2.1×10^{-8}, while that of arsenic acid, H_3AsO_4, in the first stage of ionization, is 4.5×10^{-3}.) Accordingly, both arsenous and arsenic salts are readily hydrolyzed in water. The common salts of the element are the arsenites and arsenates. Solutions of the acids as well as the salts of these acids contain very small, but appreciable amounts of As^{+++} and As^{+++++} ions respectively in equilibrium with the corresponding acid anions.

Arsenic shows a marked tendency to form amphoteric sulfides in both valence states; i.e., thioarsenites and thioarsenates. Since both antimony and tin behave in a similar manner, whereas the ions of the copper group differ in this respect, advantage is taken of this difference for the analytical separation of the two groups of ions.

Arsenous oxide in water solution forms the amphoteric hydroxide, $As(OH)_3$,

$$As_2O_{3(s)} + 3H_2O = 2As(OH)_{3(s)} \tag{32}$$

which is in equilibrium with arsenous and arsenite ions,

$$H_2O + H^+ + AsO_2^- = \left\{ \begin{array}{c} As(OH)_3 \\ H_3AsO_3 \end{array} \right\}_{(s)} = As^{+++} + 3OH^- \tag{33}$$

Hence, in the presence of a strong base, the equilibrium is shifted to the left and the production of AsO_2^- ion is favored, while in the presence of a strong acid the equilibrium is shifted to the right with the production of As^{+++} ion.

Arsenic oxide is the anhydride of **arsenic acid.**

$$As_2O_{5(s)} + 3H_2O = 2H_3AsO_4 \tag{34}$$

In this solution As^{+++++} ions are also present, as a result of a dissociation process similar to that expressed in equation (33) for arsenous acid.

In general, arsenites and arsenates of the alkali and alkaline earth metals are soluble in water; arsenites and arsenates of other positive ions are usually found to be insoluble.

Arsenous sulfide is precipitated by H_2S from acid solutions of arsenites.

$$2AsO_2^- + 2H^+ + 3H_2S = As_2S_{3(s)} + 4H_2O \tag{35}$$

Alkali sulfides and $(NH_4)_2S$ likewise precipitate the yellow As_2S_3 which is soluble in an excess of the reagent due to the formation of the **thioarsenite** ion, $AsS_3{}^{---}$.

$$As_2S_{3(s)} + 3S^{--} = 2AsS_3{}^{---} \tag{36}$$

Alkali hydroxides also dissolve As_2S_3 forming arsenites and thioarsenites.

$$As_2S_{3(s)} + 4OH^- = AsS_3{}^{---} + AsO_2{}^- + 2H_2O \tag{37}$$

Use is made of the solubility of sulfides of arsenic in ammonium polysulfide to separate arsenic, together with antimony and tin, from the copper group ions. In this reaction As_2S_3 is oxidized to the pentavalent state.

$$As_2S_{3(s)} + 3S_2{}^{--} = 2AsS_4{}^{---} + S_{(s)} \tag{38}$$

Arsenic sulfide, As_2S_5, is formed by passing H_2S into strongly acid solutions of arsenic acid.

$$2H_3AsO_4 + 5H_2S = As_2S_{5(s)} + 8H_2O \tag{39}$$

This reaction is relatively slow in cold solution. Since H_2S tends to reduce the pentavalent arsenic to the trivalent state, the precipitate contains a mixture of As_2S_3 and As_2S_5. By increasing the temperature and the concentration of the H^+ ion of the solution, the formation of As_2S_3 is favored. Like arsenous sulfide, arsenic sulfide is readily dissolved by alkali hydroxides and also by alkali sulfides.

$$As_2S_{5(s)} + 3S^{--} = 2AsS_4{}^{---} \tag{40}$$

Hot concentrated HNO_3 dissolves both As_2S_3 and As_2S_5.

$$As_2S_{3(s)} + 10NO_3{}^- + 10H^+$$
$$= 2H_3AsO_4 + 3S_{(s)} + 10NO_2 + 2H_2O \tag{41}$$
$$As_2S_{5(s)} + 10NO_3{}^- + 10H^+$$
$$= 2H_3AsO_4 + 5S_{(s)} + 10NO_2 + 2H_2O \tag{42}$$

Stannous chloride reduces all compounds of arsenic in hot concentrated HCl solution to metallic arsenic.

$$2As^{+++} + 3Sn^{++} = 2As_{(s)} + 3Sn^{++++} \tag{43}$$

Antimony compounds are not reduced by Sn^{++} ion.

Magnesium salts in the presence of NH_4Cl and NH_4OH precipitate from solutions of arsenates, $MgNH_4AsO_4 \cdot 6H_2O$, a white crystalline compound which is readily soluble in acids.

$$AsO_4^{---} + Mg^{++} + NH_4^+ = MgNH_4AsO_{4(s)} \quad (44)$$

Ammonium molybdate, in HNO_3 solution warmed to 60–70°, gives with a solution of an arsenate a yellow precipitate of **ammonium arsenomolybdate,** $(NH_4)_3AsO_4 \cdot 12MoO_3$. This precipitate is very similar in appearance and properties to ammonium phosphomolybdate, except that the latter precipitates from cold solutions. Arsenites do not give a precipitate with ammonium molybdate.

Small amounts of arsenic may be readily detected by means of the Marsh test which involves the reduction of arsenic compounds by a highly electropositive element, such as zinc, to arsine, AsH_3, and the subsequent decomposition of the gas to metallic arsenic. The latter appears in the exit tube of the apparatus as a metallic mirror. The reactions which take place in the test are the following:

$$As_2O_{3(s)} + 6Zn_{(s)} + 12H^+ = 2AsH_{3(g)} + 6Zn^{++} + 3H_2O \quad (45)$$

or $\quad H_3AsO_4 + 4Zn_{(s)} + 8H^+ = AsH_{3(g)} + 4Zn^{++} + 4H_2O \quad (46)$

and $\qquad\qquad 2AsH_{3(g)} = 2As_{(s)} + 3H_{2(g)} \qquad\qquad (47)$

Another test for arsenic is the reduction of Ag^+ ion by AsH_3 to metallic silver.

$$6Ag^+ + AsH_{3(g)} + 3H_2O = 6Ag_{(s)} + H_3AsO_3 + 6H^+ \quad (48)$$

Antimonous Ion and Antimonic Ion. As in the case of arsenic, antimony exists in two valence states, plus three and plus five. However, since antimony falls below arsenic in the fifth group of the periodic table, it is more electropositive than arsenic. Thus, the hydroxides of antimony are more basic than those of arsenic although both are amphoteric. Accordingly, antimonites and antimonates may be formed but they are rather extensively hydrolyzed in water solution. Even as bases, the above hydroxides are weak and their salts are highly hydrolyzed; strong acids must be added to their solutions to prevent the basic salts from precipitating.

Antimonous and **antimonic oxides**, Sb_2O_3 and Sb_2O_5, behave very much like the corresponding oxides of arsenic, the small differences being due to the more basic character of the former.

Solutions of alkali hydroxides, ammonium hydroxide, or alkali carbonates, when added to solutions containing Sb^{+++} ion, precipitate the white hydrated **antimonous oxide**, $Sb_2O_3 \cdot H_2O$, which in solution undoubtedly forms some **metantimonous acid**, $HSbO_2$.

$$2HSbO_2 = Sb_2O_{3(s)} + H_2O \tag{49}$$

The oxide is decidedly amphoteric in nature as the following equations indicate:

$$Sb_2O_{3(s)} + 2OH^- = 2SbO_2^- + H_2O \tag{50}$$

$$Sb_2O_{3(s)} + 6H^+ = 2Sb^{+++} + 3H_2O \tag{51}$$

Thus, the oxide is soluble in strong bases with the production of SbO_2^- ion, and is soluble in strong acids forming Sb^{+++} ion.

The halides of antimony are readily hydrolyzed in water solution, with the formation of basic salts.

$$SbCl_3 + H_2O = SbOCl_{(s)} + 2H^+ + 2Cl^- \tag{52}$$

The reaction is reversible so that the addition of HCl to the solution will dissolve the basic salt; in other words, shift the equilibrium to the left. In a saturated solution of SbOCl there are sufficient Sb^{+++} ions so that the addition of H_2S will precipitate Sb_2S_3. Antimonous sulfide may be precipitated from any solution containing Sb^{+++} ions provided the H^+ ion concentration is not too great.

$$2Sb^{+++} + 3H_2S = Sb_2S_{3(s)} + 6H^+ \tag{53}$$

Sb_2S_3 is soluble in moderately strong HCl solutions (reversal of above equation) due to the fact that a saturated solution of the sulfide furnishes sufficient S^{--} ions to form H_2S.

Like arsenous sulfide, Sb_2S_3 is soluble in $(NH_4)_2S_x$ with the formation of the **thioantimonate** ion, SbS_4^{---}.

$$Sb_2S_{3(s)} + 3S_2^{--} = 2SbS_4^{---} + S_{(s)} \qquad (54)$$

If the thioantimonate solution is treated with HCl, a precipitate of Sb_2S_5 and some free sulfur is formed. The sulfur produced in this reaction is due to the decomposition of the polysulfide ion.

$$2SbS_4^{---} + 6H^+ = Sb_2S_{5(s)} + 3H_2S \qquad (55)$$

and

$$S_2^{--} + 2H^+ = H_2S + S_{(s)} \qquad (56)$$

Since antimony falls below iron in the oxidation-reduction series of the elements, the latter will reduce Sb^{+++} ion to metallic antimony in acid solution.

$$2Sb^{+++} + 3Fe_{(s)} = 2Sb_{(s)} + 3Fe^{++} \qquad (57)$$

From moderately strong acid solutions of Sb^{+++++} ion, H_2S precipitates **antimonic sulfide,** Sb_2S_5, which is redissolved by the addition of concentrated HCl with the production of Sb^{+++} ion.

$$2H_3SbO_4 + 5H_2S = Sb_2S_{5(s)} + 8H_2O \qquad (58)$$

An oxidation-reduction reaction takes place which involves the reduction of the Sb_2S_5 to the Sb^{+++} ion and the oxidation of the S^{--} ion to free sulfur.

$$Sb_2S_{5(s)} + 6H^+ = 2Sb^{+++} + 2S_{(s)} + 3H_2S \qquad (59)$$

Antimonic sulfide resembles Sb_2S_3 in that it is soluble in solutions of $(NH_4)_2S$ or $(NH_4)_2S_x$, as well as in solutions of the alkali sulfides. The product of the reaction is the **thioantimonate** ion, SbS_4^{---}.

$$Sb_2S_{5(s)} + 3S^{--} = 2SbS_4^{---} \qquad (60)$$

Antimony gives the Marsh test through the procedure commonly used for arsenic. However, the antimony mirror which is obtained is not soluble in NaOBr solution, while the arsenic mirror dissolves readily.

Stannous Ion, Sn^{++} — Stannic Ion, Sn^{++++}. Tin is an element of the fourth group of the periodic table and occupies a position between germanium and lead. Like both of these elements, tin forms two series of compounds which exhibit valences of plus two and plus four respectively; the former are known as stannous compounds and the latter, stannic. Since the hydroxides corresponding to both valence states, namely $Sn(OH)_2$ and $Sn(OH)_4$, are amphoteric, stannite ion, SnO_2^{--}, and stannate ion, SnO_3^{--}, are readily formed in alkaline solution. In acid solution Sn^{++} and Sn^{++++} ions are present. All four types of tin compounds undergo hydrolysis in aqueous solution.

Stannous chloride combines with water to form a hydrate, $SnCl_2 \cdot 2H_2O$. However, in water solution hydrolysis occurs with the formation of a basic salt.

$$Sn^{++} + Cl^- + H_2O = Sn(OH)Cl_{(s)} + H^+ \qquad (61)$$

In order to prevent hydrolysis, it is necessary to add an excess of HCl to the solution as the above equilibrium indicates.

A solution of $SnCl_2$ after exposure to the atmosphere is found to contain considerable amounts of Sn^{++++} ion due to the oxidation of the Sn^{++} ion by oxygen.

$$2Sn^{++} + O_2 + 4H^+ = 2Sn^{++++} + 2H_2O \qquad (62)$$

However, oxidation may be prevented here by the addition of metallic tin to the solution.

$$Sn^{++++} + Sn_{(s)} = 2Sn^{++} \qquad (63)$$

Solutions of alkali hydroxides, ammonium hydroxide or of alkali carbonates give with Sn^{++} ion a white precipitate of $Sn(OH)_2$ (in the acid form, H_2SnO_2).

$$Sn^{++} + 2OH^- = Sn(OH)_{2(s)} (H_2SnO_2) \qquad (64)$$

The equilibrium involving both stannous and stannite ions may be expressed by

$$H^+ + HSnO_2^- = \left\{ \begin{array}{c} Sn(OH)_2 \\ H_2SnO_2 \end{array} \right\}_{(s)} = Sn^{++} + 2OH^- \qquad (65)$$

Thus, a strong base shifts the equilibrium to the left with the production of $HSnO_2^-$ ions, while a strong acid shifts the equilibrium to the right favoring the production of Sn^{++} ions.

From solutions of Sn^{++} ion containing H^+ ion at moderate concentration, **stannous sulfide** (brown) is precipitated by H_2S.

$$Sn^{++} + H_2S = SnS_{(s)} + 2H^+ \tag{66}$$

SnS is soluble in concentrated HCl, practically insoluble in solutions of $(NH_4)_2S$, which distinguishes Sn^{++} ion from As^{+++}, Sb^{+++} and Sn^{++++} ions, but is readily soluble in hot $(NH_4)_2S_x$ solution with the formation of **thiostannate ion.**

$$SnS_{(s)} + S_2^{--} = SnS_3^{--} \tag{67}$$

Mercuric chloride solution oxidizes Sn^{++} ion to Sn^{++++} ion.

$$Sn^{++} + 2HgCl_2 = Hg_2Cl_{2(s)} + Sn^{++++} + 2Cl^- \tag{68}$$

If an excess of Sn^{++} ion is used in this reaction, further reduction of the Hg_2Cl_2 takes place to form metallic mercury.

$$Sn^{++} + Hg_2Cl_{2(s)} = 2Hg_{(s)} + Sn^{++++} + 2Cl^- \tag{69}$$

Stannic hydroxide does not exist as such in the solid state. The partially **hydrated oxide,** H_2SnO_3, known as **alpha stannic acid,** may be produced by the action of sodium hydroxide on stannic chloride solutions. The **beta** form, which is better known as **metastannic** acid, results from the action of strong HNO_3 on metallic tin. The former is readily soluble in acids and bases giving a series of salts known as normal or alpha stannic compounds. Metastannic acid does not dissolve in acids but when heated for a short time with concentrated HCl, a compound is formed which is soluble in water. The compositions of these compounds are not definitely known.

Alpha stannic acid (or dehydrated stannic hydroxide) is decidedly amphoteric.

$$H_2SnO_{3(s)} + 2OH^- = SnO_3^{--} + 2H_2O \tag{70}$$

$$H_2SnO_{3(s)} + 4H^+ = Sn^{++++} + 3H_2O \tag{71}$$

From acid solutions H_2S produces a yellow precipitate of **stannic sulfide, SnS_2.** Under some conditions of precipitation this sulfide forms colloidal solutions. This may be prevented or minimized by the addition of a salt and by heating. SnS_2 dissolves readily in 6 M HCl with the liberation of H_2S. It is likewise soluble in $(NH_4)_2S$ solutions with the formation of the **thiostannate ion, SnS_3^{--}.**

$$SnS_{2(s)} + S^{--} = SnS_3^{--} \tag{72}$$

SnS_2 is distinguished from SnS by its solubility in $(NH_4)_2S$ solution. The higher valence compound is more acidic in character and therefore shows a greater tendency to form the corresponding amphoteric ion. SnS is soluble in $(NH_4)_2S_x$ solution, in which reaction it is oxidized to the tetravalent state.

Preliminary Experiments

1. Mix 1 ml. of 0.1 M solutions of each of the following salts: $Pb(NO_3)_2$, $Hg(NO_3)_2$, $Cu(NO_3)_2$ and $Cd(NO_3)_2$. To the mixture in a saturating flask add H_2S until the solution is saturated. Collect the precipitates on a small filter, or centrifuge, and wash very thoroughly to eliminate NO_3^- ion. Pour 2 ml. of 6 M HCl over the precipitate, and stir if the centrifuge is used. Now add sufficient NH_4OH to the HCl solution to neutralize it. Make the solution 0.2 M in H^+ ion by adding the correct amount of HCl. Pass H_2S gas into the latter solution and note the result. Explain.

2. Prepare 10 ml. of each of the following HCl solutions: 6 M, 2 M, 0.2 M, .02 M and .002 M. In making the dilutions use the medicine dropper to measure 1 ml. portions and a graduate for larger volumes. (For example, to make 10 ml. of .002 M HCl, add 1 ml. of .02 M solution to the graduate and dilute with water to 10 ml.) Add 2 ml. of each of the above HCl solutions to 2 ml. of each of the following salt solutions: 0.1 M $CuSO_4$, 0.1 M $CdSO_4$ and 0.1 M $ZnSO_4$. Thus, the resulting solutions (15 in all) contain H^+ ion at a concentration of one-half that of the original solution, and the positive metal ion at a concentration of .05 M. Pass H_2S gas into each of these solutions and note the appearance and the color of any precipitate which may form.

Record your observations in a chart similar to that given below. Explain the results on the basis of the ionization of H_2S in acid solution and the solubilities of the different sulfides.

(H^+)	0.05 M CuSO$_4$	0.05 M CdSO$_4$	0.05 M ZnSO$_4$
0.001 M			
0.01 M			
0.1 M			
1.0 M			
3.0 M			

3. Prepare the following $Pb(NO_3)_2$ solutions: (a) .01 M, by adding 9 ml. of water to 1 ml. of 0.1 M $Pb(NO_3)_2$; (b) .001 M, by adding 9 ml. of water to 1 ml. of solution (a); (c) .0001 M, by adding 9 ml. of water to 1 ml. of solution (b); (d) .00001 M, by adding 9 ml. of water to 1 ml. of solution (c); and (e) .000001 M, by adding 9 ml. of water to 1 ml. of solution (d). Saturate 3 ml. of each of these solutions with H_2S and note the limiting concentration which gives a distinctly visible precipitate. (Note: Very finely divided suspensions appear as colored solutions.) The concentration of the S^{--} ion in these solutions is approximately 1×10^{-15} M. From the $K_{S.P.}$ for PbS (7×10^{-30}) calculate the minimum concentration of Pb^{++} that should give a precipitate provided a supersaturated solution of PbS is not formed. Compare this calculated value of (Pb^{++}) with that corresponding to the limit of visibility determined above.

4. In the chart on page 354 the ions of the copper-arsenic group are listed horizontally and a number of reagents vertically. In the blank spaces provided in a similar chart made in your notebook give the products of the reactions when the given reagent is added drop by drop to a solution of the ion in question. If the product is a precipitate, indicate this fact by denoting the solid phase as, for example, $CuS_{(s)}$. Indicate the color of all precipitates and solutions containing new products. If the reaction does not give a precipitate but produces new ions, indicate these in the appropriate places. If no reaction takes place as far as you can ascertain, write *no reaction*. From your knowledge of the chemical properties of these ions, *fill in as many blank spaces as possible* *without carrying out the experiments. If you are not familiar with the reaction in question perform an experiment to obtain the desired information.*

Reagent added	Hg^{++}	Pb^{++}	Bi^{+++}	Cu^{++}	Cd^{++}	As^{+++}	Sb^{+++}	Sn^{++}	Sn^{++++}
6 M NaOH									
6 M NaOH in excess									
3 M NH$_4$OH									
3 M NH$_4$OH in excess									
0.1 M NaCl									
H$_2$S in 0.3 M HCl									

5. The sulfides of the copper-arsenic group are listed horizontally and reagents vertically, in the following chart. Indicate in the appropriate space in a similar chart in your notebook whether the given reagent will dissolve the sulfide. Also give the formula of any new substances formed in the reaction. *Perform experiments only if necessary.*

	HgS	PbS	Bi$_2$S$_3$	CuS	CdS	As$_2$S$_3$	Sb$_2$S$_3$	SnS	SnS$_2$
0.3 M HCl									
Dilute HNO$_3$									
Aqua regia									
(NH$_4$)$_2$S									
(NH$_4$)$_2$S$_x$									

6. BiCl$_3$ is hydrolyzed in water solution to the basic salt, BiOCl. Devise and perform an experiment to show that the reaction is reversible.

7. Devise and carry out experiments to verify the order of CuC_2O_4, $Cu(OH)_2$, $Cu(NH_3)_4^{++}$, and CuS in Table 26.

8. To 2 drops of $0.1\ M$ $Pb(NO_3)_2$ solution add 3 drops of $0.1\ M$ $(NH_4)_2SO_4$ solution to precipitate $PbSO_4$. To the solution containing the precipitate add $3\ M$ NH_4Ac solution, drop by drop, until the $PbSO_4$ dissolves. Lead acetate is very soluble. What conclusions can you draw regarding the extent of ionization of $Pb(Ac)_2$ in solution? Now add to the solution about 10 drops of $1\ M$ $(NH_4)_2SO_4$ solution to reprecipitate $PbSO_4$. Explain.

9. To 5 drops of $0.1\ M$ $SnCl_2$ solution add 1 ml. of water and saturate with H_2S. Brown SnS is precipitated. Add to the suspension an equal volume, about 1 ml., of $15\ M$ NH_4OH and again saturate with H_2S. Note that the brown SnS does not dissolve.

To 5 drops of $0.1\ M$ $SnCl_2$ solution add 1 ml. of water and then add 2 drops of 3% H_2O_2 solution. Warm gently. Saturate the solution with H_2S; a yellow precipitate appears. Now add to the suspension an equal volume of $15\ M$ NH_4OH and saturate with H_2S, if necessary. The precipitate is found to dissolve. Explain the results of these two experiments.

10. To a small test tube containing 12 drops of $0.1\ M$ $Cu(NO_3)_2$ solution and 12 drops of $0.1\ M$ $Cd(NO_3)_2$ solution add enough water to make the total volume 3 ml. Add 6 drops of $6\ M$ HCl solution and then saturate the solution with solid NH_4Cl. Pass H_2S into the solution, centrifuge, and divide the centrifugate into two equal portions. To one portion add 1 ml. of $2\ M$ NaAc solution. To the other portion add 10 volumes of water. In each case a precipitate is obtained. Explain what happens in each step of this experiment. (Note: Cd^{++} ion in the presence of large amounts of Cl^- ion forms a complex ion, presumably having the composition, $CdCl_4^{--}$. For every $CdCl_4^{--}$ ion which dissociates, one Cd^{++} ion and four Cl^- ions are produced.)

11. To 12 drops of $0.1\ M$ arsenic test solution add 2 ml. of water, 3 drops of $6\ M$ HCl, 1 drop of $1\ M$ NH_4I, and heat the solution to boiling. Saturate the solution for several minutes with H_2S. Centrifuge or filter. If centrifuged, add 1 ml. of water to the precipitate in the test tube; if filtered, transfer the precipitate on the filter paper to a 10 ml. test tube with 1 ml. of water. Now add 2 ml. of $6\ M$ NaOH solution. Place a few drops of $0.1\ M$ $AgNO_3$ solution on a piece of filter paper large enough to cover the mouth of the test tube. Have ready a very small piece of absorbent cotton. Now add a few granules of metallic aluminum to the test tube containing the solution, place the absorbent cotton into the mouth of the test tube, and cap the test tube with the piece of filter paper wet with the $AgNO_3$ solution. Heat the solution very gently to start the reaction between the aluminum and the NaOH solution. In the course of a minute or two the filter paper will turn black. Aluminum reacts with NaOH solution with the liberation of hydrogen. In the presence of trivalent arsenic, arsine is also produced. When the arsine gas comes in contact with the $AgNO_3$ on the filter paper, the Ag^+ ion is reduced to metallic silver. Equations for the reactions are:

$$2Al + 2OH^- + 2H_2O = 2AlO_2^- + 3H_2$$
$$As_2S_{3(s)} + 4OH^- = AsS_3^{---} + AsO_2^- + 2H_2O$$
$$AsO_2^- + 2Al + OH^- + H_2O = 2AlO_2^- + AsH_{3(g)}$$
$$6Ag^+ + AsH_{3(g)} + 3H_2O = 6Ag_{(s)} + H_3AsO_3 + 6H^+.$$

12. To each of three test tubes add 2 drops of 0.1 M $SnCl_2$ solution. To one of these add 2 ml. of water, to the second add 1 ml. of water and 1 ml. of 12 M HCl, and to the third add 2 ml. of 12 M HCl. Now add 2 drops of 0.1 M $HgCl_2$ solution to each of these three solutions, and allow them to stand for a minute or two. Write the equations for the reactions involved in the formation of Hg_2Cl_2 and metallic mercury. Postulate an explanation for the inhibiting effect of the high Cl^- ion concentration present in the second and third tubes. (Ammonium chloride produces the same effect as the HCl.)

13. Place 2 drops of 0.1 M $SbCl_3$ solution in a small test tube and add 10 drops of water. Make the solution alkaline with $6M$ NH_4OH solution and then add 6 M HAc until just acidic. (Do not be concerned about the fact that the precipitate does not dissolve in the HAc.) Add 1 drop of 6 M HAc in excess. Heat the solution almost to boiling and drop into it a few small crystals of $Na_2S_2O_3$, sodium thiosulfate. Note the formation of the orange-red antimony oxysulfide at the interface.

Procedure for the Analysis of the Copper-Arsenic Group

SCHEMATIC OUTLINE

Solution: Cu^{++}, Hg^{++}, Bi^{+++}, Cd^{++}, Pb^{++}, H_3AsO_4, H_3AsO_3, H_3SbO_4, Sb^{+++}, Sn^{++} and Sn^{++++}.

Make 0.3 M in H^+ ion — Add 3% H_2O_2 — Heat — Add 1 M NH_4I — Add H_2S — Cool — Add H_2S.

(C–D)

Precipitate: CuS, HgS, Bi_2S_3, CdS, PbS, As_2S_3, Sb_2S_3, SnS_2.
Treat with 15 M NH_4OH, 6 M NH_4OH and H_2S.

(C–D–1)

Residue: CuS, HgS, Bi_2S_3, CdS, PbS.
Treat with 6 M HNO_3.

(C)

Solution: AsS_3^{---}, SbS_3^{---}, SnS_3^{--}.
Add 12 M HCl.

(D)

Residue: HgS.
Dissolve in aqua regia. Add 0.1 M $SnCl_2$.

(C–1)

Precipitate: Hg_2Cl_2 and Hg.

Solution: Bi^{+++}, Cd^{++}, Pb^{++}, Cu^{++}.
Add concentrated H_2SO_4. Evaporate.

Ppt.: $PbSO_4$.
Add 3 M NH_4Ac. Add 1 M K_2CrO_4.

(C–2)

Solution: Bi^{+++}, Cd^{++}, Cu^{++}.
Add 15 M NH_4OH.
Blue color of $Cu(NH_3)_4^{++}$ indicates Cu^{++}.

(C–3)

Ppt.: $PbCrO_4$.

Ppt.: $Bi(OH)_3$. Add Na_2SnO_2 Solution.

(C–4)

Solution: $Cd(NH_3)_4^{++}$, $Cu(NH_3)_4^{++}$.
Add 6 M HCl.
Add NH_4Cl.
Add H_2S.

(C–5)

Ppt.: Bi. (black)

Ppt.: CuS

Solution: $CdCl_4^{--}$
Add 2 M NaAc.
Add H_2S.

Ppt.: CdS. (yellow)

Residue: As_2S_3.
Add 6 M NaOH and Al.

(D–1)

Black ppt. with $AgNO_3$. Test for arsenic.

Solution: Sb^{+++}, Sn^{++++}.

Evaporate. Introduce iron wire. Add 0.1 M $HgCl_2$.

(D–2)

Ppt.: Hg_2Cl_2 and Hg. Test for tin.

Add 6 M NH_4OH. Add 6 M HAc. Add solid $Na_2S_2O_3$.

(D–3)

Red color. Test for Sb.

Obtain a sample of an unknown from the laboratory instructor. In this sample each unknown ion is present at a minimum concentration of about .02 mole per liter. Reserve a part of this solution to make any tests you see fit (other than adding H_2S), to obtain preliminary information as to which ions may be present (Preliminary Experiment #4 will be of assistance here). If the original solution is alkaline and clear, it cannot contain Hg^{++} and Bi^{+++} ions. If the solution is alkaline and clear and NH_4OH is absent, then Hg^{++}, Bi^{+++}, Cd^{++}, and Cu^{++} ions are not present. Why?

C–D. Precipitation of the Copper-Arsenic Group. Test the solution with litmus paper * [1] to determine whether it is neutral, acidic, or alkaline. If acidic, add 5 drops of 3% H_2O_2 [2] to 3 ml. of the solution in a 25 ml. Erlenmeyer flask, heat to boiling and then add 15 M NH_4OH drop by drop until the solution gives an alkaline reaction with litmus paper. Test the solution for alkalinity after the addition of each drop. Add 6 M HCl drop by drop until the solution is acidic to litmus (this will not require more than two or three drops). Now add one drop of 6 M HCl for each ml. of solution. The solution should be 0.3 M with respect to hydrogen ion.[3,4]

If the original solution is alkaline, add 6 M HCl drop by drop until just acidic and then add one drop of 6 M HCl for each ml. of solution. Now add the 5 drops of H_2O_2 and heat to boiling.

Add one drop of 1 M NH_4I solution.[5] (Do not be disturbed if a precipitate appears either at this point or when NH_4OH is added.) Heat the solution to boiling and saturate for one minute with H_2S according to the procedure described on page 279. Heat to boiling again, and again saturate with H_2S for another minute (even with iodide ion present the precipitation of arsenous sulfide may be slow). Cool the solution under the tap and saturate with H_2S once more.[6]

Pour the solution into a 10 ml. test tube; wash out the Erlenmeyer flask with 1 ml. of water, and add to the original solution in the test tube. Centrifuge for one minute. Decant the solution into the 25 ml. Erlenmeyer flask

Pour the solution over a previously prepared filter. Wash the Erlenmeyer flask with 1 ml. of water and also pour this through the filter, adding

* All notes indicated by superior numbers are to be found at the end of their respective sections.

(which has in the meantime been cleaned). If the solution which is decanted contains a small amount of sulfide which, because of surface tension, has not settled during the centrifugation, it should be passed through a filter before pouring into the Erlenmeyer flask. Test this solution with methyl violet paper (see note 3). Adjust the H^+ ion concentration *if necessary* to 0.3 M by adding a drop or two of 3 M NH_4OH.[7] Again pass H_2S into the cold solution to test for completeness of sulfide precipitation.[8] If precipitation is not complete saturate again with H_2S and add this solution to the test tube containing the previously precipitated sulfides and centrifuge again. When precipitation is complete discard the supernatant solution after centrifugation. To the sulfides left in the bottom of the 10 ml. test tube after centrifugation add 2 ml. of water. Wash down the side of the test tube with an additional ml. of water. Stopper the test tube and shake to bring the sulfides into suspension. Centrifuge or filter again and discard the supernatant wash water.[9,10] Wash again. Add 1 ml. of 15 M NH_4OH to the precipitate in the 10 ml. test tube.

this wash water to the previously filtered solution. Test this solution with methyl violet paper (see note 3). Adjust the H^+ ion concentration if necessary to 0.3 M by adding a drop or two of 3 M NH_4OH.[7] Again pass H_2S into it to test for completeness of precipitation. If the precipitation is not complete,[8] pour the solution in the Erlenmeyer flask over the previously filtered precipitate in the filter and discard the filtrate. Wash the precipitate several times using 2 ml. of water each time.[9,10] Discard the wash water. Puncture a hole in the apex of the filter and with the capillary syringe wash the precipitate into a 10 ml. test tube with 1 ml. of 15 M NH_4OH.

NOTE 1. *In making tests with litmus, dip a thin glass rod into the solution to be tested and press the end of the rod against the paper.*

NOTE 2. *The H_2O_2 is added to bring about the oxidation of Sn^{++} ion to Sn^{++++} ion. SnS forms a gelatinous precipitate which is dissolved only in $(NH_4)_2S_x$, while SnS_2 is readily soluble in this reagent. By converting Sn^{++} ion to Sn^{++++} ion it is possible to use $(NH_4)_2S$ instead of $(NH_4)_2S_x$ in separating the arsenic from the copper group. This procedure has two distinct advantages: (1) CuS is retained practically completely in the copper group, and (2) the objectionable later precipitation of free sulfur together with the sulfides is eliminated.*

NOTE 3. *If the ions of weak acids (such as acetate) are present it is advisable to determine and adjust the H^+ ion concentration to 0.3 M by means of methyl violet paper. To determine the color of methyl violet which corre-*

sponds to 0.3 M make a solution of 3 drops of 6 M HCl in 3 ml. of water and use this solution as a standard for comparison. If no methyl violet paper is available it may be made by "chalking" a piece of filter paper with an indelible pencil, wetting it with water and then drying it high over the Bunsen burner. In testing the acidity with methyl violet paper, make certain the paper is dry before judging its color.

NOTE 4. *Ignore any precipitate which may be present in the original unknown solution, or in the solution after the H^+ ion concentration has been adjusted. Owing to the extremely low solubility of the sulfides of this group, any other slightly soluble salts will be converted to the corresponding sulfides by H_2S.*

NOTE 5. *The precipitation of arsenic acid as As_2S_5 is a slow one while the precipitation of arsenous acid as As_2S_3 is rapid. The iodide ion reduces the arsenic acid to arsenous acid and allows the precipitation to take place relatively rapidly. The iodine formed in this reaction is reduced to the iodide ion by the H_2S and can then react again with more arsenic acid. The iodide ion is therefore a catalyst for the precipitation of As_2S_3 from arsenic acid.*

NOTE 6. *The precipitation of CdS is much faster in a cold solution.*

NOTE 7. *H^+ ion is produced when the sulfides are precipitated.*

$$M^{++} + H_2S = MS_{(s)} + 2H^+$$

NOTE 8. *Free sulfur is usually formed when H_2S is passed into the acid solution. The original unknown or test solution may contain NO_3^- ion which in acid solution reacts with H_2S to form sulfur.*

$$3H_2S + 2NO_3^- + 2H^+ = 3S_{(s)} + 2NO + 4H_2O$$

NOTE 9. *If Cl^- ion is carried over with the precipitate when washing is insufficient, it will interfere in the separation of HgS from the other sulfides later. HgS is not soluble in HNO_3 but it will dissolve in HNO_3 if Cl^- is present.*

NOTE 10. *If a colloidal suspension is formed add 1 ml. of 5 M NH_4NO_3 to it or to 3 ml. of distilled water and use this solution for washing.*

C–D–1. Separation of the Arsenic Group from the Copper Group. To the suspension obtained from **C–D** add 6 M NH_4OH to make a total volume of about 3 ml. Now saturate this solution with H_2S. In carrying out this operation use a glass tube drawn to a fine tip, connect this tube to the hydrogen sulfide generator and insert the tip into the test tube (see page 295). After saturating with H_2S, heat the solution gently but do not boil. Centrifuge or filter and reserve the supernatant liquid which contains the dissolved sulfides of arsenic, antimony, and tin.

Repeat the $NH_4OH–H_2S$ treatment of the precipitate and combine supernatant liquid with the one previously obtained. Label this solution D.

Add 3 ml. of water to the precipitate C in the test tube. Shake to obtain a suspension and centrifuge discarding the supernatant wash water. Repeat the washing (see note 10). Add 1 ml. of water to the precipitate.

Wash the precipitate C in the filter with 3 ml. of water and discard the wash water (see note 10). Wash the precipitate into a 10 ml. test tube with 1 ml. of water.

C. Separation of HgS. To the suspended copper group sulfides **C** add an equal volume of 6 M HNO$_3$. Heat the mixture to boiling and continue to boil until no more precipitate appears to dissolve. If any residue remains, it should be either black or almost white (not brown) in color. Continue further treatment immediately. (It will be recalled that HgS does not dissolve in dilute HNO$_3$ while all other sulfides of the copper group dissolve readily. However, if chloride ion remains with the precipitate, dilute aqua regia will be formed upon the addition of the nitric acid and mercury may dissolve. It was for this reason that the precipitate had to be washed thoroughly.) Cool the solution and centrifuge or filter. The residue may contain HgS and free sulfur, and may also contain undissolved sulfides.[11] Pour the supernatant liquid into (or collect the filtrate in) another 10 ml. test tube and label it **C-2.**

With the aid of a pointed glass rod transfer the globule of free sulfur back to the test tube which may contain the HgS. Add 1 ml. of 15 M NH$_4$OH. Saturate the solution with H$_2$S. If necessary agitate the globule of sulfur to bring it into solution. Any imbedded sulfides will not dissolve. Centrifuge if necessary and discard the supernatant liquid. Wash twice with 3 ml. of water, centrifuge, and discard the wash water. Add 10 drops of water and 10

Puncture a hole in the filter paper and wash the residue into a 10 ml. test tube with 1 ml. of 15 M NH$_4$OH. Saturate the solution with H$_2$S. If necessary agitate the globule of sulfur to bring it into solution. Any imbedded sulfides will not dissolve. Filter if necessary and discard the filtrate. Wash with 3 ml. of water twice and filter again, discarding the wash water. Puncture a hole in the filter and wash the residue into a 10 ml. test tube with 1 ml. of water.

NOTE 11. *The free sulfur formed in this reaction may imbed into it an appreciable amount of the sulfides which will then be protected against the action of the HNO$_3$. The sulfur must therefore be separated from the sulfides and the residual sulfides again treated with this reagent.*

drops of 6 M HNO$_3$. Heat to dissolve residual copper group sulfides other than HgS. Centrifuge. Decant the solution, combining it with **C–2**. Any residue may now contain HgS, free sulfur, or both.[12]

Add 1 ml. of 6 M HNO$_3$. Heat to dissolve the residual copper group sulfides other than HgS. Filter the solution combining the filtrate with **C–2**. Any residue may contain HgS, free sulfur, or both.[12]

NOTE 12. *A black residue is not in itself sufficient evidence for the presence of mercury. The specific test for Hg^{++} ion should be made. Nor does a white residue indicate the absence of mercury. With more concentrated HNO$_3$ a white insoluble double salt of mercuric nitrate and mercuric sulfide is formed.*

C–1. Test for Hg^{++} Ion. The residue from **C** which may contain HgS is to be dissolved in aqua regia and this solution is to be tested for the presence of Hg^{++} ion.

To the precipitate in the 10 ml. test tube add 2 drops of 15 M HNO$_3$ and 10 drops of 12 M HCl.

Puncture a hole in the filter paper and wash the precipitate into a 10 ml. test tube with 1 ml. of cold 12 M HCl. To the solution add 4 drops of 15 M HNO$_3$.

Heat to boiling and agitate with a stirring rod until the greater part of the residue is dissolved. Add 1 ml. of water, centrifuge or filter, if necessary, and then transfer the supernatant liquid or filtrate to a small casserole. Evaporate the solution over an open flame (*use hood*) until only 2 or 3 drops of liquid remain.[13] (Do not evaporate to dryness; HgCl$_2$ is volatile.) Add 1 ml. of water and transfer the solution to a small test tube. Filter, if necessary. Add 2 or 3 drops of 0.1 M SnCl$_2$ solution. If Hg^{++} ion is present a white precipitate of Hg$_2$Cl$_2$ will appear which will turn gray or black due to the further reduction of the Hg$_2$Cl$_2$ to metallic mercury.

NOTE 13. *A high Cl$^-$ ion concentration inhibits the reaction between Sn^{++} and HgCl$_2$. Therefore it is necessary to remove the greater part of the HCl before this test is made. (See Preliminary Experiment 12.)*

C–2. Test for Pb^{++} Ion. Transfer the filtrate **C–2** to a small casserole, and add 8 drops of 6 M H$_2$SO$_4$. Evaporate the solution until white, *dense* fumes of SO$_3$ appear.[14] These fumes are not to be confused with steam. They will appear only when there is practically no liquid left in the casserole. *Cool well*, and *very cautiously* add 1 ml. of water.[15] After cooling, pour the solution into a 10 ml. test tube; rinse the casserole with 0.5 ml. of water, and add the wash water to the solution. If a finely divided white precipitate of $PbSO_4$ appears, centrifuge or filter. Pour the supernatant liquid into another test tube and label it **C–3.** (If filtered, label the filtrate **C–3.**) Wash the precipitate with 0.5 ml. of water, centrifuge or filter, and add the wash water to **C–3.** Do not allow any $PbSO_4$ to be carried over into solution **C–3.**

To the precipitate in the test tube add 1 ml. of 3 M NH_4Ac solution and heat. If a precipitate still appears in the solution, centrifuge and discard the residue.	Dissolve the precipitate on the filter paper with 1 ml. of hot 3 M NH_4Ac solution. Use the capillary syringe.

Add 2 drops of 1 M K_2CrO_4 to the clear solution. A yellow precipitate of $PbCrO_4$ confirms the presence of Pb^{++} ion. This precipitate should be centrifuged or filtered to be sure that it is yellow. Any white precipitate in the yellow test solution, which might have appeared inadvertently because of a previous error, might be mistaken for a yellow precipitate if the solution is not centrifuged or filtered.

NOTE 14. *The purpose of heating until dense SO_3 fumes appear is to make certain that all HNO_3 has been removed. $PbSO_4$ does not precipitate in the presence of HNO_3. The nitric acid is distilled from the solution just before the white fumes appear. Both the NO_3^- ion and excess H^+ ion interfere with the precipitation of $PbSO_4$. With large H^+ ion concentration HSO_4^- is formed and the concentration of SO_4^{--} is consequently diminished. Furthermore, lead nitrate is a relatively weak salt. Therefore in HNO_3 solution both the Pb^{++} ion and SO_4^{--} ion are present in relatively low concentrations.*

NOTE 15. *Except when dealing with very small quantities, water should never be added to concentrated H_2SO_4; rather H_2SO_4 is added to water. When adding water to H_2SO_4 the water may run down the side of the vessel below the surface of the H_2SO_4. Then the large amount of heat evolved may cause the rapid evaporation of the unmixed water and give rise to an explosion.*

C–3. Test for Cu^{++} Ion. To solution **C–3** add 15 M NH_4OH solution drop by drop until alkaline. If copper is present, a deep blue color is obtained. If this is the case, add a few drops of NH_4OH in excess to be sure that the copper hydroxide first formed is dissolved with the formation of $Cu(NH_3)_4^{++}$ ion. Shake well while adding NH_4OH. The deep blue color is sufficient evidence for the presence of Cu^{++} ion. This solution which may contain a precipitate is to be labeled **C–4**.

C–4. Test for the Bi^{+++} Ion. If a precipitate appears [16] when NH_4OH is added in the test for Cu^{++} ion (a deep blue color may obscure the precipitate), centrifuge or filter the solution. Label the clear supernatant solution or filtrate **C–5** and save for the test for Cd^{++} ion. Add 3 ml. of water to the test tube; shake and centrifuge or filter again. Discard the washings. Repeat the washing [17] and again discard the wash water.

Now pour on the precipitate in the test tube a freshly prepared cold solution of sodium stannite, Na_2SnO_2,[18] and heat. If bismuth is present, a black precipitate of metallic bismuth will appear. Allow to stand for five minutes if the black precipitate does not appear immediately.

Pour a cold freshly prepared solution of sodium stannite, Na_2SnO_2 [18] over the precipitate on the filter paper. A black color on the filter paper indicates the presence of bismuth.

NOTE 16. *Even though copper is absent and the solution is "water-white" the $Bi(OH)_3$ precipitate may be so slight that it is not easily recognized. Therefore the confirmatory test for bismuth with sodium stannite should be made in all cases.*

NOTE 17. *NH_4^+ ion interferes with the reaction between Na_2SnO_2 solution and $Bi(OH)_3$. Therefore a thorough washing of the precipitate is necessary.*

NOTE 18. *In preparing Na_2SnO_2 solution add 6 M NaOH drop by drop to 2 ml. of 0.1 M $SnCl_2$ solution until the precipitate of $Sn(OH)_2$, which first forms, just dissolves. The final solution probably will not be clear but will be opalescent.*

C–5. Test for Cd^{++} Ion. *If Cu^{++} ion is present* in the solution proceed as follows. To the solution **C–5** contained in a 10 ml. test tube add 6 M HCl dropwise until the solution is just acidic. Then add 6 drops of 6 M HCl in excess. Saturate the solution with solid NH_4Cl. Decant and saturate the solution with H_2S. Filter (do not centrifuge), and discard the precipitate which is CuS. To the solution add 1 ml. of 2 M NaAc solution. When the H^+ ion concentration is sufficiently low a yellow precipitate of CdS will form if Cd^{++} ion is present.[19] If no precipitate appears saturate again with H_2S. No yellow precipitate indicates the absence of Cd^{++} ion in the original solution.

If Cu^{++} ion is not present, merely add 6 M HCl dropwise to solution **C–5** until it is just acidic. Saturate the solution with solid NH₄Cl. Add 1 ml. of 2 M NaAc and saturate with H₂S. A yellow precipitate of CdS indicates the presence of Cd^{++} ion in the original solution.[19]

NOTE 19. *The high Cl^- ion concentration in this solution forms the $CdCl_4^{--}$ ion, thereby lowering the Cd^{++} ion concentration to such an extent that the CdS is not precipitated if the H^+ ion concentration is 0.3 M or greater. As the H^+ ion concentration is lowered by the addition of NaAc solution the S^{--} ion concentration increases sufficiently to precipitate the CdS. If Pb^{++} ion is not completely removed by the H_2SO_4 treatment (C–2) one might expect some PbS to precipitate with the CdS. However, Pb^{++} ion also forms complex ions with both Cl^- and Ac^- ions and does not precipitate as PbS in this solution even when the H^+ ion concentration is lowered to less than 10^{-3} M.*

D. Reprecipitation of the Arsenic Group Sulfides and the Separation of As₂S₃. Pour the solution **D** into a 25 ml. Erlenmeyer flask. Carefully add 12 M HCl drop by drop until just acidic, stirring after the addition of each drop. Be particularly careful when nearing the neutral point. At this point one drop of the HCl may cause a violent evolution of H₂S. Do not add more than one drop of HCl in excess (SnS₂ is soluble in relatively dilute HCl solution). Near the end-point test the solution for acidity as each drop of 12 M HCl is added.

When the solution is acidic, i.e., after one drop of 12 M HCl in excess has been added, transfer the solution and precipitate to a 10 ml. test tube. Use 10 drops of water to wash out the Erlenmeyer flask and add this to the transferred solution. Centrifuge or filter and discard the supernatant liquid or filtrate. Wash the precipitate with 3 ml. of water and discard the wash water.

Drain the test tube well from excess water. Add 2 ml. of 12 M HCl and heat gently for two minutes or longer. Do not boil. Centrifuge the solution; pour the supernatant liquid into a test tube and label it **D–2.** Repeat the HCl treatment of the residue and combine supernatant with **D–2.**

With a pointed glass rod make a hole in the bottom of the filter and with 2 ml. of 12 M HCl wash the precipitate into a test tube (use the capillary syringe for this operation). Heat gently for two minutes or longer. Do not boil. Decant the supernatant liquid and repeat HCl treatment of residue. Combine the supernatant liquids, add 1 ml. of water, filter the solution, and label the filtrate **D–2.**

The test **D–1** is to be made with the residue, which should be yellow if it consists only of As_2S_3.

D–1. Test for Arsenic. In this test any As_2S_3 is converted into AsH_3 which in turn reacts with $AgNO_3$ solution to produce black metallic silver.

To the residue from **D** add 1 ml. of water.	Make a hole in the filter paper (from **D**) and, using the capillary syringe, transfer the residue to a 10 ml. test tube with 1 ml. of water.

Add 2 ml. of 6 M NaOH solution. Any As_2S_3 will dissolve. Wet a piece of filter paper, large enough to cover the mouth of the test tube, with 0.1 M $AgNO_3$ solution. Have ready a small piece of absorbent cotton. Now add a few small pieces of metallic aluminum (pellets, not powder) to the solution; place the cotton well into the mouth of the test tube, and then cap the test tube with the filter paper, wet with the $AgNO_3$ solution. Heat the solution gently to initiate the reaction between the aluminum and the NaOH solution. If arsenic is present the underside of the filter paper will turn a gray or black color[20] due to the free silver formed by the reaction between the gas AsH_3 and the $AgNO_3$ solution,[21] (see Preliminary Experiment 11).

NOTE 20. *Do not carry out this experiment near the H_2S generator. Any appreciable amount of H_2S in the air will also discolor the $AgNO_3$ paper.*

NOTE 21. *This test is only applicable to arsenic in the trivalent state. Antimony in any form will not interfere.*

D–2. Test for Tin. Transfer 1 ml. of the solution **D–2** to a casserole. Label the rest of the solution **D–3**, and reserve it for the antimony test. To **D–2** in the casserole add a few very small pieces of fine iron wire [22] and carefully heat the casserole over the open flame *in the hood* until all but a drop or two of the solution has evaporated (see note 13). Add 1 ml. of water and pour the solution into a small test tube. If a few small pieces of carbon (from the wire) or metallic antimony carry over into the test tube, do not be concerned; they will not interfere. Add 2 drops of 0.1 M $HgCl_2$ solution. A white or gray precipitate of Hg_2Cl_2 and Hg indicates the presence of tin in the original solution.

NOTE 22. *The iron reduces the stannic to stannous chloride. The Fe^{++} ion also formed does not interfere with the test.*

D–3. Test for Antimony. Transfer about 1 ml. of solution D–3 to a casserole and evaporate about one-half of it (*use the hood*). Transfer the solution to a small test tube and add 6 M NH_4OH dropwise until the solution is just alkaline. Make acidic with 6 M HAc. Add 1 drop of 6 M HAc in excess and heat to boiling. (Do not be disturbed if a precipitate which appeared in this procedure does not dissolve.) Drop into the hot solution a small pinch of sodium thiosulfate, $Na_2S_2O_3$, crystals. A two-phased system will form with the $Na_2S_2O_3$ in the bottom of the test tube and an orange-red colored antimony oxysulfide is produced at the interface if Sb^{+++} ion is present. If no orange-red color appears, heat very gently and allow to stand. No red coloration at the end of a few minutes indicates that Sb^{+++} ion was not present in the original solution.

Equations for Pertinent Reactions

$$H_2O_2 + Sn^{++} + 2H^+ = Sn^{++++} + 2H_2O$$
$$Sn^{++++} + 2H_2S = SnS_{2(s)} + 4H^+$$
$$2H_3AsO_3 + 3H_2S = As_2S_{3(s)} + 6H_2O$$
$$2Sb^{+++} + 3H_2S = Sb_2S_{3(s)} + 6H^+$$
$$M^{++} + H_2S = MS_{(s)} + 2H^+$$

(M⁺⁺ is bivalent metal ion)

$$2Bi^{+++} + 3H_2S = Bi_2S_{3(s)} + 6H^+$$
$$H_3AsO_4 + 2I^- + 2H^+ = I_2 + H_3AsO_3 + H_2O$$
$$I_2 + H_2S = 2H^+ + 2I^- + S_{(s)}$$
$$NH_4OH + H_2S = NH_4^+ + HS^- + H_2O$$
$$SnS_{2(s)} + HS^- + OH^- = SnS_3^{--} + H_2O$$
$$As_2S_{3(s)} + 3HS^- + 3OH^- = 2AsS_3^{---} + 3H_2O$$
$$Sb_2S_{3(s)} + 3HS^- + 3OH^- = 2SbS_3^{---} + 3H_2O$$
$$3MS_{(s)} + 2NO_3^- + 8H^+ = 3M^{++} + 2NO + 3S_{(s)} + 4H_2O$$
$$3HgS_{(s)} + 2NO_3^- + 6Cl^- + 8H^+$$
$$= 3HgCl_2 + 2NO + 3S_{(s)} + 4H_2O$$
$$2HgCl_2 + Sn^{++} = Sn^{++++} + Hg_2Cl_{2(s)} + 2Cl^-$$
$$Pb^{++} + SO_4^{--} = PbSO_{4(s)}$$
$$PbSO_{4(s)} + 2Ac^- = Pb(Ac)_2 + SO_4^{--}$$
$$Pb(Ac)_2 + CrO_4^{--} = PbCrO_{4(s)} + 2Ac^-$$
$$Cu^{++} + 4NH_3 = Cu(NH_3)_4^{++}$$
$$Bi^{+++} + 3NH_4OH = Bi(OH)_{3(s)} + 3NH_4^+$$
$$Sn^{++} + 4OH^- = SnO_2^{--} + 2H_2O$$

$3SnO_2^{--} + 2Bi(OH)_{3(s)} = 2Bi_{(s)} + 3SnO_3^{--} + 3H_2O$

$Cd^{++} + 4Cl^- = CdCl_4^{--}$

$CdCl_4^{--} + H_2S = CdS_{(s)} + 2H^+ + 4Cl^-$

$SnS_3^{--} + 2H^+ = SnS_{2(s)} + H_2S$

$2AsS_3^{---} + 6H^+ = As_2S_{3(s)} + 3H_2S$

$2SbS_3^{---} + 6H^+ = Sb_2S_{3(s)} + 3H_2S$

$SnS_{2(s)} + 4H^+ = Sn^{++++} + 2H_2S$

$Sb_2S_{3(s)} + 6H^+ = 2Sb^{+++} + 3H_2S$

$As_2S_{3(s)} + 4OH^- = AsS_3^{---} + AsO_2^- + 2H_2O$

$AsO_2^- + 2Al + OH^- + H_2O = 2AlO_2^- + AsH_{3(g)}$

$6Ag^+ + AsH_{3(g)} + 3H_2O = 6Ag_{(s)} + H_3AsO_3 + 6H^+$

$Sn^{++++} + Fe = Fe^{++} + Sn^{++}$

$Sn^{++} + 2HgCl_2 = Sn^{++++} + Hg_2Cl_{2(s)} + 2Cl^-$

$Hg_2Cl_{2(s)} + Sn^{++} = Sn^{++++} + 2Hg_{(s)} + 2Cl^-$

$2Sb^{+++} + 2Na_2S_2O_3 + 3H_2O$
$$= Sb_2OS_{2(s)} + 4Na^+ + 2SO_4^{--} + 6H^+$$

CHAPTER XVI

The Aluminum–Zinc Group

Al^{+++}, Cr^{+++}, Fe^{+++}, Co^{++}, Ni^{++}, Fe^{++}, Mn^{++} and Zn^{++} Ions

The aluminum-zinc group is precipitated in a solution which contains ammonium hydroxide, ammonium chloride and ammonium sulfide ($NH_4OH + H_2S$). In this procedure the hydroxides of Al^{+++} and Cr^{+++} and the sulfides of Fe^{+++}, Fe^{++}, Ni^{++}, Co^{++}, Mn^{++} and Zn^{++} ions are precipitated. With the silver and copper-arsenic groups eliminated, no other ions precipitate.

The Al^{+++}, Cr^{+++} and Fe^{+++} ions constitute what is commonly called the aluminum group; the other ions make up the zinc group. The ions of the aluminum group are trivalent while those of the zinc group are bivalent. The ions of the latter group form stronger and more soluble bases than those of the aluminum group and, accordingly, their salts are hydrolyzed to a smaller extent in water solution. Of the members of the zinc group, only zinc hydroxide is amphoteric.

The ions of the aluminum group form very insoluble hydroxides. These ions are appreciably hydrolyzed by water, and when treated with solutions of $(NH_4)_2S$, $(NH_4)_2CO_3$ or Na_2CO_3, their hydroxides are precipitated. Both aluminum and chromium hydroxides are amphoteric while ferric hydroxide does not display this property.

Of the alkaline earth group hydroxides, magnesium hydroxide is quite insoluble but it is by no means as insoluble as the hydroxides of aluminum and chromium. One might predict magnesium hydroxide to be precipitated with aluminum and chromium hydroxides according to the procedure indicated above. The precipitation of magnesium hydroxide is prevented by the addition of ammonium chloride to the precipitating reagent. The effect of the ammonium chloride is apparent; the high concentration of NH_4^+ ion, by the

369

common ion effect, reduces the concentration of the OH^- ion sufficiently so that the product, $(Mg^{++})(OH^-)^2$, is less than the solubility product constant. Consequently, a mixture of ammonium hydroxide, ammonium chloride and ammonium sulfide serves to precipitate the aluminum-zinc group, thereby separating the ions of this group from those of the alkaline earth and alkali groups.

Aluminum Ion, Al^{+++}. Aluminum shows only one valence, plus three, in all its compounds. All the common salts of aluminum are colorless and are appreciably soluble in water or dilute acid solution. The salts of aluminum show a marked tendency to form hydrates and double salts. Since aluminum hydroxide is decidedly amphoteric, a series of salts is formed in which the aluminum is found as a part of the anion, as for example, in the aluminate ion, AlO_2^-.

Ammonium hydroxide precipitates **aluminum hydroxide** from solutions containing Al^{+++} ions.

$$Al^{+++} + 3NH_4OH = Al(OH)_{3(s)} + 3NH_4^+ \qquad (73)$$

Alkali hydroxides likewise precipitate $Al(OH)_3$ from solutions of aluminum salts. However, the precipitate is readily soluble in an excess of the reagent, with the formation of AlO_2^- ion. If HCl is added gradually to the solution containing the AlO_2^- ion, $Al(OH)_3$ is reprecipitated. An excess of the acid will again redissolve the $Al(OH)_3$. These changes are explained by the following equilibrium. (See Chapter VIII for a discussion of the properties of amphoteric hydroxides.)

$$Al^{+++} + 3OH^- = \left\{ \begin{matrix} Al(OH)_3 \\ H_3AlO_3 \end{matrix} \right\}_{(s)} = H^+ + AlO_2^- + H_2O \qquad (74)$$

Aluminum hydroxide is only slightly soluble in excess NH_4OH because of the low concentration of OH^- ion in this reagent. The addition of NH_4Cl to the NH_4OH solution reduces the OH^- ion concentration and therefore decreases the solubility of $Al(OH)_3$. Therefore, to precipitate $Al(OH)_3$ as completely as possible with NH_4OH, some soluble ammonium salt, such as NH_4Cl, should be added.

The presence of the ammonium salt serves another purpose; it tends to prevent the formation of colloidal $Al(OH)_3$.

While freshly precipitated $Al(OH)_3$ dissolves readily in solutions of strong bases or strong acids, yet if allowed to stand in air or to become partially dehydrated in any manner, its solubility in acids changes greatly and very often it is found to be difficult to dissolve. However, under such conditions, it may be dissolved by prolonged treatment with hot concentrated acid. This is true of many other hydroxides.

In the precipitation of $Al(OH)_3$ with NH_4OH or with any of several suitable reagents, substances such as tartrates, citrates, oxalates and phosphates must be absent, due to the fact that either complex ions may be formed or precipitation of some of the ions of the alkaline earth group may result. (It is evident that the latter interference appears only in the general scheme of analysis, that is, when ions of all groups may be present.) The formation of a complex ion decreases the number of available Al^{+++} ions and this effect may even prevent the precipitation of $Al(OH)_3$. Chromium hydroxide and ferric hydroxide behave in a similar manner. Therefore, it is necessary to remove organic matter and other interfering ions before an attempt is made to precipitate $Al(OH)_3$. The removal of organic matter may be accomplished by the addition of sodium carbonate and sodium nitrate to the solution, by subsequent evaporation of the solution to dryness, and ignition of the residue. The PO_4^{---} ion may be removed by precipitation as $FePO_4$ after tests have been made on the original solutions for the presence of iron.

Sodium carbonate, $BaCO_3$, $(NH_4)_2CO_3$ and $(NH_4)_2S$ all behave alike when added to solutions containing Al^{+++} ions, in that the result in each case is the precipitation of $Al(OH)_3$. All of these substances undergo extensive hydrolysis with the production of OH^- ions in quantities sufficient to exceed the solubility product constant for $Al(OH)_3$.

$$CO_3^{--} + H_2O = HCO_3^- + OH^- \qquad (75)$$

$$S^{--} + H_2O = HS^- + OH^- \qquad (76)$$

Even the slightly soluble $BaCO_3$ ($K_{s.p.} = 8.1 \times 10^{-9}$) produces sufficient CO_3^{--} ions in its saturated solution that the OH^- ion concentration produced by hydrolysis precipitates $Al(OH)_3$.

Aurin tricarboxylic acid (**aluminon**) forms a red lake with $Al(OH)_3$. This is a good confirmatory test for the Al^{+++} ion. $Cr(OH)_3$ and $Fe(OH)_3$ behave similarly, but in the analysis these hydroxides are separated before this test is applied.

Chromic Ion, Cr^{+++}. Chromium shows a valence of plus two in chromous compounds, plus three in chromic compounds, and its valence state in chromates and dichromates is plus six. Chromous ion, Cr^{++}, is very easily oxidized to the chromic condition. The H^+ ion in water is sufficient to promote this oxidation, though all air be excluded. Consequently, chromous salts possess little stability and we shall have no occasion to deal with them in the analytical procedures.

Chromic ion, Cr^{+++}, resembles aluminum ion, Al^{+++}, in many ways. It is readily hydrolyzed with the formation of **chromic hydroxide,** $Cr(OH)_3$, which possesses amphoteric properties. For this reason chromic hydroxide is soluble in the presence of excess hydroxide ion, forming another series of salts known as chromites.

$$Cr(OH)_{3(s)} + OH^- = CrO_2^- + 2H_2O \qquad (77)$$

Chromic sulfate, like aluminum sulfate, forms alums with the sulfates of the alkali metals and the ammonium radical. Chromic ion, however, differs markedly from Al^{+++} ion in that it shows a pronounced tendency to form many **complex ions** (see Chapter IX of text). The **chloride, bromide, iodide, sulfate, acetate** and **nitrate** of Cr^{+++} ion are soluble in water; while the **phosphate** and **hydroxide** are only slightly soluble. The **carbonate** and **sulfide** cannot exist in water solutions because of hydrolysis.

Chromate — Dichromate Equilibrium. In both chromates and dichromates the valence state of the chromium is plus six. The CrO_4^{--} ion predominates in basic solution while the $Cr_2O_7^{--}$ ion predominates in an acid medium. However, both ions are always present in solutions as follows:

$$2CrO_4^{--} + 2H^+ = 2HCrO_4^- = Cr_2O_7^{--} + H_2O \quad (78)$$

From equation (78) it is evident that an excess of H^+ ions shifts the equilibrium to the right, thereby producing $Cr_2O_7^{--}$ ions, while a strong base removes H^+ ions and causes the equilibrium to shift to the left with the production of CrO_4^{--} ions. Considering (78) in two steps, we have

$$HCrO_4^- = CrO_4^{--} + H^+ \quad (79)$$

and

$$2HCrO_4^- = Cr_2O_7^{--} + H_2O \quad (80)$$

The equilibrium constant for (79) has a value of 7×10^{-7} while that for (80) has a value of 60. Multiplying equation (79) by two and then subtracting (80), we obtain

$$2CrO_4^{--} + 2H^+ = Cr_2O_7^{--} + H_2O \quad (81)$$

The equilibrium expression is

$$\frac{(Cr_2O_7^{--})}{(CrO_4^{--})^2(H^+)^2} = K_{eq} = 1.2 \times 10^{14} \quad (82)$$

According to the value of the equilibrium constant $Cr_2O_7^{--}$ ion predominates in solution provided the H^+ ion concentration is appreciable. If the solution is neutral, H^+ concentration of 1×10^{-7}, the ratio of the concentration of the $Cr_2O_7^{--}$ ion to the concentration of the CrO_4^{--} ion squared is about unity. In a basic medium this ratio is less than unity and accordingly CrO_4^{--} ion predominates. The addition of a metal ion to a solution of a chromate or a dichromate will result in the precipitation of one or the other salt, depending upon which is the less soluble and whether the solution contains an excess of H^+ ions or of OH^- ions.

Ammonium hydroxide, alkali hydroxides, alkali carbonates, barium carbonate and alkali sulfides precipitate **chromic hydroxide** from solutions containing Cr^{+++} ion.

$$Cr^{+++} + 3OH^- = Cr(OH)_{3(s)} \quad (83)$$

Like $Al(OH)_3$, the $Cr(OH)_3$ is only slightly soluble in excess NH_4OH, but in excess cold NaOH or KOH solution it is readily soluble, because of its amphoteric properties, with the formation of chromite ion, CrO_2^- (see equation 77). If the alkaline solution containing CrO_2^- ion is heated to boiling, a less soluble crystalline form of the hydroxide is precipitated. Aluminum hydroxide does not behave in this manner; aluminates are stable in boiling water.

Chromic hydroxide is also soluble in strong acid solution.

$$Cr(OH)_{3(s)} + 3H^+ = Cr^{+++} + 3H_2O \qquad (84)$$

Thus, the complete equilibrium involving Cr^{+++} and CrO_2^- ions is

$$Cr^{+++} + 3OH^- = \left\{ \begin{array}{l} Cr(OH)_3 \\ H_3CrO_3 \end{array} \right\}_{(s)} = H^+ + CrO_2^- + H_2O \qquad (85)$$

The effect of excess acid or base upon this equilibrium is apparent in light of previous discussions of similar equilibria.

Chromic salts when fused with a nitrite or a nitrate and alkali carbonate give a soluble chromate. Iron and aluminum salts do not show similar reactions. In alkaline solution the oxidation of CrO_2^- ion to CrO_4^{--} ion may be carried out with any of several oxidizing agents, such as Br_2, Cl_2, Na_2O_2, H_2O_2 and MnO_4^- ion (see Table 20). For example, with H_2O_2 in alkaline solution

$$2CrO_2^- + 3HO_2^- = 2CrO_4^{--} + H_2O + OH^- \qquad (86)$$

Dichromate ion is easily reduced to Cr^{+++} ion in acid solution.

$$Cr_2O_7^{--} + 3H_2S + 8H^+ = 2Cr^{+++} + 3S_{(s)} + 7H_2O \qquad (87)$$

In neutral or alkaline solutions $Cr(OH)_3$ rather than Cr^{+++} ion is formed.

For the identification of chromium in analysis, the Cr^{+++} ion (or the CrO_2^- ion) is oxidized to CrO_4^{--} ion, and Pb^{++} ion is introduced to precipitate $PbCrO_4$, a slightly soluble, yellow compound.

Ferric Ion, Fe^{+++} — Ferrous Ion, Fe^{++}. Iron shows two principal valences in its compounds and therefore forms two well known series of salts. The compounds of iron in both valence states are of importance in analytical procedures. The ferrous salts form green hydrates while the hydrated ferric salts are yellow or brown in color. The ferrous ion is a strong reducing agent having a marked tendency to go to the ferric condition. For this reason, solutions of ferrous salts when exposed to air have a tendency to change to the higher valence state.

The Fe^{++} ion forms a hydroxide, $Fe(OH)_2$, which is stronger and more soluble than the hydroxide of the Fe^{+++} ion, $Fe(OH)_3$. Though both Fe^{++} and Fe^{+++} ions undergo hydrolysis in water solution the effect is decidedly greater in the case of the latter ion since it is derived from the weaker and less soluble base. Both these ions form double salts and basic salts; the formation of the latter class is due to partial hydrolysis. Neither the ferrous nor the ferric hydroxide possesses any amphoteric properties. Both ions are distinguished by their ability to combine with negative ions to produce complex anions.

The **acetate, chloride, bromide, iodide, nitrate, thiocyanate** and **sulfate** of Fe^{++} ion are soluble in water, while the **oxalate, hydroxide, sulfide, carbonate** and **phosphate** of this ion are very slightly soluble. Of the compounds of the Fe^{+++} ion, the **thiocyanate, nitrate, chloride, bromide** and **oxalate** are soluble, while the **phosphate, sulfide, sulfate** and **hydroxide** are relatively insoluble.

Ammonium hydroxide, NaOH or KOH added to neutral solutions of ferrous salts precipitate white gelatinous **ferrous hydroxide,** $Fe(OH)_2$, which is rapidly oxidized in air, passing through several stages of color: green to reddish-brown, the latter color being due to **ferric hydroxide.**

$$4Fe(OH)_{2(s)} + O_2 + 2H_2O = 4Fe(OH)_{3(s)} \qquad (88)$$

The same reagents, as well as alkali carbonates and barium carbonate, precipitate $Fe(OH)_3$ from solutions containing Fe^{+++} ion. It is practically insoluble in an excess of the alkali hydroxide and in this way $Fe(OH)_3$ differs from the corresponding hydroxides of aluminum and chromium. Ferric hydroxide also differs from the hydroxides of cobalt, nickel and zinc, in that the latter are soluble in an excess NH_4OH, due to the formation of complex ions.

Ferrous ion in the presence of cyanide ion, CN^-, gives a precipitate of the yellow-red **ferrous cyanide,**

$$Fe^{++} + 2CN^- = Fe(CN)_{2(s)} \qquad (89)$$

which is soluble in excess CN^- ion with the formation of the complex **ferrocyanide ion.**

$$Fe(CN)_{2(s)} + 4CN^- = Fe(CN)_6{}^{----} \qquad (90)$$

But CN^- ion, in the presence of Fe^{+++} ion, causes the precipitation of ferric hydroxide since the CN^- ion is appreciably hydrolyzed.

$$CN^- + H_2O = HCN + OH^- \qquad (91)$$

and $\qquad Fe^{+++} + 3OH^- = Fe(OH)_{3(s)} \qquad (92)$

Potassium ferrocyanide, $K_4Fe(CN)_6$, in the presence of Fe^{++} ion undergoes the following reaction, with the formation of the slightly soluble **potassium ferro-ferrocyanide.**

$$Fe^{++} + 2K^+ + Fe(CN)_6{}^{----} = K_2Fe[Fe(CN)_6]_{(s)} \qquad (93)$$

However, upon exposure to air the latter is readily oxidized to Prussian blue, **ferric ferrocyanide,** $Fe_4[Fe(CN)_6]_3$.

The same final result may be obtained through the direct combination of the Fe^{+++} ion with the $Fe(CN)_6{}^{----}$ ion.

$$4Fe^{+++} + 3Fe(CN)_6{}^{----} = Fe_4[Fe(CN)_6]_{3(s)} \qquad (94)$$

This is a very sensitive test for the Fe^{+++} ion.

The **ferricyanide ion,** $Fe(CN)_6{}^{---}$. may be formed by treating solutions containing Fe^{+++} ion with an excess of CN^- ion; the $Fe(OH)_3$ first produced reacts with the CN^- ion.

$$Fe(OH)_{3(s)} + 6CN^- = Fe(CN)_6{}^{---} + 3OH^- \qquad (95)$$

With Fe^{++} ion the $Fe(CN)_6{}^{---}$ ion forms a dark blue precipitate known as Turnbull's blue, which is a test for Fe^{++} ion.

$$3Fe^{++} + 2Fe(CN)_6^{---} = Fe_3[Fe(CN)_6]_{2(s)} \qquad (96)$$

According to their formulae Prussian blue and Turnbull's blue contain 45.5 and 47.2 per cent iron respectively. However, within the limits of experimental error, both have the same composition. Prussian blue, instead of Turnbull's blue, could be produced by the reaction

$$Fe^{++} + Fe(CN)_6^{---} = Fe^{+++} + Fe(CN)_6^{----} \qquad (97)$$

followed by reaction (94). In reaction (97) the Fe^{++} and Fe^{+++} ions merely change places in the complex ion. Prussian blue and Turnbull's blue are therefore thought to be identical.

The color reactions of the Fe^{++} and Fe^{+++} ions with the $Fe(CN)_6^{----}$ and $Fe(CN)_6^{---}$ ions are given in the following chart.

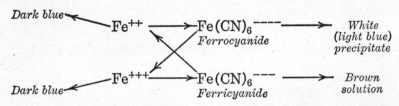

Thiocyanate ion, CNS^-, gives no color reaction with Fe^{++} ion, but with Fe^{+++} ion produces a blood red complex ion, either $Fe(CNS)_6^{---}$ or one of the possible complexes containing less than six CNS coordinating groups.

$$Fe^{+++} + 6CNS^- = Fe(CNS)_6^{---} \qquad (98)$$

Organic acids and salts of these acids as well as phosphates and mercuric chloride interfere in this test.

Nitric acid readily oxidizes Fe^{++} ion to Fe^{+++} ion,

$$3Fe^{++} + 4H^+ + NO_3^- = 3Fe^{+++} + NO + 2H_2O \qquad (99)$$

If a layer of cold concentrated sulfuric acid is also present in the solution, **ferrous nitroso sulfate,** $FeNOSO_4$, forms at the interface. This is known as the "brown ring" test for Fe^{++} ion and also for NO_3^- ion.

Hydrogen sulfide has no effect upon Fe^{++} ion in acid solution. From alkaline solutions H_2S precipitates **ferrous sulfide** quite completely.

$$Fe(OH)_{2(s)} + H_2S = FeS_{(s)} + 2H_2O \qquad (100)$$

Sodium sulfide furnishes a relatively high concentration of S^{--} ion compared to that furnished by a solution of H_2S, so this reagent when added to a solution of Fe^{++} ion will precipitate FeS. Ammonium sulfide may also be used to precipitate FeS.

When H_2S is passed into acid solutions containing Fe^{+++} ion, the latter is reduced to Fe^{++} ion.

$$2Fe^{+++} + H_2S = 2Fe^{++} + 2H^+ + S_{(s)} \qquad (101)$$

In acid solution $(NH_4)_2S$ produces with Fe^{+++} ion FeS and free sulfur; whereas in alkaline solution the black Fe_2S_3 is precipitated. Therefore, when Fe_2S_3 produced in alkaline solution is dissolved in acid, the H_2S produced by the reaction reduces the iron to the ferrous state.

$$Fe_2S_{3(s)} + 4H^+ = 2Fe^{++} + 2H_2S + S_{(s)} \qquad (102)$$

Cobaltous Ion, Co^{++}. Cobalt forms two classes of salts, in which it exhibits valences of plus two and plus three. The compounds of the latter class are extremely unstable at ordinary temperatures, so the chemistry of cobalt will be here confined almost entirely to the more stable cobaltous compounds. Complex ions containing the cobalt atom in the three plus state are numerous and possess great stability (see Chapter IX).

Hydrated crystallized cobaltous compounds and their dilute solutions are pink in color while concentrated solutions and the anhydrous salts are blue.

The soluble salts of the Co^{++} ion include the **chloride, bromide, iodide, nitrate, sulfate, thiosulfate** and **thiocyanate,** while the common slightly soluble compounds are the **carbonate, chromate, cyanide, ferricyanide, ferrocyanide, hydroxide, oxalate, phosphate, tartrate** and **sulfide.**

Alkali hydroxides precipitate **cobaltous hydroxide,** Co(OH)$_2$, from solutions containing Co^{++} ion. The hydroxide is blue in color in cold solutions but pink or rose colored in warm solutions. It is only very slightly soluble in excess alkali, so it does not possess appreciable amphoteric properties. On exposure to air cobaltous hydroxide becomes brown in color due to partial oxidation. The hydroxide is soluble in solutions containing large amounts of NH_4^+ ion. Therefore it is not precipitated completely in the presence of this ion.

Ammonium hydroxide, in the absence of ammonium salts, precipitates cobaltous hydroxide which is soluble in excess reagent.

$$Co^{++} + 2NH_4OH = Co(OH)_{2(s)} + 2NH_4^+ \quad (103)$$

In the presence of air oxidation results and a complex compound of the type $[Co(NH_3)_5Cl]Cl_2$ is probably formed.

Potassium cyanide precipitates in neutral solution the light brown **cobaltous cyanide,** $Co(CN)_2$, which is soluble in the presence of excess CN^- ion.

$$Co^{++} + 2CN^- = Co(CN)_{2(s)} \quad (104)$$

and $\quad Co(CN)_{2(s)} + 4CN^- = Co(CN)_6^{----} \quad (105)$

When the latter solution is heated in contact with air a bright yellow color appears due to the oxidation of the **cobaltocyanide ion** to the **cobalticyanide ion,** $Co(CN)_6^{---}$. The cobalticyanide ion is more stable than the cobaltocyanide ion since the latter is readily decomposed by HCl solution to give Co^{++} ion and HCN; the former ion is not affected by HCl.

Potassium nitrite added to solutions of Co^{++} ion which have been acidified with acetic acid gives a yellow precipitate of **potassium cobaltinitrite,** $K_3[Co(NO_2)_6]$.

$$Co^{++} + 2HAc + 7NO_2^- + 3K^+$$
$$= NO + H_2O + 2Ac^- + K_3[Co(NO_2)_6]_{(s)} \quad (106)$$

In the presence of Na^+ ion the relatively insoluble

$$K_2Na[Co(NO_2)_6]$$

is formed. Nickelous ion does not give this reaction.

Hydrogen sulfide precipitates **cobaltous sulfide,** CoS, from solutions of Co^{++} ion.

$$Co^{++} + H_2S = CoS_{(s)} + 2H^+ \qquad (107)$$

If strong acids are present CoS fails to precipitate. This result is apparent from the equation given above, for an excess of H^+ ion shifts the equilibrium to the left, which process is identical with the dissolving of the sulfide. However, if acetate ion is present it will capture H^+ ion with the formation of slightly ionized acetic acid, thereby shifting the equilibrium to the right and causing the CoS to be precipitated to a greater extent. Ammonium hydroxide exerts a similar effect since OH^- ions also capture H^+ ions. Freshly precipitated CoS is readily soluble in HCl solution, but after the sulfide has been allowed to stand in air its solubility in this medium is greatly reduced. This is probably due to a change in composition or in crystalline form. The *rate* of solution of CoS in HCl is very low after the precipitate has been allowed to stand. Advantage is taken of this property to separate CoS from some of the other sulfides of this group. It is obvious that $(NH_4)_2S$ precipitates CoS from neutral or alkaline solutions of Co^{++} ion.

A concentrated solution of NH_4CNS may also be used to identify Co^{++} ion.

$$Co^{++} + 4CNS^- = Co(CNS)_4^{--} \qquad (108)$$

The complex ion formed has a characteristic blue color, the intensity of which may be increased by shaking the solution with acetone. Ferric ion interferes with this test but this interference may be avoided by the addition of potassium-sodium tartrate, which removes Fe^{+++} ion through the formation of a complex ion.

Cobaltous compounds impart a deep blue color to a borax bead.

Nickelous Ion, Ni^{++}. Nickel, unlike cobalt and iron, forms only one series of compounds in which the nickel atom exhibits the valence of plus two. In many respects the chemistry of Ni^{++} ion is very similar to that of Co^{++}

ion. Nickelous salts in the hydrated form and in solution are green in color; the anhydrous salts are yellow. The Ni^{++} ion also enters in the formation of several complex ions but in general these ions possess much less stability than those of cobalt. Nickelous hydroxide shows no amphoteric properties. The **nitrate, chloride, bromide, iodide, sulfate, acetate, thiosulfate** and **thiocyanate** of Ni^{++} ion are all soluble. The more insoluble compounds of this ion are the **carbonate, sulfide, chromate, cyanide, hydroxide, oxalate** and **phosphate.**

Alkali hydroxides precipitate light green **nickelous hydroxide,** $Ni(OH)_2$, from solutions of Ni^{++} ion.

$$Ni^{++} + 2OH^- = Ni(OH)_{2(s)} \qquad (109)$$

It is soluble in solutions containing NH_4^+ ion or NH_4OH due to the formation of the **complex ion,** $Ni(NH_3)_4^{++}$.

$$Ni(OH)_{2(s)} + 4NH_3 = Ni(NH_3)_4^{++} + 2OH^- \qquad (110)$$

Nickelous hydroxide in alkaline solution may be readily oxidized to a hydrated dioxide, NiO_2. In acid solution this oxide is a very strong oxidizing agent. It is the oxidizing constituent in the Edison storage cell. The dioxide may very well be a peroxide but there is no experimental evidence to justify a definite conclusion.

Alkali carbonates precipitate a green **basic carbonate** from Ni^{++} ion solutions; the normal **hydrated carbonate,** $NiCO_3 \cdot 6H_2O$, is obtained if carbonic acid is also present.

Ammonium hydroxide, in dilute solution and in the absence of ammonium salts, precipitates a green basic salt. If the chloride is used, the reaction is

$$Ni^{++} + Cl^- + NH_4OH = Ni(OH)Cl_{(s)} + NH_4^+ \qquad (111)$$

The presence of ammonium salts reduces the OH^- concentration, through the common ion effect, to such a small value as to prevent the precipitation of either the basic salt or the normal hydroxide. The basic salt, however, is soluble in an excess of NH_4OH with the formation of the complex ion noted above.

Alkali cyanides precipitate **nickelous cyanide** from solutions of Ni^{++} ions.

$$Ni^{++} + 2CN^- = Ni(CN)_{2(s)} \tag{112}$$

The precipitate is soluble in excess CN^- ion due to the formation of a **nickel-cyanide complex ion.**

$$Ni(CN)_{2(s)} + 2CN^- = Ni(CN)_4^{--} \tag{113}$$

When HCl is added to solutions of the complex ion, $Ni(CN)_2$ is first precipitated. This effect is to be expected on the basis of H^+ ions combining with CN^- ions to form the slightly ionized HCN.

Thiocyanate ion, CNS^-, does not show a color reaction nor give a precipitate with Ni^{++} ion. This property distinguishes Ni^{++} ion from Co^{++} and Fe^{+++} ions.

Potassium nitrite, in acetic acid solution, does not give a precipitate with Ni^{++} ion, again distinguishing this ion from Co^{++} ion.

Hydrogen sulfide precipitates **nickel sulfide** from solutions of Ni^{++} ions.

$$Ni^{++} + H_2S = NiS_{(s)} + 2H^+ \tag{114}$$

If the H^+ ion concentration of the solution is high, NiS fails to precipitate. Even in neutral solution the precipitation of NiS is not analytically complete, since as the reaction proceeds to the right the H^+ ion concentration increases. The latter may reach a sufficiently high value to prevent further precipitation. If Ac^- ion is present in the solution, the precipitation of NiS will proceed to a greater extent, since Ac^- ion removes H^+ ion by the formation of HAc. Any ion which tends to remove H^+ ion will produce the same effect. Like CoS, NiS is dissolved slowly by dilute HCl. The effect here appears to be one involving only the *rate* of solution. Undoubtedly, at equilibrium NiS would be found quite soluble in HCl, but the rate of solution in attaining equilibrium conditions is very low. Advantage of this property is taken both in the case of CoS and NiS in the separation of these ions from some of the other ions of the zinc group. The sulfides of the other ions of the zinc group are readily soluble in HCl solution. NiS, as well as CoS, may be dissolved by HNO_3 or by aqua regia.

$$NiS_{(s)} + 2NO_3^- + 4H^+ = Ni^{++} + 2NO_2 + S_{(s)} + 2H_2O \quad (115)$$

Dimethylglyoxime in alcohol solution yields with solutions of Ni^{++} ion, alkaline with NH_4OH, a characteristic red precipitate of nickel dimethylglyoxime.

$$Ni^{++} + 2NH_3 + 2C_4H_6N_2O_2H_2$$
$$= NiC_8H_{14}N_4O_{4(s)} + 2NH_4^+ \quad (116)$$

This is a very sensitive test for the Ni^{++} ion. Ag^+, Mn^{++}, Fe^{++}, Fe^{+++} and Co^{++} ions also give precipitates with this same reagent, under suitable conditions. In NH_4OH solution Co^{++} does not precipitate unless present in high concentrations.

Manganous Ion, Mn^{++}. Manganese forms several series of compounds in accordance with its marked variability in valence. In these compounds the manganese atom shows the following valence states: plus two, plus three, plus four, plus six and plus seven. All types of compounds possess specific chemical properties and impart characteristic colors to their solutions. The hydroxides, oxides or acids representing all the valence states of manganese are: manganous hydroxide, $Mn(OH)_2$; manganic hydroxide, $Mn(OH)_3$; manganese dioxide, MnO_2; manganic acid, H_2MnO_4; and permanganic acid, $HMnO_4$. As the valence number increases the acidic properties of the oxides or their hydrates become more pronounced.

Manganous ion, at one end of the series, is a good reducing agent, while MnO_4^- ion, at the other end, is a strong oxidizing agent. In acid solution the Mn^{++} ion is highly stable. Accordingly, ions containing manganese in a higher oxidized state are readily reduced to Mn^{++} ion in this medium. In alkaline or neutral solutions tetravalent manganese has a high stability and therefore the reduction of manganese in higher valence states in this medium gives MnO_2. Trivalent manganese ion is stable only in the presence of a high concentration of H^+ ion, while manganese with a valence number of plus six is stable only in the presence of a high concentration of OH⁻ ion.

Manganous salts are white when anhydrous and pink when hydrated or in water solution. Manganic salts are purple. Anhydrous manganates have a violet color but in solution the MnO_4^{--} ion is green. Permanganates are violet to black in the solid state, and the MnO_4^- ion is deep purple in color.

The more common soluble salts of Mn^{++} ion are the **chloride, bromide, iodide, nitrate, thiosulfate, thiocyanate** and **sulfate,** while the **acetate, oxalate, carbonate, hydroxide, phosphate, cyanide** and **sulfide** are relatively insoluble. The following table gives the equilibria involving Mn^{++} ion in saturated solutions of some of its compounds; the arrangement is based on decreasing concentration of Mn^{++} at equilibrium.

TABLE 29

EQUILIBRIA INVOLVING MANGANOUS ION

Decreasing Concentration of Mn^{++} ion	
$Mn^{++} + 2Ac^-$	$= Mn(Ac)_{2(s)}$
$Mn^{++} + C_2O_4^{--}$	$= MnC_2O_{4(s)}$
$Mn^{++} + CO_3^{--}$	$= MnCO_{3(s)}$
$Mn^{++} + 2OH^-$	$= Mn(OH)_{2(s)}$
$Mn^{++} + S^{--}$	$= MnS_{(s)}$

Some of the chemical properties of the MnO_4^{--} and MnO_4^- ions are expressed in the following equations.

$$2MnO_4^- + 10Fe^{++} + 16H^+$$
$$= 2Mn^{++} + 10Fe^{+++} + 8H_2O \quad (117)$$

$$2MnO_4^- + 10Cl^- + 16H^+ = 2Mn^{++} + 5Cl_2 + 8H_2O \quad (118)$$

$$2MnO_4^- + 3HSnO_2^- + OH^-$$
$$= 3SnO_3^{--} + 2MnO_{2(s)} + 2H_2O \quad (119)$$

$$2MnO_4^- + 5C_2O_4^{--} + 16H^+$$
$$= 2Mn^{++} + 10CO_2 + 8H_2O \quad (120)$$

$$3MnO_4^{--} + 4H^+ = 2MnO_4^- + MnO_{2(s)} + 2H_2O \quad (121)$$

$$2MnO_4^{--} + Cl_2 = 2MnO_4^- + 2Cl^- \quad (122)$$

The reactions as expressed by these equations proceed from left to right when concentrations of the substances involved are each 1 M.

Alkali hydroxides precipitate from solutions of Mn^{++} ion white **manganous hydroxide** which readily oxidizes in air. It is insoluble in excess alkali, thereby showing no amphoteric properties, but is soluble in solutions containing an appreciable concentration of NH_4^+ ion. Ammonium hydroxide precipitates $Mn(OH)_2$ from solutions of Mn^{++} ion, provided the concentration of NH_4^+ ion is not high. A high concentration of NH_4^+ ion reduces the OH^- ion concentration sufficiently to prevent the precipitation of the hydroxide.

Ammonium sulfide precipitates pink **manganous sulfide.**

$$Mn^{++} + S^{--} = MnS_{(s)} \qquad (123)$$

MnS is readily soluble in dilute acids since it is one of the more soluble sulfides and thereby furnishes a relatively high concentration of S^{--} ions. A low H^+ ion concentration is sufficient to form the slightly ionized HS^- ion, as shown by the fact that MnS is soluble even in acetic acid. It is therefore evident that H_2S passed into solutions containing Mn^{++} will not precipitate MnS unless the solution is alkaline. It will be recalled that CoS and NiS are not readily dissolved by non-oxidizing acids. This difference in the behavior of these sulfides permits a satisfactory separation of manganese from cobalt and nickel.

Nitric acid in the presence of ClO_3^- ion, Br_2, PbO_2, BiO_3^- ion, or other oxidizing agents converts Mn^{++} ion to MnO_4^- ion which is readily detected by its characteristic color. This procedure serves as a sensitive test for the identification of manganese.

Zinc Ion, Zn^{++}. Zinc is a member of sub-group two of the periodic table. It forms only one series of compounds in which the zinc atom shows a positive valence of two. Zinc hydroxide shows decided amphoteric properties, forming a second series of compounds known as zincates. The Zn^{++} ion is somewhat hydrolyzed in water, forming $Zn(OH)_2$

and H^+ ion. It also shows a pronounced tendency to form complex ions with NH_3 and CN^- ion.

Many zinc salts are very soluble in water, the more common ones being the **chloride, bromide, iodide, nitrate, thiosulfate, thiocyanate** and **acetate**. The more insoluble compounds of Zn^{++} ion include the **carbonate, oxalate, hydroxide, sulfide, chromate, cyanide** and **phosphate**.

In the following table equilibria involving the Zn^{++} ion are listed in order of decreasing concentration of Zn^{++} ion at equilibrium. The equilibria are of two types, one involving saturated solutions in which the zinc ion is in equilibrium with the solid salt in question, and the other involving complex ions. One molar solutions of the complex ions have been taken in determining their relative positions.

TABLE 30

EQUILIBRIA INVOLVING ZINC ION

$Zn^{++} + CO_3^{--}$	$= ZnCO_{3(s)}$
$Zn^{++} + C_2O_4^{--}$	$= ZnC_2O_{4(s)}$
$Zn^{++} + 2OH^-$	$= Zn(OH)_{2(s)}$
$Zn^{++} + 4NH_3$	$= Zn(NH_3)_4^{++}$
$Zn^{++} + S^{--}$	$= ZnS_{(s)}$

(Decreasing Concentration of Zn^+ Ion ↓)

Alkali hydroxides precipitate **zinc hydroxide** from solutions of Zn^{++} ion,

$$Zn^{++} + 2OH^- = Zn(OH)_{2(s)} \qquad (124)$$

which is readily soluble in excess alkali due to its amphoteric properties. Thus, in a saturated solution of $Zn(OH)_2$ the following equilibrium is involved:

$$Zn^{++} + 2OH^- = \left\{ \begin{matrix} Zn(OH)_2 \\ H_2ZnO_2 \end{matrix} \right\}_{(s)} = H^+ + HZnO_2^- \qquad (125)$$

It is apparent that the addition of a strong base shifts the equilibrium to the right and the addition of a strong acid, to the left. In this respect $Zn(OH)_2$ behaves like $Al(OH)_3$ and $Cr(OH)_3$ but differs from $Fe(OH)_3$, the latter being insoluble in excess alkali hydroxide.

When NH_4OH is added to a neutral solution of Zn^{++} ion, in the absence of ammonium salts, a white precipitate of $Zn(OH)_2$ is first formed.

$$Zn^{++} + 2NH_4OH = Zn(OH)_{2(s)} + 2NH_4^+ \qquad (126)$$

A high concentration of NH_4^+ ion in the solution shifts the equilibrium to the left, thereby preventing the precipitation of $Zn(OH)_2$. The same effect may be expressed in other words: the excess NH_4^+ ion from the ammonium salt represses the ionization of NH_4OH to such an extent that an insufficient number of OH^- ions are present to cause the precipitation of $Zn(OH)_2$.

Zinc hydroxide is readily soluble in excess NH_4OH due to the formation of the **zinc-ammonia complex ion**, $Zn(NH_3)_4^{++}$.

$$Zn(OH)_{2(s)} + 4NH_3 = Zn(NH_3)_4^{++} + 2OH^- \qquad (127)$$

In this respect $Zn(OH)_2$ resembles $Ni(OH)_2$ and $Co(OH)_2$. (See Chapters IX and X.)

Hydrogen sulfide does not precipitate **zinc sulfide** from solutions containing Zn^{++} ion if H^+ ion be present at moderate concentrations. Even the production of H^+ ion by the reaction tends to prevent the precipitation from being analytically complete, though the Zn^{++} ion solution is originally neutral. The equation for the reaction illustrates this point.

$$Zn^{++} + H_2S = ZnS_{(s)} + 2H^+ \qquad (128)$$

If acetate ion or any other captor of H^+ ion is present in the solution when H_2S is added, H^+ ions are removed and then ZnS will precipitate quite completely. If the solution is first made alkaline, $HZnO_2^-$ ion is produced, and subsequently H_2S will precipitate most of the Zn^{++} ion as ZnS.

$$HZnO_2^- + H_2S = ZnS_{(s)} + OH^- + H_2O \qquad (129)$$

The lower the H^+ ion concentration of the solution, the more favorable are the conditions for the precipitation of ZnS by H_2S. Obviously $(NH_4)_2S$ may be used in place of H_2S.

Alkali carbonates precipitate from solutions of Zn^{++} ion a **basic carbonate**, $5ZnO \cdot 2CO_2 \cdot 4H_2O$, which is soluble in either $(NH_4)_2CO_3$ or NH_4OH solutions. It is also readily dissolved by alkali hydroxides. These results are in accord with the positions of $ZnCO_3$, $Zn(OH)_2$ and $Zn(NH_3)_4^{++}$ ion in Table 30.

Alkali ferrocyanides precipitate **zinc ferrocyanide,** $Zn_2Fe(CN)_6$ (white). With ferricyanides, **zinc ferricyanide** (yellow), $Zn_3[Fe(CN)_6]_2$, is precipitated.

Preliminary Experiments

1. In the following chart the ions of the zinc-aluminum group are listed horizontally and a number of reagents vertically. In the blank spaces provided in a similar chart made in your notebook give the products of the reactions when the specified reagent is added drop by drop to a solution of the ion in question. If the product is a precipitate, indicate this fact by denoting the solid phase as, for example, $Al(OH)_{3(s)}$. Indicate the color of all

Reagent Added	Al^{+++}	Cr^{+++}	Fe^{+++}	Fe^{++}	Co^{++}	Ni^{++}	Mn^{++}	Zn^{++}
6 M NaOH								
6 M NaOH in excess								
6 M NH$_4$OH								
6 M NH$_4$OH in excess								
NH$_4$OH + NH$_4$Cl (soln. 1 M in NH$_4$Cl)								
0.5 M Na$_2$CO$_3$								
H$_2$S in 0.3 M HCl								
(NH$_4$)$_2$S								

precipitates and solutions containing new products. If the reaction does not give a precipitate but produces new ions, indicate these in the appropriate places. If no reaction takes place as far as you can ascertain, write *no reaction*. From your knowledge of the chemical properties of these ions *fill in as many blank spaces as possible without carrying out the experiments. If you are not familiar with the reaction in question perform an experiment to obtain the desired information.*

2. Devise an experiment for the detection of Fe⁺⁺ ion in the presence of Fe⁺⁺⁺ ion. Carry out the experiment to verify your conclusion. Use solutions containing these ions at a concentration of .02 molar.

3. Devise and perform an experiment to identify Co⁺⁺ ion in the presence of Ni⁺⁺ ion. (.02 M solutions.)

4. Devise and carry out procedures to separate and identify the individual ions in each of the following groups. In each case use 3 ml. of solution containing each of the three ions in question at a concentration of .02 M.

(a) Al⁺⁺⁺, Cr⁺⁺⁺ and Fe⁺⁺⁺
(b) Al⁺⁺⁺, Mn⁺⁺ and Zn⁺⁺
(c) Fe⁺⁺⁺, Zn⁺⁺ and Co⁺⁺
(d) Cr⁺⁺, Ni⁺⁺ and Mn⁺⁺

5. To 2 ml. of a solution containing Fe⁺⁺ and Zn⁺⁺ each at .02 M concentration, add 1 ml. of 1 M HAc and saturate with H₂S. Write the equation for the reaction which takes place. To the above solution now add NH₄OH until alkaline. What happens? Explain your results on the basis of the difference in solubility between ZnS and FeS.

6. Devise experiments to determine the position of zinc-ammonia complex ion in Table 30.

7. To 3 ml. of 0.5 M Na₂HPO₄ solution add 4.8 ml. of 0.5 M NaH₂PO₄ solution. The concentration of the HPO₄⁻⁻ ion in the mixture is approximately 0.192 M, while that of the H₂PO₄⁻ ion is 0.31 M. Since the equilibrium constant for the following expression has a value of 6.3 × 10⁻⁸,

$$\frac{(H^+)(HPO_4^{--})}{(H_2PO_4^-)} = 6.3 \times 10^{-8}$$

it is evident that the concentration of the H⁺ ion in this mixture is 1 × 10⁻⁷ mole per liter, the same as that of pure water. Such a solution is one of the more common "buffer" solutions. In order to understand the manner in which a buffer solution functions, carry out the following experiments:

(a) To one-half (3.9 ml.) of the above mixture in a 25 ml. graduated cylinder add a few drops of phenolphthalein indicator and then slowly pour into this solution 0.1 M NaOH until the indicator changes color. Note the amount of NaOH solution used. What is the concentration of the H^+ ion at this point? (See indicator chart.)

(b) To the other portion of the buffer mixture add a few drops of methyl orange indicator in a 25 ml. graduated cylinder and then add 0.1 M HCl until the indicator changes color. Note the amount of HCl solution used. Now what is the concentration of the H^+ ion at this point? (See indicator chart.)

(c) Using 3.9 ml. of pure water instead of the buffer solution repeat experiments (a) and (b). (Note: The H^+ ion concentration is the same in pure water as in the buffer solution.)

(d) If the same amount of base and of acid used in (a) and (b) respectively were added separately to pure water, what would be the concentration of the H^+ ion in each case? Compare with the results of (a) and (b). Explain the difference in behavior of these solutions.

(e) Write equations for the reactions taking place in (a) and (b). Disregard any reaction involving either H_3PO_4 or PO_4^{---} ion.

(f) Explain how a solution containing both NH_4OH and NH_4Cl can act as a buffer.

8. To 1 ml. of 6 M HNO_3 contained in a small casserole add 1 drop of 0.1 M $Mn(NO_3)_2$ solution. Add a small spatula-full of solid sodium bismuthate and heat to boiling. Add 1 ml. of water and pour into a test tube. Allow the solid to settle and note the purple color of the MnO_4^- ion.

9. To 1 ml. of water contained in a test tube add 3 drops of 0.1 M $Mn(NO_3)_2$ solution. Add 6 M NaOH until alkaline and then add 5 drops of the reagent in excess. Now add 5 drops of 3% H_2O_2 solution. Note the formation of black MnO_2. The equation for the reaction is

$$Mn(OH)_{2(s)} + HO_2^- = MnO_{2(s)} + H_2O + OH^-$$

Centrifuge or filter and transfer the MnO_2 to a casserole. Add 1 ml. of 6 M HNO_3 and then add a small spatula-full of solid sodium bismuthate. Heat to boiling. Dilute with 1 ml. of water and pour the mixture into a 10 ml. test tube. After the residue has settled, note the purple color of the MnO_4^- ion in the solution.

10. Add 12 drops of 0.1 M $FeSO_4$ solution and 12 drops of 0.1 M $Zn(NO_3)_2$ solution to 2 ml. of water in a 10 ml. test tube.

Make alkaline with 6 M NH$_4$OH and saturate with H$_2$S. Centrifuge or filter and wash the precipitate with 3 ml. of water. To the precipitate in a 10 ml. test tube add 3 ml. of a solution made by combining 2 parts of a saturated Na$_2$SO$_4$ solution with 1 part of a 2 M NaHSO$_4$ solution. Heat to boiling. Stir well or shake. Note that the FeS is dissolved by this reagent while the ZnS is not. Explain on the basis of the difference in the solubility product constants of ZnS and FeS.

11. To a small casserole add 12 drops of 0.1 M Co(NO$_3$)$_2$ solution, 12 drops of 0.1 M Ni(NO$_3$)$_2$ solution, 2 drops of 0.1 M Zn(NO$_3$)$_2$ solution, and then add 2 drops of 6 M HCl. Evaporate to dryness. Now add 2 ml. of a saturated solution of Na$_2$SO$_4$, 1 ml. of 2 M NaHSO$_4$ solution, and 10 drops of 3 M NH$_4$Ac solution. Saturate the solution with H$_2$S for at least one minute. No precipitate should appear at this point. Warm in the flame and gradually raise the temperature almost to boiling. A white precipitate of ZnS appears. Centrifuge or filter the solution and to the supernatant liquid or the filtrate, as the case may be, add 6 M NH$_4$OH solution until alkaline. If no precipitate appears, saturate again with H$_2$S. A black precipitate is a mixture of CoS and NiS. Explain this experiment.

12. Add 1 drop of 0.1 M Fe(NO$_3$)$_3$ solution to 10 ml. of water. Shake thoroughly. What is the concentration of the Fe^{+++} ion in this solution? Now add 6 drops of this solution to 3 ml. of water. What is the concentration of the Fe^{+++} ion in the latter solution? To the latter solution add 1 drop of 3 M HCl and 2 drops of 1 M KCNS solution. Note the sensitivity of this test.

13. Place 3 drops of 0.1 M Al(NO$_3$)$_3$ solution in a 10 ml. test tube, add 3 ml. of water, 3 drops of 3 M NH$_4$Ac solution, and 4 drops of aluminon reagent. Make the solution alkaline with 6 M NH$_4$OH, and heat. Note the formation of the red lake.

14. Prepare 3 ml. of a solution 0.02 M with respect to Fe^{++} and Zn^{++} ions and 0.1 M in HAc. Saturate with H$_2$S; ZnS should precipitate. Now make the solution 0.1 M with respect to NaAc. FeS should now precipitate.

(a) What were the H$^+$ and S^{--} ion concentrations when the ZnS began to precipitate?

(b) What were their concentrations when NaAc was added?

(c) Show by calculation that the FeS could not have precipitated before the NaAc was added.

Procedure for the Analysis of the Aluminum-Zinc Group

SCHEMATIC OUTLINE

Solution: Al^{+++}, Cr^{+++}, Fe^{+++}, Fe^{++}, Mn^{++}, Zn^{++}, Co^{++} and Ni^{++}.
Add 5 M NH_4Cl and 15 M NH_4OH.
Add H_2S.

(E–F)

Precipitate: $Al(OH)_3$, $Cr(OH)_3$, Fe_2S_3, FeS, MnS, ZnS, CoS, NiS.
Add saturated Na_2SO_4 and 2 M $NaHSO_4$.

(E–F–1)

Residue: ZnS, CoS, NiS.
Dissolve in 6 M HCl and 6 M HNO_3.
Evaporate to dryness.
Add saturated Na_2SO_4, and 2 M $NaHSO_4$.

(E)

Solution: Zn^{++}, Co^{++}, Ni^{++}.
Add H_2S.

(E–1)

Ppt.: ZnS. (white).	Solution: Co^{++}, Ni^{++}. Boil — Add Br_2 water.	
	Add 6 M KNO_2. (E–2)	Add 3 M NH_4OH and dimethylglyoxime. (E–3)
	Precipitate: $K_3Co(NO_2)_6$. (yellow).	
		Precipitate: Nickel dimethylglyoxime. (red).

Solution: Al^{+++}, Cr^{+++}, Fe^{+++}, Fe^{++}, Mn^{++}.
Add 6 M H_2SO_4 — boil.
Add Br_2 water. Boil — Add 6 M NH_4OH.

(F)

Precipitate: $Al(OH)_3$, $Cr(OH)_3$, $Fe(OH)_3$, $[Mn(OH)_3]$.
Dissolve in 3 M HCl.
Treat with 6 M NaOH.
Add 3% H_2O_2.

(F–2)

Residue: $Fe(OH)_3$. (MnO_2). (F–2)	Solution: AlO_2^-, CrO_4^{--}. Add 12 M HCl. Add 6 M NH_4OH. (F–3)	
Add 3 M HCl. Add 1 M KCNS. (red).	Ppt.: $Al(OH)_3$. Add 3 M HCl. Add aluminon reagent. Add 6 M NH_4OH.	Solution: CrO_4^{--}. Add 6 M HAc and 2 M $Pb(Ac)_2$. (F–4)
	Ppt.: $Al(OH)_3$ + dye (red).	Ppt.: $PbCrO_4$. (yellow).

Solution: Mn^{++}.
Add 6 M HNO_3.
Add sodium bismuthate.

(F–1)

Solution: MnO_4^-.
(purple).

Obtain from the laboratory instructor a sample of a solution containing ions of the aluminum-zinc group only. If the solution is strongly alkaline and contains no NH_4OH, it is evident from the properties of the ions of this group that only Al^{+++}, Cr^{+++} and Zn^{++} ions can be present. If the solution is acidic, all ions of the group may be present.

E–F. Precipitation of the Aluminum-Zinc Group. Place 3 ml. of this solution in an Erlenmeyer flask. Reserve the rest to make any tests you may see fit (other than adding $NH_4OH + H_2S$), to obtain preliminary information as to which ions may be present.

To 3 ml. of the unknown solution add 1 ml. 5 M NH_4Cl solution; make alkaline with 15 M NH_4OH and add 10 drops of the latter solution in excess. If no precipitate appears at this point, Al^{+++}, Cr^{+++}, and Fe^{+++} ions are absent. Saturate the solution, which may contain a precipitate, with H_2S.[1] Centrifuge or filter and test the filtrate or supernatant solution for complete precipitation by adding 2 drops of 15 M NH_4OH,[2] heating, and again saturating with H_2S.[3] Combine any precipitate with that obtained originally. Wash the precipitate with 3 ml. of water and discard the washings. The collected precipitate may contain $Al(OH)_3$, $Cr(OH)_3$, Fe_2S_3, FeS, NiS, CoS, MnS, and ZnS.

NOTE 1. *In a hot solution any $Cr(OH)_3^{-}$ present may be transformed into an insoluble form. This transformation is prevented by keeping the solution cold during the first precipitation.*

NOTE 2. *If the solution is not sufficiently alkaline during the first addition of H_2S, MnS will not precipitate. When more NH_4OH is added and the solution is again saturated with H_2S, the Mn^{++} ion, if present, may then be precipitated as the pink MnS.*

NOTE 3. *All the Zn^{++} ion may not be removed from the solution as ZnS during the first saturation with H_2S since under some circumstances the rate of the precipitation of this sulfide is slow when the solution is cold. The ZnS would then precipitate from the hot solution.*

E–F–1. Separation of ZnS, CoS and NiS.

To the combined precipitates from **E–F,** contained in a 10 ml. test tube, add 3 ml. of a solution made by combining one part, by volume, of a saturated solution of Na_2SO_4 and one part of 2 M $NaHSO_4$.[4]

With a pointed glass rod puncture the filter paper and with 3 ml. of a solution, made by combining one part, by volume, of a saturated solution of Na_2SO_4 and one part of 2 M $NaHSO_4$,[4] wash the precipitate into a 10 ml. test tube.

Agitate and stir the mixture vigorously for about two minutes. If any reaction occurs during this time, as may be observed by the evolution of gas, continue to stir until the reaction ceases. Do not heat. Centrifuge or filter. Test residue, if any, with a small portion of the buffer solution (freshly prepared) to insure complete reaction and solution of $Al(OH)_3$, $Cr(OH)_3$, Fe_2S_3, FeS and MnS, which may be present. Label the supernatant liquid or filtrate **F**. This solution contains any or all of the ions: Cr^{+++}, Al^{+++}, Fe^{+++}, Fe^{++}, and Mn^{++}. The precipitate **E** may contain the undissolved sulfides of zinc, cobalt and nickel. Wash the precipitate with 3 ml. of water and discard the washings. Add 1 ml. of 6 M HCl and 1 ml. of 6 M HNO_3 to the precipitate in the test tube. Heat to boiling and then transfer to a small casserole. Work the mass of sulfur with a stirring rod for several minutes; then remove and discard the sulfur.

Evaporate the solution to dryness. Remove the flame under the casserole just as the last drop is evaporating; that is, do not overheat the dry salt. With the aid of the capillary syringe add 1 ml. of 2 M $NaHSO_4$ solution to the salt in the casserole, after it has cooled, and pour into a 10 ml. test tube. Label this **E–1**. Rinse the casserole with 2 ml. of saturated Na_2SO_4 solution and add to **E–1**.

NOTE 4.   *The Na_2SO_4 and $NaHSO_4$ produce a buffer solution with a hydrogen ion concentration of about 10^{-2} mole per liter. HSO_4^- ion is a relatively weak acid with a dissociation constant of 10^{-2}.*

$$\frac{(H^+)(SO_4^{--})}{(HSO_4^-)} = 10^{-2}$$

Since the ratio $\dfrac{(SO_4^{--})}{(HSO_4^-)}$ is approximately equal to one, the H^+ ion concentration is therefore approximately equal to 10^{-2} mole per liter. ZnS, CoS, and NiS do not dissolve rapidly in a solution of this H^+ ion concentration.

E–1.   Test for Zn^{++} Ion.   Add 10 drops of 3 M NH_4Ac solution to solution **E–1** which may contain the ions Zn^{++}, Ni^{++}, and Co^{++}. Saturate the cold solution with H_2S for at least one minute. Warm in a flame and gradually raise the temperature amost to boiling. If zinc is present, a white or very light gray [5] precipitate of ZnS will appear.[6]

Filter or centrifuge and retain filtrate or supernatant, which may contain Co^{++} and Ni^{++} ions.

In case the precipitate is too dark to identify it as ZnS, treat it with 1 ml. of cold 1 M HCl, centrifuge, decant the solution to another test tube, and make alkaline with 3 M NH$_4$OH. Any residual H$_2$S in the solution may precipitate ZnS at this point. If no precipitate of ZnS appears, saturate the solution with H$_2$S. This procedure should give a white or light gray precipitate if zinc is present, and eliminate any NiS or CoS which may have precipitated with ZnS in the buffer solution. If the precipitate is still too dark this operation may be repeated.

Heat the filtrate or supernatant, which may contain Co^{++} and Ni^{++} ions, to boiling for several minutes to expel the H$_2$S. Add a few drops of bromine water [7] and continue heating. Add 1 ml. of water. Divide this solution into two equal portions to use for tests for Ni^{++} and Co^{++} ions. Label one of these portions **E–2** and the other **E–3**.

NOTE 5. *If this precipitate is allowed to stand, it may become darker in color due to the precipitation of some CoS or NiS or both. An initial white or gray precipitate is sufficient evidence for the presence of Zn^{++} ion. If equilibrium were attained CoS and NiS would be precipitated, but the rate of precipitation of these two sulfides is much lower than that for ZnS.*

NOTE 6. *A slight turbidity may be due to free sulfur. To distinguish sulfur from ZnS, make the solution distinctly acidic with HCl. The sulfur will not dissolve while the ZnS will.*

NOTE 7. *The purpose of adding the bromine water is to complete the removal of H$_2$S by oxidation to free sulfur.*

$$H_2S + Br_2 = S_{(s)} + 2Br^- + 2H^+$$

E–2. Test for Co^{++} Ion. To the solution **E–2** add an equal volume of 6 M KNO$_2$ solution. Warm and allow to stand for a few minutes. A yellow or olive colored precipitate of K$_3$[CO(NO$_2$)$_6$] indicates the presence of Co^{++} ion. If no yellow precipitate appears, add 3–5 drops of 6 M HAc and warm again before reaching final conclusion.

E–3. Test for Ni^{++} Ion. To solution **E–3** add 6 M NH$_4$OH drop by drop [8,9] until the solution is alkaline. Add 4 drops of dimethylglyoxime reagent. A red precipitate of nickel dimethylglyoxime indicates the presence of Ni^{++} ion.

If Co^{++} ion is present a brown soluble cobalt dimethylglyoxime is first formed. In such a case it may be necessary to add more of the dimethylglyoxime reagent to bring about the precipitation of the nickel salt. If there is any doubt about the color of the precipitate, centrifuge or filter the solution.

NOTE 8. *If Fe^{+++} ion has not been completely removed, some $Fe(OH)_3$ may be precipitated at this point. Centrifuge or filter the solution to remove it.*

NOTE 9. *If the solution turns black at this point, it is because the H_2S has not been previously completely removed and NiS precipitates. If this is the case, make acidic with 6 M HCl, add 10 drops in excess, add 10 drops of 6 M HNO_3, place in a casserole and evaporate to dryness again. After dissolving the residue in water, add 6 M NH_4OH drop by drop until just alkaline and proceed as before.*

F. Separation of Mn^{++} from Al^{+++}, Cr^{+++}, and Fe^{++} Ions.

If solution **F** is not clear, centrifuge or filter it and discard the precipitate. To the clear solution **F** add 10 drops of 6 M H_2SO_4, place it in a casserole and boil until the volume is reduced to about 1 ml. Add 3 drops of bromine water and continue heating to remove any excess Br_2.[10] Add water to restore the volume to 2 ml. Transfer to a 10 ml. test tube. Carefully make alkaline with 6 M NH_4OH and add 10 drops in excess.[11] (The solution should now be decidedly alkaline to litmus paper.) If Al^{+++}, Cr^{+++}, or Fe^{+++} ions are present a precipitate of the corresponding hydroxides will appear.[12] $Mn(OH)_2$ does not precipitate with this low OH^- ion concentration. Centrifuge or filter and retain the solution for the Mn^{++} ion test. Label it **F–1**. Wash the precipitate with 2 ml. of water and add wash water to **F–1**. Repeat the washing and discard the wash water.

Dissolve the precipitate in 1 ml. of 3 M HCl and label it **F–2**. (If filtered, wash filter with 1 ml. of water and add to **F–2**.)

NOTE 10. *The H_2S must be completely removed from the solution; otherwise MnS will form when the NH_4OH is added. This will vitiate the separation of Mn^{++} ion from the other ions. Besides oxidizing the H_2S to free sulfur, the bromine oxidizes Fe^{++} ion to Fe^{+++} ion. This procedure is carried out in order to obtain $Fe(OH)_3$ rather than $Fe(OH)_2$. $Fe(OH)_3$ is less soluble and not as gelatinous as $Fe(OH)_2$.*

NOTE 11. *Excess NH_4OH is added here to retain in solution, as $Zn(NH_3)_4^{++}$ ion, any Zn^{++} ion which may be present because of the partial solution of ZnS by the buffer solution in E–F–1.*

NOTE 12. *In alkaline solution oxygen of the air oxidizes Mn^{++} ion with the consequent formation of insoluble $Mn(OH)_3$. A small amount of $Mn(OH)_3$ appearing at this point will be later converted to MnO_2. This will not interfere with other tests unless present in relatively large amounts. It is therefore desirable that the student make this separation as rapidly as possible.*

F–1. Test for Mn^{++} Ion. Transfer 5 drops of the solution **F–1**, which may contain Mn^{++} ion, to a casserole and add 1 ml. of 6 M HNO$_3$. Now add a very small amount of solid sodium bismuthate (from the tip of the spatula). If Mn^{++} ion is present, a purple color will form due to the MnO$_4^-$ ion. If this color does not appear, heat to boiling. If the brown color of the sodium bismuthate obscures the color of the solution, allow it to stand for a time until the effervescence has stopped, and centrifuge or filter. If the color is very intense, dilute the solution with water.[13,14]

If Zn^{++} ion was not found in test **E–1** and if it was present in the original solution in small amount, an appreciable amount of the ZnS may have been dissolved by the buffer solution in **E–F–1**. In such a case, reserve the remainder of solution **F–1** for the auxilliary Zn^{++} ion test **E–X**. If Zn^{++} ion was found in **E–1**, the remainder of solution **F–1** may be discarded.

NOTE 13. *The MnO$_4^-$ ion first formed may be destroyed by reaction with the Br$^-$ ion.*

$$10Br^- + 2MnO_4^- + 16H^+ = 2Mn^{++} + 5Br_2 + 8H_2O$$

If no purple color is obtained, heat the solution to drive off the Br$_2$ and then add another pinch of sodium bismuthate. This reaction also takes place with Cl$^-$ ion. It is for this reason that reagents contributing this ion to the solution have been avoided.

NOTE 14. *If no positive test for Mn^{++} ion is obtained, it is possible that the manganese was retained with the hydroxides of Fe(OH)$_3$, Cr(OH)$_3$, and Al(OH)$_3$ as Mn(OH)$_3$. In such an event the Mn^{++} ion may be detected in F–2.*

E–X. Auxilliary Zn^{++} Ion Test. To the remainder of solution **F–1** add 6 M HCl until acidic and then add 2 drops of the reagent in excess. Transfer the solution to a casserole and evaporate to dryness. Now add 10 drops of 2 M NaHSO$_4$ solution, 1 ml. of saturated Na$_2$SO$_4$ solution, and 5 drops of 3 M·NH$_4$Ac solution. Pour the solution into a small test tube, cool if necessary, and saturate with H$_2$S for at least one minute. Warm in a flame and gradually raise the temperarure almost to boiling. If Zn^{++} ion is present at this point, a white or very light gray precipitate of ZnS will appear. If no precipitate of ZnS appears either here or in **E–1**, Zn^{++} ion is absent in the original solution.

F–2. Test for Fe^{+++} Ion. Add 2 ml. of 6 M NaOH to the acid solution **F–2** which may contain Fe^{+++}, Cr^{+++}, and Al^{+++}

ions. At this point a reddish brown precipitate indicates the presence of Fe^{+++} ion although this color may be somewhat obscured if Cr^{+++} ion is also present. Add 1 ml. of 3% H_2O_2.[15] Heat to boiling and keep hot for several minutes. Centrifuge or filter the solution, retaining the filtrate or supernatant liquid for the tests for aluminum and chromium and label it **F–3**. Wash the precipitate with 3 ml. of water and centrifuge or filter again, discarding the wash water. Repeat the washing.[16]

To the precipitate add 1 ml. of 3 M HCl. Centrifuge the solution, if necessary, and pour the supernatant solution into another test tube. (Save the residue.) [17] Dilute with 1 ml. of water.	To the precipitate on the filter paper add 1 ml. of 3 M HCl. Wash with 1 ml. of water and combine with the solution. (Retain any residue left on the filter.) [17]

Add 2 drops of 1 M KCNS solution. A deep red color indicates or confirms the presence of Fe^{+++} ion. A very light pink color which might appear at this point may be due to a small amount of iron which has crept into the solution as an impurity in the reagents.

NOTE 15. *If Mn^{++} ion was originally present and was not washed out of the hydroxides or was withheld as $Mn(OH)_3$, a black precipitate of MnO_2 will appear at this point. It will not interfere with the test for Fe^{+++} ion.*

If black precipitate does appear here, separate it either by decantation or centrifugation, wash, and then carry out test for manganese by the addition of HNO_3 and $NaBiO_3$ as described in F–1, page 397.

NOTE 16. *If the precipitate is not thoroughly washed, the NaOH retained with the precipitate will neutralize the HCl added later and the $Fe(OH)_3$ may not be completely dissolved.*

NOTE 17. *If Mn^{++} ion was not detected in F–1 and if a black residue remains at this point, carry out the following test for Mn^{++} ion. Transfer the residue to a small casserole with 2 ml. of 6 M HNO_3. Add one small spatulafull of solid sodium bismuthate and heat to boiling. Dilute with 2 ml. of water and centrifuge or filter if necessary. If the black residue contained MnO_2 the resulting solution will appear purple in color due to the MnO_4^- ion. (See F–1.)*

F–3. Test for Al^{+++} Ion. The solution **F–3** may contain AlO_2^- and CrO_4^{--} ions. Carefully neutralize the solution with 12 M HCl. Make alkaline with 6 M NH_4OH and add 10 drops of the NH_4OH in excess. Heat. A white gelatinous precipitate indicates the presence of Al^{+++} ion in the original solution. If the solution is not yellow an appreciable amount of CrO_4^{--} ion is not present. Filter [18] (do not centrifuge) this solution, even though it may appear to contain no precipitate. Retain the filtrate for the test for chromium and label it **F–4**. Wash the precipitate with 1 ml. of water. Discard the wash water. Wash again. Pour 1 ml. of 3 M HCl over the filter and collect the solution in a 10 ml. test tube. Wash the filter with 1 ml. of water and add this to the acid solution. Add 3 drops of 3 M NH_4Ac solution and 3 drops of aluminon reagent.[19] Stir the solution and add 6 M NH_4OH until slightly alkaline. Heat gently. A red flocculent precipitate of $Al(OH)_3$ with the red dye adsorbed to it indicates presence of Al^{+++} in the original solution.

It is imperative that the color of the final aluminon precipitate be compared with that obtained by the identical treatment of an 0.02 M $Al(NO_3)_3$ solution before deciding whether Al^{+++} ion is present.

If the color obtained in the aluminon test is not identical with that of the blank, the difference may be due to the presence of $Fe(OH)_3$ or $Cr(OH)_3$, small amounts of which may have inadvertently been carried through. If such is the case, add 2 drops of concentrated HNO_3 to the aluminon precipitate, heat, and repeat procedures **F–2** and **F–3**.

NOTE 18. *The $Al(OH)_3$ precipitate is often very difficult to observe at this point. Any H_2O_2 which may be present may decompose and the oxygen liberated will adhere to the $Al(OH)_3$ causing it to rise to the surface of the solution. This effect makes centrifugation inadvisable.*

NOTE 19. *These reagents must be added to the solution in the order given in the test. The conditions for the formation of the red lake have been determined empirically.*

F–4. Test for CrO_4^{--} Ion. To the solution which contains the CrO_4^{--} ion (it should be yellow if present) add 6 M acetic acid [20] drop by drop until the solution is just acidic. Add a few drops of 0.2 M $Pb(Ac)_2$ solution. A deep yellow precipitate of $PbCrO_4$ indicates the presence of chromium in the original solution.

NOTE 20. *If the yellow color of the CrO_4^{--} ion disappears when the HAc is added, the CrO_4^{--} has probably been reduced to the green Cr^{+++} ion by H_2O_2 which was previously not removed by boiling. If this should happen, $Cr(OH)_3$ may again be precipitated upon the addition of NH_4OH. The $Cr(OH)_3$ may then be converted to the CrO_4^{--} ion and the test repeated.*

Equations for Pertinent Reactions

$$Al^{+++} + 3NH_4OH = Al(OH)_{3(s)} + 3NH_4^+$$

$$Cr^{+++} + 3NH_4OH = Cr(OH)_{3(s)} + 3NH_4^+$$

$$2Fe^{+++} + 3S^{--} = Fe_2S_{3(s)}$$

$$M^{++} + S^{--} = MS_{(s)} \qquad (M^{++} = Co^{++}, Ni^{++}, Mn^{++} \text{ and } Zn^{++})$$

$$Al(OH)_{3(s)} + 3H^+ = Al^{+++} + 3H_2O$$

$$MnS_{(s)} + 2H^+ = Mn^{++} + H_2S$$

$$CoS_{(s)} + 2NO_3^- + 4H^+ = Co^{++} + 2NO_2 + S_{(s)} + 2H_2O$$

$$H_2S + Br_2 = S_{(s)} + 2H^+ + 2Br^-$$

$$Co^{++} + 2HAc + 7NO_2^- + 3K^+$$
$$= NO + H_2O + 2Ac^- + K_3Co(NO_2)_{6(s)}$$

$$Ni^{++} + 2NH_4OH + 2C_4H_6N_2O_2H_2$$
$$= NiC_8H_{14}N_4O_{4(s)} + 2NH_4^+ + 2H_2O$$

$$Fe^{+++} + 3NH_4OH = Fe(OH)_{3(s)} + 3NH_4^+$$

$$4Mn^{++} + O_2 + 8NH_4OH + 2H_2O = 4Mn(OH)_{3(s)} + 8NH_4^+$$

$$2Mn^{++} + 5NaBiO_{3(s)} + 14H^+$$
$$= 2MnO_4^- + 5Bi^{+++} + 5Na^+ + 7H_2O$$

$$10Br^- + 2MnO_4^- + 16H^+ = 2Mn^{++} + 5Br_2 + 8H_2O$$

$$Fe^{+++} + 3OH^- = Fe(OH)_{3(s)}$$

$$Al(OH)_{3(s)} + OH^- = AlO_2^- + 2H_2O$$

$$Cr(OH)_{3(s)} + OH^- = CrO_2^- + 2H_2O$$

$$2CrO_2^- + 3HO_2^- = 2CrO_4^{--} + OH^- + H_2O$$

$$Fe(OH)_{3(s)} + 3H^+ = Fe^{+++} + 3H_2O$$

$$Fe^{+++} + 6CNS^- = Fe(CNS)_6^{---}$$

$$2Mn(OH)_{3(s)} + HO_2^- = 2MnO_{2(s)} + OH^- + 3H_2O$$

$$2MnO_{2(s)} + 3NaBiO_{3(s)} + 10H^+$$
$$= 2MnO_4^- + 3Bi^{+++} + 3Na^+ + 5H_2O$$

$$Cr_2O_7^{--} + 2Pb(Ac)_2 + H_2O = 2PbCrO_{4(s)} + 2HAc + 2Ac^-$$

CHAPTER XVII

The Alkaline Earth Group of Ions

Ba^{++}, Sr^{++}, Ca^{++} and Mg^{++} Ions

The alkaline earth metals and magnesium are all included in the second main group of the periodic table. All exhibit a single valence, plus two; accordingly, they form only one series of compounds. These elements are highly electropositive and therefore they are excellent reducing agents. The hydroxides of these elements are strong and may be regarded as completely ionized in aqueous solutions; they show no amphoteric properties. The ions of these elements are not hydrolyzed, nor do they show any tendency to form complex ions. However, they are characterized by the formation of a relatively large number of slightly soluble salts.

Calcium, strontium and barium resemble each other very closely in their physical and chemical properties. Magnesium, on the other hand, is less electropositive than the alkaline earth elements and differs chemically from them in many respects. In the analytical procedures magnesium is separated from the alkaline earth ions and treated separately.

Barium Ion, Ba^{++} — Strontium Ion, Sr^{++} — Calcium Ion, Ca^{++}. The tables on page 402 list some of the slightly soluble compounds of these ions in equilibrium with their saturated solutions. These compounds are arranged according to decreasing concentration of the metal ion at equilibrium. Although there are many other slightly soluble compounds of these ions, the tables give those most frequently encountered by the student in the separation and identification of the ions according to the analytical procedures. In addition, where accurate quantitative data are lacking regarding the solubility of the compounds, no attempt has been made to place them in the tables. An examination of the three tables demonstrates the similarity of the alkaline earth ions.

TABLE 31

Equilibria Involving Barium Ion

Decreasing Concentration of Ba^{++} Ion

$$Ba^{++} + 2OH^- = Ba(OH)_{2(s)}$$
$$Ba^{++} + 2F^- = BaF_{2(s)}$$
$$Ba^{++} + S_2O_3^{--} = BaS_2O_{3(s)}$$
$$Ba^{++} + SiF_6^{--} = BaSiF_{6(s)}$$
$$Ba^{++} + SO_3^{--} = BaSO_{3(s)}$$
$$Ba^{++} + C_2O_4^{--} = BaC_2O_{4(s)}$$
$$Ba^{++} + 2IO_3^- = Ba(IO_3)_{2(s)}$$
$$Ba^{++} + CO_3^{--} = BaCO_{3(s)}$$
$$Ba^{++} + CrO_4^{--} = BaCrO_{4(s)}$$
$$Ba^{++} + SO_4^{--} = BaSO_{4(s)}$$
$$3Ba^{++} + 2PO_4^{---} = Ba_3(PO_4)_{2(s)}$$

TABLE 32

Equilibria Involving Strontium Ion

Decreasing Concentration of Sr^{++} Ion

$$Sr^{++} + 2OH^- = Sr(OH)_{2(s)}$$
$$Sr^{++} + CrO_4^{--} = SrCrO_{4(s)}$$
$$Sr^{++} + 2F^- = SrF_{2(s)}$$
$$Sr^{++} + SO_4^{--} = SrSO_{4(s)}$$
$$Sr^{++} + C_2O_4^{--} = SrC_2O_{4(s)}$$
$$Sr^{++} + CO_3^{--} = SrCO_{3(s)}$$
$$3Sr^{++} + 2PO_4^{---} = Sr_3(PO_4)_{2(s)}$$

TABLE 33

Equilibria Involving Calcium Ion

Decreasing Concentration of Ca^{++} Ion

$$Ca^{++} + CrO_4^{--} = CaCrO_{4(s)}$$
$$Ca^{++} + 2OH^- = Ca(OH)_{2(s)}$$
$$Ca^{++} + 2IO_3^- = Ca(IO_3)_{2(s)}$$
$$Ca^{++} + C_4H_4O_6^{--} = CaC_4H_4O_{6(s)}$$
$$Ca^{++} + SO_4^{--} = CaSO_{4(s)}$$
$$3Ca^{++} + 2PO_4^{---} = Ca_3(PO_4)_{2(s)}$$
$$Ca^{++} + 2F^- = CaF_{2(s)}$$
$$Ca^{++} + SO_3^{--} = CaSO_{3(s)}$$
$$Ca^{++} + CO_3^{--} = CaCO_{3(s)}$$
$$Ca^{++} + C_2O_4^{--} = CaC_2O_{4(s)}$$

The molar solubility of some of the members of these tables is very nearly the same. Accordingly, the order may be reversed by making the concentration of the anion of the more soluble salt relatively high. For example, $BaCO_3$ is only slightly less soluble than $Ba(IO_3)_2$. On the basis of the order given in Table 31; CO_3^{--} ion reacts with a saturated solution of $Ba(IO_3)_2$ to produce solid $BaCO_3$. It must be remembered that the order in these tables is based entirely upon the concentration of the positive ion at equilibrium with the slightly soluble salt.

Ammonium hydroxide does not give a precipitate with solutions containing the ions, Ba^{++}, Ca^{++} and Sr^{++}. The most insoluble hydroxide of the three ions is $Ca(OH)_2$, but even in this case NH_4OH does not furnish a high enough concentration of OH^- to precipitate $Ca(OH)_2$. A small amount of precipitate of $CaCO_3$ might be formed with this reagent due to the presence of CO_3^{--} ions produced by absorption of CO_2 from the atmosphere. In dealing with this group it is therefore essential that all precipitating reagents be as free as possible from CO_3^{--} ions.

Ammonium carbonate or sodium carbonate precipitates from neutral or alkaline solutions of these ions the corresponding relatively insoluble **carbonates**. These carbonates are somewhat soluble in solutions containing ammonium salts of strong acids. This effect is due to the hydrolysis of the NH_4^+ with the eventual production of HCO_3^- ions as the following equilibrium system demonstrates.

$$MCO_{3(s)} = M^{++} + CO_3^{--}$$
$$+$$
$$NH_4^+ + H_2O = NH_4OH + H^+ \qquad (130)$$
$$\updownarrow$$
$$HCO_3^-$$

This process uses up CO_3^{--} which can be regenerated only by more MCO_3 going into solution.

The alkaline earth carbonates are readily soluble in solutions of acids.

$$MCO_{3(s)} = M^{++} + CO_3^{--}$$
$$+$$
$$H^+ \tag{131}$$
$$\Updownarrow$$
$$HCO_3^- + H^+ = H_2CO_3 = H_2O + CO_{2(g)}$$

The H^+ ion combines with CO_3^{--} to first produce HCO_3^- ion. With relatively high H^+ ion concentration the H_2CO_3 produced exceeds the solubility of CO_2 in water at one atmosphere pressure. This effect demands a supply of HCO_3^- ions which in turn requires the production of more CO_3^{--} ions, and the latter process involves solution of MCO_3. Acetic acid produces sufficient H^+ ions to dissolve the carbonates of this group with the liberation of CO_2. The alkaline earth metal carbonates are also somewhat soluble in H_2CO_3 solutions. Obviously, in this case CO_2 is not liberated, but the increased solubility is due to formation of HCO_3^- ion.

$$MCO_{3(s)} = M^{++} \quad + CO_3^{--}$$
$$+$$
$$H_2CO_3 = HCO_3^- + H^+ \tag{132}$$
$$\Updownarrow$$
$$HCO_3^-$$

Water of "temporary hardness" contains Ca^{++} and HCO_3^- ions in appreciable quantities, which have been produced by the above process (132) from limestone and water containing H_2CO_3.

The addition of SO_4^{--} ion to solutions containing the alkaline earth metal ions causes the precipitation of the **sulfate** in each case. Of these, $BaSO_4$ is the least and $CaSO_4$ the most soluble. The molar solubility of $CaSO_4$ is about 800 times as great as that of $BaSO_4$. The solubility of all insoluble sulfates is increased only slightly by the addition of very strong acids. This small solubility effect of H^+ ion is due to the fact that H^+ and SO_4^{--} ions have some tendency to combine to form HSO_4^- ion. In contrast to the HCO_3^- ion, the HSO_4^- ion is a moderately strong acid. In .01 M solutions the extent of ionization of the HSO_4^- ion is about 50%. Since a saturated solution of $BaSO_4$ produces such a small concentration of SO_4^{--} ion its solubility is increased only to an inappreciable extent in the presence of strong acids. $SrSO_4$ and $CaSO_4$, however, are considerably more soluble in such solutions.

A solution containing an appreciable concentration of CrO_4^{--} ion will precipitate **barium chromate, strontium chromate** and **calcium chromate**. $BaCrO_4$ is the least soluble and $CaCrO_4$ the most soluble of the group. The molar solubility of $CaCrO_4$ is almost 10,000 times as great as that of $BaCrO_4$, while the molar solubility of $SrCrO_4$ is about 400 times that of $BaCrO_4$. Since the $HCrO_4^-$ ion is a very weak acid, strong acids will dissolve $BaCrO_4$. The equilibrium involved is

$$BaCrO_{4(s)} = Ba^{++} + CrO_4^{--}$$
$$+$$
$$H^+ \qquad\qquad (133)$$
$$\text{⇅}$$
$$2HCrO_4^- = Cr_2O_7^{--} + H_2O$$

It is obvious that $BaCrO_4$ cannot be precipitated from solutions of high H^+ ion concentration.

Acetic acid does not furnish sufficient H^+ ions to shift the equilibrium (133) to the right appreciably. The situation is somewhat different with $SrCrO_4$ and $CaCrO_4$. Since these chromates are so much more soluble than $BaCrO_4$ they furnish considerable quantities of CrO_4^{--} ions in their saturated solutions. In these solutions the concentration of the CrO_4^{--} ion is sufficiently high so that acetic acid will dissolve the solid chromate. In other words, solutions containing acetic acid and Sr^{++} or Ca^{++} ions will not give a precipitate of $SrCrO_4$ or of $CaCrO_4$ upon the addition of soluble chromate. This serves as a means of separating Ba^{++} ion from Sr^{++} and Ca^{++} ions.

Ammonium oxalate precipitates **barium, strontium** and **calcium oxalates**. The solubility of all three salts is of the same order of magnitude; BaC_2O_4 is only about 8 times as soluble as CaC_2O_4 and twice as soluble as SrC_2O_4 in terms of moles per liter of solution. Strong acids and even hot acetic acid will dissolve BaC_2O_4 readily. The same is true for SrC_2O_4 but CaC_2O_4 is somewhat less soluble and although it is soluble in solutions containing a high concentration of H^+ ion, it fails to dissolve to a large extent in acetic acid solutions. This result gives a method for separating Ca^{++} ion from Sr^{++} and Ba^{++} ions. Since both $H_2C_2O_4$ and $HC_2O_4^-$ ion are moderately weak acids the solubility of relatively insoluble oxalates in solutions of strong acids can be explained by equilibrium considerations similar to those of equations (131) and (133). In the precipitation of CaC_2O_4 by ammonium oxalate solution it is desirable to add NH_4OH. The latter tends to prevent the hydrolysis of the NH_4^+ ion, thereby decreasing the concentration of H^+ ion in the solution, a condition necessary for more complete precipitation.

In neutral solutions containing Ba^{++}, Sr^{++} and Ca^{++} ions, Na_2HPO_4 solution precipitates the corresponding salts of these ions.

$$M^{++} + HPO_4^{--} = MHPO_{4(s)} \qquad (134)$$

In the presence of NH_4OH the normal salts are precipitated since

$$HPO_4^{--} + OH^- = PO_4^{---} + H_2O \qquad (135)$$

and

$$3M^{++} + 2PO_4^{--} = M_3(PO_4)_{2(s)} \qquad (136)$$

The dihydrogen phosphate salts, $M(H_2PO_4)_2$, are relatively soluble. Both $M_3(PO_4)_2$, and $MHPO_4$ are readily soluble in dilute solutions of strong acids and even in acetic acid, due to the formation of the HPO_4^{--} and $H_2PO_4^-$ ions respectively.

Flame Tests. When heated in the Bunsen flame, barium salts impart to it a yellowish green color; strontium salts, a bright red color; and calcium salts, a brick red color. When present in a mixture of salts the color due to either barium or calcium does not persist long.

Magnesium Ion, Mg^{++}. Magnesium differs markedly from the alkaline earth metals in that its sulfate and chromate are highly soluble and its oxalate and carbonate are moderately soluble. It is apparent that the same reagents cannot be used for the precipitation and separation of magnesium as for the alkaline earth metal ions. The following table gives a list of slightly soluble magnesium compounds in equilibrium with their ions and arranged in the order of decreasing Mg^{++} ion concentration.

TABLE 34

EQUILIBRIA INVOLVING MAGNESIUM ION

$Mg^{++} + C_2O_4^{--}$	$= MgC_2O_{4(s)}$
$Mg^{++} + CO_3^{--}$	$= MgCO_{3(s)}$
$Mg^{++} + 2F^-$	$= MgF_{2(s)}$
$3Mg^{++} + 2PO_4^{---}$	$= Mg_3(PO_4)_{2(s)}$
$Mg^{++} + 2OH^-$	$= Mg(OH)_{2(s)}$
$Mg^{++} + NH_4^+ + PO_4^{---}$	$= MgNH_4PO_{4(s)}$

Decreasing Concentration of Mg^{++} Ion (arrow pointing down along the left side)

Alkali hydroxides and ammonium hydroxide precipitate **magnesium hydroxide** from solutions containing Mg^{++} ion. The $Mg(OH)_2$ is not soluble in an excess of any of these reagents. On the other hand, it is soluble in the presence of appreciable amounts of NH_4^+ ion. The precipitation of the hydroxide by NH_4OH may be expressed by

$$Mg^{++} + 2NH_4OH = Mg(OH)_{2(s)} + 2NH_4^+ \quad (137)$$

It is evident that the presence of NH_4^+ ions in excess decreases the concentration of the OH^- ion; this effect is sufficient to cause the $Mg(OH)_2$ to dissolve. In other words, the equilibrium above is shifted to the left. Advantage is taken of this property in the separation of Ba^{++}, Sr^{++} and Ca^{++} ions from Mg^{++} ion. To the solution containing all these ions is added a solution containing NH_4OH and $(NH_4)_2CO_3$. $CaCO_3$, $SrCO_3$ and $BaCO_3$ precipitate since the CO_3^{--} ion concentration is sufficiently high to exceed the respective solubility product constants. $MgCO_3$ does not precipitate since it is moderately soluble, nor does $Mg(OH)_2$ precipitate since the concentration of the NH_4^+ ion in the solution is high and the concentration of the OH^- ion too low to exceed the solubility product constant for $Mg(OH)_2$.

In dilute solutions, ammonium oxalate does not give a precipitate with Mg^{++} ion. However, in the more concentrated solutions of the reagent a precipitate appears having the composition, $MgC_2O_4 \cdot 2H_2O$.

A solution of Na_2HPO_4 when added to one containing Mg^{++} ions gives a white precipitate of $MgHPO_4 \cdot 7H_2O$. On the other hand, if NH_4OH and NH_4Cl are present, PO_4^{---} ion gives a characteristic white, crystalline precipitate of $MgNH_4PO_4$ since,

$$HPO_4^{--} + NH_4OH = PO_4^{---} + NH_4^+ + H_2O \quad (138)$$

and

$$PO_4^{---} + Mg^{++} + NH_4^+ = MgNH_4PO_{4(s)} \quad (139)$$

It is evident that $MgNH_4PO_4$ is soluble in relatively weak acids.

Several organic reagents have been found applicable as characteristic tests for Mg^{++} ion. Of these one of the most sensitive and successful makes use of **p-nitrobenzeneazoresorcinol** as the reagent (*S.* and *O. reagent*). It is claimed that as little as 1/500 milligram of Mg^{++} ion can be detected by this reagent. A convenient concentration for its use is a 0.5% solution of the dye in 1% sodium hydroxide solution.

Preliminary Experiments

1. In the following chart the ions of the alkaline earth group are listed horizontally and a number of reagents vertically. In the blank spaces provided in a similar chart made in your notebook give the products of the reactions when the specified reagent is added drop by drop to a solution of the ion in question. If the product is a precipitate, indicate this fact by denoting the solid phase as, for example, $BaCO_{3(s)}$. Indicate the color of all precipitates and solutions containing new products. If no reaction takes place as far as you can ascertain, write *no reaction. From your knowledge of the chemical properties of these ions fill in as many blank spaces as possible without carrying out the experiments. If you are not familiar with the reaction in question, perform an experiment to obtain the desired information.*

Reagent added	Ba^{++}	Sr^{++}	Ca^{++}	Mg^{++}
6 M NH$_4$OH				
6 M NaOH				
6 M NH$_4$OH + H$_2$S				
(NH$_4$)$_2$CO$_3$				
1 M K$_2$CrO$_4$ in 1 M HAc solution				
6 M H$_2$SO$_4$				
0.1 M (NH$_4$)$_2$C$_2$O$_4$				

2. On the basis of the relative positions of BaCO$_3$ and BaSO$_4$ in Table 31, predict what would take place if solid BaCO$_3$ were treated with Na$_2$SO$_4$ solution. Prepare some solid BaCO$_3$ by adding Na$_2$CO$_3$ solution to one of BaCl$_2$. Centrifuge or filter and wash the precipitate to remove any excess CO$_3^{--}$ ion. Test your prediction by adding some of the solid BaCO$_3$ to hot 1 M Na$_2$SO$_4$ solution. After centrifuging or filtering, test the filtrate for CO$_3^{--}$ ion by adding HCl, noting evolution of CO$_2$. Write the equation for the reaction taking place.

3. How may the reaction of (2) be reversed? Devise an experiment to determine whether it is possible to carry out this reversal to an appreciable extent. Make certain the BaSO$_{4(s)}$ is free from excess SO$_4^{--}$ ion. Use a saturated solution of K$_2$CO$_3$. In making a test for SO$_4^{--}$ ion in the presence of CO$_3^{--}$ ion, the CO$_3^{--}$ ion must first be removed by the addition of excess HCl or HNO$_3$.

4. Prepare the two following solutions: (a) 2 drops of 0.1 M Mg(NO$_3$)$_2$ solution and 2 ml. of water, (b) 2 drops of 0.1 M Mg(NO$_3$)$_2$ solution, 1 ml. of 5 M NH$_4$Cl solution, and 1 ml. of water. To each of these solutions add 2 drops of 15 M NH$_4$OH. Explain why a precipitate of Mg(OH)$_2$ is obtained in solution (a) but not in solution (b).

5. Add 6 drops of 0.1 M Mg(NO$_3$)$_2$ solution to 2 ml. of water and with this solution perform test **H** on page 415 for the Mg^{++}

ion. Note particularly the appearance of the precipitate $MgNH_4PO_4$ and of the lake formed between the S. and O. reagent and the $Mg(OH)_2$.

6. The purpose of this experiment is to acquaint the student with the principles of equilibrium as applied to the precipitation of $CaSO_4$ and $SrSO_4$.

HSO_4^- ion is a weak acid with a dissociation constant equal to 10^{-2}.

$$\frac{(H^+)(SO_4^{--})}{(HSO_4^-)} = 10^{-2}$$

Under the conditions existing in this problem the H^+ ion concentration is about 1.3 M and the HSO_4^- ion concentration about 1 M. The SO_4^{--} ion concentration is therefore approximately equal to 10^{-2} M. Since the solubility product constant for $SrSO_4$ has a value of 2.9×10^{-7}, the concentration of the Sr^{++} ion, after the $SrSO_4$ has been precipitated, is only approximately 3×10^{-5} M.

The solubility product constant for $CaSO_4$ is equal to 6×10^{-5}, and with the SO_4^{--} ion concentration equal to about 10^{-2} (as it is in this solution), the Ca^{++} ion concentration can be as high as 6×10^{-3} M without the precipitation of $CaSO_4$. The concentration of the SO_4^{--} ion in the solution remains practically constant even though a small amount is removed by the precipitation of $SrSO_4$. As SO_4^{--} ion is consumed, it is regenerated from the HSO_4^- ion. The SO_4^{--} ion concentration is therefore "buffered."

One of the difficulties sometimes encountered in the precipitation of these sulfates is that they tend to form supersaturated solutions when incipient crystals are not present. Because of this difficulty the analytical procedure adopted for the alkaline earth group is not based upon the principle stated above. The following experiments will illustrate these points.

Prepare each of the following test solutions: (a) 3 drops of 0.1 M $Ca(NO_3)_2$ and 3 drops of 0.1 M $Sr(NO_3)_2$, (b) 6 drops of 0.1 M $Sr(NO_3)_2$, (c) 6 drops of 0.1 M $Ca(NO_3)_2$, and (d) 10 drops of 0.1 M $Sr(NO_3)_2$ and 1 drop of 0.1 M $Ca(NO_3)_2$. On each of these solutions perform the following operations (work with one solution at a time).

Add 10 drops of 6 M HNO_3 and 1.5 ml. of 2 M $NaHSO_4$ solution. Heat to boiling. Any precipitate formed is $SrSO_4$. If $SrSO_4$ does not precipitate in (a), (b) and (d), seed the solution with $SrSO_4$. This can be done by making a suspension of $SrSO_4$ from solutions of Na_2SO_4 and $Sr(NO_3)_2$ and then by dipping the stirring rod into this suspension and transferring the adhering crystals to the solution in question. A small drop of the suspension may be added instead.

Cool the solution under the tap and centrifuge or filter. Reserve the precipitate for a later flame test. Label it (1). To the filtrate or supernatant liquid add 15 M NH$_4$OH dropwise until alkaline, cooling the solution under the tap as the NH$_4$OH is added. Now heat the solution. If Ca^{++} ion is present, a precipitate of CaSO$_4$ should form when the solution is heated. Filter or centrifuge. Reserve any precipitate for a later test. Label it (2).

Make calculations involving the solubility products of CaSO$_4$ and SrSO$_4$ to determine whether the precipitation of these salts is behaving according to expectation.

To the filtrate or supernatant liquid add 1 ml. of 0.1 M (NH$_4$)$_2$C$_2$O$_4$ solution. Shake the solution and allow it to stand for a few minutes. If Ca^{++} ion is present, a faint precipitate of CaC$_2$O$_4$ may appear (CaC$_2$O$_4$ does not precipitate readily when the SO$_4$$^{--}$ ion concentration is high).

Wash the precipitate (2) with water. Discard the wash water and to the precipitate add 1 ml. of (NH$_4$)$_2$CO$_3$ reagent. (If filtration is used, puncture the filter paper in this operation.) Stir and heat the solution. Any solid sulfate will be converted to carbonate. Centrifuge or filter. Wash and discard the wash water. Now dissolve the precipitate in 1 ml. of 1 M HCl. Add 6 M NH$_4$OH until alkaline and then add only one drop of 0.1 M (NH$_4$)$_2$C$_2$O$_4$ solution. If Ca^{++} ion is present, a white precipitate of CaC$_2$O$_4$ will appear.

Wash the precipitate (1), if any was formed, and treat it with 1 ml. of (NH$_4$)$_2$CO$_3$ reagent. Heat and stir. The SrSO$_4$ is converted to SrCO$_3$. Centrifuge or filter. To the solid SrCO$_3$ add 3 drops of 6 M HC$_3$ and with this solution make a flame test for strontium.

7. Carry out flame tests on different solutions containing the ions of the alkaline earth group. Add a few drops of 6 M HCl to each solution. It is essential to become familiar with these tests.

8. For each of the following cases devise a method for separating and identifying the two ions in question.

(a) Ba^{++} and Ca^{++}
(b) Mg^{++} and Ca^{++}
(c) Ba^{++} and Mg^{++}
(d) Sr^{++} and Mg^{++}
(e) Ba^{++} and Sr^{++}

Procedure for the Analysis of the Alkaline Earth Group

SCHEMATIC OUTLINE

Solution: Ba^{++}, Sr^{++}, Ca^{++} and Mg^{++}. Add 5 M NH_4Cl, 15 M NH_4OH and $(NH_4)_2CO_3$. (G–H)				
Precipitate: $BaCO_3$, $SrCO_3$, $CaCO_3$. Dissolve in 6 M HAc. Add 3 M NH_4Ac. Add 1 M K_2CrO_4. (G)			Solution: Mg^{++} (H)	
Precipitate: $BaCrO_4$. Dissolve in 6 M HCl. Add 6 M H_2SO_4. (G–1) Precipitate: $BaSO_4$.	Solution: Sr^{++}, Ca^{++}. Add $N(C_2H_4OH)_3$ and $(NH_4)_2SO_4$.		Add 5 M NH_4Cl. Add 15 M NH_4OH. Add 0.5 M Na_2HPO_4. Precipitate: $MgNH_4PO_4$	Add 6 M NaOH. Heat to dryness. Add 6 M HCl and water. Add S. and O. reagent. Add 6 M NaOH.
	Precipitate: $SrSO_4$. Add $(NH_4)_2CO_3$. (G–2) Precipitate: $SrCO_3$. Dissolve in 6 M HCl. Apply flame test.	Solution: Ca^{++} Add $(NH_4)_2C_2O_4$ (G–3) Precipitate: CaC_2O_4.		Precipitate: $Mg(OH)_2$ + dye (blue).

G–H. Precipitation of the Alkaline Earth Group. Obtain from the laboratory instructor a sample of the unknown to be analyzed. Saturate 3 ml. of this sample with solid NH_4Cl, decant the supernatant liquid into a 10 ml. test tube, make alkaline with 15 M NH_4OH solution and add 5 drops of 15 M NH_4OH in excess. Heat the solution almost to boiling [1] (*do not boil*) and with constant stirring add 2 ml. of the prepared $(NH_4)_2CO_3$ reagent. Allow the solution to stand for a few minutes and centrifuge or filter. To the filtrate or supernatant liquid add a few drops of the $(NH_4)_2CO_3$ reagent to test for completeness of precipitation, and combine any precipitate formed with that originally obtained. Continue testing for completeness of precipitation until no more precipitate is formed. The white carbonates of Ba^{++}, Ca^{++}, and Sr^{++} ions may be present in the precipitate (**G**). The filtrate (**H**) may contain the Mg^{++} ion.[2]

NOTE 1. *The purpose of heating at this point is to prevent the formation of too gelatinous a precipitate which is not easily washed.*

NOTE 2. *$Mg(OH)_2$ has a sufficiently large solubility product constant that it will not precipitate when the OH^- ion concentration is as low as in this buffered solution.*

G–1. Test for Ba^{++} Ion. Wash the white carbonate precipitate (**G**) with 3 ml. of warm water, centrifuge or filter and discard the washings. Repeat the washing.

To the precipitate in the test tube add dropwise 6 M HAc until the precipitate is just dissolved. Use the stirring rod to agitate the precipitate and solution after the addition of each drop of 6 M HAc.

To the precipitate on the filter add 1 ml. of 3 M HAc with the aid of the capillary syringe, collecting the solution in a 10 ml. test tube. If the precipitate is not completely dissolved, add 10 drops of 3 M HAc to the solution already collected and again pour this over the precipitate, collecting the solution in a 10 ml. test tube.

Add 10 drops of 3 M NH_4Ac solution and dilute with 3 ml. of water. Now add 10 drops of 1 M K_2CrO_4 solution. A yellow precipitate of $BaCrO_4$ indicates the presence of Ba^{++} ion in the original solution. Heat the solution and centrifuge or filter. Retain the filtrate and label it **G–2**. This will contain any Ca^{++} and Sr^{++} ions present in the original solution. Wash the collected

$BaCrO_4$ precipitate twice, using 3 ml. of water each time. Discard the washings.

To confirm the presence of Ba^{++} ion, dissolve the yellow $BaCrO_4$ with 1 ml. of 6 M HCl. Add to the solution 2 drops of 6 M H_2SO_4 to precipitate the white $BaSO_4$. The color of the solution will make the precipitate appear yellow. Filter or centrifuge to ascertain whether the precipitate is white.

G–2. Test for Sr^{++} Ion. Adjust the volume of the orange-yellow solution which is to be tested for both Sr^{++} and Ca^{++} ions to 3 ml. either by evaporation or dilution as the case may be. Place 10 drops of this solution in a small test tube and add 10 drops of triethanolamine [3] and 1 ml. of 1 M $(NH_4)_2SO_4$ solution. Heat to boiling. A white precipitate or clouding of the solution indicates the presence of Sr^{++} ion. If a precipitate appears, centrifuge or filter the solution and retain the filtrate (**G–3**) to test for the Ca^{++} ion.

To confirm the presence of Sr^{++} ion, first wash the precipitate of $SrSO_4$ several times with water.

To the precipitate now add 2 ml. of the $(NH_4)_2CO_3$ reagent, heat and stir. The $SrSO_4$ will be converted to $SrCO_3$. Centrifuge and to the precipitate add 3 drops of 6 M HCl, and with a piece of Chromel wire looped at the end make the flame test for Sr^{++} ion. The strontium salts impart a deep red color to the flame.

Puncture a hole in the apex of the filter paper and with 2 ml. of the $(NH_4)_2CO_3$ solution wash it into a 10 ml. test tube. Heat the solution and stir. The $SrSO_4$ will be converted to the less soluble $SrCO_3$. Filter the solution. With a piece of Chromel wire looped at the end gather up some of the precipitate from the filter paper, dip it into a drop of 6 M HCl previously placed on a watch glass and insert into a flame. Strontium salts impart a deep red color to the flame.

NOTE 3. *Triethanolamine, $N(C_2H_4OH)_3$, is an organic derivative of ammonia and forms a more stable complex with the Ca^{++} ion than with Sr^{++} ion, thereby preventing the precipitation of $CaSO_4$.*

G–3. Test for Ca^{++} Ion. Add to the centrifugate or filtrate **G–3** 10 drops of 0.25 M $(NH_4)_2C_2O_4$ solution. Heat to boiling. A white precipitate or clouding of the solution indicates the presence of Ca^{++} ion.[4] (The appearance of the white precipitate is more easily distinguishable if compared with a blank prepared by adding 4 drops of 0.1 M K_2CrO_4, 1 drop of 0.1 M $Ca(NO_3)_2$, and 1 drop of 0.25 M $(NH_4)_2C_2O_4$ solutions to 10 drops of water).

NOTE 4. *The calcium triethanolamine complex is not so stable that it prevents the precipitation of the relatively insoluble CaC_2O_4.*

H. Test for the Mg^{++} Ion. To one-half of the filtrate **H** add 10 drops of 5 M NH_4Cl, 5 drops of 15 M NH_4OH, and 10 drops of 0.5 M Na_2HPO_4 solution in the order named. Stir the mixture and allow it to stand for a few minutes. The appearance of a white crystalline precipitate of $MgNH_4PO_4$ is a test for the Mg^{++} ion.

To the other portion of solution **H** add 2 ml. of 6 M NaOH solution, place in a casserole, and heat almost to dryness.[5] Add 6 M HCl until the solution is acidic, dilute with water to 2 ml., and transfer the solution to a test tube. Add 1 drop of S. and O. reagent[6] and then add 6 M NaOH dropwise until alkaline. Add 3 drops of 6 M NaOH in excess. If Mg^{++} ion is present, $Mg(OH)_2$ will precipitate with the dye adsorbed to it to give a characteristic blue colored lake.

NOTE 5. *The purpose of heating at this point is to eliminate the NH_4^+ ion which is present in the basic solution as NH_3. The NH_4^+ ion interferes with the formation of the lake.*

NOTE 6. *S. and O, refers to Suitsu and Okuma who first proposed the use of this reagent, p-nitrobenzeneazoresorcinol, in the test for Mg^{++} ion.*

Equations for Pertinent Reactions

$$M^{++} + CO_3^{--} = MCO_{3(s)} \qquad (M^{++} = Ba^{++}, Ca^{++} \text{ or } Sr^{++})$$
$$MCO_{3(s)} + 2HAc = M^{++} + CO_2 + 2Ac^- + H_2O$$
$$Ba^{++} + CrO_4^{--} = BaCrO_{4(s)}$$
$$2BaCrO_{4(s)} + 2SO_4^{--} + 2H^+ = 2BaSO_{4(s)} + Cr_2O_7^{--} + H_2O$$
$$Sr^{++} + SO_4^{--} = SrSO_{4(s)}$$
$$SrSO_{4(s)} + CO_3^{--} = SrCO_{3(s)} + SO_4^{--}$$
$$SrCO_{3(s)} + 2H^+ = Sr^{++} + CO_2 + H_2O$$
$$Ca^{++} + C_2O_4^{--} = CaC_2O_{4(s)}$$
$$Mg^{++} + NH_4^+ + PO_4^{---} = MgNH_4PO_{4(s)}$$
$$Mg^{++} + 2OH^- = Mg(OH)_{2(s)}$$

CHAPTER XVIII

Analysis of the Positive Ions

In the analysis of all of the common metal ions the procedure employed is that of first separating them into several groups, each of which contains ions exhibiting a common chemical property which is the basis for the separation. For example, only Ag^+, Hg_2^{++} and Pb^{++} ions react with Cl^- ion to form relatively insoluble chlorides. These three ions then constitute one group in the analytical classification. A second group is made up of those ions which form insoluble sulfides with H_2S in acid solution. A third group consists of ions which form either insoluble hydroxides or sulfides when treated with NH_4OH, NH_4Cl and H_2S. A fourth group consists of Ca^{++}, Sr^{++}, Ba^{++} and Mg^{++} ions. These groups, together with the alkali metal group, have already been considered in the five previous chapters.

We shall now devote our attention to the analysis of unknown samples which may contain ions belonging to any of the five groups. In this chapter we shall consider these group separations and a number of complications which may arise due to the presence of certain anions. Specific directions for the separations will be given up to a point where the student can conveniently be referred back to the group procedure with which he is familiar.

At this point we cannot emphasize too strongly the need for making certain that any given group is completely separated from the solution and that the group precipitate is thoroughly washed. The presence of any ion foreign to a group may well give rise to unnecessary complications and lead to error in the analysis.

The following procedure applies to ions already in solution. If the unknown sample is an alloy, a salt, or a mixture of solid substances, it will be necessary to bring the sample into solution as completely as possible. To accomplish this the unknown must be treated according to the directions given in Chapter XIX. If a suspended precipitate is present in the unknown solution, this must be separated from the solution and treated as a solid (Chapter XIX).

SCHEMATIC OUTLINE FOR SEPARATION OF GROUPS

Solution: Ions of groups **A, B, C D, E–F,** and **G–H.**
Test for ions of group **A.**
Add HCl.

Precipitate: AgCl Hg$_2$Cl$_2$ PbCl$_2$ (B)	Solution: Ions of groups **C–D, E–F,** and **G–H.** Make (H$^+$) 0.3 M, add H$_2$O$_2$, and saturate with H$_2$S.			
	Precipitate: (C–D). CuS As$_2$S$_3$ HgS Sb$_2$S$_3$ Bi$_2$S$_3$ SnS$_2$ CdS PbS Treat with NH$_4$OH + H$_2$S.	Solution: Ions of groups **E–F** and **G–H.** Add NH$_4$OH, NH$_4$Cl, and H$_2$S.		
		Precipitate: (E–F). ZnS Al(OH)$_3$ CoS Cr(OH)$_3$ NiS FeS MnS Treat with Na$_2$SO$_4$ and NaHSO$_4$.	Solution: Ions of group **G–H.** Add NH$_4$OH and (NH$_4$)$_2$CO$_3$.	
	Residue: CuS HgS Bi$_2$S$_3$ CdS PbS (C)	Solution: AsS$_3$$^{---}$ SbS$_3$$^{---}$ SnS$_2$$^{--}$ (D)		Precipitate: CaCO$_3$ SrCO$_3$ BaCO$_3$ (G)	Solution: Mg^{++} (H)
			Residue: ZnS CoS NiS (E)	Solution: Al^{+++} Cr^{+++} Fe^{++} Mn^{++} (F)

The solution containing the unknown should first be tested with litmus. If it is strongly alkaline, several positive ions are evidently absent. If it is acidic, all positive ions may be present provided Cl$^-$ ion is absent. Reserve 1 ml. of the solution for making any tests you may see fit to determine the presence or absence of some ions, and thereby simplify or confirm the analysis.

A. The Alkali Metal Group. Carry out tests for NH$_4$$^+$, Na$^+$ and K$^+$ ions, using the original solution, according to the procedures **A–1, A–2** and **A–3** described on pages 320–321.

B. Precipitation of the Silver Group.[1] If the clear original solution is alkaline, add 6 M HCl until neutral. To 3 ml. of the neutral solution, or to 3 ml. of the clear original solution if acidic, add 1 drop of 6 M HCl. If no precipitate appears, the ions of the silver group are absent; proceed directly to the copper-arsenic group. In the event of the formation of a precipitate, add 4 more drops of 6 M HCl,[2] stir, and pour the contents of the test tube into a filter supported by a 40 mm. funnel.[3] Test the filtrate for completeness of precipitation by adding one drop of 6 M HCl. Make certain that precipitation is complete.[4] Wash the precipitate **B** with 1 ml. of 1.5 M HCl and add the wash solution [5] to the filtrate. Label the filtrate **C–H**; it may contain ions of all groups excepting the silver group. Again wash the precipitate with 1 ml. of 1.5 M HCl and *discard* the wash solution. The precipitate **B** may consist of AgCl, Hg_2Cl_2 and $PbCl_2$. It should be examined for the presence of these ions according to procedures **B–1, B–2** and **B–3** outlined on pages 334 and 335.

NOTE 1. *In the original unknown solution a white solid may be present due to the hydrolysis of bismuth, antimony, arsenic or tin ions. This solid must be removed by centrifugation or filtration before the test is made for the presence of the silver group (white precipitate upon the addition of HCl). After the removal of the silver group chlorides, the original white solid should be added to the filtrate containing the ions of the remaining groups. In the precipitation of the ions of the copper-arsenic group, the white hydrolysis products will be converted to the less soluble sulfides.*

NOTE 2. *If Sb^{+++} and Bi^{+++} ions are present in the original solution (acidic), the addition of HCl may initially cause the oxychlorides, SbOCl and BiOCl, to precipitate. However, further addition of HCl will dissolve these oxychlorides. Care should be taken not to confuse the oxychloride precipitate with the silver group chloride precipitate.*

NOTE 3. *In the analysis of the silver group it is much more convenient to use filtration rather than centrifugation operations.*

NOTE 4. *The solubility of $PbCl_2$ in the acid solution is much greater than that of AgCl and Hg_2Cl_2. Therefore Pb^{++} ion is only partially removed at this point. However, it will appear again in the copper group as PbS. If the original solution contains Pb^{++} ion in small amount, no $PbCl_2$ may be precipitated in the silver group.*

NOTE 5. *The silver group precipitate is washed to remove occluded liquid which may contain ions of other groups. An HCl solution is used instead of water to reduce the amount of $PbCl_2$ in the wash solution and to prevent the precipitation of SbOCl and BiOCl on the filter.*

C–D.   Precipitation of the Copper-Arsenic Group.[6]   To the filtrate **C–H** obtained from the separation of the silver group, and contained in a 25 ml. Erlenmeyer flask, add 5 drops of 3% H_2O_2 and heat the solution to boiling. Before precipitation is carried out with H_2S the H^+ ion concentration must be made approximately equal to 0.3 M. Since the solution may contain an excess of H^+ ion it must first be neutralized before the proper amount of acid is added. Add 6 M NH_4OH dropwise until the solution is just alkaline. Disregard any precipitate which may appear. Add a drop or two of 6 M HCl to make the solution just acidic and then add 1 drop of 6 M HCl for each ml. of the solution (see footnote 3, page 359). Add 1 drop of 1 M NH_4I solution. (Do not be disturbed if a precipitate appears here.)

Heat the solution to boiling and saturate for one minute with H_2S. Heat to boiling again, and again saturate with H_2S. Cool the solution under the tap and saturate with H_2S once more.[7,8]

Pour the solution into a 10 ml. test tube; wash out the Erlenmeyer flask with 1 ml. of water, and add to the solution in the test tube. Centrifuge for one minute. Dip the end of a small stirring rod into the supernatant liquid to obtain enough solution to be tested with methyl violet paper for the H^+ ion concentration (see footnote 3, page 359). If necessary, pour the supernatant liquid into another 10 ml. test tube, adjust the H^+ ion concentration by adding a drop or two of 3 M NH_4OH, and again pass H_2S into the cold solution to test for completeness of precipitation. Centrifuge, decant the supernatant liquid, and combine any precipitate with that previously formed. Label the supernatant liquid **E–H**; it may contain ions of the aluminum-zinc and alkaline earth groups. The precipitate **C–D** contains the sulfides of any of the copper-arsenic group ions which may be present.

Pour the solution over a previously prepared filter. Wash the Erlenmeyer flask with 1 ml. of water and also pour this through the filter, adding this wash water to the previous filtrate. Dip the end of a small stirring rod into the filtrate to obtain enough solution to be tested with methyl violet paper for the H^+ ion concentration (see footnote, 3 page 359). If necessary, adjust the H^+ ion concentration by adding a drop or two of 3 M NH_4OH, and again pass H_2S into the cold solution to test for completeness of precipitation. If a precipitate appears, pour the solution over the previously filtered precipitate in the filter, collect the filtrate in a 10 ml. test tube, and label it **E–H**. This solution may contain ions of the aluminum-zinc and alkaline earth groups. The precipitate **C–D** contains the sulfides of

If it was not found necessary to adjust the H^+ ion concentration after the methyl violet test, decant the supernatant liquid E–H from the precipitate C–D.

To the sulfide precipitate C–D add 2 ml. of water and then wash down the side of the test tube with an additional ml. of water. Use a stirring rod to bring the sulfides into suspension. Centrifuge and add the supernatant wash water to solution E–H. Wash twice with 3 ml. of water and discard the wash water each time. Now add 1 ml. of 15 M NH_4OH to precipitate C–D.

any of the copper-arsenic group ions which may be present.

If it was not found necessary to adjust the H^+ ion concentration after the methyl violet test, set aside the filtrate E–H and retain the precipitate C–D.

Wash the sulfide precipitate C–D on the filter with 3 ml. of water and add the wash solution to filtrate E–H. Wash the precipitate twice with 2 ml. of water and discard the washings. Puncture a hole in the apex of the filter and with the capillary syringe wash the precipitate into a 10 ml. test tube with 1 ml. of 15 M NH_4OH solution.

Carry out the procedure for separating the copper group from the arsenic group as described under C–D–1, page 360, and continue the analysis of these two groups from that point on.

Note 6. *Notes 1–10 on pages 359 and 360 apply to this separation and should be consulted at this point.*

Note 7. *If the Cl^- ion concentration should be inordinately high, as would be the case if the original solution were clear and contained $SbCl_3$, $BiCl_3$, or $SnCl_4$ in HCl solution, then it might prevent the precipitation of CdS because of the formation of the $CdCl_4^{--}$ complex ion. If the CdS is not completely precipitated in the copper-arsenic group, it will appear with the final ZnS precipitate in group E–F and can be detected there.*

Note 8. *If chromium is present in the original solution as $Cr_2O_7^{--}$ ion or the manganese as MnO_4^- ion, these ions will be reduced by the H_2S in the acid solution to Cr^{+++} and Mn^{++} ions respectively.*

The Removal of Interfering Anions. If an unknown sample contains ions of the alkaline earth group (Ca^{++}, Sr^{++}, Ba^{++} or Mg^{++}) and if BO_2^-, $C_2O_4^{--}$, F^-, AsO_2^-, AsO_4^{---} or PO_4^{---} ions are also present, the corresponding insoluble salts will precipitate when the solution is made alkaline with NH_4OH in the initial step of the procedure for the precipitation of the aluminum-zinc group. As long as any combination of these ions is restricted to an acidic medium, as is the case in the precipitation of the silver and of the copper-arsenic groups, no interference arises. Though the alkaline earth salts of AsS_3^{---} and AsS_4^{---} ions are not soluble, these ions will be removed as As_2S_3 in the precipitation of the copper-arsenic group. In the systematic analysis of a sample it is essential that tests first be made for the anions, and if any of the interfering anions listed above are found they must be eliminated before proceeding with the precipitation of the aluminum-zinc group.

If BO_2^- ion is found to be present heat solution **E–H** in a casserole to remove H_2S and then continue the heating, with the addition of a few drops of 12 M HCl and a few drops of methyl alcohol from time to time, until the solution is evaporated to dryness. Do not heat the dry salt, but remove the flame at the point of dryness. In this procedure boric acid, H_3BO_3, reacts with the methyl alcohol to form methyl borate, $(CH_3O)_3B$, which is volatile and escapes from the solution. If BO_2^- ion is the only interfering ion found to be present, dissolve the residue in 2 ml. of 0.3 M HCl solution and continue the analysis for the metal ions at the point indicated as **E–F**, the precipitation of the aluminum-zinc group.

If $C_2O_4^{--}$ ion is found to be present add to solution **E–H** 1 ml. of 12 M HCl and 10 drops of 15 M HNO$_3$. Transfer the solution to a casserole and evaporate slowly almost to dryness, until not more than one or two drops of liquid remain. During the course of the evaporation test the solution for the presence of $C_2O_4^{--}$ ion by adding a small drop of the solution, obtained by using the capillary syringe, to 10 drops of a very dilute (pink) solution of $KMnO_4$. MnO_4^- ion oxidizes any $C_2O_4^{--}$ ion to CO_2; during the reaction Mn^{++} ion is produced and the solution becomes colorless. If the color of the $KMnO_4$ solution persists, $C_2O_4^{--}$ ion is then absent. In any event continue heating the solution almost to dryness, dissolve the residue in 2 ml. of water, add 1 or 2 drops of 6 M HCl if necessary, and continue the analysis for the metal ions at the point indicated as **E–F**, the precipitation of the aluminum-zinc group.

If F^- ion is found to be present the procedure used to remove $C_2O_4^{--}$ with aqua regia will suffice. However, carry out the evaporation in a Pyrex test tube. If porcelain ware is used, some etching will take place with the result that aluminum will be introduced into the unknown.

If PO_4^{---} ion is found to be present it may conveniently be removed as $FePO_4$. In acid solution Fe^{+++} ion forms a complex ion with PO_4^{---} ion, but when the solution is only slightly acidic, $FePO_4$ is precipitated. Under these conditions the phosphates of the alkaline earth metals are not precipitated. Al^{+++} and Cr^{+++} ions also form insoluble phosphates and will be removed along with $FePO_4$ if all three positive ions are present. In such a case it is necessary to examine the phosphate precipitate for Al^{+++} and Cr^{+++} ions. If the concentration of the PO_4^{---} ion should be relatively high in the unknown solution, there might not be sufficient Al^{+++}, Cr^{+++}, and Fe^{+++} ions to precipitate all of the phosphate present. To make certain that the phosphate is precipitated completely, excess Fe^{+++} ion is added to the solution; then the unreacted Fe^{+++} ion is removed by boiling the solution in the presence of HAc. Under these conditions an insoluble basic ferric acetate, $Fe(OH)_2Ac$, is formed. Obviously, before any Fe^{+++} ion is added to the solution, it is first necessary to test the unknown for the presence of this ion.

Heat solution **E–H** to boiling to remove H_2S. Add 5 drops of Br_2 water to remove the last traces of H_2S and to oxidize Fe^{++} ion to Fe^{+++} ion. With the aid of the capillary syringe remove 2 drops of the solution to a small test tube. Add 10 drops of water and then add 1 drop of 1 M KCNS solution. A deep red color shows the presence of Fe^{+++} ion in the original unknown solution.

To the bulk of solution **E–H**, now free from H_2S, add 6 M NH_4OH dropwise until the solution is alkaline and then add 3 drops of the reagent in excess. Now add 6 M HAc until the solution is acidic, and add 3 drops in excess. If Al^{+++}, Cr^{+++}, or Fe^{+++} ions are present with PO_4^{---}, the precipitate may consist of any or all of the corresponding phosphates. If the solution is deep reddish-brown in color, the precipitation of the phosphate is complete; if it is not this color, add 0.1 M $FeCl_3$ solution dropwise until this color is obtained. Heat to boiling until the volume is reduced to 1 ml. and then add 3 ml. of water. Centrifuge or filter. The filtrate may contain Co^{++}, Ni^{++}, Zn^{++} and Mn^{++} ions of the zinc group as well as ions of the alkaline earth group. It should be treated according to procedure **E–F** below, but in the analysis of the group it should be kept in mind that tests are to be made only for CO^{++}, Ni^{++}, Zn^{++} and Mn^{++} ions. The precipitate may contain the phosphates of Fe^{+++}, Cr^{+++} and Al^{+++} ions and the basic acetate of Fe^{+++} ion.

Add 1 ml. of water to the precipitate, stir to produce a suspension, and then pour the contents into a small casserole. (If filtration is used, puncture the apex of the filter and wash the precipitate into a small casserole with 1 ml. of water from the capillary syringe.) Add 1 ml. of 6 M NaOH solution, 5 drops of 3% H_2O_2 solution, and stir while heating for one minute. Add 1 ml. of water and then centrifuge or filter. The precipitate of $Fe(OH)_3$ may be discarded. The filtrate or supernatant liquid may contain AlO_2^- and CrO_4^{--} ions and should be examined for their presence according to procedures **F–3** and **F–4**, pages 398 and 399.

E–F. Precipitation of the Aluminum-Zinc Group. Place the filtrate **E–H** in a casserole or small beaker and evaporate until the solution has a volume of about 2 ml. Add 3 drops of Br_2 water and heat for one minute to remove the last traces of H_2S. Then transfer the solution to a 25 ml. Erlenmeyer flask, wash the casserole or beaker with 1 ml. of water (use the capillary syringe), and add the wash water to the evaporated solution. Cool the solution.

To the solution add 10 drops of 5 M NH_4Cl[9,10]; make alkaline with 15 M NH_4OH and add 10 drops of the reagent in excess. If no precipitate is obtained here, Al^{+++}, Cr^{+++}, and Fe^{+++} ions are absent. Saturate the solution, which may already contain a precipitate, with H_2S. Centrifuge or filter, and test the supernatant liquid or filtrate for completeness of precipitation by adding 2 drops of 15 M NH_4OH, heating, and again saturating with H_2S. Combine any precipitate with that obtained previously. Save the filtrate or supernatant liquid for later tests and label it **G–H**. It may contain the ions of the alkaline earth group. Wash the precipitate, **E–F–1**, with 3 ml. of water and add the wash water to **G–H**. Wash the precipitate again and discard the wash water. Using this precipitate continue the analysis of the aluminum-zinc group by beginning with the procedure described in **E–F–1** on page 393.[11]

Note 9. *If the original solution was strongly acidic and a relatively large amount of NH_4OH was needed to neutralize it in operation C–D, then the NH_4Cl may be omitted here.*

Note 10. *The solution must contain a relatively large amount of NH_4^+ ion so that the OH^- ion concentration will be decreased to such a low level that $Mg(OH)_2$ will not be precipitated with this group.*

Note 11. *If the Cl^- ion concentration was high in the precipitation of the copper-arsenic group, cadmium would not be completely removed there* (*see footnote 7*). It would appear as CdS in the precipitation of the aluminum-zinc group and it would not be dissolved by the Na_2SO_4–$NaHSO_4$ buffer. In the test for Zn^{++} ion, in which ZnS is precipitated in HAc solution, CdS would also precipitate if present. If the ZnS precipitate has a decided yellow color it should be tested for the presence of Cd^{++} ion as follows. Centrifuge the solution and reserve the filtrate for Ni^{++} and Co^{++} ion tests. Wash the precipitate twice with 2 ml. of water containing 2 drops of 6 M HAc, and discard the wash water in each case. Dissolve the precipitate in 3 M HCl added dropwise with constant stirring. Add 2 ml. of water, then neutralize the solution with 6 M NH_4OH. Add 3 M HCl until the solution is just acidic and then add 1 drop of 6 M HCl in excess for each ml. of solution (about 3 drops will be required). Saturate the solution with H_2S, keeping the solution cold. If Cd^{++} ion is present in appreciable amounts, CdS will precipitate. Centrifuge or filter and to the filtrate add 10 drops of 2 M $NaAc$ solution. If Zn^{++} ion is present, ZnS will precipitate at this point due to the increase in the S^{--} ion concentration brought about by the lowering of the H^+ ion concentration by Ac^- ion.

G–H.   Precipitation of the Alkaline Earth Group.   Evaporate solution **G–H** in a casserole until the volume is reduced to about 3 ml. If the solution contains an appreciable amount of NH_4Cl (see footnotes 9 and 10), it will not be necessary to add the salt at this point. Test with litmus to make certain that the solution is alkaline. If it is alkaline, add 3 drops of 15 M NH_4OH; if it is not alkaline, make alkaline with 15 M NH_4OH and then add 3 drops of the reagent in excess. Heat the solution almost to boiling (*do not boil*) and with constant stirring add 2 ml. of $(NH_4)_2CO_3$ reagent. Allow the solution to stand for a few minutes and then centrifuge or filter. To the filtrate or supernatant liquid add a few drops of the $(NH_4)_2CO_3$ reagent to test for completeness of precipitation, and combine any precipitate formed with that originally obtained. Continue testing for completeness of precipitation until no more precipitate is formed. The filtrate may contain Mg^{++} ion and should be examined according to procedure **H**, page 415. The precipitate should be washed twice with 3 ml. of warm water and then examined for the presence of Ba^{++}, Ca^{++}, and Sr^{++} ions according to procedures **G–1**, **G–2** and **G–3**, pages 413–414.

CHAPTER XIX

The Preparation of a Sample for Analysis — Analysis of Solids

The schemes of analysis outlined in this text are based entirely upon "wet" methods. Blow-pipe analysis and high temperature non-aqueous methods are omitted. Before the analysis proper can be undertaken, it is therefore necessary that the salts of as many of the ions as possible be converted into a soluble form. When making an analysis for the metallic ions, the salts of these ions are usually converted into the soluble nitrates or chlorides and analyses for the anions are usually not made with this solution. Such a solution is either neutral or acidic. Conversely, when analyses are to be made for anions, as many of these ions as possible are converted into the soluble sodium salts. The interfering cations are removed from such a solution by a process which leaves the solution either neutral or alkaline. We shall consider separately the preparation of solutions for anion and cation analysis.

Before the sample is analyzed, valuable preliminary information often may be obtained by an examination of its physical properties, particularly its color (see Table 35 on page 426). If the sample is in solution, such preliminary information is somewhat limited. The positive ions: Cu^{++}, Ni^{++}, Co^{++}, Mn^{++}, Fe^{+++} and Cr^{+++} and the anions: CrO_4^{--} (or $Cr_2O_7^{--}$), $Fe(CN)_6^{---}$ and $Fe(CN)_6^{----}$ are the only ions considered here which are colored. If the sample is a solid but not an alloy, a great deal of information may be obtained from such an examination. The following table, arranged according to color, may be helpful. If the sample is a pure compound, the analysis (usually for one anion and one cation) is simple, and its color will often serve to eliminate a great number of tests. If the solid is a mixture of salts, it may be examined under a magnifying glass and again certain ions can often be eliminated by such an inspection.

TABLE 35

THE MORE COMMON COLORED SALTS [1]

Black — CuO, NiO, Fe_3O_4, FeO, FeS, CuS, Cu_2S, HgS, Hg_2S, Ag_2S, PbS, NiS, CoS, MnO_2 and finely divided free metals.

Brown — CdO, Bi_2O_3, SnS, Bi_2S_3, $Fe_2(CrO_4)_3$, $CuCrO_4$ and PbO_2.

Blue — Hydrated copper and cobalt salts.

Green — Nickel salts, hydrated ferrous salts, chromic salts, manganates and some copper salts.

Yellow — Most chromates, HgO, CdS, SnS_2, As_2S_3, As_2S_5, free sulfur, some ferrocyanides, some iodides, and oxides of Pb.

Red — Ag_2CrO_4, Fe_2O_3, HgI_2, Cu_2O, HgO, HgS, Sb_2S_3, Pb_3O_4, some iodides, some chromates and dichromates.

Orange — Sb_2S_5 and some dichromates.

Pink — Manganous salts and hydrated cobaltous salts.

Purple — Permanganates and some chromic salts.

The colors of anhydrous salts (usually white) are often different from the hydrated forms. Too great a reliance must not be placed on a preliminary color examination. Such an examination should be used rather as a check on the chemical analysis.

NOTE. 1. *The colors of some metallic oxides and sulfides of minerals are different from those of the same compounds precipitated from solution.*

PREPARATION OF SOLUTION FOR ANION ANALYSIS

Two distinctly different cases present themselves: (1) when the sample is completely soluble in water or is already in the dissolved form, and (2) when the sample is either partially or wholly insoluble in water. A preliminary test with a small amount of the solid will determine to which class it belongs.

I. Sample Soluble in Water. If the sample is soluble in water, dissolve about 0.15 g. (150 mg.) in 10 ml. of water.[2] Test this solution (or the sample already in the dissolved form) with litmus. If acidic, add 6 M NaOH drop by drop until just alkaline or until a precipitate first forms. To this solution, or to the original solution which was found to be alkaline, add one drop of 1.5 M Na_2CO_3

solution.[3] If no precipitate forms either with NaOH or Na_2CO_3, this alkaline solution is ready for anion analysis.

If a precipitate forms, add 2 ml. of 1.5 M Na_2CO_3 solution to the 10 ml. sample in a casserole and boil for ten minutes. Continually add water as it is lost by evaporation. Note whether any NH_3 is evolved (note odor or test with wet litmus paper). The mixture should then be centrifuged or filtered. If necessary add enough water to make the final volume 10 ml. This solution is then ready for the anion analysis. The Na_2CO_3 treatment should convert all insoluble salts except silicates, phosphates, most sulfides and the halides and thiocyanate of silver into soluble sodium salts and insoluble carbonates.[4-9]

If the precipitate consists entirely of carbonates, when washed, it should be completely soluble in 3 M HAc. If the precipitate is not soluble in 3 M HAc, the residue should be treated according to the directions given on pages 429–431.

II. When Sample is Completely or Partially Insoluble in Water. The sample to be treated should be very finely divided. If it is not, grind it thoroughly in a mortar. Place about 150 mg.[2] of the finely ground sample in a small casserole and add 2 ml. of 1.5 M Na_2CO_3 solution.[3] Cover the casserole with a small watch glass and boil for ten minutes. At frequent intervals replace the water that boils away. After cooling the mixture, pour into a 10 ml. test tube and centrifuge or filter. Wash the precipitate with 2 ml. of water, centrifuge or filter and add the wash water to the previously obtained filtrate.

If the precipitate consists entirely of converted carbonates,[4-9] it should be soluble in 3 M HAc. If it does not completely dissolve, treat the residue, after washing it, with 1 ml. of 1.5 M Na_2CO_3 solution and again heat for ten minutes. Centrifuge or filter and add the filtrate to the solution to be tested for anions. If after this second Na_2CO_3 treatment, an appreciable amount of the solid is not dissolved by 3 M HAc, save it for subsequent direct analysis of the solid. The prepared sample should be diluted sufficiently to give a total volume of 10 ml.

NOTE. 2. *If a sufficiently delicate balance is not available, weigh out 1 gram of some finely divided salt taken from the reagent shelf. Place this on a piece of paper and divide into 6 equal parts. This procedure will give the student an idea of what approximate quantity of the solid unknown 150 mg. represents.*

NOTE 3. *The sodium carbonate should be sulfate free. The test for sulfate may be made by acidifying the Na_2CO_3 solution with an excess of 6 M HCl and adding $BaCl_2$ solution. No precipitate of $BaSO_4$ should form.*

NOTE 4. *With the exception of those salts listed above, the carbonates of the heavy metals are less soluble in alkaline solution than other insoluble salts.*

NOTE 5. *The carbonate treatment would not completely remove ions bound in solution as ammonia complexes. If the alkaline solution when boiled evolves NH_3, such ions may possibly be present. If such is the case, they can be detected by the addition of H_2S to a few drops of the alkaline solution. Under these conditions the insoluble sulfides will form. These and amphoteric ions may be removed by adding NH_4NO_3 and H_2S to the solution. In such a case, tests for the S^{--} and NO_3^- ions must be made on separate samples.*

NOTE 6. *It is recommended to the instructor that samples which will produce the silver-ammonia complex ion in carbonate solution (e.g. $AgNO_3$ and NH_4NO_3) should not be used. When such a solution is evaporated, it often explodes.*

NOTE 7. *Many of the sulfides, many phosphates and the halides of silver are not acted upon by the Na_2CO_3 solution. Tests for the sulfides can be made on the residue according to the directions given on page 430. The phosphate ion can be obtained in acid solution and detected in the cation analysis as described on page 431. The halides of silver may be changed to Ag_2S by the action of NH_4OH and H_2S as described on page 431. The tests for the Cl^-, Br^-, and I^- ions should be made separately on the sulfide solution after the excess H_2S has been removed by boiling.*

NOTE 8. *Strong oxidizing agents will react with strong reducing agents in the Na_2CO_3 treatment. Such cases need hardly be considered since combinations of this kind are unstable and are not encountered in samples having any practical significance.*

NOTE 9. *The extent to which this conversion takes place is determined by the solubility product constants of the salt in question and its corresponding carbonate. As an example let us determine to what extent $BaCrO_4$ can be converted into $BaCO_3$ by 1.5 M Na_2CO_3 solution. The reaction is*

$$BaCrO_{4(s)} + CO_3^{--} = BaCO_{3(s)} + CrO_4^{--}$$
$$K_{S.P.}(BaCrO_4) = (Ba^{++})(CrO_4^{--}) = 2.4 \times 10^{-10} \quad \text{(A)}$$
$$K_{S.P.}(BaCO_3) = (Ba^{++})(CO_3^{--}) = 8.1 \times 10^{-9} \quad \text{(B)}$$

When the solution is in equilibrium with both these solids, the ratio of the CrO_4^{--} ion concentration to that of CO_3^{--} ion is obtained by dividing (A) by (B):

$$\frac{(Ba^{++})(CrO_4^{--})}{(Ba^{++})(CO_3^{--})} = \frac{(CrO_4^{--})}{(CO_3^{--})} = \frac{2.4 \times 10^{-10}}{8.1 \times 10^{-9}} = .03$$
$$(CrO_4^{--}) = .03\,(CO_3^{--})$$

If the CO_3^{--} ion concentration is 1.5 M, the CrO_4^{--} ion concentration is therefore approximately equal to .03 × 1.5 or .045 M. This concentration is more than adequate for testing. However it should be borne in mind that this is the maximum CrO_4^{--} ion concentration obtainable with 1.5 Na_2CO_3 solution.

This calculation is only an approximation since no account has been taken of the lowering of the CO_3^{--} ion concentration through the formation of $BaCO_3$. Furthermore, the Mass Law as we have stated it does not apply rigorously to such highly concentrated solutions.

With $BaSO_4$ and $BaCO_3$ the ratio is even smaller, but still large enough to dissolve an appreciable amount of the SO_4^{--} ion.

In the case of $PbSO_4$ and $PbCO_3$ the ratio

$$\frac{(SO_4^{--})}{(CO_3^{--})} = \frac{(Pb^{++})(SO_4^{--})}{(Pb^{++})(CO_3^{--})} = \frac{1.1 \times 10^{-8}}{4 \times 10^{-14}} = 2.8 \times 10^5$$

The $PbSO_4$ is therefore easily converted to $PbCO_3$ even with dilute Na_2CO_3 solution.

Tests for Ions not Converted into Soluble Form by Sodium Carbonate Treatment

The Carbonate Ion. If the solid sample must be treated with Na_2CO_3 solution to convert the anions into soluble salts, it is obvious that the carbonate test must be made on the original solid sample.

Place about 10 mg. of the solid sample (a small amount on the tip of a spatula) on a watch glass and carefully cover it with 2 drops of 3 M HCl. If a gas is evolved, it may be any of the following, SO_2, H_2S or CO_2, and the more definite test for CO_3^{--} ion described below must be made. If no gas is observed, CO_3^{--} ion probably is not present; in any event, the test for the ion should be carried out since some carbonates react slowly even with strong acids. The S^{--} ion may be in the form of such an insoluble salt (e.g. CuS) that it will not react with the HCl.

For the carbonate test place 20 mg. of the finely ground solid sample in a 10 ml. test tube (**A**). Cover the sample with a small amount of finely divided zinc.[10] Insert into a one-hole rubber stopper which fits the test tube a short length of glass tubing bent at a right angle. (Draw out glass tubing to a smaller size, if necessary, in order to fit stopper.) Connect to the exit end of the glass tubing a piece of rubber tubing about 4 inches long. Attach to the other end of the rubber tubing a glass nozzle (similar to medicine dropper), about 3 inches long, made by drawing out a piece of glass tubing. Place nozzle into a 10-ml. test tube (**B**) containing 2 ml. of saturated $Ba(OH)_2$ solution. Mount this apparatus on a ring stand, clamping test tube (**A**) at a slight angle in a position so it can be heated.

To test tube (**A**), containing the sample and zinc, add 1 ml. of 3% H_2O_2 solution [11] and 1 ml. of 3 M HCl, and then stopper immediately. (If the evolution of gas is slow, heat gently; do not boil.) The CO_2 generated in the reaction will produce a white precipitate of $BaCO_3$ in test tube (**B**). To make certain that the precipitate is $BaCO_3$, remove test tube (**B**) and add to it 6 M HAc until the solution is definitely acid. $BaCO_3$ should dissolve, thus confirming the presence of CO_3^{--} ion.

If the sample to be analyzed is already in solution, if no Na_2CO_3 has been added, and if by the preliminary test **1-A** (page 442) CO_3^{--} is possibly present, repeat the above test using 10 drops of the unknown solution in place of the solid.

NOTE 10. *The Zinc has two functions.* (a) *It reduces some H_2SO_3 to H_2S.* (*SO_2 will also give a precipitate with the $Ba(OH)_2$.*) (b) *With HCl it generates hydrogen gas which drives the CO_2 out of the test tube.*

NOTE 11. *The H_2O_2 oxidizes H_2SO_3 to SO_4^{--} ion. The rate of the reaction between H_2O_2 and $H_2C_2O_4$ is very low.*

The Sulfide Ion. Sulfides which are converted to the soluble form by the Na_2CO_3 treatment will be detected in the analysis of the anion solution. Those which are not so converted may be detected by the following procedure.

Place about 5 mg. of the residue left from the Na_2CO_3 treatment (insoluble in HAc) in a small test tube. Cover this with a small amount of finely granulated zinc.[12] Add 1 ml. of 3 M HCl and with the forefinger and thumb hold across the mouth of the test tube a small strip of filter paper, on which a drop of 0.2 M $Pb(Ac)_2$ solution has been placed. If sulfide is present, the spot of $Pb(Ac)_2$ will turn black, due to the formation of PbS.[13]

NOTE 12. *Those sulfides which are not dissolved by HCl nevertheless can be decomposed with the liberation of H_2S by the action of a mixture of HCl and metallic zinc. Taking CuS as an example this reaction is*

$$CuS_{(s)} + Zn_{(s)} + 2H^+ = Cu_{(s)} + Zn^{++} + H_2S_{(g)}$$

The equilibrium constant for this reaction may be calculated by the method outlined in Chapter XI, making use of Tables 20, 44 and 46. The value of the constant, so calculated, is $10^{21.6}$. This figure indicates that the equilibrium is far to the right.

NOTE 13. *This test if performed on the original sample may not give the sulfide ion test when excess sulfite ion is present. The H_2S and SO_2 (or H_2SO_3) react rapidly to give free sulfur and water.*

$$2H_2S + H_2SO_3 = 3H_2O + 3S_{(s)}$$

However, all insoluble sulfites are converted into the soluble sodium sulfite by the Na_2CO_3 treatment. If the sulfide ion test is made on the residue from the Na_2CO_3 treatment, no sulfite will be present.

The Phosphate Ion. To a few milligrams of the residue left from the Na_2CO_3 treatment (insoluble in 3 M HAc) add 1 ml. of 3 M HNO_3 and heat to boiling. Centrifuge or filter. The residue may be used in the test for the silver halides. Heat (*do not boil*) the solution and then add about 3 drops of 0.1 M $(NH_4)_2MoO_4$ solution. A yellow precipitate indicates the presence of phosphate. Centrifuge or filter and wash the precipitate to be certain that it is yellow. (Precipitated MoO_3 is white.)

Test for Silver Halides. To a few milligrams of the residue left from the Na_2CO_3 treatment (treated with 3 M HAc) add 1 ml. 3 M HNO_3 and boil. Centrifuge or filter. Place the residue in a small test tube, add 1 ml. of 6 M NH_4OH and using the drawn glass tube (see page 293), saturate with H_2S. The halides of silver will be transposed into Ag_2S leaving the anions in solution. Continue the tests for the anions as directed on page 449.

PREPARATION OF THE SOLUTION FOR CATION ANALYSIS

Sample Soluble in Water. If the sample is soluble in water, it is ready for analysis without further treatment. 150 mg. (approximately $\frac{1}{7}$ g. or about the volume occupied by 2 drops of water) in 10 ml. water should give a solution sufficiently concentrated for most analyses.[14]

NOTE 14. *Do not make the solution too concentrated since the amounts of precipitates obtained later may then be too great for convenient filtration or centrifugation, and washing.*

The Removal of Organic Matter. Place a few milligrams of the solid sample in a small test tube and without adding any water heat to a relatively high temperature in the Bunsen flame. If interfering organic matter is present, the sample will turn black or dark brown or a film of oil will distill onto the sides of the test tube. If it is found that such organic matter is present proceed as directed below; otherwise proceed with the acid treatment.

If the previously described charring test has shown that organic material is present, place about 200 mg. (proportionately more if much organic matter is present) of the sample in a small casserole and to this add 1 ml. of 18 M H_2SO_4. Heat in a hood until the dense white fumes of SO_3 appear. The sample should now be charred. Cool and carefully add 10 drops of 15 M HNO_3 and again heat. If the mixture is not light colored (free from carbon), add more H_2SO_4 and HNO_3 and continue the operation until the oxidation is complete, as evidenced by the light color of the mixture. Evaporate the solution almost to dryness and very carefully add 2 ml. of water and then add 2 drops of 6 M H_2SO_4. Transfer to a test tube, wash the casserole with 1 ml. of water and add the wash water to the solution. Centrifuge or filter. Retain the liquid for the cation analysis and treat the residue, if any, with Na_2CO_3 solution as directed in the following section.

Sample not Soluble in Water. If the solid sample is not soluble in water, use very small portions of it to determine its solubility in the following solvents, both cold and hot: 6 M HCl, 12 M HCl, 6 M HNO_3, 15 M HNO_3 and aqua regia (1 part 15 M HNO_3 to 3 parts 12 M HCl). Some deductions can be drawn regarding the nature of the solid from its solubility in these various reagents. For example, the carbonates of all metals are soluble in dilute HNO_3, while dilute HCl will leave a precipitate of AgCl, $PbCl_2$ or Hg_2Cl_2 if the corresponding carbonates are present. Ag_2S and CuS are soluble in concentrated nitric acid but not in concentrated HCl, while HgS is soluble only in aqua regia. It must be borne in mind that aged precipitates do not behave like those freshly prepared. Aged ZnS, for example, may not dissolve in HCl. If solution has been effected with any of these reagents, 150 mg. of the sample should be dissolved in the one selected. It should then be evaporated almost to dryness (only a few drops of liquid remaining) and then dissolved in 10 ml. of water.

The common substances not soluble in these reagents are $BaSO_4$, $CaSO_4$, $SrSO_4$, $PbSO_4$, the halides of silver, CaF_2, oxides and ignited salts, free sulfur, and carbon.

If HCl, HNO_3, or aqua regia do not completely dissolve the solid, place the residue from the acid treatment in a casserole and, after adding 2 ml. of 1.5 M Na_2CO_3, boil the solution for ten minutes, replacing the water that is lost by evaporation. This process will convert many insoluble salts into insoluble carbonates. Centrifuge or filter this mixture, discard the supernatant liquid, wash the residue well with water and add a few drops of 6 M HNO_3. Dilute with a few ml. of water and add this solution to the original acid solution which is to be evaporated. If a residue still remains, repeat the treatment with the Na_2CO_3 solution. All substances should be dissolved by this process except silicates, sulfur, carbon and the halides of silver.

To dissolve the silver halides add a few grains of metallic zinc and 1 ml. of 1 M H_2SO_4. The zinc will reduce the silver to the metallic form. Wash the silver free from the H_2SO_4, dissolve it in a few drops of 6 M HNO_3 and make a separate test for the Ag^+ ion by adding HCl and by noting the solubility of the AgCl in NH_4OH.

If there is still some constituent which is not dissolved, it will be necessary to subject the residue to a carbonate fusion.

Solution of the Residue by Carbonate Fusion. The residue after the treatments with acid, Na_2CO_3 solution, and Zn plus H_2SO_4 may contain silicates, some oxides or calcined salts. If such is the case, solution can be effected by fusing the sample with sodium carbonate. To carry out such a fusion proceed as follows.

Transfer the residue left after the Zn and H_2SO_4 acid treatment to a small nickel crucible, obtained from the instructor. (The residue from the treatment with the Na_2CO_3 solution, not treated with Zn and H_2SO_4, may be used if desired.) Place the crucible in a small clay triangle; then cover the residue with a small pinch of solid Na_2CO_3 and a small pinch of solid K_2CO_3. After covering the crucible, heat it in the hot flame of a blast lamp or Meeker burner. The carbonate mixture should fuse and dissolve the sample. If small particles appear to be present in the melt, add a very small amount (a few mg.) of solid $NaNO_3$ and heat again for several minutes.[18] Cool the crucible and place it in a casserole. Cover it with water and boil until the solid mass has disintegrated. Filter or centrifuge the solution, and label the filtrate or centrifugate (**A**). To the residue add 10 drops of 6 M HNO_3, then add 1 ml. of water.[15,16] Filter or centrifuge, and label the filtrate or centrifugate (**B**). If (**A**) or (**B**) is alkaline, make acidic with 6 M HNO_3, evaporate to volume of about 1–2 ml., and then analyze each separately for cations.[17] In the analysis cognizance should be taken of the fact that nickel from the crucible may be introduced into the solutions.

NOTE 15. *During the fusion with the carbonate mixture, a reaction takes place in which the insoluble salts are converted to carbonates or oxides which in turn are dissolved by HNO_3.*

NOTE 16. *When the carbonate fusion extract is neutralized with HNO_3, silicic acid, and metastannic acid may precipitate. This precipitate is coagulated by first heating the mixture to dryness. Water is added to the residue and the precipitate is then separated from the solution by filtration or centrifugation. If H_2S and NH_4OH are added to a suspension of this precipitate which has been thoroughly washed, SnS_2, a yellow compound, will be formed directly from the precipitate if tin is present in the insoluble residue. The silicic acid is discarded.*

NOTE 17. *If the halides of silver are present, these are reduced to free silver in accordance with the reaction.*

$$4AgCl + 2Na_2CO_3 = 4Ag + 4NaCl + 2CO_2 + O_2$$

The Ag is subsequently dissolved by the HNO_3.

NOTE 18. *The $NaNO_3$ serves to oxidize some substances to more soluble forms, for example, chromites to chromates.*

SOLUTION OF A METAL OR AN ALLOY

The usual solvent for the commonest metals and alloys is dilute HNO_3. Hydrochloric acid is not used to such a large extent, particularly on alloys the composition of which is not known, for with this acid the volatile hydrides of arsenic, antimony and phosphorous are likely to form. The strongly oxidizing HNO_3 is therefore preferred. On the other hand, aluminum is not readily attacked by HNO_3 inasmuch as this acid forms an acid-resisting coat of aluminum oxide on the surface of the metal. For alloys containing appreciable amounts of aluminum, a mixture of Br_2 and HCl is often used as the acid solvent.

With HNO_3 as the solvent, the oxides of antimony and tin (or metastannic acid) may be formed. These are insoluble in the dilute nitric acid, particularly when heated. They may be converted to the corresponding sulfides. The sulfides can then be dissolved in HNO_3 and added to the original solution.[19]

The size of the sample to be used will depend upon the number of constituents. A conveniently small sample should first be used and if a larger sample is used later to test for those elements present in smaller amounts, the scheme of analysis can be slightly modified to remove the relatively large quantities of those ions found to be present by the first analysis.

The metal sample should be converted into a form offering a large surface for the acid. This may be accomplished with a hammer or even a mortar and pestle if the alloy is brittle. In some cases a steel file may be used or the sample may be turned in a lathe. If the metal is very soft, it may be cut into small chips with a knife.

NOTE 19. *Metastannic acid and the insoluble oxides of antimony are formed when HNO₃ reacts directly with the metals and not so readily when the sulfides of these metals are dissolved by this reagent.*

PROCEDURE

Try the action of 6 M HNO₃ on a small sample of the metal to determine whether it can be dissolved by this reagent. Heat if necessary. If the sample dissolves (with or without a resulting white precipitate), proceed according to the directions in the following paragraph. If it does not dissolve readily, try the effect of 10 drops of 12 M HCl to which 1 drop of liquid bromine has been added (see instructor for specific directions in handling free bromine). Specific directions for the use of this solvent are given on page 436.

Solution by HNO₃. Place about 100 mg. of the sample in a small casserole and add 2 ml. of 6 M HNO₃ and heat (*do not boil*). If a white residue forms, agitate and press these particles with a glass rod to remove the coating from the surface of the metal particles. Add more HNO₃ if necessary. After the metal is dissolved, evaporate to dryness. Add a few drops of 15 M HNO₃ and again evaporate to dryness. Add 5 drops of 6 M HNO₃ and 1 ml. of water and transfer to a test tube. Repeat this operation to rinse the casserole. If the solution is not clear, centrifuge or filter.

If the sample dissolves without leaving a residue, proceed with the analysis for the cations. If there is a residue, it will most probably consist of the oxides of tin and antimony or silicic acid.[20]

The oxides are converted to the sulfides by digesting the solids with (NH₄)₂S solution. To the residue add 1 ml. of 3 M NH₄OH and saturate with H₂S. Warm the mixture very gently and agitate with a stirring rod. Neutralize the solution or the suspension with 3 M HNO_3 and then add 1 drop of the acid in excess. Filter or centrifuge the mixture and, after washing with water, treat the residue with 5 to 10 drops of 6 M HNO_3. Heat — do not boil. Add 1 ml. of water and after centrifuging or filtering,[21] add the centrifugate to the original nitric acid solution which is to be used for the cation analysis. Dilute with water to a total volume of 10 ml. and proceed with the cation analysis.

NOTE 20. *The purpose of heating to dryness is to coagulate the tin and antimony oxides. Black particles of carbon, which usually float on the surface, are to be discarded.*

It is not likely that appreciable amounts of silicic acid are formed together with the oxides of tin and antimony and vice versa. Silicon and either or both of these metals are usually not present together in the same alloy.

NOTE 21. *Any residue remaining at this point may contain carbon, sulfur, silicic acid and incompletely converted metallic oxides.*

Solution by Br_2 and HCl. If HNO_3 does not dissolve the alloy and if the previous small-scale test has shown that HCl and Br_2 will do so, place about 50 mg. of the sample in a casserole. Add 2 ml. of 12 M HCl and then add a few drops of liquid bromine (see the instructor for directions). Heat gently and agitate with the glass rod if necessary. Evaporate the solution to dryness. Add a few drops of 6 M HNO_3, dilute to 10 ml., and then proceed with the cation analysis. Any residue may consist of insoluble chlorides or bromides and should be treated with 1.5 M Na_2CO_3 solution, as directed on page 427, or should be subjected to a carbonate fusion, if necessary (see page 433).

CHAPTER XX

Identification of the Negative Ions

In this section we shall consider the methods for identifying the more common negative ions (anions). Consideration will be given only to the following ions and their acid or complex derivatives.

TABLE 36

Arsenate	AsO_4^{---}	Iodide	I^-
Arsenite	AsO_3^{---}	Nitrate	NO_3^-
Borate	BO_2^-	Nitrite	NO_2^-
Bromide	Br^-	Oxalate	$C_2O_4^{--}$
Carbonate	CO_3^{--}	Phosphate	PO_4^{---}
Chlorate	ClO_3^-	Sulfate	SO_4^{--}
Chloride	Cl^-	Sulfide	S^{--}
Chromate	CrO_4^{--}	Sulfite	SO_3^{--}
Ferricyanide	$Fe(CN)_6^{---}$	Thiocyanate	CNS^-
Ferrocyanide	$Fe(CN)_6^{----}$	Thiosulfate	$S_2O_3^{--}$
Fluoride	F^-		

It is obvious that in any given unknown sample, containing positive and negative ions, the larger the number of positive ions present the smaller must be the number of negative ions, and *vice versa*. As the number of positive and negative ions increases, the greater is the probability that pairs of ions of relatively insoluble or very slightly soluble salts will be present. A knowledge of the positive ions present in a solution immediately eliminates certain negative ions; likewise, a knowledge of the negative ions eliminates certain positive ions. Thus, if Ag^+ ion is found to be present and if the solution is not ammoniacal, S^{--}, Cl^-, Br^-, I^-, CNS^-, $Fe(CN)_6^{---}$, and $Fe(CN)_6^{----}$ ions cannot be present. Likewise, if Pb^{++} or Ba^{++} ions are found in the unknown and the unknown sample is soluble in water or dilute acid solution, it is evident that SO_4^{--} ion must be absent.

Strong oxidizing ions will not exist in solutions containing ions which function as reducing agents and *vice versa*. When the positive ions of a given unknown have been identified, it is advisable to consult the Solubility Table (No. 48) in the Appendix and thereby eliminate as many of the negative ions as possible. Such a procedure often leads to a simplification of the detection of negative ions.

The detection of most negative ions derived from weak acids should be carried out in basic, neutral, or only slightly acidic solution. In a solution which is strongly acidic the concentration of such ions will be much lower than in basic solution, and probably too low for precipitation by a positive ion. Designating the negative ion as A^- and the positive metal ion as M^+, these conditions can be readily explained by the following equilibrium:

$$HA = H^+ + A^-$$
$$+$$
$$M^+ \qquad\qquad (140)$$
$$\updownarrow$$
$$MA_{(s)}$$

If the unknown solution is strongly acidic, the equilibrium will be shifted to the left, which effect increases the concentration of the HA molecules and in turn decreases the concentration of A^- ions. The concentration of the latter may be decreased in this manner to such an extent as to escape detection. On the other hand, the introduction of a strong base to such a solution serves to remove H^+ ions, thereby shifting the equilibrium to the right and increasing the concentration of A^- ions sufficiently to precipitate the salt MA. Negative ions considered here which show a pronounced tendency to combine with H^+ ion are: AsO_4^{---}, AsO_3^{---}, BO_2^-, CO_3^{--}, CrO_4^{--}, $Fe(CN)_6^{---}$, $Fe(CN)_6^{----}$, F^-, NO_2^-, $C_2O_4^{--}$, PO_4^{---}, S^{--}, SO_3^{--}, CNS^-, and $S_2O_3^{--}$.

If, however, the weak acid derived from the negative ion produces a gas, then the presence of H^+ ion is a favorable condition for the detection of the negative ion. The ions, S^{--}, SO_3^{--}, $S_2O_3^{--}$, and CO_3^{--} fall into this category and the equilibria involved in these cases are as follows:

$$S^{--} + 2H^+ = H_2S_{(aq.)} = H_2S_{(g)} \uparrow \tag{141}$$

$$SO_3^{--} + 2H^+ = H_2SO_3 = H_2O + SO_{2(g)} \uparrow \tag{142}$$

$$CO_3^{--} + 2H^+ = H_2CO_3 = H_2O + CO_{2(g)} \uparrow \tag{143}$$

$$S_2O_3^{--} + 2H^+ = H_2S_2O_3 = H_2O + SO_{2(g)} \uparrow + S_{(s)} \tag{144}$$

The addition of a strong acid to solutions containing S^{--}, SO_3^{--}, $S_2O_3^{--}$, and CO_3^{--} ions shifts the equilibrium in each case to the right. When the solubility of the substances produced is exceeded, H_2S, SO_2, or CO_2 will escape from solution as gases. These gases may then be detected by suitable methods. These equilibria can also be shifted to the right by the application of heat since gases are less soluble at high than at low temperatures.

Many of the positive metal ions interfere with the tests for the negative ions and therefore it is necessary at the outset to remove these positive ions from the solution. Inasmuch as the carbonates of most positive ions are relatively insoluble in alkaline solution, these ions may be precipitated as such in this medium. It is obvious that the test for CO_3^{--} ion must be made before this same ion is added as a reagent.

No such systematic scheme of analysis as that applied to the positive ions is applicable to the negative ions. Instead of using the same solution throughout the analysis it has been found necessary or expedient to make a number of isolated tests on different portions of the unknown solution. The procedure adopted here is that of making preliminary elimination tests in order that individual characteristic tests applied later may be reduced to as small a number as possible. The elimination tests are given schematically in Table 37 and, in detail, on the following pages. Some of the elimination tests are subsidiary to others and in some cases it will not be necessary to make all of these tests. These tests as outlined in Table 37 apply only to those anions in solution. Additional tests must be made on solids the anions of which cannot be converted into a soluble form by the carbonate treatment. After the elimination tests have been made, it will be possible to determine which ions cannot be present and conclusive characteristic tests for these particular ions may therefore be omitted.

Some confusion may arise in the use of elimination tests if the student does not thoroughly understand their purpose. The elimination tests are to be carried out with the definite view in mind to determine which ions are *not present* rather than to make positive tests for those ions which are present. The positive tests are to be made *after* the elimination tests have been made. If, for example, no precipitate is obtained when a solution containing HNO_3 and $AgNO_3$ is added to a solution prepared for the anion analysis, then Cl^-, Br^-, I^-, and CNS^- ions are absent. On the other hand, if a precipitate were obtained upon the addition of HNO_3 and $AgNO_3$, then no definite information would be forthcoming since such a precipitate might contain any or all of the silver salts of these ions. If all the anions listed in the table were present, the elimination tests would be practically worthless. The fewer the number of anions present the greater is the amount of information obtainable from the elimination tests.

In the analysis of most commercial and natural substances the student will encounter relatively few cases in which more than two or three anions are present in a single sample. For such cases the elimination tests are very valuable.

The detailed procedure given here for the analysis of the anions is only one of many possible schemes. The student is encouraged to use his ingenuity, together with his knowledge of the chemical properties of both anions and cations, to make variations in the scheme. He should also devise additional confirmatory tests when his knowledge of facts and originality of thought permit.

TABLE 37

PRELIMINARY ELIMINATION TESTS

Test	Positive tests to be made for	CO_3^{--}	S^{--}	SO_3^{--}	CrO_4^{--}	SO_4^{--}	F^-	$C_2O_4^{--}$	PO_4^{---}	AsO_3^{---}	AsO_4^{---}	BO_2^-	$S_2O_3^{--}$	Cl^-	Br^-	I^-	CNS^-	$Fe(CN)_6^{---}$	$Fe(CN)_6^{----}$	NO_3^-	NO_2^-	ClO_3^-
5	No dark brown or black color upon addition of $MnCl_2$ in 12 M HCl indicates absence of				CrO_4^{--}													$Fe(CN)_6^{---}$		NO_3^-	NO_2^-	ClO_3^-
4	No blue precipitate when original solution is treated with HCl, $Fe(NO_3)_3$, and $K_3Fe(CN)_6$ indicates absence of		S^{--}	SO_3^{--}												I^-		$Fe(CN)_6^{---}$			NO_2^-	
3-E	If no precipitate is obtained when HNO_3 is added to filtrate from 3-D, it indicates absence of													Cl^-								
3-D	If precipitate obtained in 3-B is completely soluble in 0.25 M NH_4OH, it indicates absence of														Br^-	I^-	CNS^-					
3-C	No precipitate when $NaNO_2$ solution is added to filtrate from 3-B indicates absence of																					ClO_3^-
3-B	No precipitate upon addition of HNO_3 and $AgNO_3$ to the filtrate from 3-A indicates absence of													Cl^-	Br^-	I^-	CNS^-					
3-A	No precipitate upon making S^{--} free solution acidic with HAc and adding $Zn(NO_3)_2$ solution indicates absence of																	$Fe(CN)_6^{---}$	$Fe(CN)_6^{----}$			
2-C	No precipitate upon making filtrate from 2-B alkaline indicates absence of								PO_4^{---}	AsO_3^{---}	AsO_4^{---}	BO_2^-										
2-B	No precipitate by $BaCl_2$ to filtrate of group 2-A indicates absence of				CrO_4^{--}	SO_4^{--}																
2-A	No precipitate by $CaCl_2$ in acidic solution of low H^+ ion concentration indicates absence of						F^-	$C_2O_4^{--}$														
1-B	No precipitate upon addition of acid to alkaline solution indicates absence of												$S_2O_3^{--}$									
1-A	No gas evolved upon addition of acid to alkaline solution indicates absence of	CO_2	S^{--}	SO_3^{--}																		
Test	Anions, or derivatives of, considered in analysis	CO_3^{--}	S^{--}	SO_3^{--}	CrO_4^{--}	SO_4^{--}	F^-	$C_2O_4^{--}$	PO_4^{---}	AsO_3^{---}	AsO_4^{---}	BO_2^-	$S_2O_3^{--}$	Cl^-	Br^-	I^-	CNS^-	$Fe(CN)_6^{---}$	$Fe(CN)_6^{----}$	NO_3^-	NO_2^-	ClO_3^-

Procedure for Detection of Anions

The following procedure is designed only for anions present in a prepared solution. The preparation of the solution which consists in converting insoluble salts of the anions to be analyzed into soluble forms and in the removal of those cations which will interfere with the anion analysis is given in the preceding chapter.

Preliminary Elimination Tests

Prepare a chart such as Table 37 leaving out the characterization of the test at the top of each column (left side of page 441) and leaving blank all spaces except those in the first column; i.e., the formulae for the ions on which tests are to be made. After each preliminary test, check off in the appropriate spaces those ions which are known to be absent. After all preliminary tests have been made, it will be obvious which ions can possibly be present (the horizontal rows which are unmarked).

Test 1–A. This test is to be performed only if the original unknown is completely soluble in water to give an alkaline solution. It must be applied before any Na_2CO_3 has been added.

Place 5 drops of the unknown solution in a small test tube and heat gently (*do not boil*). Holding the tube to the light observe carefully whether a gas is evolved when 2 drops of 6 M HCl are added. If no gas is observed here, test the solid unknown directly for the evolution of gas by adding concentrated HCl. If no gas is evolved in either case, CO_3^{--}, S^{--} and SO_3^{--} ions cannot be present. Note that the absence of any gas also indicates the absence of $S_2O_3^{--}$ ion. (Check these ions in columns 1–A and 1–B of the chart if they are shown to be absent; leave spaces blank if a gas is observed.)

Test 1–B. This test must be applied to the Na_2CO_3 prepared solution.[1]

Add 5 drops of 6 M HCl to 5 drops of the prepared solution in a small test tube and heat gently. If a white gelatinous precipitate is formed, it may be due to silicic acid.[2] If $S_2O_3^{--}$ ion is present in the original solution, a precipitate of free sulfur will form.[3]

NOTE 1. *The Na_2CO_3 prepared solution must be used here since the addition of HCl to the original unknown could precipitate insoluble chlorides and oxychlorides.*

NOTE 2. *The test for SiO₃⁻⁻ ion has been omitted from this scheme because of the expense (platinum) and danger (HF) involved in making a satisfactory confirmatory test.*

NOTE 3. *If Ag⁺ and NH₄⁺ ions were both present in the original solution and if the Ag⁺ ion was not removed, the addition of HCl will produce a precipitate of AgCl which is soluble in NH₄OH. The free sulfur is not soluble in this reagent.*

Test 2–A. To 10 drops of the Na_2CO_3 prepared solution in a small test tube add 10 drops of water and insert into the solution a small fragment of litmus paper. Add 3 M HAc (made by diluting 1 ml. of 6 M HAc with 1 ml. of water) drop by drop, counting the number of drops added, until the litmus paper just turns pink. Now continue to add the same number of drops of 3 M HAc as have already been added. To the resulting solution add 4 drops of 0.1 M CaCl₂ solution. If no precipitate forms, F^- and $C_2O_4^{--}$ ions are absent. If a precipitate forms, either or both of these ions may be present. Record your findings in the chart if these ions are absent. Centrifuge or filter. Save the precipitate for the characteristic tests for F^- and $C_2O_4^{--}$ ions (page 446). Label it. After the filtrate has been tested for completeness of precipitation by adding 2 more drops of CaCl₂ solution, continue with the next test.

Test 2–B. To the filtrate from **2–A** from which insoluble calcium salts have been removed, add 2 drops of 0.1 M BaCl₂ solution. If a precipitate is not formed, CrO_4^{--} and SO_4^{--} ions are absent. In such a case make a record of it in the chart. If a yellow precipitate is formed, CrO_4^{--} ion is known to be present. (SO_4^{--} ion may also be present.) If the precipitate is white, SO_4^{--} ion is present and CrO_4^{--} ion is absent. Test for completeness of precipitation and add 2 drops of 0.1 M BaCl₂ solution in excess. Filter or centrifuge the solution and reserve the filtrate for the next test.

If SO_3^{--} ion is present in the original solution in relatively large amounts, BaSO₃ may precipitate here. Unless SO_3^{--} ion has been found to be absent in test **1–A,** wash the precipitate thoroughly with water, and add a few drops of 6 M HCl to the precipitate. Determine whether SO_3^{--} ion is present by noting any evolution of gas. Note that BaSO₃ and BaCrO₄ will dissolve in HCl while BaSO₄ will not.

Test 2–C. Add 5 drops of 12 M HCl to the filtrate from **2–B** and heat in a casserole to expel SO₂ and CO₂. Note if free sulfur is formed from any $S_2O_3^{--}$ ion which may be present. Now add 15 M NH_4OH to the clear solution until it is decidedly alkaline to litmus. Add several drops NH_4OH in excess. If no precipitate forms, PO_4^{---}, AsO_4^{---} and BO_2^- ions are absent.

If no precipitate is observed BO_2^- ion may still be present in small amounts since $Ba(BO_2)_2$ may form a supersaturated solution. Therefore, in any case, carry out the specific flame test for boron using the prepared Na_2CO_3 solution as described on page 451.

Test 3–A. Add 1 drop of 0.1 M $Pb(NO_3)_2$ solution to 2 drops of the Na_2CO_3 prepared solution to test for the presence of S^{--} ion. If a black precipitate of PbS is formed, the S^{--} ion must be removed completely before tests for ferro- and ferricyanide ions may be made. To accomplish this, add 1 ml. of water to 1 ml. of the Na_2CO_3 prepared solution in a 10 ml. test tube. Now add 0.1 M $Pb(NO_3)_2$ solution drop by drop until further addition produces a white precipitate. Stop the addition at this point. It may be necessary to allow the solution to stand or to centrifuge it for a very short time between additions of the $Pb(NO_3)_2$ solution, to be able to ascertain whether the newly formed precipitate is white. Centrifuge or filter and discard the precipitate. Add one more drop of $Pb(NO_3)_2$ solution to the filtrate. A white precipitate of $PbCO_3$ should form instead of the black sulfide.

To the original Na_2CO_3 prepared solution free from S^{--} ion, or to the solution from which S^{--} ion has been removed, as the case may be, add 6 M HAc drop by drop until acidic. (Use litmus paper.) Add 4 drops of 6 M HAc in excess and then add 1 drop of 0.1 M $Zn(NO_3)_2$ solution. If a precipitate forms, add 10 more drops of the $Zn(NO_3)_2$ solution. Centrifuge or filter, discard the precipitate and save the filtrate for the next elimination test. If no precipitate forms, $Fe(CN)_6^{---}$ and $Fe(CN)_6^{----}$ ions are absent.[4,5]

NOTE 4. *$Zn_2Fe(CN)_6$ (white) and $Zn_3[Fe(CN)_6]_2$ (yellow) are relatively insoluble in dilute HAc solution.*

NOTE 5. *$Zn_3(AsO_4)_2$ may precipitate slowly as a gelatinous colorless precipitate if the H^+ ion concentration is too small. This precipitate can be easily distinguished from the white or yellow granular precipitates of zinc ferrocyanide and zinc ferricyanide The appearance of any zinc arsenate will therefore not interfere.*

Test 3–B. To the filtrate from **3–A** add 10 drops of 6 M HNO_3 and heat. Filter if necessary. To the cooled solution add 5 drops of 0.1 M AgNO₃. If no precipitate forms, Cl⁻, Br⁻, I⁻ and CNS⁻ ions are absent. Make a record of absence. If no precipitate forms, do not carry out tests **3–D** and **3–E**. If a precipitate forms [6] test for completeness of precipitation by adding more AgNO₃ solution. Filter or centrifuge and save the precipitate for test **3–D** and **3–E**. Save the filtrate for test **3–C**.

NOTE 6. *The $S_2O_3^{--}$ ion is decomposed by the acidic solution. If either the $S_2O_3^{--}$ or S^{--} ions have not been completely removed, a black precipitate of Ag_2S may be formed.*

Test 3–C. Add 1 drop of chloride-free 6 M KNO₂ to the filtrate [7] from **3–B** or to the solution if no precipitate was formed. If no precipitate of AgCl appears, ClO_3^- ion is absent. A precipitate at this point indicates positively that ClO_3^- ion is present.

NOTE 7. *HNO_2 reduces the ClO_3^- ion to Cl^- ion.*
$$ClO_3^- + 3HNO_2 = Cl^- + 3NO_3^- + 3H^+$$
AgCl is insoluble while $AgClO_3$ is quite soluble.

Test 3–D. To the *thoroughly* washed precipitate from **3–B** add 4 ml. of water, 4 drops of 6 M NH₄OH and 10 drops of 0.1 M AgNO₃ solution. (The relative amounts of water, NH₄OH and AgNO₃ are important in this test. Follow directions closely.) Agitate the precipitate with a glass rod. If the precipitate dissolves completely, Br⁻, I⁻ and CNS⁻ ions are not present. Save this mixture for **3–E**. The complete solution of the precipitate by NH₄OH at this concentration is sufficient evidence that Cl⁻ ion is present.

Test 3–E. If the precipitate in **3–D** is completely dissolved by NH₄OH, carry out this test only to confirm the presence of Cl⁻ ion. If the precipitate did not dissolve completely in the NH₄OH, it may have dissolved partially.

Filter or centrifuge the ammoniacal solution from **3–D** if necessary. Acidify the solution with HNO₃. If no precipitate forms, Cl⁻ ion is absent. A heavy [8] white precipitate confirms the presence of the Cl⁻ ion.

NOTE 8. *A very faint precipitate at this point may be due to Br⁻ or CNS⁻ ion.*

Test 4. To 3 drops of the Na₂CO₃ prepared solution add 1 ml. of water, 2 drops of 6 M HCl, 2 drops of 0.1 M FeCl₃, and 1 drop of *freshly prepared* saturated $K_3Fe(CN)_6$ (ferricyanide) solution. Allow the mixture to stand several minutes. If a deep blue precipitate does not form, S^{--}, SO_3^{--}, I^-, $Fe(CN)_6^{----}$ and NO_2^- ions are absent.[9, 10, 11]

NOTE 9. *This test depends upon the fact that the above ions in acidic solution reduce Fe^{+++} ion to Fe^{++} ion. The Fe^{++} ion then combines with the $Fe(CN)_6^{---}$ ion to give Prussian Blue. (See page 377.)*

NOTE 10. *To be sure that none of the reagents contains either Fe^{++} ion or a reducing agent, make a blank test using all reagents, omitting only the prepared solution. Compare the intensities of the blue color obtained here with that obtained with the unknown solution.*

NOTE 11. *To prepare a saturated solution of $K_3Fe(CN)_6$, place a few crystals of the salt in a small test tube, add 10 drops of water and agitate with a stirring rod.*

Test 5. To 3 drops of the prepared solution add dropwise 12 drops of a saturated solution of $MnCl_2$ in 12 M HCl and heat the mixture to boiling. If no dark brown or black color appears, the following ions are absent: CrO_4^{--}, $Fe(CN)_6^{---}$, NO_3^-, NO_2^- and ClO_3^-.[12] A slight darkening, which indicates the presence of oxidizing ions, may be overlooked unless the color of the solution is compared with that of the original solution.

NOTE 12. *Any one of the above mentioned ions in strong acid solution oxidizes $MnCl_2$ solution to the dark colored $MnCl_3$ solution.*

After all preliminary tests have been made and checks for absent ions have been placed in the appropriate spaces in the prepared chart, note which ions have not been checked. *Confirmatory tests need to be made for these ions only.*

POSITIVE TESTS FOR ANIONS

The following tests are based on the assumption that all negative ions included in this scheme are present in the solution. However, only the tests for those ions which have not been previously eliminated should be carried out. If the instructor does not include all ions given here as possibilities, the student can merely strike out those ions not considered.

OXALATE AND FLUORIDE IONS

Make the tests for these ions on any precipitate which may have been formed in the previous test 2–A.

Test for $C_2O_4^{--}$ Ion. The precipitate should be washed twice with 2 ml. of water. The first wash water is discarded and the second retained. Add 10 drops of 6 M H_2SO_4 solution to the second wash water and now add dropwise .001 M $KMnO_4$[13] solution until a faint pink color persists. Count and record the number of drops necessary.

To about one-half of the precipitate in a small test tube add 2 ml. of water and 10 drops of 6 M H_2SO_4, and shake. Again add .001 M $KMnO_4$ solution dropwise. If $C_2O_4^{--}$ ion is present, at least several drops more of the .001 M $KMnO_4$ solution than was required for the above blank test will be necessary to impart the permanent pink color to the solution.[14]

NOTE 13. *Make up the .001 M KMnO₄ solution by placing 10 drops of .01 M KMnO₄ in a 10 ml. test tube and adding water until the test tube is half filled.*

NOTE 14. *The MnO_4^- ion in acid solution oxidizes oxalic acid (or $C_2O_4^{--}$) to CO_2.*

$$5H_2C_2O_4 + 2MnO_4^- + 6H^+ = 10CO_2 + 2Mn^{++} + 8H_2O$$

Test for F^- Ion. With a piece of Chromel wire having a small loop at one end, transfer the remainder of the precipitate from test **2–A**, which may contain both CaF_2 and CaC_2O_4, onto a flat piece of filter paper. The purpose of this operation is to extract the greater part of the water. With the looped end of the wire gather up as much as possible of the precipitate, place it in the flame of a Bunsen burner, and heat to redness.[15]

Wash the surface of a small watch glass with alcohol to remove grease, and make certain that the glass is perfectly clean and clear before using.

With the aid of another wire or a pin scrape the ignited precipitate onto the surface of the watch glass. Confine the precipitate to as small an area as possible (1 or 2 mm.²) and add to the precipitate on the watch glass a very small crystal of dry $(NH_4)_2SO_4$ (equivalent to the volume of the fused precipitate). Dip a pointed glass rod (previously used to puncture filter paper) into 18 M H_2SO_4 and apply the point to the solid on the watch glass. A very small drop of H_2SO_4 should be retained by the solid.

Now hold the watch glass 8 or 10 inches above the Bunsen flame to heat the mixture gently. Keep it warm for 5 minutes and then allow it to stand for an hour or so. (The test may appear in a few minutes, depending upon the concentration of the F^- ion; however, if no etching is observed, allow the glass to stand for several hours before reaching a decision). Then wash the watch glass thoroughly and with a magnifying glass examine the area subjected to any hydrofluoric acid which may have formed. If the spot is etched, F^- ion is present in the unknown. In case the test is still negative and even in case elimination test **2–A** indicated the absence of F^- ion, repeat the test, using the original solid unknown instead of the precipitate from **2–A** and allow to stand over night before arriving at any conclusion.

NOTE 15. *All water must be removed to make this test successful.*

SULFATE, SULFITE, AND CHROMATE IONS

Test for SO_4^{--} Ion. Place 5 drops of the prepared Na_2CO_3 solution in a small test tube and dilute with 1 ml. of water. Acidify by adding 6 M HCl dropwise. Add 2 drops of 6 M HCl in excess. Now add 1 ml. of 0.1 M $BaCl_2$ solution. A white precipitate of $BaSO_4$ indicates the presence of SO_4^{--} ion in the original solution. Centrifuge or filter the solution and discard the precipitate. Save the filtrate for tests for the SO_3^{--} and CrO_4^{--} ions. Add 1 drop of 0.1 M $BaCl_2$ to insure completeness of precipitation.

Test for SO_3^{--} Ion. To the filtrate obtained in the test for SO_4^{--} ion add 5 drops of bromine water.[16] A white precipitate indicates the presence of SO_3^{--} ion in the original solution. If no precipitate is obtained, add 1 drop of 0.1 M $BaCl_2$ to be certain that Ba^{++} ion is present in excess. Centrifuge or filter the solution.

NOTE 16. *Bromine oxidizes H_2SO_3 to SO_4^{--} ion in acid solution.*

$$H_2SO_3 + Br_2 + H_2O = SO_4^{--} + 2Br^- + 4H^+$$

Test for CrO_4^{--} Ion. If CrO_4^{--} ion is present in the solution, a yellow precipitate would have been obtained in preliminary test **2–B**. The solution would also have a yellow color (do not be confused by the color due to bromine).

To confirm, or again test for CrO_4^{--} ion, add to the filtrate from the test for SO_3^{--} ion 10 drops of 2 M NaAc.[17] If CrO_4^{--} (or $Cr_2O_7^{--}$) ion is present, a yellow precipitate of $BaCrO_4$ will form.[18]

NOTE 17. *The addition of Ac^- ion lowers the H^+ ion concentration by the formation of weak HAc. When the H^+ ion concentration is lowered, the*

CrO_4^{--} *ion concentration is increased sufficiently to combine with* Ba^{++} *ion to form solid* $BaCrO_4$.

$$H_2O + Cr_2O_7^{--} \text{ (acid solution)} = 2H^+ + 2CrO_4^{--}$$

NOTE 18. *If* F^- *or* $C_2O_4^{--}$ *ions are present in large concentration, the corresponding barium salt may precipitate. However, both these precipitates are white and will not obscure the yellow color of* $BaCrO_4$.

FERROCYANIDE, FERRICYANIDE, AND THIOCYANATE IONS

If the previous tests have shown either ferro- or ferricyanide ions to be present, make the following test.

To 1 ml. of water in a small test tube add 5 drops of the prepared Na_2CO_3 solution. Add 6 M HNO_3 dropwise until the solution is acidic. Now add 3 drops of 0.1 M $Fe(NO)_3$ solution. If a dark blue precipitate forms, $Fe(CN)_6^{----}$ ion is present. If the precipitate forms, heat and centrifuge or filter the solution. Discard the precipitate and to the filtrate again add 1 drop of 0.1 M $Fe(NO_3)_3$ to insure completeness of precipitation. If the solution has a bright red color, CNS^- ion is present.

Now add 3 drops of 0.1 M $FeSO_4$ solution. If a dark blue precipitate is formed, $Fe(CN)_6^{---}$ ion is present. See page 377 for the chemistry involved in these tests.[19]

NOTE 19. *In making this test why could not the* $FeSO_4$ *solution be added first, the solution then filtered, and then the* $Fe(NO_3)_3$ *added?*

CHLORIDE, BROMIDE, AND IODIDE IONS

If the previous elimination test **3–D** has shown that Br^-, I^- and CNS^- ions are absent, do not make this test. The positive chloride test was made in the elimination test **3–E** and no further test for this ion need be made.

If the elimination tests showed that Br^- or I^- ions may possibly be present, proceed as follows.

Test for I^- Ion. Place 5 drops of the prepared Na_2CO_3 solution in a small test tube and dilute with 10 drops of water. Neutralize with 6 M HNO_3; add 2 drops of the HNO_3 in excess. Now cover the surface of the liquid with about 10 drops of CCl_4. Add a quantity of 0.1 M $Fe(NO_3)_3$ solution [20] equal in volume to the aqueous solution already in the test tube and shake. A violet color in the CCl_4 layer indicates the presence of I^- ion.[21]

If the CCl_4 layer turns purple, remove it from the surface with the capillary syringe and add more CCl_4 and shake again. Again discard the CCl_4 layer. Repeat this operation until the CCl_4 layer remains colorless.

NOTE 20. *The Fe^{+++} ion oxidizes the I^- ion to free iodine.*

NOTE 21. *Other ions may react with the Fe^{+++} ion added but these reactions will not interfere with the iodine formation if an excess of the Fe^{+++} ion is present.*

Test for Br^- Ion. Now transfer the solution to a casserole and heat to boiling to drive off any residual iodine. After cooling, pour the solution back into the test tube. Add 10 drops of 6 M HNO_3, again add 1 ml. of CCl_4 and then add 0.1 M $KMnO_4$ solution [22] dropwise until the aqueous solution is distinctly purple. Shake the mixture. A yellow or orange color in the CCl_4 layer indicates the presence of Br^- ion. If the concentration of the bromine in the CCl_4 layer is small and it is found difficult to distinguish its color, remove about one half of the CCl_4 with a medicine dropper and transfer it to a 3 ml. test tube. Compare the color of this solution with that of an equal volume of pure CCl_4.

NOTE 22. *The Fe^{+++} ion is not a strong enough oxidizing agent to oxidize Br^- ion to free bromine. Note the positions of Fe^{+++} ion, I_2, Br_2 and $MnO_4^- + H^+$ ion in the oxidation reduction table page 269 (#63, 68, 83 and 102).*

PHOSPHATE, ARSENATE, AND ARSENITE IONS

Do not make these tests if preliminary test **2–C** showed these ions to be absent.

Tests for PO_4^{---} and AsO_4^{---} Ions. Add 5 drops of the prepared Na_2CO_3 solution to a small test tube and dilute with 10 drops of water. Add 6 M HNO_3 dropwise until one drop turns blue litmus red (place a small fragment of the litmus paper in the solution). Filter if a precipitate forms. Add 1 ml. of magnesia mixture. Allow the solution to stand 10 minutes or longer, shaking occasionally. If a white precipitate appears, either AsO_4^{---} ion or PO_4^{---} ion or both are present.[23]

Filter or centrifuge the solution and save the filtrate for the arsenite test (label it). Wash the precipitate with 2 ml. of water to which 1 ml. of 3 M NH_4OH has been added. To the precipitate now add (or if filtration was used, pour over the filter paper) 1 ml.

of 0.1 M AgNO$_3$ solution to which 2 drops of 6 M HAc have been added. If AsO$_4$$^{---}$ ion is present, the magnesium ammonium arsenate will be converted to silver arsenate which is red in color. Silver phosphate would also be formed. This is yellow in color.

In case arsenate is shown to be present the color of the yellow silver phosphate will be obscured and a separate test for phosphate must be made. In such a case the arsenic must be removed before the phosphate test can be applied.

NOTE 23. *AsO$_4$$^{---}$ and PO$_4$$^{---}$ ions, under the conditions of the above test, are precipitated as MgNH$_4$AsO$_4$ and MgNH$_4$PO$_4$ respectively. To prevent the precipitation of magnesium arsenite, Mg$_3$(AsO$_3$)$_2$, the OH$^-$ ion concentration cannot be too high.*

Test for Phosphate in Presence of Arsenate. To 5 drops of the prepared Na$_2$CO$_3$ solution in a 10 ml. test tube add 10 drops of water and add 6 M HCl drop by drop until the solution turns methyl violet paper a blue green color. Add 1 drop of 1 M NH$_4$I, heat to boiling and saturate with H$_2$S (use the small glass tube drawn to a narrow tip). Centrifuge or filter and again add H$_2$S to test for completeness of precipitation. Pour the filtrate into a small casserole and evaporate almost to dryness. Add to the residue in the casserole 5 drops of 15 M HNO$_3$ and 5 drops of water. Add a few drops of this solution to 10 drops of hot ammonium molybdate solution.[24] A yellow precipitate of ammonium phospho-molybdate indicates the presence of phosphate ion. If no precipitate appears, warm the solution (do not boil) before deciding whether phosphate ion is absent.

Owing to the exacting conditions necessary for carrying out this test successfully, it is advisable to perform it first with a "known" solution containing phosphate ion.

NOTE 24. *Ammonium molybdate solution deteriorates slowly and should not be used if more than one month old.*

Test for AsO$_2$$^-$ Ion. To the filtrate from the test for AsO$_4$$^{---}$ and PO$_4$$^{---}$ ions add 6 M HCl until it is acidic to litmus paper. Saturate with H$_2$S. A yellow precipitate of As$_2$S$_3$ indicates the presence of AsO$_2$$^-$ ion.

BORATE, NITRATE, NITRITE, AND CHLORATE IONS

Test for BO$_2$$^-$ Ion. To prevent spreading of the solution rub your finger over the surface of a watch glass to give it a fine film of oil (there is sufficient oil on the hand) and then place on the watch glass 5 drops of the prepared Na_2CO_3 solution. To this add 2 drops of 15 M HNO_3 and heat the watch glass gently, high over the flame, until the solution has evaporated to dryness. Allow it to cool. Scrape the solid residue into a small pile and add to it an equal amount of finely ground CaF_2. With the pointed glass rod moisten the powder with a very small amount of 18 M H_2SO_4 and gather the paste into a very small loop made at the end of a piece of Chromel wire. Bring the looped end of the wire up to the edge of the flame (not into it). If boron is present, the edge of the flame will assume a green color. [25, 26]

NOTE 25. *In acid solution borates are converted to boric (or boracic) acid. Example:*

$$5H_2O + B_4O_7^{--} + 2H^+ = 4H_3BO_3$$

Boric acid combines with HF to produce volatile boron trifluoride, BF_3.

$$H_3BO_3 + 3HF = BF_3 + 3H_2O$$

The volatile BF_3 escapes readily from the above mixture when warmed gently and imparts a green color to the flame.

NOTE 26. *Copper and barium salts also give a green color to the flame but these ions have been removed in preparing the solution with Na_2CO_3.*

Test for NO_2^- Ion. To 5 drops of the Na_2CO_3 prepared solution add 2 drops of 6 M H_2SO_4. The solution should be acidic. If it is not, add another drop of the H_2SO_4. To the acidic solution add 5 drops of 0.1 M $FeSO_4$ solution.[27] If NO_2^- ion is present the entire solution will turn dark brown.[28] If NO_2^- ion is not present and if Br^-, I^-, CrO_4^{--}[29] and ClO_3^-[30] ions are also absent, use this solution for NO_3^- ion test.

NOTE 27. *The $FeSO_4$ solution should be freshly prepared.*

NOTE 28. *Fe^{++} ion in dilute acid solution reduces HNO_2 to NO which in turn combines with excess Fe^{++} ion to form $Fe(NO)^{++}$ ion. This ion has a characteristic dark brown color.*

NOTE 29. *CrO_4^{--} (or $Cr_2O_7^{--}$) ion and HNO_2 cannot exist together in acid solution. The HNO_2 will be oxidized to NO_3^- ion.*

NOTE 30. *If ClO_3^- ion is present NO_2^- ion cannot be present since the latter would be oxidized to NO_3^- ion by the former, in acid solution.*

Test for NO_3^- Ion. If Br^-, I^-, CrO_4^{--}, ClO_3^- and NO_2^- ions are absent proceed as follows.

To the acidified solution obtained in making the NO_2^- ion test add 3 drops of 18 M H_2SO_4 by holding the small test tube in an inclined position thereby permitting the concentrated H_2SO_4 to run down the side of the test tube. The H_2SO_4 should submerge to the bottom of the test tube and form a separate layer. Do not agitate the mixture. If NO_3^- ion is present a brown ring will form at the junction of the two liquids in the course of a few minutes.[31]

NOTE 31. *The NO_3^- ion in acid solution is reduced by the Fe^{++} ion to NO which in turn reacts with excess Fe^{++} ion to produce the brown colored $Fe(NO)^{++}$ ion. With the NO_3^- ion (in contrast to NO_2^- ion) this reaction takes place rapidly only in a solution of very high H^+ ion concentration and at relatively higher temperatures. Such a condition exists at the junction of the two liquids.*

Test for NO_3^- Ion in the Presence of NO_2^- Ion. If NO_2^- ion is present it must be removed before the NO_3^- ion test is applied.

To 5 drops of the Na_2CO_3 prepared solution add 6 M H_2SO_4 until acidic. Now add 3 drops of 1 M $(NH_4)_2SO_4$ solution, place in a casserole and very carefully and slowly evaporate until the mixture is in the form of a thick paste. Do not heat to dryness. After cooling redissolve the paste in 1 ml. of water and pour the solution into a small test tube. Disregard any undissolved residue. Add 10 drops of 0.1 M $FeSO_4$ solution and add 3 or 4 drops of 18 M H_2SO_4 as directed in the preceding paragraph. A brown ring indicates the presence of NO_3^- ion.[32]

NOTE 32. *If the NO_2^- ion is not removed the whole solution will be brown colored and the typical brown "nitrate" ring will not be visible.*

Test for NO_3^- Ion in the Presence of Br^-, I^- and CrO_4^{--} Ions. Acidify 5 drops of the Na_2CO_3 prepared solution dropwise with 6 M HAc. Add 10 drops of water and pour into a previously cleaned small mortar. Add about 10 to 20 mg. of solid nitrate free Ag_2SO_4. With a clean pestle triturate (grind) the mixture for two minutes. Pour the supernatant liquid into a test tube and centrifuge if necessary. To this solution add 2 drops of 6 M H_2SO_4. Centrifuge or filter if a precipitate of Ag_2SO_4 forms. To the clear solution add 5 to 10 drops of 0.1 M $FeSO_4$ solution and then add 3 to 4 drops of 18 M H_2SO_4 as directed above.[33, 34]

NOTE 33. *If Br^- and I^- ions are not removed, Br_2 and I_2 may be formed at the interface and be confused with the "nitrate" ring.*

NOTE 34. $Cr_2O_7^{--}$ *ion in acid solution is reduced by* Fe^{++} *ion to the* *green* Cr^{+++} *ion.   The green color thus produced will interfere with the* *nitrate test.*

Test for NO_3^- Ion in the Presence of ClO_3^- Ion.   To remove the ClO_3^- ion add a very small amount of metallic zinc [35] to any of the above solutions which may contain NO_3^- ion, after acidifying with H_2SO_4 and before the $FeSO_4$ solution has been added.[36]   The zinc should be in contact with the solution for several minutes before it is decanted, centrifuged, or filtered.   To the clear solution add $FeSO_4$ solution and 18 M H_2SO_4 as directed above.

NOTE 35.   *The metallic zinc in acid solution reduces the* ClO_3^- *ion to* Cl^- *ion.   The latter does not interfere with the* NO_3^- *ion test.*

NOTE 36.   *If* ClO_3^- *ion is not removed* ClO_2, *a yellow colored gas soluble* *in water, will form and obscure the test.*

Test for ClO_3^- Ion.   A sufficient test for the ClO_3^- ion was made in preliminary elimination test **3-C**

CHAPTER XXI

The Chemical Properties of Negative Ions

Carbonate Ion, CO_3^{--}. When water is saturated with CO_2, carbonic acid is formed. The concentration of the H_2CO_3 in solution is proportional to the pressure of the CO_2 gas (Henry's Law). At a pressure of one atmosphere the concentration of the H_2CO_3 (total concentration of dissolved CO_2) is .034 mole per liter. In such a solution the following equilibria are maintained:

$$CO_{2(g)} + H_2O = H_2CO_3 = H^+ + HCO_3^-$$
$$\Updownarrow \qquad (145)$$
$$CO_3^{--} + H^+$$

In fact the above equilibrium holds for any solution to which CO_2, a bicarbonate (e.g. $NaHCO_3$) or a carbonate (e.g. Na_2CO_3) has been added. If a strong acid is added to such a solution the equilibrium is shifted to the left with the production of CO_2. The latter may be readily detected by passing it through limewater, with which $CaCO_3$ is formed.

$$CO_{2(g)} + Ca^{++} + 2OH^- = CaCO_{3(s)} + H_2O \quad (146)$$

This is one of the best methods for the detection of carbonates. A solution of $Ba(OH)_2$ may be used in place of limewater in this test.

The addition of OH^- ion shifts the equilibrium (145) to the right with the production of HCO_3^- and CO_3^{--} ions. Since the CO_3^{--} ion concentration in H_2CO_3 is not great enough to precipitate any of the relatively insoluble carbonates the precipitation of this ion must always be carried out in alkaline solution.

The carbonates of several of the positive ions show a limited solubility in water. Table 38 gives a list of the more common slightly soluble carbonates in order of decreasing CO_3^{--} ion concentration at equilibrium.

TABLE 38

EQUILIBRIA INVOLVING CARBONATE ION

$CO_3^{--} + Mg^{++}$	$= MgCO_{3(s)}$
$CO_3^{--} + 2Ag^{+}$	$= Ag_2CO_{3(s)}$
$CO_3^{--} + Ca^{++}$	$= CaCO_{3(s)}$
$CO_3^{--} + Ba^{++}$	$= BaCO_{3(s)}$
$CO_3^{--} + Sr^{++}$	$= SrCO_{3(s)}$
$CO_3^{--} + Pb^{++}$	$= PbCO_{3(s)}$

(Decreasing Concentration of CO_3^{--} Ion)

The carbonates of the alkali metals and NH_4^+ ion are soluble; those of Al^{+++}, Fe^{+++}, Cr^{+++}, As^{+++}, Sb^{+++}, Sn^{++}, and Sn^{++++} ions are unknown in aqueous solution since they would be extensively hydrolyzed. All carbonates or basic carbonates of the other ions considered in this text are insoluble.

Sulfide Ion, S^{--}. Hydrogen sulfide and the HS^- ion are both very weak acids the properties of which have already been thoroughly discussed in previous sections of the text. (See Chapter VII.) Many of the sulfides of the positive ions show a very limited solubility in water. The more common of these slightly soluble sulfides are listed in Table 39 in order of decreasing concentration of S^{--} ion at equilibrium.

TABLE 39

EQUILIBRIA INVOLVING SULFIDE ION

$S^{--} + Mn^{++}$	$= MnS_{(s)}$
$S^{--} + Fe^{++}$	$= FeS_{(s)}$
$S^{--} + Zn^{++}$	$= ZnS_{(s)}$
$S^{--} + Ni^{++}$	$= NiS_{(s)}$
$S^{--} + Co^{++}$	$= CoS_{(s)}$
$S^{--} + Cd^{++}$	$= CdS_{(s)}$
$S^{--} + Pb^{++}$	$= PbS_{(s)}$
$S^{--} + 2Cu^{+}$	$= Cu_2S_{(s)}$
$S^{--} + 2Ag^{+}$	$= Ag_2S_{(s)}$
$S^{--} + Cu^{++}$	$= CuS_{(s)}$
$S^{--} + Hg^{++}$	$= HgS_{(s)}$

(Decreasing Concentration of S^{--} Ion)

The more soluble of the slightly soluble sulfides (those above Cu_2S in Table 39) as well as the soluble sulfides, such as those of the alkali metals, alkaline earth metals, ammonium ion, etc., are dissolved by moderately strong HCl with the liberation of H_2S gas. Taking ZnS as an example the equilibria involved in this reaction are

$$ZnS_{(s)} = Zn^{++} + S^{--}$$
$$+$$
$$H^+ \qquad\qquad H_2S \ (gas) \qquad (147)$$
$$\updownarrow \qquad\qquad \updownarrow$$
$$HS^- + H^+ = H_2S \ (diss.)$$

The addition of H^+ ion shifts the equilibrium to the right with the ultimate liberation of H_2S gas. The latter may be readily detected by moistened lead acetate paper placed in the stream of the gas which forms a black coloration due to PbS.

One of the most insoluble sulfides is Ag_2S. (See Table 39.) When a solution of $AgNO_3$ is added to one containing S^{--} ion, Ag_2S is precipitated. The precipitate is not dissolved by NH_4OH, CN^- ion, nor by non-oxidizing acids. Hence, under favorable conditions, Ag^+ ion may be used to detect S^{--} ion.

Thiosulfate Ion, $S_2O_3^{--}$. Thiosulfate ion may be regarded as a sulfate ion with one of the oxygen atoms replaced by sulfur.

Thiosulfuric acid is not known in the pure state inasmuch as it is extremely unstable, dissociating to give free sulfur and sulfurous acid. If a solution of a soluble thiosulfate is made acidic this reaction takes place and sulfur precipitates. With a sufficient amount of the strong acid present, SO_2 is liberated from the solution.

$$H_2S_2O_3 = S_{(s)} + H_2SO_3$$
$$H_2SO_3 = H_2O + SO_2 \qquad (148)$$

The most important salt of $S_2O_3^{--}$ ion is sodium thiosulfate, $Na_2S_2O_3 \cdot 5H_2O$, which is also known as "hypo" and is used in the "fixing" of photographic films and plates.

The $S_2O_3^{--}$ ion forms a soluble complex ion with Ag^+ ion provided an excess of the former is present.

$$S_2O_3^{--} + 2Ag^+ = Ag_2S_2O_{3(s)} \qquad (149)$$

$$Ag_2S_2O_{3(s)} + 2S_2O_3^{--} = Ag_2(S_2O_3)_3^{----} \qquad (150)$$

Therefore most silver salts can be readily dissolved in a solution of sodium thiosulfate.

Thiosulfate ion shows the properties of a reducing agent in its reaction with iodine; the iodine is reduced to I^- ion and the $S_2O_3^{--}$ ion is oxidized to the tetrathionate ion, $S_4O_6^{--}$.

$$2S_2O_3^{--} + I_2 = S_4O_6^{--} + 2I^- \qquad (151)$$

Oxalate Ion, $C_2O_4^{--}$. Oxalate ion is derived from oxalic acid, a dibasic acid, which ionizes in two stages,

$$
\begin{aligned}
(1) \qquad & H_2C_2O_4 = H^+ + HC_2O_4^- \\
(2) \qquad & HC_2O_4^- = H^+ + C_2O_4^{--}
\end{aligned}
\qquad (152)
$$

The ionization constant for the first stage has a value of 3.8×10^{-2} while that for the second stage is 5×10^{-5}. Accordingly, $H_2C_2O_4$ is a moderately strong acid while the bioxalate ion, $HC_2O_4^-$, is one of the stronger of the acid ions.

Most oxalates are relatively insoluble in water, at the most slightly soluble; those of the alkali metals and magnesium are notable exceptions. However, the slightly soluble oxalates are readily soluble in solutions of strong acids. Others are found to be soluble in the presence of a high concentration of $C_2O_4^{--}$ ion due to the formation of complex ions. In Table 40 some of the more slightly soluble oxalates are arranged in order of decreasing concentration of $C_2O_4^{--}$ ion at equilibrium.

Since calcium oxalate is one of the more insoluble oxalates, it is used to identify the $C_2O_4^{--}$ ion. When a saturated solution of $CaSO_4$ is added to a solution containing an appreciable quantity of $C_2O_4^{--}$ ion, CaC_2O_4 is precipitated. Calcium sulfate, while not very soluble in water, is more soluble than CaC_2O_4 and consequently the following equi-

TABLE 40

EQUILIBRIA INVOLVING OXALATE ION

	$C_2O_4^{--} + Mg^{++} = MgC_2O_{4(s)}$
	$C_2O_4^{--} + Ba^{++} = BaC_2O_{4(s)}$
Decreasing Concentration of $C_2O_4^{--}$ Ion	$C_2O_4^{--} + Sr^{++} = SrC_2O_{4(s)}$
	$C_2O_4^{-} + Cu^{++} = CuC_2O_{4(s)}$
	$C_2O_4^{--} + Cd^{++} = CdC_2O_{4(s)}$
	$C_2O_4^{--} + Ca^{++} = CaC_2O_{4(s)}$
	$C_2O_4^{--} + Zn^{++} = ZnC_2O_{4(s)}$
	$C_2O_4^{--} + Pb^{++} = PbC_2O_{4(s)}$

librium is favored toward the right, even in dilute HAc solution.

$$Ca^{++}(sat.\ CaSO_4\ sol'n) + C_2O_4^{--} = CaC_2O_{4(s)} \quad (153)$$

Calcium oxalate is readily soluble in strong acids due to the formation of the bioxalate ion, $HC_2O_4^-$, but it is not appreciably dissolved by HAc. The latter does not furnish a sufficient concentration of H^+ ion to shift the above equilibrium (153) to the left.

If potassium permanganate and dilute H_2SO_4 are added to a solution containing $C_2O_4^{--}$ ion, decolorization of the permanganate ion takes place, due to the oxidation of the $C_2O_4^{--}$ ion to CO_2 and the simultaneous reduction of the MnO_4^- ion to Mn^{++} ion.

$$5H_2C_2O_4 + 2MnO_4^- + 6H^+ = 10CO_2 + 2Mn^{++} + 8H_2O \quad (154)$$

An organic reagent known as resorcinol may be used to identify $C_2O_4^{--}$ ion. When a dilute solution of resorcinol in concentrated H_2SO_4 is added to a solid oxalate or oxalic acid and heated until SO_3 fumes appear, a blue color is imparted to the solution. A modification of the resorcinol test employs the following procedure. The oxalate solution is introduced into a test tube to which are added a few drops of dilute H_2SO_4 and a very small amount of magnesium powder. After the magnesium has disappeared, a few drops of the dilute resorcinol solution is added and concentrated H_2SO_4 is allowed to run down the walls of the test tube slowly in order to establish two liquid layers. If $C_2O_4^{--}$ ion is present a blue color will appear at the junction of the two liquids.

Fluoride Ion, F⁻. Hydrofluoric acid is a gas at room temperature (the liquid boils at 19° C.) and is readily soluble in water. Since it attacks glassware the commercial solution which contains 48% of hydrofluoric acid by weight is packed in Cerosene or paraffin bottles. The molecular weight of the gas is in agreement with the simple formula HF at low pressures, but when the pressure is increased or the temperature is decreased it has been shown that an equilibrium mixture of HF and H_6F_6 molecules exists.

In dilute solutions the acid for the most part is present as HF molecules, but undoubtedly forms polymers in the more concentrated solutions. It is a fairly weak acid, since its ionization constant has a value of about 7×10^{-4}. With the exception of lithium fluoride, the fluorides of the alkali metals are soluble as are also the fluorides of Ag^+, Hg^{++}, Fe^{+++}, Al^{+++}, Sb^{+++}, and Sn^{++++} ions. Since hydrofluoric acid is not an extremely weak acid the insoluble fluorides are not dissolved by strong acids such as HCl.

Hydrofluoric acid reacts with silica, SiO_2, or silicates to produce the gas SiF_4. It is this reaction which takes place when glass is etched by hydrofluoric acid and can therefore be used as a test for fluorides. If the solid containing the fluoride is placed on glass and if sulfuric acid is added, HF will be generated and this in turn will react with the silicates in the glass to form SiF_4.

$$CaF_2 + H_2SO_4 = CaSO_4 + 2HF \qquad (155)$$

$$SiO_2 + 4HF = SiF_4 + 2H_2O \qquad (156)$$

Sulfate Ion, SO_4^{--}. Sulfuric acid, H_2SO_4, is known in the free state but in this condition exhibits none of the characteristic properties of an acid; it is an exceedingly poor conductor of electricity and is relatively inactive chemically. When added to water the resulting solution is a very good conductor of the electric current and is capable of taking part in many metathetic reactions. The first stage of ionization, $H_2SO_4 = H^+ + HSO_4^-$ is practically complete and for our purposes may be considered as 100%. On the other hand, the bisulfate ion, HSO_4^-, behaves like a moderately weak acid, $HSO_4^- = H^+ + SO_4^{--}$. (See Chapter VII.)

The SO_4^{--} ion differs from many other negative ions in that it is derived from a moderately strong acid and therefore relatively insoluble sulfates may be precipitated from acid solutions.

The sulfates of most of the positive ions are soluble in water. The slightly soluble and moderately soluble sulfates are listed in Table 35 in order of decreasing concentration of SO_4^{--} ion at equilibrium. Of these sulfates $BaSO_4$ is the most insoluble. Consequently it is used for the detection of SO_4^{--} ion. The procedure employed here is to first make the unknown solution acid with HNO_3 so as to reduce the concentration of anions of weak acids which form slightly soluble salts with Ba^{++} ion, and then to add $BaCl_2$ to produce a precipitate of white $BaSO_4$.

TABLE 41

Equilibria Involving Sulfate Ion

Decreasing Concentration of SO_4^{--} Ion		
$SO_4^{--} + 2Ag^+$	$=$	$Ag_2SO_{4(s)}$
$SO_4^{--} + Ca^{++}$	$=$	$CaSO_{4(s)}$
$SO_4^{--} + Sr^{++}$	$=$	$SrSO_{4(s)}$
$SO_4^{--} + Hg_2^{++}$	$=$	$Hg_2SO_{4(s)}$
$SO_4^{--} + Pb^{++}$	$=$	$PbSO_{4(s)}$
$SO_4^{--} + Ba^{++}$	$=$	$BaSO_{4(s)}$

Sulfite Ion, SO_3^{--}. Sulfurous acid, H_2SO_3, is a weak dibasic acid capable of existence only in solution. It ionizes in two stages.

$$(1) \qquad H_2SO_3 = H^+ + HSO_3^-$$
$$(2) \qquad HSO_3^- = H^+ + SO_3^{--} \qquad (157)$$

The ionization constant for stage (1) is 1.7×10^{-2}, and that for stage (2), 5×10^{-6}. The values for these constants show that sulfurous acid is one of the stronger of the weak acids.

A solution of sulfurous acid in water contains many different ions and molecules; the equilibria involved here may be represented as follows:

$$SO_{2(g)} + H_2O = H_2SO_3 = H^+ + \quad HSO_3^-$$
$$\updownarrow \qquad (158)$$
$$H^+ + SO_3^{--}$$

At 25° and at a pressure of 1 atmosphere, SO_2 dissolves in water to produce a solution containing about 1.2 M H_2SO_3, assuming that all of the dissolved SO_2 is present as such.

From the above equilibria it is seen that the effect of the addition of a strong acid to a solution of sulfurous acid is to shift all of the equilibria to the left with the ultimate liberation of SO_2 from the solution as a gas. This effect is made more evident if the solution is heated, since under these conditions the solubility of SO_2 is considerably less. The liberated SO_2 may be readily detected by its odor or it may be oxidized to H_2SO_4 and subsequently detected as $BaSO_4$ (see #43 of Table 20).

Most sulfites of positive ions with the exception of the alkali metal ions are insoluble in water while the bisulfites are soluble. Since the sulfur atom of the SO_3^{--} ion exists in the plus four valence state, this ion may act either as a reducing agent or as an oxidizing agent. When it acts as a reducing agent it is oxidized to the SO_4^{--} ion in which the valence number of the sulfur atom is plus six. When the SO_3^{--} ion functions as an oxidizing agent it is usually reduced to free sulfur. Permanganate ion, I_2, $Cr_2O_7^{--}$, and Fe^{+++} ions are readily reduced by H_2SO_3 in acid solution. On the other hand, S^{--} ion and Sn^{++} ion are oxidized by SO_3^{--} ion. Solutions of sulfurous acid and of sulfites are slowly oxidized by oxygen when exposed to the atmosphere.

Chromate Ion, CrO_4^{--}; Dichromate Ion, $Cr_2O_7^{--}$. In chromates and dichromates the chromium has a valence number of plus six. The CrO_4^{--} ion predominates in basic solution while $Cr_2O_7^{--}$ ion predominates in an acid solution. (For a discussion of the equilibrium between the two ions, see page 372.) Whether a relatively insoluble dichromate or chromate will be precipitated with a given metal ion will depend upon the relative solubilities of the chromate and dichromate and upon the H^+ ion concentration of the solution. In general the dichromates are more soluble than the chromates. Thus, if a precipitate is produced it is usually a chromate. The more insoluble chromates are those of Sr^{++}, Ag^+, Ba^{++} and Pb^{++} ions, named in the order of decreasing solubility. Thus Ba^{++} ion and Pb^{++} ion are the most suitable for analytical purposes in the identification of CrO_4^{--} ion. Other slightly or very slightly soluble chromates are those of Hg^{++}, Hg_2^{++}, Bi^{+++}, and Mn^{++} ions. The chromates of the alkali metals, zinc, copper, calcium, and magnesium are soluble. Since the $HCrO_4^-$ ion is a relatively weak acid ($K_I = 7 \times 10^{-7}$), slightly soluble chromates are soluble in solutions of strong acids.

Since the $Cr_2O_7^{--}$ ion in an acid medium is a strong oxidizing agent, it is readily reduced by reducing agents such as H_2S, I^-, Fe^{++}, Sn^{++}, etc. to Cr^{+++} ion. In these reactions a change in color takes place from the orange of the $Cr_2O_7^{--}$ ion to the green Cr^{+++} ion. (See Table 20.) Therefore, if reducing ions are present in an unknown sample the chromium will be present as Cr^{+++} ion and the appropriate tests are those previously described.

Ferrocyanide Ion, $Fe(CN)_6^{----}$. The ferrocyanide ion is a complex ion which may be regarded as being composed of one ferrous ion and six cyanide ions.

$$Fe^{++} + 6CN^- = Fe(CN)_6^{----} \qquad (159)$$

It can be formed, as equation (159) indicates, by treating a solution of a ferrous salt with an excess of KCN solution. The complex ion is very stable and its dissociation constant is therefore very small. As a matter of fact the $Fe(CN)_6^{----}$ ion does not dissociate to a large enough extent in solution to give a test for free Fe^{++} ion, though the most sensitive testing reagents be used.

Ferrocyanic acid, $H_4Fe(CN)_6$, is a white crystalline solid which is readily soluble in water. The water solution is strongly acidic. Neither the solid nor the aqueous solution of the acid is stable when exposed to air. Under these conditions an insoluble blue precipitate is formed. The acid is formed by treating a concentrated solution of the potassium salt, $K_4Fe(CN)_6$, with H_2SO_4. When this is done the white crystalline acid precipitates.

All of the salts of the $Fe(CN)_6^{----}$ ion, with the exception of those with the alkali metal ions, are relatively insoluble. In fact some of these are so insoluble that they are stable in acid solution. It is therefore necessary to remove this ion together with the ferricyanide ion, $Fe(CN)_6^{---}$, before any analysis is made on the cations. The salt formed when $Fe(CN)_6^{----}$ ion reacts with Fe^{+++} ion has a deep blue color and Fe^{+++} ion is, therefore, one of the reagents used for detecting the $Fe(CN)_6^{----}$ ion (see page 377). The calcium and strontium salts are relatively soluble in weak acid solution while the zinc salt is relatively insoluble.

Ferrocyanide ion is a weak reducing agent; it can be oxidized by MnO_4^- ion in acid solution with the formation of the ferricyanide ion, $Fe(CN)_6^{---}$.

Ferricyanide Ion, $Fe(CN)_6^{---}$. The ferricyanide ion, $Fe(CN)_6^{---}$, which is similar to the ferrocyanide ion, $Fe(CN)_6^{----}$, may be formed when a solution containing Fe^{+++} ion is treated with an excess of a solution containing CN^- ion (see page 376). A relatively small amount of CN^- ion produces a precipitate of $Fe(OH)_3$ since the CN^- is appreciably hydrolyzed.

$$CN^- + H_2O = HCN + OH^- \qquad (160)$$

$$Fe^{+++} + 3OH^- = Fe(OH)_{3(s)} \qquad (161)$$

But in the presence of a large excess of CN^- ion, $Fe(CN)_6^{---}$ ion is obtained.

$$Fe(OH)_{3(s)} + 6CN^- = Fe(CN)_6^{---} + 3OH^- \qquad (162)$$

Again, $Fe(CN)_6^{---}$ ion is exceedingly stable and does not dissociate to any appreciable extent to give Fe^{+++} ion in solution.

Ferricyanic acid, $H_3Fe(CN)_6$, is a solid which can be prepared by the reaction between a concentrated solution of the potassium salt and concentrated HCl. This substance is brown in color and is readily soluble in water. The salts of all ferricyanides except those of the alkali and alkaline earth metals and of iron are insoluble. The compound formed with the ferric salt, $Fe[Fe(CN)_6]$, is soluble; it has a dark brown color while the salt formed with Fe^{++} ion, $Fe_3[Fe(CN)_6]_2$, has a deep blue color exactly like that produced by Fe^{+++} ion and ferrocyanide ion, $Fe_4[Fe(CN)_6]_3$. In fact it has been proposed that these two salts are identical inasmuch as the Fe^{+++} ion can be reduced to the Fe^{++} ion and $Fe(CN)_6^{----}$ ion can be oxidized to $Fe(CN)_6^{---}$ ion and *vice versa*. If equilibrium conditions were established when all of these ions are put into the solution, the same compound might always result. The zinc and cobalt ferricyanides are very insoluble even in hydrochloric acid solution.

Thiocyanate Ion, CNS⁻. Thiocyanic acid is very unstable; it decomposes very rapidly to produce HCN and perthiocyanic acid, $H_2C_2N_2S_3$. All thiocyanates are soluble with the exception of the lead, mercury, silver, and copper salts. The thiocyanate ion forms a deep red complex ion with Fe^{+++} ion. (See page 377.)

$$Fe^{+++} + 6CNS^- = Fe(CNS)_6^{---} \qquad (163)$$

This reaction serves as a very sensitive test for both Fe^{+++} and CNS^- ions.

Chloride Ion, Cl⁻. The chlorides of positive ions are soluble in water with the exception of $AgCl$, $PbCl_2$, Hg_2Cl_2, Cu_2Cl_2, and the basic chlorides of Sb^{+++} and Bi^{+++} ions. In solutions containing a very high concentration of Cl^- ion, even these salts dissolve, with the formation of complex ions such as $HgCl_4^{--}$, $HgCl_3^-$, $AgCl_2^-$, etc. All chlorides are strong electrolytes and are completely ionized with the exception of $CdCl_2$, $HgCl_2$, and $PbCl_2$. The formation of complex anions may be responsible in part for the behavior of these slightly ionized salts.

Silver ion gives with Cl^- ion a precipitate of AgCl which is soluble in solutions containing NH_4OH, or CN^- ion, due to the formation of complex ions. In carrying out the test for Cl^- ion it is advisable to make the unknown solution acid with HNO_3, then precipitate it as AgCl, dissolve this precipitate in NH_4OH, and reprecipitate the AgCl by the addition of HNO_3. This test is applicable only in the absence of Br^-, I^-, S^{--} and CNS^- ions.

Oxidizing agents stronger than chlorine will oxidize chlorides to free chlorine which in turn may be detected by suitable reagents. Permanganate ion in acid solution, H_2O_2, and others are suitable oxidizing agents for the conversion of Cl^- ion to free chlorine (see #94, Table 20). Starch iodide paper is an excellent reagent for the detection of free chlorine. However, bromine gives the same test.

Bromide Ion, Br^-. Hydrogen bromide is a colorless gas at ordinary temperatures and is highly soluble in water. In solution it is known as hydrobromic acid which is completely ionized to give H^+ and Br^- ions. Most bromides are soluble in water; AgBr, Hg_2Br_2, $PbBr_2$ and Cu_2Br_2 show a limited solubility. In fact all bromides are less soluble than the corresponding chlorides. There are two properties of the Br^- ion which makes its identification possible in the presence of Cl^- and I^- ions, (1) the bromides are less soluble than the chlorides and (2) the Br^- ion is a much stronger reducing agent than is the Cl^- ion but is not nearly as strong in this respect as the I^- ion. Thus, bromides are quite readily oxidized to free bromine whereas chlorides are oxidized to chlorine with greater difficulty (see Table 20, ##62, 83 and 94).

When Ag^+ ion is added to a solution containing Br^- ion, a light yellow precipitate of AgBr appears. It is insoluble in dilute HNO_3, but is readily dissolved by CN^- ion. It dissolves in NH_4OH if the concentration of the reagent is relatively high. As a matter of fact, a molar solution of $Ag(NH_3)_2^+$ ion furnishes more Ag^+ ions than a saturated solution of AgBr (see Table 22, page 319), but since the concentration of the Ag^+ ion in these two solutions is of the same order of magnitude it is possible to reverse the equilibrium in the direction of the formation of the complex ion by using a relatively high concentration of ammonia.

There are several oxidizing agents which are capable of converting Br^- ion to free Br_2. The following equations illustrate the reactions involved:

$$Cl_2 + 2Br^- = 2Cl^- + Br_2 \qquad (164)$$

$$2MnO_4^- + 10Br^- + 16H^+ = 2Mn^{++} + 5Br_2 + 8H_2O \qquad (165)$$

$$SO_4^{--} + 2Br^- + 4H^+ = SO_2 + Br_2 + 2H_2O \qquad (166)$$

$$MnO_{2(s)} + 2Br^- + 4H^+ = Mn^{++} + Br_2 + 2H_2O \qquad (167)$$

$$Cr_2O_7^{--} + 6Br^- + 14H^+ = 2Cr^{+++} + 3Br_2 + 7H_2O \qquad (168)$$

In each case free Br_2 is liberated, though in some instances it may be necessary to heat the mixture. In order to identify the free bromine it is essential to add some organic compound in which bromine is readily soluble. For this purpose carbon tetrachloride, chloroform or carbon bisulfide may be used.

Iodide Ion, I^-. Hydrogen iodide is a gas at ordinary temperatures which is exceedingly soluble in water. Its water solution is known as hydriodic acid, a strong acid which is completely ionized to H^+ and I^- ions. All the common iodides with the exception of AgI, Hg_2I_2, PbI_2 and Cu_2I_2 are soluble in water. These iodides show a lower solubility than the corresponding bromides. The I^- ion is a much stronger reducing agent than the Br^- ion and is therefore readily oxidized by oxidizing agents to free iodine.

Iodide ion shows a marked tendency to combine with free iodine to form the complex tri-iodide ion, I_3^- ($I^- + I_2 = I_3^-$). While the I^- ion is colorless in water solution the I_3^- ion is brown in color. Many other complex ions containing iodine in the anion are known. Thus HgI_2 reacts with I^- ion to form HgI_4^{--} ion.

$$HgI_2 + 2I^- = HgI_4^{--} \qquad (169)$$

Cuprous iodide likewise dissolves in the presence of excess I^- ion to form a complex ion.

$$Cu_2I_2 + 2I^- = 2CuI_2^- \qquad (170)$$

Bismuth iodide, BiI_3, behaves similarly.

$$BiI_3 + I^- = BiI_4^- \qquad (171)$$

Silver ion gives with I^- ion a yellow precipitate of AgI, insoluble in HNO_3 as well as in NH_4OH but readily soluble in solutions containing CN^- ion. Silver iodide is not appreciably soluble in NH_4OH, AgBr is soluble only when the concentration of the NH_4OH is relatively high, and AgCl is readily soluble. By the use of this reagent it is possible to effect a qualitative separation of iodides from bromides and chlorides.

The I^- ion is easily oxidized by many oxidizing agents some of which are included in the following equations:

$$Cl_2 + 2I^- = I_2 + 2Cl^- \qquad (172)$$

$$Br_2 + 2I^- = I_2 + 2Br^- \qquad (173)$$

$$2NO_2^- + 2I^- + 4H^+ = I_2 + 2NO + 2H_2O \qquad (174)$$

$$2MnO_4^- + 10I^- + 16H^+ = 2Mn^{++} + 5I_2 + 8H_2O \qquad (175)$$

$$Cr_2O_7^{--} + 6I^- + 14H^+ = 2Cr^{+++} + 3I_2 + 7H_2O \qquad (176)$$

$$H_2O_2 + 2I^- + 2H^+ = I_2 + 2H_2O \qquad (177)$$

$$2Fe^{+++} + 2I^- = 2Fe^{++} + I_2 \qquad (178)$$

The free iodine produced may be detected by the violet color it imparts to such solvents as chloroform, carbon bisulfide or carbon tetrachloride in which it is readily soluble. A very sensitive test for free iodine is starch solution or prepared starch paper; a characteristic blue color appears in the presence of this reagent.

Some of the above oxidation-reduction reactions do not take place when a bromide or a chloride is used in place of an iodide. This fact renders possible the identification of an iodide in the presence of the other halide ions. Thus, NO_2^- ion in the presence of dilute H_2SO_4 oxidizes I^- ion but will not oxidize Cl^- or Br^- ions. Likewise, Fe^{+++} ion in dilute H_2SO_4 solution will oxidize I^- ion but not Br^- ion. An examination of Table 20 reveals many possibilities relative to the oxidation of the halide ions. The differences found here are due to the fact that I^- ion is the strongest reducing agent of the halide ions under consideration while the Cl^- ion is the weakest. Thus, much stronger oxidizing agents are required to oxidize Cl^- ion than Br^- ion, and in turn much stronger oxidizing agents are necessary for the oxidation of the Br^- ion than for the I^- ion.

Phosphate Ion, PO_4^{---}. Phosphorus forms several oxyacids in which the valence number of the phosphorus is plus five. Of these the most important is orthophosphoric acid, H_3PO_4. Since it is a tribasic acid, it ionizes in water solution in three stages (see Chapter VII). The HPO_4^{--} ion is such a weak acid that in strong acid solution the concentration of the PO_4^{---} ion is too small to precipitate any of the relatively insoluble phosphates of the aluminum, zinc, or alkaline earth groups. If the H^+ ion concentration is maintained at about 10^{-5} M by the use of a buffer of sodium acetate and acetic acid, the phosphates of Fe^{+++}, Cr^{+++}, and Al^{+++} may be precipitated. In basic solution all of the phosphates of the ions of these two groups and of most of the others are insoluble. The phosphates of alkali metal ions are soluble. Many of the monohydrogen phosphates are also insoluble while in general the dihydrogen phosphates are soluble in water.

Silver nitrate gives with solutions of phosphates the slightly soluble silver phosphate, Ag_3PO_4, yellow in color. It is soluble in nitric acid and also in ammonium hydroxide.

Magnesia mixture, which is a solution containing $MgCl_2$, NH_4Cl and NH_4OH, precipitates white magnesium ammonium phosphate, $MgNH_4PO_4$, soluble in acids.

$$Mg^{++} + NH_4^+ + PO_4^{---} = MgNH_4PO_{4(s)} \qquad (179)$$

Solutions of phosphates react with ammonium molybdate reagent, $(NH_4)_2MoO_4$, to produce a yellow precipitate of ammonium phosphomolybdate, $(NH_4)_3PO_4 \cdot 12MoO_3$. This is a very delicate test for the PO_4^{---} ion. Alkalies and NH_4OH dissolve the precipitate. In appearance it closely resembles the corresponding ammonium arsenomolybdate, but differs from the latter in that it is soluble in ammonium oxalate solution.

Arsenite Ion, AsO_3^{---}. Arsenous acid has never been isolated, yet its anhydride, As_2O_3, is one of the most common compounds of arsenic. This substance dissolves slightly in water to produce an acid solution which may be regarded as a solution of arsenous acid. Most of the known salts of arsenous acid are derived from the meta-acid, $HAsO_2$.

Arsenites appear in various forms as the orthoarsenites, the metarsenites and the pyroarsenites. Examples of these three forms are barium metarsenite, $Ba(AsO_2)_2$, silver ortho-arsenite, Ag_2AsO_3, and ammonium pyroarsenite, $(NH_4)As_2O_5$ respectively. In all of these compounds the arsenic atom has the valence number of plus three. The arsenites of the alkali metals are all soluble in water and those of all other metals are soluble in weak acid solution. When a strong acid is added to a solution of a soluble arsenite, the weak arsenous acid (in solution) is formed. However, this will react with H_2S to precipitate As_2S_3.

Arsenous acid is amphoteric and therefore is dissolved both by strong acids and by strong bases. The acid ionization constant for arsenous acid has a value of about 2×10^{-8}. (See page 344 for a discussion of the chemistry of the compounds of arsenic.)

The Arsenate Ion, AsO_4^{---}. Arsenic acid may be made by dissolving As_2O_3 in nitric acid. The arsenic in the plus three state is thereby oxidized to arsenic in the plus five state and arsenic acid results. This substance may be crystallized from the solution as $2H_3AsO_4 \cdot H_2O$. When this substance is heated it dissociates into water and As_2O_5, which in turn may be dissolved in water to give a solution of arsenic acid.

Like the phosphates the arsenates occur in various forms such as the metarsenates, the orthoarsenates and the pyroarsenates. The arsenates resemble the phosphates in their properties. Many of the arsenates are isomorphous with the phosphates. When arsenates are dissolved in acid solution, the weak arsenic acid, H_3AsO_4, is formed. However, as an acid H_3AsO_4 is very much stronger than arsenous acid, since its ionization constant has a value of about 5×10^{-3}. If a solution of arsenic acid is saturated with hydrogen sulfide in the cold, As_2S_5 is formed. This reaction, however, is exceedingly slow.

$$2H_3AsO_4 + 5H_2S = As_2S_{5(s)} + 8H_2O \qquad (180)$$

When the solution is hot the arsenic acid is reduced by the hydrogen sulfide to arsenous acid and the arsenous acid in turn gives As_2S_3 with H_2S. This reaction is catalyzed by the I^- ion (see NOTE 5 on page 360).

The Borate Ion, BO_2^-. The borate ion may exist in several forms, as metaborate, BO_2^-, orthoborate, BO_3^{---}, and tetraborate, $B_4O_7^{--}$. Very few orthoborates are known. Most of the borates exist in the meta form. Borax is sodium tetraborate, $Na_2B_4O_7$.

Boric acid of commerce is sometimes known as boracic acid and has the formula H_3BO_3. Upon heating, water is lost and metaboric acid HBO_2 is formed, which upon further heating again is changed to tetraboric acid, $H_2B_4O_7$. Boric acid is a very weak acid; the ionization constant for the first stage of ionization has a value of 1×10^{-9}. In fact it is so weak that a saturated solution of it may be used as an eye wash without any irritation. The formula for borax, $Na_2B_4O_7$, may be written as $Na_2O \cdot 2B_2O_3$ while the formula for sodium metaborate, $NaBO_2$, may be written as $Na_2O \cdot B_2O_3$. From these formulae it is apparent that there is an excess of B_2O_3 in the sodium tetraborate. When borax is fused this excess B_2O_3 acts as an acid anhydride and dissolves the oxide of other metals, thereby often forming a colored borax. For example when cobalt oxide, CoO, dissolves in borax to produce the characteristic deep blue colored bead, the reaction may be regarded as

$$Na_2O \cdot 2B_2O_3 + CoO = Na_2O \cdot B_2O_3 + CoO \cdot B_2O_3 \quad (181)$$

With methyl alcohol in acid solution the borates form methyl borate $(CH_3O)_3B$. This compound is volatile and when burned gives rise to a characteristic green flame which is often used as a test for the borates.

When a drop of a solution containing a borate and acidified with HCl is placed on a piece of turmeric paper which is then dried above a flame, a characteristic reddish-brown color is observed. This color changes to green when a drop of 0.1 M NaOH solution is placed on the spot.

Nitrate Ion, NO_3^-. Anhydrous nitric acid is miscible with water in all proportions and in dilute solution is completely ionized. It is a powerful oxidizing agent and acting in this capacity the nitrogen atom is reduced from the plus five valence state to one of the lower valence states. The possible reduction states of the nitrogen atom are plus four as in NO_2; plus three as in N_2O_3; plus two as in NO; plus one as in N_2O; and minus three as in NH_3. In general, the lower the concentration of the HNO_3, the higher the temperature and the more powerful the reducing agent, the lower will be the valence of the nitrogen atom in the reduction product.

All nitrates are soluble in water with the exception of a few basic salts. This fact makes it impossible to separate nitrates from a mixture of ions by precipitation methods. To identify the NO_3^- ion it is necessary to resort to some of its characteristic properties as an oxidizing agent and then identify the products of oxidation.

Dilute H_2SO_4 does not react with nitrates, but when concentrated H_2SO_4 is heated with a solid nitrate, HNO_3 is produced and is partially decomposed to NO_2 which appears in the form of brown fumes.

$$2HNO_3 = 2NO_{2(g)} + H_2O + \tfrac{1}{2}O_{2(g)} \quad (182)$$

The "brown ring" test for the nitrate ion is carried out in the following way. To 10 drops of the solution to be tested, if alkaline, add 1 M H_2SO_4 dropwise until acid. Add

2 drops 1 M FeSO$_4$ solution and, with the test tube held in a slanting position, allow 0.5 ml. concentrated H$_2$SO$_4$ to run down the wall of the test tube. The H$_2$SO$_4$ forms a separate layer at the bottom of the test tube. If NO$_3^{--}$ ion is present a brown ring forms at the junction of the two liquids in the course of a few minutes (compare with the action of NO$_2^-$ ion — see below). The brown color is due to the formation of ferrous nitroso sulfate, FeNOSO$_4$. The NO$_3^-$ ion is reduced to nitric oxide, NO, which in turn reacts with the Fe^{++} ion to form a complex ion, Fe(NO)$^{++}$. ClO$_3^-$, I$^-$, Br$^-$ and NO$_2^-$ ions interfere with this test.

If concentrated H$_2$SO$_4$ is added to brucine (an alkaloid) and the mixture is then added to a small amount of a solution containing NO$_3^-$ ion, a deep red color changing quite rapidly to yellow appears. Subsequent addition of SnCl$_2$ produces a violet color. NO$_2^-$ does not interfere but ClO$_3^-$ ion does.

Aluminum powder added to alkaline solutions of nitrates reduces the NO$_3^-$ ion to NH$_3$. When the solution is heated NH$_3$ is liberated and may be detected by litmus paper in the usual manner. Naturally, the unknown solution must not contain ammonium salts. If present, they must first be removed by treating with NaOH and boiling; then the test for NO$_3^-$ ion can be applied. The formation of ammonia is given by the following equation:

$$8Al_{(s)} + 3NO_3^- + 5OH^- + 2H_2O = 3NH_3 + 8AlO_2^- \quad (183)$$

Other tests for NO$_3^-$ are known which involve the reduction of NO$_3^-$ ion to NO$_2^-$ and a subsequent test for the latter. These tests are described under the properties of the NO$_2^-$ ion.

Nitrite Ion, NO$_2^-$. Nitrous acid is not known in the pure state but in water solution it has the properties of a weak acid. Since the ionization constant for this acid is 4.6×10^{-4}, it is to be regarded as one of the stronger of the weak acids.

All nitrites are soluble in water with the exception of silver nitrite which is slightly soluble. Many salts are known containing the nitrite radical in complex anions. Some of these show a rather limited solubility, such as potassium cobaltinitrite, $K_3Co(NO_2)_6$.

The valence state of the nitrogen atom in the NO_2^- ion is plus three; consequently, this ion can function either as a reducing or as an oxidizing agent. The following equations illustrate this dual behavior of the NO_2^- ion.

$$2MnO_4^- + 5NO_2^- + 6H^+ = 2Mn^{++} + 5NO_3^- + 3H_2O \quad (184)$$

$$Cr_2O_7^{--} + 3NO_2^- + 8H^+ = 2Cr^{+++} + 3NO_3^- + 4H_2O \quad (185)$$

$$ClO_3^- + 3NO_2^- = 3NO_3^- + Cl^- \quad (186)$$

$$2NO_2^- + 2I^- + 4H^+ = 2NO + I_2 + 2H_2O \quad (187)$$

$$NO_2^- + Fe^{++} + 2H^+ = NO + Fe^{+++} + H_2O \quad (188)$$

$$2NO_2^- + H_2S + 2H^+ = 2NO + S_{(s)} + 2H_2O \quad (189)$$

Other oxidation-reduction reactions involving the NO_2^- ion may be found by examining Table 20.

If a nitrite is treated with a small amount of dilute HCl and the mixture warmed so as to allow escaping gases to come in contact with moistened starch-potassium iodide paper, the latter will assume a deep blue color. This test may also be applied by dipping the paper into a nitrite solution acidified with HCl.

If $FeSO_4$ is added to a dilute acid solution of a nitrite (acetic acid suffices), the NO_2^- ion is reduced to NO which in turn combines with the Fe^{++} ion to form the brown, $Fe(NO)^{++}$ complex ion. This reaction can be applied to the detection of NO_3^- ion, provided concentrated H_2SO_4 is used. Since HNO_2 and HNO_3 have approximately the same strength as oxidizing agents (#79 and #81, Table 20) the great difference in their behavior in forming $Fe(NO)^{++}$ ion must be due to the relative velocities of the two reactions.

Chlorate Ion, ClO_3^-. Chloric acid, $HClO_3$, is not known in the free condition. Dilute solutions of the acid may be prepared and concentrated by evaporation to about 40% of the acid; beyond this point decomposition takes place.

Chloric acid is a strong acid and hence its solutions may be considered as being practically completely ionized. All chlorates are soluble in water, but a low H^+ ion concentration is necessary to prevent the precipitation of basic salts of a few of the positive ions.

Concentrated H_2SO_4 reacts with the chlorates with the liberation of ClO_2 which when heated decomposes explosively. (Great care should be exercised when treating chlorates with sulfuric acid.) The ClO_2 gas is quite unstable and possesses an odor similar to that of chlorine.

Chlorates are readily reduced by H_2SO_3 to chlorides.

$$ClO_3^- + 3SO_3^{--} = Cl^- + 3SO_4^{--} \qquad (190)$$

The presence of Cl^- ion may be detected by adding HNO_3 and $AgNO_3$ and heating the mixture gently; a precipitate of AgCl forms slowly.

Nitrite ion also reduces ClO_3^- ion in acid solution.

$$ClO_3^- + 3NO_2^- = Cl^- + 3NO_3^- \qquad (191)$$

Obviously these two ions cannot be present in the same solution.

The usual procedure for the identification of a chlorate consists first of its reduction to Cl^- ion by a suitable reagent and then the precipitation of AgCl.

APPENDIX

LIST OF DESK APPARATUS

2 beakers, 50 ml.
2 beakers, 100 ml.
14 bottles, dropper reagent, 1 ounce
1 glass-stoppered bottle, 1 ounce (tincture)
1 Bunsen burner
1 casserole, 30 ml.
2 clamps (test tube)
1 clamp holder
1 clay triangle
2 cobalt glass pieces (5 cm. × 5 cm.)
1 crucible, porcelain (small)
1 crucible tongs, iron
1 cylinder, graduated, 10 ml.
1 cylinder, graduated, 25 ml.
1 evaporating dish, #00
1 evaporating dish, #000
1 file, triangular
1 flask, Florence, 250 ml.
2 flasks, Erlenmeyer, 25 ml.
1 box filter paper, 40 mm.
1 box filter paper, 55 mm.
2 funnels, 30–40 mm., short stem
1 funnel stand
1 gauze, wire
1 box labels
1 box matches
6 medicine droppers (standard)
1 mortar (small)
1 pipette, 5 ml.

2 lengths 3 mm. glass rod, 30 cm. each
4 lengths 6 mm. glass tubing, 30 cm. each
1 bar soap
1 stand, iron (small)
1 spatula (micro)
1 sponge
1 two-hole rubber stopper to fit 250 ml. flask
1 one-hole rubber stopper to fit 25 ml. flask
1 one-hole rubber stopper to fit 10 ml. test tube
1 tube litmus paper, blue
1 tube litmus paper, red
1 tube methyl violet paper
2 pieces 8 mm. gum rubber tubing, 30 cm. each
1 piece 1 cm. gas tubing, 60 cm.
1 test tube holder (small)
10 test tubes, 7.5 cm. × 1 cm.
12 test tubes (Pyrex), 10 cm.
2 test tubes, 15 cm.
1 test tube brush (small)
1 test tube rack (small)
2 towels
1 tray for 14 reagent bottles
2 watch glasses, 50 mm.
1 wing top
2 pieces wire, iron or Chromel, 15 cm. in length to be used for flame tests

LIST OF REAGENTS

ACIDS	CONCENTRATION (MOLAR)
Acetic, dilute	6
Hydrochloric, conc.	12
Hydrochloric, dilute	6
Hydrochloric	3
Nitric, conc.	15
Nitric, dilute	6
Sulfuric, conc.	18
Sulfuric, dilute	6

BASES	
Ammonium hydroxide, conc.	15
Ammonium hydroxide, dilute	6
Ammonium hydroxide	3
Potassium hydroxide	6
Sodium hydroxide	6
Sodium hydroxide	0.1

SALT SOLUTIONS, TEST SOLUTIONS, AND SPECIAL REAGENTS

Aluminon reagent, 1 g. of the ammonium salt of aurin tricarboxylic acid in 1 liter of water.

*Aluminum nitrate	0.1
Ammonium acetate	3

Ammonium carbonate reagent, dissolve 200 g. of ammonium carbonate in 500 ml. of 3 M ammonium hydroxide and dilute to 1 liter.

Ammonium chloride	5
Ammonium iodide	1

Ammonium molybdate, dissolve 40 g. of MoO_3 in a mixture of 100 ml. of water and 60 ml. of 15 M NH_4OH. Add this solution slowly and with vigorous stirring to one containing 200 ml. of 15 M HNO_3 and 450 ml. of water.

*Ammonium nitrate	0.1
Ammonium nitrate	4
*Ammonium oxalate	0.2

* Reagents indicated by an asterisk are to be used as test solutions both for cations and anions. Some of these reagents are also needed for other purposes.

Ammonium sulfate.................................. 1
Ammonium sulfate.................................. 0.1
*Antimony trichloride, dissolve in 500 ml. of 6 M HCl and
    dilute to 1 liter................................... 0.1
*Arsenic oxide, dissolve in hot water and add a small
    amount of HCl to obtain a clear solution............ 0.1
*Arsenous oxide, dissolve in 30 ml. of 6 M HCl and dilute
    to 1 liter....................................... 0.1
Barium chloride.................................... 0.1
Barium hydroxide (saturated)
*Barium nitrate.................................... 0.1
*Bismuth nitrate, add to 1 liter of 1.5 M HNO_3......... 0.1
Bromine, liquid (not on shelf)
Bromine water, saturate water with a few drops of liquid
    bromine.
*Cadmium nitrate.................................. 0.1
Cadmium sulfate................................... 0.1
Calcium chloride................................... 0.1
Calcium nitrate.................................... 0.1
Carbon tetrachloride
*Chromium nitrate................................. 0.1
*Cobalt nitrate.................................... 0.1
*Cupric nitrate.................................... 0.1
Cupric sulfate..................................... 0.1
Dimethylglyoxime, 1% solution, dissolve 10 g. in 1 liter
    of alcohol.
Ferric chloride.................................... 0.1
*Ferric nitrate.................................... 0.1
Ferrous sulfate.................................... 0.1
Hydrogen peroxide, 3% solution
Lead acetate...................................... 0.2
*Lead nitrate..................................... 0.1
Magnesia mixture, dissolve 50 g. of $MgCl_2 \cdot 6H_2O$ and
    70 g. of NH_4Cl in 400 ml. of water, add 100 ml. of 15 M
    NH_4OH and dilute to 1 liter. Should be filtered.
*Magnesium nitrate............................... 0.1
*Manganous nitrate............................... 0.1
Manganous chloride, saturated in 12 M HCl
Mercuric chloride.................................. 0.1
*Mercuric nitrate................................. 0.1

*Mercurous nitrate.. 0.1
Methyl alcohol
Methyl orange (1 g. in 1 liter)
*Nickel nitrate... 0.1
Phenolphthalein, 1% solution in 50% alcohol
*Potassium bromide....................................... 0.1
Potassium carbonate, saturated solution
*Potassium chlorate....................................... 0.1
Potassium chromate....................................... 1
*Potassium chromate....................................... 0.1
*Potassium ferricyanide.................................... 0.1
*Potassium ferrocyanide.................................... 0.1
*Potassium iodide... 0.1
*Potassium nitrate.. 0.1
Potassium nitrite.. 6
Potassium permanganate.................................. .01
Potassium thiocyanate.................................... 1
*Potassium thiocyanate.................................... 0.1
S. and O. reagent for magnesium — *p*-nitrobenzeneazore-
   sorcinol. Dissolve 1.2 g. of the dye in 250 ml. of 0.25 *M*
   NaOH.
*Silver nitrate... 0.1
Sodium acetate.. 2
*Sodium arsenate... 0.1
*Sodium arsenite... 0.1
*Sodium tetraborate (borax).............................. .05
Sodium carbonate.. 1.5
*Sodium carbonate.. 0.1
*Sodium chloride... 0.1
*Sodium fluoride... 0.1
*Sodium nitrite.. 0.1
Sodium dihydrogen phosphate............................. 0.5
Sodium hydrogen phosphate.............................. 0.5
*Sodium hydrogen phosphate.............................. 0.1
Sodium sulfate, saturated
Sodium sulfate.. 1
Sodium hydrogen sulfate................................. 2
*Sodium sulfide.. 0.1
*Sodium sulfite.. 0.1
Sodium thiosulfate...................................... 0.1

*Stannic chloride.................................... 0.1
*Stannous chloride, dissolve 22 g. of $SnCl_2 \cdot 2H_2O$ in 75 ml.
  of 12 M HCl, allow to stand for several hours and then
  dilute to 1 liter.................................. 0.1
*Strontium nitrate.................................. 0.1
  Triethanolamine
*Zinc nitrate....................................... 0.1
  Zinc sulfate...................................... 0.1

SOLID REAGENTS

In addition to the following list of solid reagents, which are essential for the procedures in this text, it is desirable that the student have available all the solids used in preparing the previously listed solutions. Substances needed for solid unknowns are of such a varied nature, that the selection of them is left to the discretion of the instructor.

Absorbent cotton	Potassium nitrate
Aluminum, granular, pellets	Potassium permanganate
Ammonium chloride	Sodium bicarbonate
Ammonium sulfate	Sodium bismuthate
Calcium fluoride	Sodium carbonate
Ferrous sulfate	Sodium chloride
Iron, very fine wire	Sodium nitrate
Mercury (not on shelf)	Sodium thiosulfate
Potassium carbonate	Zinc, powdered, granular
Potassium ferricyanide	

TABLE 42

DENSITY-MOLARITY

In making solutions of H_2SO_4, HCl, HNO_3 and NH_3 the concentration of the solution which is to be diluted should always be determined. This can easily be done with the aid of a hydrometer and the following table. If no hydrometer is available a pycnometer may be used or a relatively large amount of the solution (500 ml.) can be weighed on a rather rough balance and the density determined by comparing the weight with an equal volume of water.

For the purposes of this course this table will apply to densities determined between 15° and 25° C.

H₂SO₄		HCl		HNO₃		NH₄OH(NH₃)	
M	d (20° C.)	M	d (20° C.)	M	d (20° C.)	M	d (20° C.)
1	1.060	1	1.016	1	1.032	1	.992
2	1.118	2	1.033	2	1.065	2	.984
3	1.177	3	1.050	3	1.097	3	.976
4	1.234	4	1.066	4	1.130	4	.969
5	1.287	5	1.082	5	1.161	5	.962
6	1.338	6	1.098	6	1.192	6	.955
7	1.388	7	1.113	7	1.221	7	.948
8	1.440	8	1.128	8	1.248	8	.942
9	1.490	9	1.143	9	1.275	9	.935
10	1.539	10	1.158	10	1.300	10	.928
11	1.586	11	1.171	11	1.324	11	.922
12	1.633	12	1.184	12	1.346	12	.916
13	1.678	13	1.196	13	1.367	13	.909
14	1.722			14	1.386	14	.903
15	1.761			15	1.403	15	.897
16	1.795			16	1.417	16	.892
17	1.822						
18	1.834						

Preparation Of Unknown Solutions

It is desirable that the student carry out tests with solutions containing given ions at concentrations comparable to those of the unknown solutions. For this purpose it is recommended that all stock solutions contain the ions in question at a concentration of 0.1 M. In making up an unknown the instructor may then conveniently use 0.6 ml. (12 drops) of a 0.1 M solution of each ion included and then dilute to a total volume of 3 ml. This procedure allows for a maximum of five ions each at a concentration of .02 M. If it is desirable to use a larger number of ions for the unknown solution the total volume may be increased to 4 ml. or more. *All test solutions should be made available to the student for carrying out the preliminary experiments.*

MATHEMATICAL OPERATIONS

In designing the problems for this course, simplicity of mathematical operations has been one of the chief objectives. Since the primary purpose of these problems is the development of an understanding of chemical equilibrium, difficulties with mathematics would tend to impair the progress of the student. There are, however, a few simple mathematical operations, notations and concepts with which it is impossible to dispense. These are given in the nature of a review since it is assumed that the student is familiar with the simplest algebra and the use of logarithms.

The Use of Exponents. The small size and the large numbers of molecules with which we have to deal make it necessary to use numbers that are often beyond everyday range of thought. For example, there are 606,000,000,000,-000,000,000,000 molecules in one mole or one gram molecule of any substance. Instead of expressing the number in this manner we use an abbreviated form, 6.06×10^{23} (6.06 times ten to the twenty-third power). The factor 10^{23} is equivalent to moving the decimal point twenty-three places to the right in the number 6.06. The number 2000 may be written 2×10^3, that is, 2×1000, for 10^3 is the product obtained when 10 is multiplied by itself three times; i.e., $10 \times 10 \times 10$. One million would be 10^6, and one billion, 10^9. The number 206,000 could be written in any one of the following ways:

$$0.206 \times 10^6 \qquad\qquad 206 \times 10^3$$
$$2.06 \ \ \times 10^5 \qquad\qquad 2060 \times 10^2$$
$$20.6 \ \ \times 10^4 \qquad\qquad 20600 \times 10$$

The first, second or third of these are obviously the most convenient.

Numbers very much smaller than 1 are expressed in a similar manner. Two-millionths may be written .000002, but for convenience it is better to write it as 2×10^{-6} (2 times ten to the minus sixth power). In order to convert the second form to the first it is necessary merely to move the decimal point six places to the left. It is the same as $2/10^6$, that is, two divided by one million. Again, this number could be written in any of the following forms:

$$2.0 \times 10^{-6} \qquad\qquad .002 \times 10^{-3}$$
$$0.2 \times 10^{-5} \qquad\qquad .0002 \times 10^{-2}$$
$$.02 \times 10^{-4} \qquad\qquad .00002 \times 10^{-1}$$
$$\qquad\qquad\qquad\qquad .000002$$

The first two of these forms are the most convenient. The number 10^{-6} is the same as $0.1 \times 0.1 \times 0.1 \times 0.1 \times 0.1 \times 0.1$.

The use of the exponential form greatly facilitates the multiplication and division of either large or small numbers. In multiplying two purely exponential numbers the exponents are added, and this algebraic sum is used as the exponent of the answer. Examples:

$$10^3 \times 10^3 = 10^6$$
$$10^3 \times 10^{-2} = 10$$
$$10^{23} \times 10^{-6} = 10^{17}$$

Multiplying 4×10^7 by 6×10^4 becomes 24×10^{11}, that is, $(4 \times 6) \times (10^{7+4})$. Likewise,

$$6000 \times 210 = 6 \times 10^3 \times 2.1 \times 10^2 = 12.6 \times 10^5$$
$$420 \times 0.000036 = 4.2 \times 10^2 \times 3.6 \times 10^{-5} = 15.12 \times 10^{-3}$$
$$.00012 \times .00007 = 1.2 \times 10^{-4} \times 7.0 \times 10^{-5} = 8.4 \times 10^{-9}.$$

The reverse operation is performed by dividing one number by another. For the purely exponential part of the number the exponent of the divisor is subtracted algebraically from that of the dividend and the algebraic difference is used as the exponent of the answer. Thus,

$$10^6 \text{ divided by } 10^2 = 10^4$$

Examples of division are:

(a) $\quad 4 \times 10^4 \div 2 \times 10^2 = \dfrac{4 \times 10^4}{2 \times 10^2} = \left(\dfrac{4}{2}\right) \times \left(\dfrac{10^4}{10^2}\right)$

$$= 2 \times 10^2$$

(b) $\quad 4 \times 10^4 \div 8 \times 10^{-6} = \left(\dfrac{4}{8}\right) \times \left(\dfrac{10^4}{10^{-6}}\right) = 0.5 \times 10^{4-(-6)}$

$\qquad\qquad = 0.5 \times 10^{4+6} = 0.5 \times 10^{10}$

(c) $\quad 3.2 \times 10^{-5} \div 4 \times 10^{-9} = \left(\dfrac{3.2}{4}\right) \times \left(\dfrac{10^{-5}}{10^{-9}}\right) = 0.8 \times 10^{-5-(-9)}$

$\qquad\qquad = 0.8 \times 10^{-5+9} = 0.8 \times 10^4 = 8 \times 10^3$

Since the squaring of any number is the operation of multiplying the number by itself, $(2 \times 10^5)^2$ becomes,

$$2 \times 10^5 \cdot 2 \times 10^5 \text{ or } 4 \times 10^{10}$$

In extracting a square root of a purely exponential number, the exponent is merely divided by two and used in the answer:

$$\sqrt{10^4} = 10^2$$

The square root of $4 \times 10^{-4} = \sqrt{4} \times \sqrt{10^{-4}} = 2 \times 10^{-2}$. It is essential that the exponent be an even number in order to simplify the procedure; if it should not be an even number it may be easily changed as shown in the following cases:

(a) $\sqrt{0.4 \times 10^5} = \sqrt{4 \times 10^4}$

(or $(4 \times 10^4)^{\frac{1}{2}}) = \sqrt{4} \times \sqrt{10^4} = 2 \times 10^2$

(b) $\sqrt{2.5 \times 10^{-9}} = \sqrt{25 \times 10^{-10}}$

(or $(25 \times 10^{-10})^{\frac{1}{2}}) = 5 \times 10^{-5}$

(c) $\sqrt{81 \times 10^6} = (81 \times 10^6)^{\frac{1}{2}} = 9 \times 10^3$

The exponent $\frac{1}{2}$ may be substituted for the usual square root sign. Thus $\sqrt{2}$ is the same as $2^{\frac{1}{2}}$, and $\sqrt{3 \times 10^2}$, the same as $(3 \times 10^2)^{\frac{1}{2}}$.

The Use of Logarithms and Exponential Numbers. The common logarithm of any number is the power to which the number 10 must be raised to equal that number. Thus the logarithm of 1000 is 3, that is, the number 10 must be raised to the third power to be equal to 1000. Examples:

Number	Number expressed exponentially	Logarithm
1000	10^3	3
100000	10^5	5
10	10^1	1
1	10^0	0*
.01	10^{-2}	-2
.00001	10^{-5}	-5

To what power must 10 be raised to equal 50? Obviously, the value of this exponent must be between 1 and 2, for 50 lies between 10, the common logarithm of which is 1, and 100, the common logarithm of which is 2. The logarithm of 50 is 1.6990, that is, $50 = 10^{1.6990}$. When the exponent of 10 is not a whole number, we cannot give it the same simple interpretation as was done in the previous section. For example, to move the decimal point 1.6990 places to the right has no meaning. Nevertheless, any number may be expressed entirely in the exponential form. Examples are:

Number	Logarithm of number	Number expressed exponentially
20	1.3010	$10^{1.3010}$
310	2.4914	$10^{2.4914}$
.013	-1.8861	$10^{-1.8861}$

What was stated previously regarding the multiplication of exponential numbers applies here; that is, for multiplication the exponents are added, and for division, the exponents are subtracted. Thus,

$$20 \times 310 = 10^{1.3010} \times 10^{2.4914} = 10^{3.7924} = 6200$$

(The logarithm of 6200 is 3.7924.)

The exponent in question may be found in logarithm tables provided for this purpose. Accordingly, the procedure used to obtain the product of any two or more numbers by the use of logarithms is as follows: The logarithms of the num-

* Any finite number raised to the zero power is equal to 1.

bers are taken from the tables and added. This sum of logarithms is the logarithm of the product of the original numbers which again may be obtained from the tables. Thus, to multiply 20 by 310 we add the logarithms of these numbers, 1.3010 and 2.4914, which gives 3.7924. By referring to the logarithm tables we find that the number 6200 corresponds to the logarithm 3.7924.

Similarly, in the process of division, the logarithms are subtracted. In order to divide 6240 by 39 we first find the logarithms for these numbers, 3.7952 and 1.5911 respectively. Subtracting the second from the first we obtain 2.2041 which, by referring to the tables, we find corresponds to 160, the answer. Another example is: Divide 3913 by 13.*

$$\begin{aligned}
\text{Logarithm of 3913} &= 3.5925 \\
\text{Logarithm of \quad 13} &= 1.1139 \\
\hline
\text{Logarithm answer} &= 2.4786
\end{aligned}$$

The answer is 301 since it is the number which corresponds to the logarithm whose value is 2.4786.

Every logarithm is made up of two parts, the characteristic and the mantissa. The characteristic is that part of the logarithm which lies to the left of the decimal point, and the mantissa that part to the right of it. If the logarithm of a number is 4.3060, the characteristic is 4 and the mantissa is .3060. Only the mantissa is found in the logarithm table since the characteristic merely depends upon the position of the decimal point. For example, the logarithm for 316 is found in the tables to be 4996, which is only the mantissa. The characteristic is one less than the number of digits in the number 316, that is, 3 − 1 or 2. So the logarithm for the number 316 is 2.4996 (or .4496 + 2). It will be observed that the mantissae for the logarithms of the numbers 316, 31.6 and 3.16 are all the same; only the characteristics are different: 2, 1 and 0 respectively.

The significance of the mantissa and the characteristic

---

* In actual practice it would not be practical to use logarithms for such a simple case.

can perhaps be better understood from the following considerations. The number 316 may be written 3.16×10^2.

logarithm of (3.16×10^2) = logarithm of 3.16 + logarithm of 10^2
logarithm of (3.16×10^2) = $.4996$ (mantissa) + 2 (characteristic)
or   logarithm of $316 = 2.4996$

The logarithm of any number less than 1 has a negative value and great care must be used in dealing with such logarithms to avoid mistakes and confusion. The logarithm of such a number may be obtained easily by the same procedure as that given above. For example, the logarithm of $.00316$ is obtained as follows:

$$.00316 = 3.16 \times 10^{-3}$$
$$\text{logarithm of } .00316 = \text{logarithm of } 3.16 + \text{logarithm of } 10^{-3}$$
$$= .4996 + (-3) = .4996 - 3 = -2.5004$$

The logarithm of any number less than 1 is usually not expressed entirely as a negative number. For example the logarithm of $.00316$ usually would not be expressed as -2.5004 but rather as $.4996 - 3$. The abbreviated form for this last expression is $\bar{3}.4996$ or $7.4996 - 10$. The reason for adopting this usage is that in this form the mantissae are always added in the process of multiplication; only the characteristics have negative values.

The characteristic of the logarithm of a number less than 1 is equal in magnitude to *one more* than the number of zeros between the first significant figure and the decimal point, and has a negative value. Thus the characteristic of the logarithm of $.0013$ is -3, and that of the logarithm of $.00006$ is -5. The logarithm of $.0013$ is then $.1139 - 3$. (This would be equal to -2.8861 but for convenience is written as $\bar{3}.1139$ or usually $7.1139 - 10$.)

Examples:

	Number	Logarithm
(a)	.0167	$8.2227 - 10$ or $\bar{2}.2227$
	.000003	$4.4771 - 10$ or $\bar{6}.4771$
	.764	$9.8831 - 10$ or $\bar{1}.8831$

(b) Divide 6309 by .0009

$$
\begin{array}{lllll}
\text{Logarithm} & 6300 & = 3.7993 & \text{or} & 13.7993 - 10 \\
\text{Logarithm} & .0009 & = \bar{4}.9542 & \text{or} & 6.9542 - 10 \\
\text{Log of answer} & & \overline{6.8451} & & \overline{6.8451}
\end{array}
$$

Answer is 7,000,000 or 7.00 $\times$ 10^6.

(c) Multiply .0016 by .0131

$$
\begin{array}{llll}
\text{Logarithm} .0016 & = \bar{3}.2041 & \text{or} & 7.2041 - 10 \\
\text{Logarithm} .0131 & = \bar{2}.1173 & \text{or} & 8.1173 - 10 \\
\text{Log answer} & = \bar{5}.3214 & & \overline{15.3214 - 20} \text{ (or } 5.3214 - 10)
\end{array}
$$

Answer is .00002096 or 2.096 $\times$ 10^{-5}

To convert any number into an exponential number on the base 10, it is necessary to use logarithms. Thus, to convert the number 50 into an exponential number we first find the logarithm of 50, which is 1.6990. The logarithm then becomes the exponent of the number 10,

$$50 = 10^{1.6990}$$

The exponential number corresponding to .000005 or 5×10^{-6} is $10^{-5.3010}$. The logarithm of $(5 \times 10^{-6}) = \log 5 + \log 10^{-6} = 0.6990 - 6$. So $5 \times 10^{-6} = 10^{.6990-6} = 10^{-5.3010}$.

The Evaluation of the Hydrogen Ion Concentration (pH values). For convenience, the concentration of the hydrogen ion is often expressed in terms of pH values. The pH value for any solution is defined as the logarithm of the reciprocal of the concentration of the hydrogen ion, that is, $p\text{H} = \log \dfrac{1}{(\text{H}^+)}$. The calculation of the pH value of any solution for which the concentration of the H^+ ion is known is a simple operation if the text of the foregoing paragraph is understood. For example, let us find the pH of a solution, the hydrogen ion concentration of which is 5.3×10^{-6} mole per liter.

$$
\begin{aligned}
p\text{H} &= \log \frac{1}{5.3 \times 10^{-6}} = \log 1 - \log (5.3 \times 10^{-6}) \\
&= - \log (5.3 \times 10^{-6}) = - \log 5.3 - \log 10^{-6} \\
&= - 0.72 \text{ (approximately)} - (- 6) = - 0.72 + 6 = 5.28
\end{aligned}
$$

The pH value is 5.28 or approximately 5.3. Without regard for the thought processes or definitions involved, the procedure is to find the logarithm of the concentration; change the sign, and the result is the pH value. Example: Find the pH value of a solution the hydrogen ion concentration of which is 7×10^{-9}.

$$\log (7 \times 10^{-9}) = \log 7 + \log 10^{-9} = 0.85 - 9 = -8.15.$$

The pH value is accordingly 8.15.

Conversely, the hydrogen ion concentration may be found by reversing the process. Example: Find the hydrogen ion concentration for a solution the pH value of which is 4.3.

$$\log \text{ concentration } H^+ \text{ ion} = -4.3 = 0.7 - 5 = \bar{5}.7$$
$$= \log 5 + \log 10^{-5}$$

(log of 5 is approximately 0.7)

So the concentration of the hydrogen ion is 5×10^{-5}.

Significant Figures and Precision Necessary in Solving Equations. If the population of a city were given as 576,334 it is obvious that the last three figures have no meaning, for enough deaths and births took place during the making of the record to change these figures an unpredictable amount. It would, therefore, be quite as accurate — even more accurate — to say that the population of the city was 576,000. At a given time, only the first three figures would have any meaning and possibly the third figure would also be of no significance, depending upon the time and method of taking the census. In giving any information in terms of numerical values only as many significant figures should be used as the accuracy warrants. It would be incorrect to say that one's weight is 126.3 pounds if it is known that the scale used was not accurate to more than a pound. Even though the scale registered 126.3 pounds it could not be relied upon to be accurate enough for this figure, so 126 pounds would give better information. Although the scale might be very accurate, the weight of the human body varies sufficiently during the day to make this accuracy of no significance.

In giving the concentration of a substance in solution, again as many significant figures should be used as the experimental information justifies. Thus, if approximately 200 ml. of 1 molar HCl solution were mixed with approximately 800 ml. of water, the concentration of the HCl in the final solution would be expressed as 0.2 molar and not 0.20 molar. The addition of the zero after 0.2 would indicate that the accuracy with which the concentration of the solution was known was about .01 molar, that the solution was not 0.19 molar nor 0.21 molar, but nearer 0.20 molar. Obviously, the manner in which the solution was prepared does not justify this accuracy. To know what figures are to be regarded as significant is often too much to ask of students in the more elementary courses of chemistry. It involves a complete understanding of the methods employed in obtaining the data from an experiment.

The precision employed in making any calculation should depend upon the expected accuracy of the result. For most problems in this course an accuracy of 10% in the answer is quite sufficient. In most cases the experimental conditions are such as to render any greater accuracy unnecessary. With this in mind, calculations and algebraic solutions can be greatly simplified. Example: Find the value of X in the following equation. (Only an accuracy within 10% is required.)

$$\frac{X}{(3 - X)} = .003$$

By neglecting the X in the term $(3 - X)$ and letting $3 - X$ be approximately equal to 3, we have

$$\frac{X}{3} = .003$$
$$X = .009$$

We neglected X in the term $(3 - X)$ because it could be seen by inspection that X was small as compared with 3. The X can only be neglected in a term in which it is added to or subtracted from some number which is much larger than

X itself. Further consideration of such solutions applied to specific examples is given in the main text of this book.

The Solution of Quadratic Equations. All quadratic equations may be expressed in the following form:

$$aX^2 + bX + c = 0,$$

in which equation the coefficients a, b and c may have positive or negative values. Such an equation has two roots; sometimes these roots are imaginary. However, equations constructed from physical data always have real roots, and of these real roots only those having positive values are of any significance.

The general solution of the above equation is given as

$$X = \frac{-b \pm \sqrt{b^2 - 4ac}}{2a}$$

The value of X may be obtained by merely substituting the numerical values of a, b and c into the above form. Example: Solve the equation

$$X^2 + .01X - 4 \times 10^{-6} = 0$$

$$(a = 1,\ b = .01 \text{ and } c = -4 \times 10^{-6})$$

$$X = \frac{-.01 \pm \sqrt{(.01)^2 + 16 \times 10^{-6}}}{2}$$

$$= \frac{-.01 \pm \sqrt{1.16 \times 10^{-4}}}{2}$$

$$= \frac{-.01 \pm .01077}{2}$$

$$= -.010385 \text{ or } +.000385$$

If X in this problem represents some physical quantity such as the concentration of the hydrogen ion, only the positive value of X has a physical significance, and

$$X = 3.85 \times 10^{-4}$$

The Slide Rule. The slide rule is an instrument consisting of two fitted pieces of wood each of which is ruled with lines which are numbered; the divisions between the different numbers and zero are proportional to the logarithms of the numbers. By sliding one piece along the other, the sum of the logarithms of two numbers can be obtained. Since the process of adding the logarithms of two numbers is the same as multiplying the numbers by each other, the slide rule can be used for multiplication. It follows that the reverse operation of division can also be performed on the slide rule.

Students are strongly urged to obtain a slide rule and use it in making the computations necessary in the course. The solutions of problems are enormously expedited by its use. The ordinary 10-inch slide rule has an accuracy of about one part in 500 which is sufficiently accurate for most work in chemistry. Complete directions for its operation accompany every slide rule.

Proportion. The three statements,

(1) A is proportional to B

(2) $A \propto B$

(3) $A = $ constant $\times B$, or $A = KB$, or $\dfrac{A}{B} = K$,

are identical in meaning. The statements (2) and (3) are abbreviations of statement (1). In statement (3), K is known as the proportionality constant. If we write

$$d = Ks$$

where d is the distance covered in a given time and s is speed, we are saying that the distance covered in a given time is proportional to the speed.

The rate of formation of hydrogen iodide from its elements, hydrogen and iodine, is expressed by the following equation:

rate $= k \times$ (*concentration of* H_2) $\times$ (*concentration of* I_2)

This means that the rate of formation of hydrogen iodide is proportional to the product of the concentrations of the hydrogen and iodine.

PROBLEMS. MATHEMATICAL OPERATIONS

1. Express the following numbers in the exponential form:

(a)	1,000,000	(m)	.01
(b)	400,000	(n)	.0032
(c)	50,000	(o)	.000007
(d)	9,000	(p)	.00107
(e)	600	(q)	.0000000009
(f)	70	(r)	.00000678
(g)	1,450,000	(s)	0.103
(h)	946,000	(t)	1.0
(i)	59,000	(u)	0.1
(j)	9,627	(v)	.00045
(k)	450	(w)	.000006
(l)	563,200		

2. Express the answers of the following in the exponential form:

(a) Multiply 4.2×10^4 by 3.0×10^4

(b) Multiply 2.5×10^{-2} by 2.0×10^5

(c) Multiply 6.06×10^{23} by 1×10^{-6}

(d) Multiply 4.0×10^{-4} by 7.0×10^{-3}

(e) Multiply .00005 by 10

(f) Multiply .00025 by 400

(g) Multiply .000007 by 1×10^{10}

(h) Multiply 60 by 5,000,000

(i) Multiply 2500 by .0025

(j) Multiply .00003 by .006

(k) Multiply 1×10^6 by .0005

3. Express the answers of the following in the exponential form:

(a) Divide 1×10^6 by 2×10^4

(b) Divide 3×10^4 by 3×10^{-3}

(c) Divide 4.2×10^{-3} by 1.3×10^{-4}

(d) Divide 4.5×10^{-6} by 1.5×10^{-5}

(e) Divide 9×10^{-20} by 2×10^{-15}

(f) Divide 4.2×10^6 by 210,000

(g) Divide 2.5×10^5 by .00005

(h) Divide 6.6×10^{-7} by 1.1×10^5

   (i) Divide 5.0×10^{-6} by 2,500,000
   (j) Divide 4×10^{-4} by .0008
   (k) Divide 64,000 by 2×10^5
   (l) Divide 2,500,000 by 5×10^{-8}
   (m) Divide .000034 by 1.7×10^3
   (n) Divide .00065 by 1.3×10^{-2}

4. Express the answers of the following operations in terms of the significant figures only: (The quantities represent experimental values.)

   (a) Add the quantities 1834.56, 50 and 0.765
   (b) Subtract 6.0 from 22.45
   (c) Subtract 6.00 from 22.45
   (d) Multiply 0.675 by $(.02)^2$
   (e) Solve for X in the following: $X(6 - X) = .0006$

5. Find the logarithm of the following:

   (a) 2156.3   (e) 67.25
   (b) 340   (f) 0.387
   (c) 1.035   (g) .004
   (d) .0000067   (h) 400

6. Give the number (antilogarithm) corresponding to the following logarithms:

   (a) 3.6745   (e) $6.4632 - 10$
   (b) 2.4362   (f) $\bar{4}.2697$
   (c) .2875   (g) $- 2.3628$
   (d) $9.3476 - 10$ (h) $- 0.2756$

7. Solve the following expressions with the use of logarithms:

   (a) $V = 350 \times \dfrac{273}{302} \times \dfrac{745}{760}$ Find V

   (b) $N = \dfrac{6.06 \times 10^{23}}{1000 \times 22.4 \times 760 \times 10^{-6}}$ Find N

   (c) $M = \dfrac{22.4 \times 10^3 \times 2.456}{150}$ Find M

   (d) $X = \dfrac{(3.65)^2 \times 24.5 \times 10^{-4} \times 376.2}{3.0 \times 26.5 \times 500}$ Find X

8. Solve the following expressions; use logarithms where desirable:

(a) $(2.54 \times 10^5)^2$

(b) $(3.6 \times 10^{-4})^2$

(c) $(1.2 \times 10^{-3})^3$

(d) $(6.56 \times 10^2)^2(3.5 \times 10^4)^2$

(e) $(9.2 \times 10^{-2})^2(2.6 \times 10^8)^2$

9. Extract the square root of the following; use logarithms where desirable:

(a) 4×10^{-6}

(b) $(4 \times 10^{-6})^2$

(c) 3.6×10^9

(d) 0.25×10^{-4}

(e) 25×10^{-5}

(f) 6.942×10^3

(g) 24.53×10^{-7}

(h) 1.44×10^{-14}

10. Solve the following equations for X:

(a) $X^2 + 4X + 7 = 0$

(b) $X^2 + 0.15X = 2.53$

(c) $X^2 + (1 \times 10^{-4})X - 3.6 \times 10^{-6} = 0$

(d) $X^2 + (1.8 \times 10^{-5})X - 1.8 \times 10^{-6} = 0$

11. Calculate the pH of solutions which contain the following concentration of the hydrogen ion respectively:

(a) 1×10^{-4}

(b) 2×10^{-12}

(c) 3.5×10^{-6}

(d) 1×10^{-7}

(e) 2.56×10^{-5}

(f) 0.1345

12. From the following pH values calculate the concentration of the hydrogen ion:

(a) 7.0

(b) 8.4

(c) 5.3

(d) 6.87

(e) 9.25

(f) 2.46

13. Express the following statements in the form of an equation:

(a) At constant temperature, the pressure of a gas varies inversely with the volume.

(b) At constant pressure, the volume of a gas varies directly with the absolute temperature.

(c) At constant volume, the pressure of a gas varies directly with the absolute temperature.

(d) The speed of diffusion of a molecule in the gaseous condition is inversely proportional to the square root of its mass.

(e) The force of attraction between two bodies is directly proportional to the product of their masses and inversely proportional to the square of the distance between them.

TABLE 43

Ionization Constants of Weak Acids

The equilibrium constants given in this and following tables appear in two forms. In the column to the right, the value of the constant is given in exponential form for convenience when used in calculations involving the half reactions of Table 20. Some of the data have been taken from the International Critical Tables; other data have been selected after a careful evaluation of the literature references.

Acid	Equilibrium	Ionization Constant (at Room Temperature)	
Acetic	$CH_3COOH = H^+ + CH_3COO^-$	1.85×10^{-5}	$10^{-4.7}$
Arsenic	$H_3AsO_4 = H^+ + H_2AsO_4^-$	4.5×10^{-3}	$10^{-2.3}$
Arsenous	$H_3AsO_3 = H^+ + H_2AsO_3^-$	2.1×10^{-8}	$10^{-7.7}$
Benzoic	$C_6H_5COOH = H^+ + C_6H_5COO^-$	6.6×10^{-5}	$10^{-4.2}$
Boric	$H_3BO_3 = H^+ + H_2BO_3^-$	1.1×10^{-9}	$10^{-9.0}$
Carbonic	$H_2CO_3 = H^+ + HCO_3^-$	3.5×10^{-7}	$10^{-6.5}$
Bicarbonate ion	$HCO_3^- = H^+ + CO_3^{--}$	7×10^{-11}	$10^{-10.2}$
Chloracetic	$ClCH_2COOH = H^+ + ClCH_2COO^-$	1.4×10^{-3}	$10^{-2.9}$
Cyanic	$HCNO = H^+ + CNO^-$	2×10^{-4}	$10^{-3.7}$
Dichloracetic	$Cl_2CHCOOH = H^+ + Cl_2CHCOO^-$	5.5×10^{-2}	$10^{-1.3}$
Formic	$HCOOH = H^+ + HCOO^-$	2.1×10^{-4}	$10^{-3.7}$
Hydrazoic	$HN_3 = H^+ + N_3^-$	1.9×10^{-5}	$10^{-4.7}$
Hydrocyanic	$HCN = H^+ + CN^-$	2.1×10^{-9}	$10^{-8.7}$
Hydrofluoric	$HF = H^+ + F^-$	6.9×10^{-4}	$10^{-3.2}$
Hydrogen peroxide	$H_2O_2 = H^+ + HO_2^-$	5×10^{-12}	$10^{-11.3}$
Hydrogen selenide	$H_2Se = H^+ + HSe^-$	1.9×10^{-4}	$10^{-3.7}$
Hydrogen sulfide	$H_2S = H^+ + HS^-$	9×10^{-8}	$10^{-7.0}$
Bisulfide ion	$HS^- = H^+ + S^{--}$	1.2×10^{-15}	$10^{-14.9}$
Hydrogen telluride	$H_2Te = H^+ + HTe^-$	2.5×10^{-3}	$10^{-2.6}$
Nitrous	$HNO_2 = H^+ + NO_2^-$	4.6×10^{-4}	$10^{-3.3}$
o-Nitrobenzoic	$C_7H_5NO_4 = H^+ + C_7H_4NO_4^-$	6.1×10^{-3}	$10^{-2.2}$
Oxalic	$H_2C_2O_4 = H^+ + HC_2O_4^-$	3.8×10^{-2}	$10^{-1.4}$
Monohydrogen oxalate ion	$HC_2O_4^- = H^+ + C_2O_4^{--}$	5×10^{-5}	$10^{-4.3}$
Phenol	$C_6H_5OH = H^+ + C_6H_5O^-$	1.0×10^{-10}	10^{-10}
Phosphoric	$H_3PO_4 = H^+ + H_2PO_4^-$	7.5×10^{-3}	$10^{-2.1}$

Acid	Equilibrium	Ionization Constant (at Room Temperature)	
Dihydrogen phosphate ion	$H_2PO_4^- = H^+ + HPO_4^{--}$	6.3×10^{-8}	$10^{-7.2}$
Monohydrogen phosphate ion	$HPO_4^{--} = H^+ + PO_4^{---}$	3.6×10^{-13}	$10^{-12.5}$
Phosphorous	$H_3PO_3 = H^+ + H_2PO_3^-$	5.0×10^{-2}	$10^{-1.3}$
Dihydrogen phosphite ion	$H_2PO_3^- = H^+ + HPO_3^{--}$	2.0×10^{-5}	$10^{-4.7}$
Propionic	$C_2H_5COOH = H^+ + C_2H_5COO^-$	1.4×10^{-5}	$10^{-4.9}$
Salicylic	$C_7H_6O_3 = H^+ + C_7H_5O_3^-$	1.1×10^{-3}	10^{-3}
Selenious	$H_2SeO_3 = H^+ + HSeO_3^-$	3.5×10^{-3}	$10^{-2.5}$
Sulfurous	$H_2SO_3 = H^+ + HSO_3^-$	1.7×10^{-2}	$10^{-1.8}$
Bisulfite ion	$HSO_3^- = H^+ + SO_3^{--}$	5×10^{-6}	$10^{-5.3}$
Tartaric	$C_4H_4O_6H_2 = H^+ + C_4H_4O_6H^-$	1.1×10^{-3}	10^{-3}
Bitartrate ion	$C_4H_4O_6H^- = H^+ + C_4H_4O_6^{--}$	6.9×10^{-5}	$10^{-4.2}$
Telluric	$H_2TeO_4 = H^+ + HTeO_4^-$	6×10^{-7}	$10^{-6.2}$
Bitellurate ion	$HTeO_4^- = H^+ + TeO_4^{--}$	4×10^{-11}	$10^{-10.4}$
Tellurous	$H_2TeO_3 = H^+ + HTeO_3^-$	2×10^{-3}	$10^{-2.7}$
Aluminum hydroxide	$Al(OH)_3 = H^+ + AlO_2^- + H_2O$	4×10^{-13}	$10^{-12.4}$
Chromium hydroxide	$Cr(OH)_3 = H^+ + CrO_2^- + H_2O$	1×10^{-16}	10^{-16}
Lead hydroxide	$Pb(OH)_2 = H^+ + HPbO_2^-$	2×10^{-16}	$10^{-15.7}$
Mercuric hydroxide	$Hg(OH)_2 = H^+ + HHgO_2^-$	1×10^{-15}	10^{-15}
Silver hydroxide	$AgOH = H^+ + AgO^-$	8×10^{-13}	$10^{-12.1}$
Stannous hydroxide	$Sn(OH)_2 = H^+ + HSnO_2^-$	6×10^{-18}	$10^{-17.2}$
Zinc hydroxide	$Zn(OH)_2 = 2H^+ + ZnO_2^{--}$	1×10^{-29}	10^{-29}

TABLE 44

IONIZATION CONSTANTS OF WEAK BASES

Base	Equilibrium	Ionization Constant (at Room Temperature)	
Ammonium hydroxide	$NH_4OH = NH_4^+ + OH^-$	1.8×10^{-5}	$10^{-4.7}$
Methyl ammonium hydroxide	$CH_3NH_3OH = CH_3NH_3^+ + OH^-$	5×10^{-4}	$10^{-3.3}$
Dimethyl ammonium hydroxide	$(CH_3)_2NH_2OH = (CH_3)_2NH_2^+ + OH^-$	7.4×10^{-4}	$10^{-3.1}$
Trimethyl ammonium hydroxide	$(CH_3)_3NHOH = (CH_3)_3NH^+ + OH^-$	7.4×10^{-5}	$10^{-4.1}$
Ethyl ammonium hydroxide	$C_2H_5NH_3OH = C_2H_5NH_3^+ + OH^-$	5.6×10^{-4}	$10^{-3.3}$
Phenyl ammonium hydroxide	$C_6H_5NH_3OH = C_6H_5NH_3^+ + OH^-$	4.6×10^{-10}	$10^{-9.3}$
Hydrazine hydroxide	$H_2N \cdot NH_3OH = H_2N \cdot NH_3^+ + OH^-$	3×10^{-6}	$10^{-5.5}$

TABLE 45

SOLUBILITY PRODUCT CONSTANTS AT ROOM TEMPERATURE

Substance	Equilibrium	Solubility Product Constant	
Acetates			
Silver acetate	$CH_3COOAg_{(s)} = Ag^+ + CH_3COO^-$	4×10^{-3}	$10^{-2.4}$
Bromates			
Silver bromate	$AgBrO_{3(s)} = Ag^+ + BrO_3^-$	6×10^{-5}	$10^{-4.2}$
Bromides			
Mercurous bromide	$Hg_2Br_{2(s)} = Hg_2^{++} + 2Br^-$	4×10^{-23}	$10^{-22.4}$
Silver bromide	$AgBr_{(s)} = Ag^+ + Br^-$	7.7×10^{-13}	$10^{-12.1}$
Carbonates			
Barium carbonate	$BaCO_{3(s)} = Ba^{++} + CO_3^{--}$	8.1×10^{-9}	$10^{-8.1}$
Calcium carbonate	$CaCO_{3(s)} = Ca^{++} + CO_3^{--}$	8.7×10^{-9}	$10^{-8.1}$
Lead carbonate	$PbCO_{3(s)} = Pb^{++} + CO_3^{--}$	4.0×10^{-14}	$10^{-13.4}$
Magnesium carbonate	$MgCO_{3(s)} = Mg^{++} + CO_3^{--}$	4.0×10^{-5}	$10^{-4.4}$
Silver carbonate	$Ag_2CO_{3(s)} = 2Ag^+ + CO_3^{--}$	6.2×10^{-12}	$10^{-11.2}$
Strontium carbonate	$SrCO_{3(s)} = Sr^{++} + CO_3^{--}$	1.6×10^{-9}	$10^{-8.8}$
Chlorides			
Mercurous chloride	$Hg_2Cl_{2(s)} = Hg_2^{++} + 2Cl^-$	1.5×10^{-18}	$10^{-17.8}$
Silver chloride	$AgCl_{(s)} = Ag^+ + Cl^-$	1.56×10^{-10}	$10^{-9.8}$
Chromates			
Barium chromate	$BaCrO_{4(s)} = Ba^{++} + CrO_4^{--}$	2.4×10^{-10}	$10^{-9.6}$
Lead chromate	$PbCrO_{4(s)} = Pb^{++} + CrO_4^{--}$	2.0×10^{-14}	$10^{-13.7}$
Silver chromate	$Ag_2CrO_{4(s)} = 2Ag^+ + CrO_4^{--}$	9.0×10^{-12}	10^{-11}
Cyanides			
Silver cyanide	$AgCN_{(s)} = Ag^+ + CN^-$	2.2×10^{-12}	$10^{-11.7}$
Dichromates			
Silver dichromate	$Ag_2Cr_2O_{7(s)} = 2Ag^+ + Cr_2O_7^{--}$	2.0×10^{-7}	$10^{-6.7}$
Fluorides			
Barium fluoride	$BaF_{2(s)} = Ba^{++} + 2F^-$	1.7×10^{-6}	$10^{-5.8}$
Calcium fluoride	$CaF_{2(s)} = Ca^{++} + 2F^-$	4.0×10^{-11}	$10^{-10.4}$
Lead fluoride	$PbF_{2(s)} = Pb^{++} + 2F^-$	3.7×10^{-8}	$10^{-7.4}$
Magnesium fluoride	$MgF_{2(s)} = Mg^{++} + 2F^-$	6.4×10^{-9}	$10^{-8.2}$
Strontium fluoride	$SrF_{2(s)} = Sr^{++} + 2F^-$	2.8×10^{-9}	$10^{-8.6}$
Hydroxides			
Aluminum hydroxide	$Al(OH)_{3(s)} = Al^{+++} + 3OH^-$	1×10^{-33}	10^{-33}
Cadmium hydroxide	$Cd(OH)_{2(s)} = Cd^{++} + 2OH^-$	1.2×10^{-14}	$10^{-13.9}$
Chromium hydroxide	$Cr(OH)_{3(s)} = Cr^{+++} + 3OH^-$	1×10^{-30}	10^{-30}

Substance	Equilibrium	Solubility Product Constant	
Copper hydroxide	$Cu(OH)_{2(s)} = Cu^{++} + 2OH^-$	6×10^{-20}	$10^{-19.2}$
Ferric hydroxide	$Fe(OH)_{3(s)} = Fe^{+++} + 3OH^-$	1.5×10^{-36}	$10^{-35.8}$
Ferrous hydroxide	$Fe(OH)_{2(s)} = Fe^{++} + 2OH^-$	2×10^{-14}	$10^{-13.7}$
Lead hydroxide	$Pb(OH)_{2(s)} = Pb^{++} + 2OH^-$	2.5×10^{-16}	$10^{-15.6}$
Magnesium hydroxide	$Mg(OH)_{2(s)} = Mg^{++} + 2OH^-$	1.5×10^{-11}	$10^{-10.8}$
Manganese hydroxide	$Mn(OH)_{2(s)} = Mn^{++} + 2OH^-$	4.5×10^{-14}	$10^{-13.3}$
Mercuric hydroxide	$HgO_{(s)} + H_2O = Hg^{++} + 2OH^-$	2×10^{-22}	$10^{-21.7}$
Nickel hydroxide	$Ni(OH)_{2(s)} = Ni^{++} + 2OH^-$	2×10^{-14}	$10^{-13.7}$
Silver hydroxide	$\frac{1}{2}Ag_2O_{(s)} + \frac{1}{2}H_2O = Ag^+ + OH^-$	1.6×10^{-8}	$10^{-7.8}$
Stannous hydroxide	$Sn(OH)_{2(s)} = Sn^{++} + 2OH^-$	5×10^{-26}	$10^{-25.3}$
Zinc hydroxide	$Zn(OH)_{2(s)} = Zn^{++} + 2OH^-$	5×10^{-17}	$10^{-16.3}$
Iodates			
Barium iodate	$Ba(IO_3)_{2(s)} = Ba^{++} + 2IO_3^-$	6.5×10^{-10}	$10^{-9.2}$
Calcium iodate	$Ca(IO_3)_{2(s)} = Ca^{++} + 2IO_3^-$	6.5×10^{-7}	$10^{-6.2}$
Cupric iodate	$Cu(IO_3)_{2(s)} = Cu^{++} + 2IO_3^-$	1.4×10^{-7}	$10^{-6.9}$
Lead iodate	$Pb(IO_3)_{2(s)} = Pb^{++} + 2IO_3^-$	2.6×10^{-13}	$10^{-12.6}$
Silver iodate	$AgIO_{3(s)} = Ag^+ + IO_3^-$	1.0×10^{-8}	10^{-8}
Iodides			
Lead iodide	$PbI_{2(s)} = Pb^{++} + 2I^-$	1.4×10^{-8}	$10^{-7.9}$
Mercurous iodide	$Hg_2I_{2(s)} = Hg_2^{++} + 2I^-$	4×10^{-29}	$10^{-28.4}$
Silver iodide	$AgI_{(s)} = Ag^+ + I^-$	1.5×10^{-16}	$10^{-15.8}$
Thallous iodide	$TlI_{(s)} = Tl^+ + I^-$	2.5×10^{-8}	$10^{-7.6}$
Oxalates			
Barium oxalate	$BaC_2O_{4(s)} = Ba^{++} + C_2O_4^{--}$	1.5×10^{-7}	$10^{-6.8}$
Cadmium oxalate	$CdC_2O_{4(s)} = Cd^{++} + C_2O_4^{--}$	1.5×10^{-8}	$10^{-7.8}$
Calcium oxalate	$CaC_2O_{4(s)} = Ca^{++} + C_2O_4^{--}$	2.6×10^{-9}	$10^{-8.6}$
Cupric oxalate	$CuC_2O_{4(s)} = Cu^{++} + C_2O_4^{--}$	2.9×10^{-8}	$10^{-7.5}$
Ferrous oxalate	$FeC_2O_{4(s)} = Fe^{++} + C_2O_4^{--}$	2.1×10^{-7}	$10^{-6.7}$
Lead oxalate	$PbC_2O_{4(s)} = Pb^{++} + C_2O_4^{--}$	2.8×10^{-11}	$10^{-10.6}$
Magnesium oxalate	$MgC_2O_{4(s)} = Mg^{++} + C_2O_4^{--}$	8.8×10^{-5}	$10^{-4.1}$
Strontium oxalate	$SrC_2O_{4(s)} = Sr^{++} + C_2O_4^{--}$	5.8×10^{-8}	$10^{-7.2}$
Zinc oxalate	$ZnC_2O_{4(s)} = Zn^{++} + C_2O_4^{--}$	1.5×10^{-9}	$10^{-8.8}$
Sulfates			
Barium sulfate	$BaSO_{4(s)} = Ba^{++} + SO_4^{--}$	1.1×10^{-10}	10^{-10}
Calcium sulfate	$CaSO_{4(s)} = Ca^{++} + SO_4^{--}$	6.1×10^{-5}	$10^{-4.2}$
Lead sulfate	$PbSO_{4(s)} = Pb^{++} + SO_4^{--}$	1.1×10^{-8}	10^{-8}
Strontium sulfate	$SrSO_{4(s)} = Sr^{++} + SO_4^{--}$	2.9×10^{-7}	$10^{-6.5}$
Sulfides			
Cadmium sulfide	$CdS_{(s)} = Cd^{++} + S^{--}$	1.0×10^{-28}	10^{-28}
Cobalt sulfide	$CoS_{(s)} = Co^{++} + S^{--}$	1.0×10^{-27}	10^{-27}
Cupric sulfide	$CuS_{(s)} = Cu^{++} + S^{--}$	3.5×10^{-38}	$10^{-37.5}$
Ferrous sulfide	$FeS_{(s)} = Fe^{++} + S^{--}$	3.7×10^{-19}	$10^{-18.4}$
Lead sulfide	$PbS_{(s)} = Pb^{++} + S^{--}$	7.0×10^{-30}	$10^{-29.2}$
Manganous sulfide	$MnS_{(s)} = Mn^{++} + S^{--}$	1.4×10^{-15}	$10^{-14.9}$

Substance	Equilibrium	Solubility Product Constant
Mercuric sulfide	$HgS_{(s)} = Hg^{++} + S^{--}$	1×10^{-50} 10^{-50}
Nickelous sulfide	$NiS_{(s)} = Ni^{++} + S^{--}$	1.4×10^{-24} $10^{-23.9}$
Silver sulfide	$Ag_2S_{(s)} = 2Ag^+ + S^{--}$	4×10^{-52} $10^{-51.4}$
Thallous sulfide	$Tl_2S_{(s)} = 2Tl^+ + S^{--}$	6.4×10^{-23} $10^{-22.2}$
Zinc sulfide	$ZnS_{(s)} = Zn^{++} + S^{--}$	1.2×10^{-23} $10^{-22.9}$
Thiocyanates		
Silver thiocyanate	$AgCNS_{(s)} = Ag^+ + CNS^-$	1.2×10^{-12} $10^{-11.9}$

TABLE 46

DISSOCIATION CONSTANTS OF COMPLEX IONS

Equilibrium	Dissociation Constant	
$[Cd(NH_3)_4]^{++} = Cd^{++} + 4NH_3$	1×10^{-7}	10^{-7}
$[Ag(NH_3)_2]^+ = Ag^+ + 2NH_3$	6.8×10^{-8}	$10^{-7.2}$
$[Zn(NH_3)_4]^{++} = Zn^{++} + 4NH_3$	2.6×10^{-10}	$10^{-9.6}$
$[HgBr_4]^{--} = Hg^{++} + 4Br^-$	2.2×10^{-22}	$10^{-21.7}$
$[HgCl_3]^- = Hg^{++} + 3Cl^-$	6.0×10^{-17}	$10^{-16.2}$
$[Cd(CN)_4]^{--} = Cd^{++} + 4CN^-$	1.4×10^{-17}	$10^{-16.9}$
$[Cu(CN)_3]^{--} = Cu^+ + 3CN^-$	5.0×10^{-28}	$10^{-27.3}$
$[Hg(CN)_4]^{--} = Hg^{++} + 4CN^-$	4×10^{-42}	$10^{-41.4}$
$[Ag(CN)_2]^- = Ag^+ + 2CN^-$	8×10^{-23}	$10^{-22.1}$
$[HgI_4]^{--} = Hg^{++} + 4I^-$	5.0×10^{-32}	$10^{-31.3}$
$[Hg(CNS)_4]^{--} = Hg^{++} + 4CNS^-$	1.0×10^{-22}	10^{-22}

TABLE 47

Electron Configurations of the Elements [1]

		K	L		M			N				O				P			Q
		1s	2s	2p	3s	3p	3d	4s	4p	4d	4f	5s	5p	5d	5f	6s	6p	6d	7s
H	1	1																	
He	2	2																	
Li	3	2	1																
Be	4	2	2																
B	5	2	2	1															
C	6	2	2	2															
N	7	2	2	3															
O	8	2	2	4															
F	9	2	2	5															
Ne	10	2	2	6															
Na	11	2	2	6	1														
Mg	12	2	2	6	2														
Al	13	2	2	6	2	1													
Si	14	2	2	6	2	2													
P	15	Neon		6	2	3													
S	16	core		6	2	4													
Cl	17	2	2	6	2	5													
A	18	2	2	6	2	6													
K	19	2	2	6	2	6		1											
Ca	20	2	2	6	2	6		2											
Sc	21	2	2	6	2	6	1	2											
Ti	22	2	2	6	2	6	2	2											
V	23	2	Argon	6	2	6	3	2											
Cr	24	2	core	6	2	6	5	1											
Mn	25	2	2	6	2	6	5	2											
Fe	26	2	2	6	2	6	6	2											
Co	27	2	2	6	2	6	7	2											
Ni	28	2	2	6	2	6	8	2											
Cu	29	2	2	6	2	6	10	1											
Zn	30	2	2	6	2	6	10	2											
Ga	31	2	2	6	2	6	10	2	1										
Ge	32	2	2	6	2	6	10	2	2										
As	33	2	Copper		2	6	10	2	3										
Se	34	2	core		2	6	10	2	4										
Br	35	2	2	6	2	6	10	2	5										
Kr	36	2	2	6	2	6	10	2	6										
Rb	37	2	2	6	2	6	10	2	6			1							
Sr	38	2	2	6	2	6	10	2	6			2							
Y	39	2	2	6	2	6	10	2	6	1		2							
Zr	40	2	2	6	2	6	10	2	6	2		2							
Cb	41	2	2	6	2	6	10	2	6	4		1							
Mo	42	2	2	Krypton			6	10	2	6	5		1						
Ma	43	2	2	core	2	6	10	2	6	6		1							
Ru	44	2	2	6	2	6	10	2	6	7		1							
Rh	45	2	2	6	2	6	10	2	6	8		1							
Pd	46	2	2	6	2	6	10	2	6	10									

[1] The electronic assignments for elements 89 to 96 are very tentative.

		K	L		M			N				O				P			Q
		1s	2s	2p	3s	3p	3d	4s	4p	4d	4f	5s	5p	5d	5f	6s	6p	6d	7s
Ag	47	2	2	6	2	6	10	2	6	10		1							
Cd	48	2	2	6	2	6	10	2	6	10		2							
In	49	2	2	6	2	6	10	2	6	10		2	1						
Sn	50	2	2	6	Silver core			2	6	10		2	2						
Sb	51	2	2	6	2	6	10	2	6	10		2	3						
Te	52	2	2	6	2	6	10	2	6	10		2	4						
I	53	2	2	6	2	6	10	2	6	10		2	5						
Xe	54	2	2	6	2	6	10	2	6	10		2	6						
Cs	55	2	2	6	2	6	10	2	6	10		2	6			1			
Ba	56	2	2	6	2 Xenon core			6	10			2	6			2			
La	57	2	2	6	2	6	10	2	6	10		2	6	1		2			
Ce	58	2	2	6	2	6	19	2	6	10	1	2	6	1		2			
Pr	59	2	2	6	2	6	10	2	6	10	2	2	6	1		2			
Nd	60	2	2	6	2	6	10	2	6	10	3	2	6	1		2			
Il	61	2	2	6	2	6	10	2	6	10	4	2	6	1		2			
Sa	62	2	2	6	2	6	10	2	6	10	5	2	6	1		2			
Eu	63	2	2	6	2	6	10	2	6	10	6	2	6	1		2			
Gd	64	2	2	6	2	6	10	2	6	10	7	2	6	1		2			
Tb	65	2	2	6	2	6	10	2	6	10	8	2	6	1		2			
Ds	66	2	2	6	2	6	10	2	6	10	9	2	6	1		2			
Ho	67	2	2	6	2	6	10	2	6	10	10	2	6	1		2			
Er	68	2	2	6	2	6	10	2	6	10	11	2	6	1		2			
Tu	69	2	2	6	2	6	10	2	6	10	12	2	6	1		2			
Yb	70	2	2	6	2	6	10	2	6	10	13	2	6	1		2			
Lu	71	2	2	6	2	6	10	2	6	10	14	2	6	1		2			
Hf	72	2	2	6	2	6	10	2	6	10	14	2	6	2		2			
Ta	73	2	2	6	2	6	10	2	6	10	14	2	6	3		2			
W	74	2	2	6	2	6	10	2	6	10	14	2	6	4		2			
Re	75	2	2	6	2	6 Hafnium core				10	14	2	6	5		2			
Os	76	2	2	6	2	6	10	2	6	10	14	2	6	6		2			
Ir	77	2	2	6	2	6	10	2	6	10	14	2	6	7		2			
Pt	78	2	2	6	2	6	10	2	6	10	14	2	6	9		1			
Au	79	2	2	6	2	6	10	2	6	10	14	2	6	10		1			
Hg	80	2	2	6	2	6	10	2	6	10	14	2	6	10		2			
Tl	81	2	2	6	2	6	10	2	6	10	14	2	6	10		2	1		
Pb	82	2	2	6	2	6	10	Gold core			14	2	6	10		2	2		
Bi	83	2	2	6	2	6	10	2	6	10	14	2	6	10		2	3		
Po	84	2	2	6	2	6	10	2	6	10	14	2	6	10		2	4		
—	85	2	2	6	2	6	10	2	6	10	14	2	6	10		2	5		
Rn	86	2	2	6	2	6	10	2	6	10	14	2	6	10		2	6		
—	87	2	2	6	2	6	10	2 Radon core				2	6	10		2	6		1
Ra	88	2	2	6	2	6	10	2	6	10	14	2	6	10		2	6		2
Ac	89	2	2	6	2	6	10	2	6	10	14	2	6	10		2	6	1	2
Th	90	2	2	6	2	6	10	2	6	10	14	2	6	10		2	6	1	2
Pa	91	2	2	6	2	6	10	2	6	10	14	2	6	10	2	2	6	1	2
U	92	2	2	6	2	6	10	2	6	10	14	2	6	10	3	2	6	1	2
Np	93	2	2	6	2	6	10	2	6	10	14	2	6	10	4	2	6	1	2
Pu	94	2	2	6	2	6	10	2	6	10	14	2	6	10	5	2	6	1	2
Am	95	2	2	6	2	6	10	2	6	10	14	2	6	10	6	2	6	1	2
Cm	96	2	2	6	2	6	10	2	6	10	14	2	6	10	7	2	6	1	2

TABLE 48

Physical Properties of Compounds of Ions of the Analytical Groups

Sol. = soluble. Insol. = insoluble. Sl. = slightly. Alk. = alkali. Alc. = alcohol. V. = very. Dec. = decomposes. (Some of the data of this table have been taken from the International Critical Tables; other data have been selected after a careful evaluation of the literature references.)

Formula	Color and Form	Solubility in H_2O (g. per 100 g. H_2O)	General Solubility
K	Cubic silvery metal	Reacts violently	Sol. acids, alc., Hg
K_2O	Cubic white-gray	V. sol., forms KOH	Sol. alc., ether
K_2O_4	Yellow leaflets	V. sol., dec.	Dec. in alc.
KOH	Rhombic white, deliquescent	112 (20°)	V. sol. alc., ether; insol. NH_3
$KC_2H_3O_2$	Lustrous white powder, deliquescent	255 (20°)	Sol. alc.; insol. ether
$KSbO_3$	White powder	Insol.	Sol. hot KOH; insol. alc.
$K_2H_2Sb_2O_7\cdot 4H_2O$	Granular, white crystalline powder	2.82 (20°)	
K_3AsO_4	White needles, deliquescent	19 (cold)	Sl. sol. alc.
K_3AsO_3	White needles	V. sol.	Sol. alc.
$KBrO_3$	Trigonal white	7.1 (20°)	Sl. sol. alc.; insol. acetone
KBr	Cubic white	64.5 (20°)	Sl. sol. alc., ether; sol. glycerine
$K_2CO_3\cdot 2H_2O$	Rhombic white	139 (20°)	Insol. alc., acetone
$KHCO_3$	Monoclinic white	33 (20°)	Insol. alc.
$KClO_3$	Monoclinic white	7.1 (20°)	Sl. sol. alc.; sol. alk.
$KClO_4$	Rhombic white	1.68 (20°)	Insol. alk., ether
KCl	Cubic white	34.4 (20°)	Sol. alc., alk., ether, glycerine
KClO	Only in solution	V. sol.	
K_2PtCl_6	Cubic yellow	0.74 (25°)	Insol. alc., ether

Formula	Color and Form	Solubility in H_2O (g. per 100 g. H_2O)	General Solubility
K_2CrO_4	Rhombic yellow	62.5 (20°)	Insol. alc.
$K_2Cr_2O_7$	Monoclinic or triclinic red	11.5 (20°)	Insol. alc.
KCNO	White needles	75 (25°)	Insol. alc.
KCN	Cubic white, white granular, deliquescent, very poisonous	72 (25°)	Sl. sol. alc., sol. glycerine, CH_3OH
$K_3Fe(CN)_6$	Monoclinic red	44 (20°)	Sol. acetone; insol. alc.
$K_4Fe(CN)_6 \cdot 3H_2O$	Monoclinic yellow	32 (20°)	Sol. acetone; insol. alc., NH_3
$KF \cdot 2H_2O$	White monoclinic prisms, deliquescent	156 (21°)	Sol. HF; insol. alc.
KIO_3	Monoclinic white	8.1 (20°)	Sol. KI; insol. alc., NH_3
KIO_4	Tetragonal white	0.66 (13°)	V. sl. sol. KOH
KI	Cubic white or white granular	143 (20°)	Sol. alc., NH_3; sl. sol. ether
KI_3	Monoclinic dark blue, deliquescent	V sol.	Sol. alc., KI
K_2MnO_4	Rhombic green	Dec.	Sol. KOH
$KMnO_4$	Rhombic purple	6.4 (20°)	Dec. by alc.; sol. H_2SO_4; v. sol. CH_3OH, acetone
KNO_3	Rhombic or trigonal white	31.1 (20°)	Insol. alc., ether
KNO_2	White prisms, deliquescent	302 (20°)	V. sol. NH_3; sl. sol. alc.
$K_2Fe(CN)_5 \cdot NO \cdot 2H_2O$	Monoclinic red	100 (16°)	Sol. alc.
$K_2C_2O_4 \cdot H_2O$	Monoclinic white	38 (20°)	
K_3PO_4	Rhombic white, deliquescent	193 (25°)	Insol. alc.
K_2HPO_4	Amorphous white, deliquescent	V. sol.	V. sol. alc.
KH_2PO_4	Tetragonal colorless, deliquescent	30 (25°)	Insol. alc.
$K_4(PO_3)_4 \cdot 2H_2O$	Amorphous white	Sl. sol.	Sol. alc.
$K_4P_2O_7 \cdot 3H_2O$	White, deliquescent	Sol.	Insol. alc.

Formula	Color and Form	Solubility in H_2O (g. per 100 g. H_2O)	General Solubility
K_2HPO_3	White powder, deliquescent	V. sol.	Insol. alc.
K_2SiO_3	Amorphous white	Sol.	Insol. alc.
$K_2NaCo(NO_2)_6 \cdot H_2O$	Yellow crystals	0.07 (25°)	Insol. alc.
K_2SO_4	Rhombic or hexagonal white	11.1 (20°)	Insol. alc., acetone, CS_2
$KHSO_4$	Monoclinic or rhombic white	36.3 (0°)	Insol. alc., acetone
$K_2S_2O_8$	Triclinic white	5.3 (20°)	Insol. alc.
K_2S	Yellow-brown, deliquescent	Sol.	Sol. alc., glycerine; ether
K_2S_2	Red-yellow crystals	Sol.	Sol. alc.
$K_2SO_3 \cdot 2H_2O$	Monoclinic yellowish-white	131 (20°)	Sl. sol. alc.; insol. NH_3
$KHSO_3$	White crystals	Sol.	Insol. alc.
$KNaC_4H_4O_6 \cdot 4H_2O$	Rhombic colorless	91 (20°)	V. sl. sol. alc.
$KCNS$	White prisms, deliquescent	215 (20°)	Sol. alc., acetone
$3K_2S_2O_3 \cdot 5H_2O$	White rhombic	181 (20°)	
Na	Cubic silvery metal	Reacts violently	Reacts with alc.; insol. C_6H_6, ether
Na_2O	Gray, deliquescent	Sol., forms NaOH	Sol. alc.
Na_2O_2	Yellow powder	Sol.	Sol. dil. acids; insol. alc.
$NaOH$	White, deliquescent	109 (20°)	Sol. alc.
$NaC_2H_3O_2 \cdot 3H_2O$	Monoclinic white	76 (20°)	Sl. sol. alc.
$2NaSbO_3 \cdot 7H_2O$	Cubic white	0.03 (12°)	Sl. sol. alc., NH_4 salts; insol. HAc
$Na_2H_2Sb_2O_7 \cdot H_2O$	Tetragonal white	Sl. sol.	Sl. sol. alc.
$Na_3AsO_4 \cdot 12H_2O$	Trigonal white	23.7 (14°)	Sl. sol. alc.
Na_2HAsO_3	White	V. sol.	Sl. sol. alc.
$NaBO_2$	White hexagonal prisms	Sol.	
$Na_2B_4O_7 \cdot 10H_2O$	Monoclinic white	4.9 (20°)	Sol. glycerine; insol. acids

Formula	Color and Form	Solubility in H_2O (g. per 100 g. H_2O)	General Solubility
$NaBrO_3$	Cubic white	27.5 (0°)	Insol. alc.
NaBr	Cubic white	90 (20°)	Sl. sol. alc.
$Na_2CO_3 \cdot H_2O$	Rhombic white	59 (30°)	Insol. alc., ether; sol. glycerine
$Na_2CO_3 \cdot 10H_2O$	Monoclinic white	60 (20°)	Insol. alc.
$NaHCO_3$	Monoclinic white	10.2 (25°)	Insol. alc.
$NaClO_3$	Cubic or trigonal white	97 (20°)	Sol. alc., glycerine
$NaClO_4 \cdot H_2O$	Rhombohedral white, deliquescent	209 (15°)	Sol. alc.
NaCl	Cubic white	35.8 (20°)	Sol. glycerine; sl. sol. alc.; insol. HCl
$Na_2PtCl_6 \cdot 6H_2O$	Triclinic yellow-red	66 (15°)	Sol. alc., chlorine water; insol. ether
$Na_2CrO_4 \cdot 10H_2O$	Monoclinic yellow, deliquescent	130 (15°)	Sl. sol. alc.
$Na_2Cr_2O_7 \cdot 2H_2O$	Monoclinic red, deliquescent	206 (20°)	Insol. alc.
NaCN	Cubic white, deliquescent	Sol.	Sl. sol. alc.
$Na_3Fe(CN)_6 \cdot H_2O$	Red deliquescent	19 (0°)	Insol. alc.
$Na_4Fe(CN)_6 \cdot 10H_2O$	Monoclinic yellow	33 (25°)	Insol. alc.
NaF	Tetragonal or cubic white	4.2 (25°)	V. sl. sol. alc.
NaHS	Rhombic white	V. sol.	Sol. alc.
$NaIO_3$	Rhombic white	8.7 (20°)	Sol. HAc; insol. alc.
$NaI \cdot 2H_2O$	Monoclinic white	223 (20°)	
$Na_2MnO_4 \cdot 10H_2O$	Monoclinic green	Sol.	
$NaMnO_4 \cdot 3H_2O$	Purple crystals, deliquescent	V. sol.	Sol. NH_3
$NaNO_3$	Trigonal white	88 (20°)	Sl. sol. alc., glycerine
$NaNO_2$	Rhombic white, hygroscopic	83 (20°)	Sl. sol. CH_3OH; v. sol. NH_3
$Na_2C_2O_4$	White crystals	3.2 (15°)	
$Na_3PO_4 \cdot 12H_2O$	Trigonal white	26 (20°)	Insol. CS_2
$Na_2HPO_4 \cdot 12H_2O$	Rhombic or monoclinic white, efflorescent	19.7 (20°)	Insol. alc.

Formula	Color and Form	Solubility in H_2O (g. per 100 g. H_2O)	General Solubility
$NaH_2PO_4 \cdot H_2O$	Rhombic white	98 (20°)	Insol. alc.
$NaPO_3$	Amorphous white, hygroscopic	Sl. sol.	Sol. acids, alk.
$Na_4P_2O_7 \cdot 10H_2O$	Monoclinic white	10.7 (20°)	Insol. alc., NH_3
$Na_2HPO_3 \cdot 5H_2O$	Rhombic white, deliquescent	Sol.	Insol. alc.
Na_2SiO_3	Monoclinic white	Sol.	Insol. alc., Na and K salts
Na_2SO_4	White crystals	49 (35°)	Insol. alc.
$Na_2SO_4 \cdot 10H_2O$	Monoclinic white	43 (20°)	Insol. alc.
$NaHSO_4$	Triclinic white	50 (0°)	Insol. NH_3
$Na_2S \cdot 9H_2O$	Tetragonal white, deliquescent	56 (20°)	Sol. alc.
$Na_2SO_3 \cdot 7H_2O$	Monoclinic white	52 (20°)	Insol. alc.
$NaHSO_3$	Monoclinic white	Sol.	Insol. alc., acetone
$NaCNS$	Rhombic white, deliquescent	V. sol.	V. sol. alc.
$Na_2S_2O_3 \cdot 5H_2O$	Monoclinic white, efflorescent	110 (20°)	Sol. NH_3; insol. alc.
$NH_4C_2H_3O_2$	White crystals, hygroscopic	148 (4°)	Sol. alc.; sl. sol. acetone
$NH_4SbO_3 \cdot 2H_2O$	White crystals	Insol.	Insol. alc.
$NH_4H_2AsO_4$	Tetragonal white	Sl. sol.	
NH_4BrO_3	Hexagonal white	V. sol.	Sl. sol. alc.
NH_4Br	Cubic white; slightly hygroscopic	76 (20°)	Sol. alc., acetone, ether, NH_3
$(NH_4)_2CO_3 \cdot H_2O$	Cubic white	74 (15°)	Insol. alc., CS_2, NH_3
NH_4HCO_3	Rhombic or monoclinic white	21 (20°)	Insol. alc., acetone
NH_4ClO_3	White monoclinic needles	V. sol.	Sl. sol. alc.
NH_4ClO_4	Rhombic white	23 (20°)	Sol. acetone; sl. sol. alc.
NH_4Cl	Cubic white	37.3 (20°)	Sl. sol. alc.; sol. NH_3
$(NH_4)_2PtCl_6$	Cubic yellow	0.50 (20°)	Insol. alc., ether, cold HCl
$(NH_4)_2CrO_4$	Monoclinic yellow	40 (30°)	Sl. sol. NH_3, acetone; insol. alc.

Formula	Color and Form	Solubility in H_2O (g. per 100 g. H_2O)	General Solubility
$(NH_4)_2Cr_2O_7$	Monoclinic orange	35 (20°)	Sol. alc.; insol. acetone
NH_4CNO	White crystals	V. sol.	Sl. sol. alc.; insol. ether
NH_4CN	Cubic white	V. sol.	V. sol. alc.
$(NH_4)_3Fe(CN)_6$	Red crystals	V. sol.	
$(NH_4)_4Fe(CN)_6$	Monoclinic yellow, turning blue in air	Sol.	Insol. alc.
NH_4F	Hexagonal white, deliquescent	V. sol.	Sol. alc.; insol. NH_3
NH_4HS	Rhombic white	Sol.	Insol. alc., ether
NH_4IO_3	Rhombic or monoclinic white	4.4 (30°)	
NH_4IO_4	Tetragonal white	2.7 (16°)	
NH_4I	Cubic white, hygroscopic	170 (20°)	V. sol. alc., acetone, NH_3; sl. sol. ether
$(NH_4)_2MoO_4$	White monoclinic prisms	Sol., dec.	Sol. acids; insol. alc., NH_3, SO_2, acetone
NH_4NO_3	Rhombic white	195 (20°)	Sol. alc., CH_3OH, acetone, NH_3
NH_4NO_2	Yellowish-white crystals	V. sol.	Sol. alc.; insol. ether
$(NH_4)_2C_2O_4 \cdot H_2O$	Rhombic white	5.1 (20°)	Insol. NH_3
$(NH_4)_2HPO_4$	Monoclinic white	59 (20°)	Insol. alc., acetone
$NH_4H_2PO_4$	Tetragonal white	37 (20°)	Insol. acetone
$NH_4H_2PO_3$	White monoclinic prisms	171 (0°)	Insol. alc.
$(NH_4)_3PO_4 \cdot 12MoO_3 \cdot 3H_2O$	Yellow powder	Sl. sol.	Sol. alk.; insol. alc., HNO_3
$(NH_4)_2SO_4$	Rhombic white	76 (20°)	Insol. alc., NH_3, acetone
NH_4HSO_4	Rhombic white	100 (cold)	Sl. sol. alc.; insol. acetone
$(NH_4)_2S$	Yellow-white crystals, hygroscopic	V. sol.	V. sol. NH_3; sol. alc.
$(NH_4)_2SO_3 \cdot H_2O$	Monoclinic white	32.4 (0°)	Sl. sol. alc.; insol. acetone
NH_4HSO_3	White hexagonal prisms	267 (0°)	
$(NH_4)_3SbS_4 \cdot 4H_2O$	Yellow prisms	137 (20°)	Insol. alc.

Formula	Color and Form	Solubility in H_2O (g. per 100 g. H_2O)	General Solubility
NH_4CNS	Monoclinic white, deliquescent	162 (20°)	Sol. alc., NH_3, acetone
$(NH_4)_2S_2O_3$	Monoclinic white	V. sol.	Sl. sol. acetone; insol. alc.
Pb	Cubic, silvery, blue-white soft metal	Insol.	Sol. 1 : 1 HNO_3, hot conc. H_2SO_4
PbO	Yellow tetragonal	1.7×10^{-3} (20°)	Sol. HNO_3, alk., Pb acetate, NH_4Cl, $CaCl_2$, $SrCl_2$
PbO_2	Brown tetragonal	Insol.	Sol. dil. HCl, acetic acid, hot conc. H_2SO_4
$Pb(OH)_2$	White amorphous powder	1.6×10^{-3} (20°)	Sol. acid, alk.; insol. HAc
$Pb(C_2H_3O_2)_2 \cdot 3H_2O$	White monoclinic crystals	5.1 (25°)	
$Pb(AsO_2)_2$	White powder	Insol.	Sol. HNO_3
$Pb(BrO_3)_2 \cdot H_2O$	White monoclinic crystals	1.38 (20°)	
$PbBr_2$	White rhombic crystals	0.84 (20°)	Sol. acids, KBr; sl. sol. NH_3
$PbCO_3$	White rhombic	1×10^{-4} (20°)	Sol. acids, alk.
$2PbCO_3 \cdot Pb(OH)_2$	White amorphous powder	Insol.	Sol. acids; sl. sol. in aqueous CO_2
$Pb(ClO_3)_2$	White monoclinic crystals	151 (18°)	
$PbCl_2$	White rhombic crystals	1.08 (25°)	Sol. conc. HCl
$PbCrO_4$	Yellow monoclinic	7×10^{-6} (20°)	Sol. acids, alk.; insol. HAc, NH_3 liq.
$Pb(CN)_2$	Yellowish-white powder	Sl. sol. cold; sol. hot water	Sol. KCN, acids
$Pb_3[Fe(CN)_6]_2 \cdot 6H_2O$	Red crystals	Sl. sol. cold; sol. hot	Sol. HNO_3, alk.
$Pb_2Fe(CN)_6 \cdot 3H_2O$	Yellowish-white powder	Insol.	Sl. sol. H_2SO_4
PbF_2	White	6.4×10^{-2} (20°)	Sol. HNO_3; insol. HAc, NH_3
$Pb(IO_3)_2$	White	3.1×10^{-3} (25°)	Sl. sol. HNO_3; insol. NH_3 liq.
PbI_2	Yellow powder	6.4×10^{-2} (20°)	Sol. alk., KI; insol. alc.

Formula	Color and Form	Solubility in H_2O (g. per 100 g. H_2O)	General Solubility
$Pb(NO_3)_2$	Cubic or monoclinic white crystals	59.6 (25°)	Moderately sol. alc.; sol. alk., liq. NH_3
$2PbO \cdot N_2O_5 \cdot H_2O$	Yellow	Very sol.	Sol. acids
$Pb(NO_2)_2 \cdot H_2O$	Yellow	Very sol.	
PbC_2O_4	Heavy white powder	1.6×10^{-4} (18°)	Sol. HNO_3; insol. alc.
$Pb_3(PO_4)_2$	White powder	1.4×10^{-5} (20°)	Sol. HNO_3, alk.; insol. HAc
$PbSO_4$	Monoclinic or rhombic white	4.06×10^{-3} (25°)	Sl. sol. conc. H_2SO_4; sol. NH_4 salts; insol. alc.
PbS	Cubic black metallic	Insol.	Sol. acids; insol. KOH, alc.
$PbSO_3$	White	Insol.	Sol. HNO_3
PbS_2O_3	White crystals	3×10^{-2} (15°)	Dec. by acids; sol. $Na_2S_2O_3$
Hg	Silvery liquid	Insol.	Sol. HNO_3; insol. HCl
HgO	Rhombic yellow or red	5×10^{-3} (25°)	Sol. acids; insol. alc., ether
Hg_2O	Brownish-black powder	7×10^{-4} (cold)	Sol. H_2SO_4, HNO_3, hot HAc; insol. dil. HCl, alk., NH_3
$Hg(C_2H_3O_2)_2$	White scales or powder	25 (10°)	Sol. alc.
$Hg_2(C_2H_3O_2)_2$	White micaceous scales	0.10 (21°)	Sol. H_2SO_4, HNO_7
$Hg_3(AsO_4)_2$	Yellow	Very sl. sol.	Sol. HCl, HNO_3
Hg_3AsO_4	Dark red	Insol.	Sol. HNO_3; insol. HAc
$Hg_3(AsO_3)_2$		Sl. sol.	Dec. by KOH
$Hg(BrO_3)_2 \cdot 2H_2O$	Crystalline, white	0.15 (cold)	Sol. HNO_3, HCl, $Hg(NO_3)_2$
$Hg_2(BrO_3)_2$	Crystalline, white	Dec.	Sl. sol. HNO_3
$HgBr_2$	Rhombic white	0.61 (25°)	Sol. alc., methyl alc.; v. sl. sol. ether
Hg_2Br_2	Tetragonal whitish-yellow	4×10^{-6} (25°)	Sol. acids; insol. alc., acetone
Hg_2CO_3	Yellowish-brown	Insol.	Sol. HNO_3, NH_4Cl; insol. alc.
$2HgO \cdot HgCO_3$	Brownish-red	Insol.	Sol. aq. CO_2, NH_4Cl

Formula	Color and Form	Solubility in H_2O (g. per 100 g. H_2O)	General Solubility
$HgNH_2Cl$	White powder or small prisms	Insol.	Dec. by acids
$Hg(ClO_3)_2$	Needles, white	25 (cold)	
$Hg_2(ClO_3)_2$	Rhombic, white	Sol.	Sol. alc., HAc
$HgCl_2$	White rhombic or powder	6.7 (20°)	Sol. alc., ether, HAc, pyridine
Hg_2Cl_2	Tetragonal white	2.1×10^{-4} (18°)	Sol. $Hg(NO_3)_2$, aq. reg.; sl. sol. hot HNO_3, HCl; insol. alc., ether
$HgCrO_4$	Rhombic red	Sl. sol., dec.	Dec. by acid; sol. NH_4Cl; insol. acetone
Hg_2CrO_4	Red needles or powder	V. sl. sol.	Sol. HNO_3, KCN
$Hg(CN)_2$	White tetragonal or powder	11.3 (25°)	Moderately sol. alc.; sol. NH_3; insol. benzene
$Hg_3[Fe(CN)_6]_2$		Very sol.	
$Hg_3Fe(CN)_6$		Insol.	
$Hg_2Fe(CN)_6$	Brown	Insol.	Insol. acids
HgF_2	Cubic white	Dec.	Sol. dil. HNO_3, HF
Hg_2F_2	Cubic yellow	Dec.	
$Hg(IO_3)_2$	White amorphous powder	Insol.	Sol. HCl, NH_4Cl, NaCl, KI; insol. HNO_3
$Hg_2(IO_3)_2$	Yellowish	Insol.	Sol. dil. HCl; insol. cold HNO_3
HgI_2	Tetragonal red or rhombic yellow crystals or powder	6×10^{-3} (25°)	Sl. sol. alc.; sol. ether, acetone, $Na_2S_2O_3$, alk. salts
Hg_2I_2	Tetragonal or amorphous yellow powder	V. sl. sol.	Sol. KI, NH_4OH; insol. alc., ether
$Hg(NO_3)_2$	Whitish-yellow deliquescent powder	V. sol.	Sol. HNO_3, NH_3, acetone; insol. alc.
$Hg_2(NO_3)_2 \cdot 2H_2O$	Monoclinic white, efflorescent	Dec.	Sol. dil. HNO_3; insol. NH_4OH
HgC_2O_4	White	Insol.	Sol. HCl; sl. sol. HNO_3
$Hg_2C_2O_4$	White	Insol.	Sl. sol. HNO_3

Formula	Color and Form	Solubility in H$_2$O (g. per 100 g. H$_2$O)	General Solubility
Hg$_3$(PO$_4$)$_2$	Yellowish-white powder	Insol.	Sol. acids, NH$_4$Cl; insol. alc.
Hg$_3$PO$_4$	White	Insol.	Sol. HNO$_3$, aq. HgNO$_3$; insol. H$_3$PO$_4$
HgSO$_4$	White rhombic or powder	Dec.	Sol. acids, NaCl; insol. alc., acetone, NH$_3$
Hg$_2$SO$_4$	Monoclinic colorless, yellowish-white powder	5.8×10^{-2} (25°)	Sol. H$_2$SO$_4$, HNO$_3$
HgS	Cubic black or amorphous black powder	Insol.	Sol. Na$_2$S, aq. reg., alk.; insol. HNO$_3$, alc.
Hg$_2$S	Black	Insol.	Insol. acid, (NH$_4$)$_2$S; sol. (NH$_4$)$_2$S$_x$
Hg(CNS)$_2$	White powder	7×10^{-2} (25°)	Sol. NH$_4$ salts, NH$_3$, HCl, KCN; sl. sol. alc., ether
Ag	Cubic white metal	Insol.	Sol. HNO$_3$, hot H$_2$SO$_4$. KCN; insol. alk.
Ag$_2$O	Cubic brownish-black	5.0×10^{-3} (25°)	Sol. acids, NH$_4$OH, KCN
AgC$_2$H$_3$O$_2$	White plates	1.12 (25°)	
Ag$_3$AsO$_4$	Cubic dark red	8.5×10^{-4} (20°)	Sol. HAc, NH$_4$OH
Ag$_3$AsO$_3$	Yellow powder	1.15×10^{-3} (20°)	Sol. HAc, NH$_4$OH, HNO$_3$; insol. alc.
AgBO$_2$	White	9×10^{-1} (25°)	Sol. acids
Ag$_2$B$_4$O$_7 \cdot$2H$_2$O	White	Sl. sol.	Sol. acids
AgBrO$_3$	Tetragonal white	1.96×10^{-1} (25°)	Sol. NH$_4$OH; sl. sol. HNO$_3$
AgBr	Cubic pale yellow	7.9×10^{-6} (20°)	Sol. KCN, Na$_2$S$_2$O$_3$; sl. sol. NH$_4$OH; insol. alc.
Ag$_2$CO$_3$	Yellow powder	3.2×10^{-3} (20°)	Sol. NH$_4$OH, NaS$_2$O$_3$; insol. alc.
AgClO$_3$	Tetragonal white	4.5×10^{-1} (20°)	Sl. sol. alc.
AgCl	Cubic white	1.87×10^{-4} (25°)	Sol. NH$_4$OH, Na$_2$S$_2$O$_3$, KCN
Ag$_2$CrO$_4$	Monoclinic red	1.4×10^{-3} (0°)	Sol. acids, NH$_4$OH, KCN

Formula	Color and Form	Solubility in H_2O (g. per 100 g. H_2O)	General Solubility
$Ag_2Cr_2O_7$	Triclinic red	$8.3 \times 10^{-3}(15°)$	Sol. acids, NH_4OH, KCN
$Ag_2(CN)_2$	Hexagonal white	$2.2 \times 10^{-5}(20°)$	Sol. HNO_3, NH_4OH, KCN, $Na_2S_2O_3$
$Ag_3Fe(CN)_6$	Orange	$6.6 \times 10^{-5}(20°)$	Sol. NH_4OH, hot $(NH_4)_2CO_3$; insol. acids
$Ag_4Fe(CN)_6 \cdot H_2O$	Yellow	Insol.	Sol. NH_4OH, KCN; insol. acids
AgF	Cubic yellow, deliquescent	180 (25°)	
$AgIO_3$	Rhombic white	$5.1 \times 10^{-3}(25°)$	Sol. NH_4OH, HNO_3, KI
AgI	Hexagonal yellow	$3 \times 10^{-7}(21°)$	Sol. KCN, $Na_2S_2O_3$; sl. sol. NH_4OH
$AgNO_3$	Rhombic white	240 (25°)	Sol. ether, glycerine; sl. sol. absolute alc.
$AgNO_2$	Rhombic white	$4.2 \times 10^{-1}(25°)$	Sol. HAc, NH_4OH, HNO_3; insol. alc.
$Ag_2C_2O_4$	White crystals	$3.4 \times 10^{-3}(18°)$	Sol. acids, NH_4OH, KCN
Ag_3PO_4	Cubic yellow	$6.5 \times 10^{-4}(19.5°)$	Sol. acids, NH_4OH, KCN; insol. NH_3
Ag_2SO_4	Rhombic white	$7.9 \times 10^{-1}(20°)$	Sol. acids, NH_4OH; insol. alc.
Ag_2S	Cubic black or rhombic gray-black	$1.4 \times 10^{-5}(20°)$	Sol. HNO_3, KCN
Ag_2SO_3	White crystals	V. sl. sol.	Sol. acids, NH_4OH, KCN; insol. HNO_3
AgCNS	White crystals or curd	$1.29 \times 10^{-5}(20°)$	Sol. NH_4OH; insol. acids
$Ag_2S_2O_3$	White	Sl. sol.	Sol. NH_4OH, $Na_2S_2O_3$
As_4	Hexagonal, silvery-grayish-black metal or amorphous black	Insol.	Sol. HNO_3
$As_2O_3 \, \alpha$	Cubic or fibrous or monoclinic white	2.13 (25°)	Sol. alc., alk., HCl
$As_2O_3 \, \beta$	Amorphous or vitreous white	3.7 (20°)	Sol. alk., HCl

Formula	Color and Form	Solubility in H_2O (g. per 100 g. H_2O)	General Solubility
As_2O_5	Amorphous white	150 (16°)	Sol. alc., acids, alk.
$H_3AsO_4 \cdot \frac{1}{2}H_2O$	White translucent crystals; hygroscopic	16.7 (cold)	Sol. alk., alc., glycerine
$HAsO_3$	White crystals	Forms H_3AsO_4	
$AsBr_3$	Yellowish-white prisms	Hydrolyzes	Sol. HCl, HBr, CS_2
$AsCl_5$	Colorless liquid	Hydrolyzes	
$AsCl_3$	Oily liquid	Hydrolyzes	Sol. HCl, HBr, PCl_3, alc., ether
AsF_5	Colorless gas	Sol.	Sol. alk., alc., ether, benzene
AsF_3	Oily liquid	Dec.	Sol. alc., ether, benzene, NH_4OH
AsI_3	Hexagonal red	Sl. sol., hydrolyzes	Sol. alc., ether, $CHCl_3$, CS_2
As_2S_5	Yellow	Insol.	Sol. alk., HNO_3, alkali sulfides
As_2S_3	Monoclinic yellow or red	5×10^{-5} (18°)	Sol. alc., alk., HNO_3, alk. carbonates
Sb	Hexagonal silvery-white metal	Insol.	Sol. hot conc. H_2SO_4, aqua regia
Sb_2O_3	Cubic or rhombic white	V. sl. sol.	Sol. HCl, KOH, HAc, tartaric acid
Sb_2O_5	Yellow powder	Insol.	Sol. HCl, acetone, NH_3, CS_2, $CHCl_3$
H_3SbO_4	White powder	Sl. sol.	Sol. KOH
$HSbO_3$	White powder	Sl. sol.	Sol. acids, KOH; insol. acetone
$H_4Sb_2O_7$	White powder	Sl. sol.	Sol. alk.
H_3SbO_3	White amorphous	Insol.	Insol. alc.
$HSbO_2$	White	Insol.	Insol. alc.
$SbBr_3$	Rhombic white	Hydrolyzes	Sol. HCl, HBr, CS_2, NH_3, alc., acetone
$SbCl_3$	Rhombic white	Hydrolyzes	Sol. alc., HCl, tartaric acid, CS_2
$SbCl_5$	Liquid, colorless	Hydrolyzes	Sol. HCl, tartaric acid
SbF_3	Octahedral grayish-white	494 (25°)	Insol. NH_3

Formula	Color and Form	Solubility in H_2O (g. per 100 g. H_2O)	General Solubility
SbF_5	Oily colorless liquid	Sol.	Sol. KF
SbI_3	Trigonal; monoclinic red; rhombic yellow	Hydrolyzes	Sol. HI, HCl, KI, alc., acetone, CS_2
SbI_5	Brown liquid	Hydrolyzes	
$Sb_2(SO_4)_3$	White powder, deliquescent	Insol.	Sol. acids
Sb_2S_5	Orange-yellow powder	Insol.	Sol. alk., NH_4HS, HCl; insol. alc.
Sb_2S_3	Rhombic red	$1.8 \times 10^{-4} (18°)$	Sol. alk., NH_4HS, K_2S, HCl; insol. HAc
Sn	Tetragonal or rhombic white, or cubic gray	Insol.	Sol. HCl, H_2SO_4, dil. HNO_3, aqua regia, hot KOH, NaOH
SnO	Tetragonal (cubic) black	Insol.	Sol. acids, fixed alk. hydroxides; sl. sol. NH_4Cl
SnO_2	Tetragonal white	Insol.	Insol. aqueous acids; sol. conc. H_2SO_4
$Sn(OH)_4 \cdot xH_2O$	White	Insol.	Sol. HNO_3
$Sn(OH)_2$	Amorphous yellow, reddish-yellow crystals	$2 \times 10^{-4} (cold)$	Sol. acids, alk.; insol. NH_4OH; sol. alk. carbonates
H_2SnO_3	Amorphous or colloidal white ppt.	Insol.	Sol. KOH, NaOH; insol. acids
$Sn(C_2H_3O_2)_2$	Yellowish powder	Decomposes	Sol. acids
$SnBr_4$	White rhombic pyramids, deliquescent	Sol., decomposes	Sol. acetone, $AsBr_3$, PCl_3
$SnBr_2$	Rhombic pale yellow	$85.2 (0°)$	
$SnCl_4$	Colorless liquid	Very sol.	
$SnCl_4 \cdot 5H_2O$	White monoclinic crystals	Very sol.	
$SnCl_2$	Rhombic white	$232 (25°)$	Sol. alc., ether, acetone, pyridine, methyl acetate
$SnCl_2 \cdot 2H_2O$	White monoclinic	$276 (25°)$	Sol. alc., ether, acetone, glacial HAc
$SnOCl_2$	White	Sol.	

Formula	Color and Form	Solubility in H_2O (g. per 100 g. H_2O)	General Solubility
$Sn(CrO_4)_2$	Brownish-yellow crystalline powder		
$SnCrO_4$	Brown	Sl. sol.	Sol. HCl
$Sn_3[Fe(CN)_6]_2$	White	Insol.	Sol. HCl
$SnFe(CN)_6$	Greenish-white gel	Insol.	Sol. hot HCl
$Sn_2Fe(CN)_6$	White gel	Insol.	Sol. HCl
SnF_4	White crystalline mass, hygroscopic	V. sol.	
SnF_2	White monoclinic crystals	Sol.	
SnI_4	Cubic yellow	Dec.	Sol. CS_2, alc., ether, $CHCl_3$, C_6H_6
SnI_2	Monoclinic yellowish-red	0.99 (20°)	Sol. KOH, HCl, HF, CS_2
$Sn(NO_3)_4$	Silky needles	Dec.	
$Sn(NO_3)_2 \cdot 20H_2O$	White leaflets	Dec.	Sol. HNO_3
SnC_2O_4	White crystals or heavy white powder	Insol.	Sol. HCl; sl. sol. NH_4Cl, $(NH_4)_2C_2O_4$
$Sn_3(PO_4)_2$	White amorphous solid	Insol.	Sol. acids, alk.
$Sn(SO_4)_2 \cdot 2H_2O$	Hexagonal prisms, deliquescent	V. sol.	Sol. ether, dil. H_2SO_4; reacts with HCl
$SnSO_4$	White-yellowish crystalline powder	19 (19°)	
SnS_2	Hexagonal golden yellow	2×10^{-5} (18°)	Sol. alk. sulfides, aqua regia, PCl_5, $SnCl_2$, alk. hydrox.; insol. HCl, HNO_3
SnS	Rhombic gray-black	2×10^{-6} (18°)	Sol. HCl, alk., $(NH_4)_2S_x$
Bi	Hexagonal silvery-white or reddish metal	Insol.	Sol. HNO_3, hot H_2SO_4, aqua regia; sl. sol. hot HCl
Bi_2O_5	Brown or dark red	Insol.	Sol. acids, KOH
Bi_2O_3	Rhombic yellow or cubic gray-black	Insol.	Sol. acids
$Bi(OH)_3$	White amorphous powder	Insol.	Sol. acids; insol. or sl. sol. conc. alk.

Formula	Color and Form	Solubility in H_2O (g. per 100 g. H_2O)	General Solubility
$BiBr_3$	Yellow crystalline powder, deliquescent	Dec.	Sol. HCl, HBr, ether; insol. alc.
BiOBr	White crystals or powder	Insol.	Sol. acids; insol. alc.
$BiCl_3$	White crystals, deliquescent	Dec.	Sol. acids, alc., ether, acetone
BiOCl	White crystals or powder	Insol.	Sol. acids; insol. acetone, tartaric acid, NH_3
$Bi_2O_3 \cdot CO_2 \cdot H_2O$	White powder	Insol.	Sol. acids
$Bi_2(CrO_4)_3$	Orange-red	8×10^{-5}	Sol. acids
BiF_3	White	Insol.	Sol. acids
BiOF	White crystals or powder	Insol.	Sol. acids
$Bi(IO_3)_3$	White	Insol.	Sl. sol., HNO_3; sol. HI, KI, abs. alc.
BiI_3	Hexagonal reddish- or brownish-gray, black	Insol.	Sol. HCl, HI, KI, abs. alc.
BiOI	Rhombic red crystals	Insol.	Sol. acids; insol. alc., $CHCl_3$, KI
$Bi(NO_3)_3 \cdot 5H_2O$	Triclinic white, sl. hygroscopic	Dec.	Very sol. HNO_3; sol. acids, acetone
$BiONO_3 \cdot H_2O$	Hexagonal plates or white powder	Insol.	Sol. acids; insol. alc.
$Bi_2(C_2O_4)_3$	White	Insol.	Sol. acids
$BiPO_4$	Monoclinic white	Insol.	Sol. HCl; insol. dil. HNO_3, alc.
$Bi_2(SO_4)_3$	White needles	Dec.	Sol. acids
Bi_2S_3	Rhombic brownish-black	$1.8 \times 10^{-5} (18°)$	Sol. HNO_3; insol. dil. acids
Cu	Cubic reddish metal	Insol.	Sol. HNO_3, hot H_2SO_4; v. sl. sol. HCl, NH_4OH
CuO	Cubic or triclinic black	Insol.	Sol. acids, NH_4Cl, KCN
Cu_2O	Cubic red	Insol.	Sol. HCl, NH_4Cl, NH_4OH; sl. sol. HNO_3; insol. alc.

Formula	Color and Form	Solubility in H_2O (g. per 100 g. H_2O)	General Solubility
$Cu(OH)_2$	Blue gel or amorphous blue powder	Insol.	Sol. acids, alc., NH_4OH, KCN
CuOH	Yellow	Insol.	Sol. acids, NH_4OH
$Cu(C_2H_3O_2)_2 \cdot H_2O$	Dark green powder	7.2 (15°)	Sol. alc., ether
$Cu_3(AsO_4)_2 \cdot 4H_2O$	Bluish-green	Insol.	Sol. acids, NH_4OH
$Cu(As_3O_2)_2$	Green	Sl. sol.	Sol. acids
$Cu(BrO_3)_2 \cdot 6H_2O$	Cubic bluish-green	V. sol.	Sol. NH_4OH
$CuBr_2$	Monoclinic black, deliquescent	V. sol.	Sol. alc., acetone, NH_3; insol. C_6H_6
Cu_2Br_2	Cubic, tetrahedral white	V. sl. sol.	Sol. HBr, HCl, HNO_3, NH_4OH; insol. acetone
Cu_2CO_3	Yellow	Insol.	Sol. acids, NH_4OH
$CuCO_3 \cdot Cu(OH)_2$	Monoclinic dark green	Insol.	Sol. acids, NH_4OH, KCN; insol. alc.
$Cu(ClO_3)_2 \cdot 6H_2O$	Cubic green, deliquescent	240 (20°)	Sol. alc., acetone
$CuCl_2 \cdot 2H_2O$	Rhombic green, deliquescent	97 (25°)	Sol. alc., ether, NH_4Cl
Cu_2Cl_2	Cubic white	1.2×10^{-2} (20°)	Sol. HCl, NH_4OH
$CuCrO_4$	Brown	Insol.	Sol. acids
$Cu_2Cr_2O_7 \cdot 2H_2O$	Black crystals, deliquescent	V. sol.	Sol. acids, alc., NH_4OH
$Cu(CN)_2$	Yellowish-green powder	Insol.	Sol. acids, alk., KCN, C_5H_5N
$Cu_2(CN)_2$	Monoclinic white	Insol.	Sol. HCl, NH_4OH, KCN; sl. sol. NH_3
$Cu_3[Fe(CN)_6]_2$	Yellowish-green	Insol.	Sol. NH_4OH; insol. HCl
$Cu_3Fe(CN)_6$	Brownish-red	Insol.	Sol. NH_4OH; insol. HCl
$Cu_2Fe(CN)_6 \cdot 7H_2O$	Reddish-brown	Insol.	Sol. NH_4OH; insol. acids, NH_3
$Cu_4Fe(CN)_6$	Brownish-red	Insol.	Sol. NH_4OH; insol. NH_4Cl
$CuF_2 \cdot 2H_2O$	Monoclinic blue	Sl. sol.	Sol. alc., HCl, HF, HNO_3; insol. acetone, NH_3
Cu_2F_2	Red crystals	Insol.	Sol. HCl, HF, HNO_3; insol. alc.

Formula	Color and Form	Solubility in H_2O (g. per 100 g. H_2O)	General Solubility
$Cu(IO_3)_2 \cdot H_2O$	Triclinic blue	0.33 (15°)	Sol. NH_4OH, dil. H_2SO_4; insol. alc., dil. HNO_3
Cu_2I_2	Cubic white	8×10^{-4} (18°)	Sol. KI, KCN, NH_4OH; insol. acids, alc.
$Cu(NO_3)_2 \cdot 3H_2O$	Blue, deliquescent	197 (30°)	Sol. alc.
$Cu(NO_3)_2 \cdot 6H_2O$	Blue crystals	233 (25°)	Sol. alc.
$CuC_2O_4 \cdot \frac{1}{2}H_2O$	Bluish-white	2.4×10^{-3} (25°)	Sol. NH_4OH; insol. HAc
$Cu_3(PO_4)_2 \cdot 3H_2O$	Rhombic blue	Insol.	Sol. acids, NH_4OH, H_3PO_4; insol. NH_3
$CuSO_4$	Greenish-white, rhombic	22.6 (25°)	Insol. alc.
$CuSO_4 \cdot 5H_2O$	Triclinic blue	35.3 (25°)	Insol. alc.
Cu_2SO_4	Gray powder	Dec.	Sol. HNO_3
CuS	Hexagonal or mono-clinic black	Insol.	Sol. HNO_3, KCN, hot conc. HCl, H_2SO_4; insol. alc., alk.
Cu_2S	Rhombic black	5×10^{-4} (18°)	Sol. HNO_3, NH_4OH; insol. acetone
$Cu_2SO_3 \cdot H_2O$	Hexagonal red or white	Sl. sol.	Sol. NH_4OH, HCl; insol. alc., ether
$Cu(SCN)_2$	Black	Dec.	Sol. NH_4OH, acids
$Cu_2(SCN)_2$	White	5×10^{-5} (20°)	Sol. NH_4OH, conc. acids, ether; insol. alc.
Cd	Hexagonal silvery-white metal	Insol.	Sol. acids, NH_4NO_3, hot H_2SO_4
CdO	Amorphous brown	Insol.	Sol. acids, NH_4 salts; insol. alk.
$Cd(OH)_2$	Trigonal or amor-phous white	2.6×10^{-4} (25°)	Sol. acids, NH_4 salts; insol. alk.
$Cd(C_2H_3O_2)_2 \cdot H_2O$	White needles	43.6 (0°)	Sl. sol. alc.
$Cd(BrO_3)_2 \cdot H_2O$	Rhombic white	125 (17°)	Insol. alc.
$CdBr_2 \cdot 4H_2O$	Small white needles, efflorescent	129 (20°)	Sol. alc., HCl
$CdCO_3$	Trigonal white	Insol.	Sol. acids, KCN, NH_4 salts; insol. NH_3

Formula	Color and Form	Solubility in H_2O (g. per 100 g. H_2O)	General Solubility
$Cd(ClO_3)_2 \cdot 2H_2O$	White prisms, deliquescent	500 (20°)	Sol. acids, acetone, alc.
$CdCl_2 \cdot 2\frac{1}{2}H_2O$	Cubic white	142 (20°)	Sl. sol. alc.; insol. acetone, ether
$CdCrO_4$	Yellow	Insol.	Sol. acids
$Cd(CN)_2$	White crystals	1.7 (15°)	Sol. acids, KCN, NH_4OH
$Cd_2Fe(CN)_6$		Insol.	Sol. HCl
CdF_2	Cubic white	4.4 (25°)	Sol. acids, HF; insol. alc., NH_3
$Cd(IO_3)_2 \cdot H_2O$	Monoclinic, small crystals	Sl. sol.	Sol. HNO_3, NH_4OH
CdI_2	Hexagonal brownish	86.3 (25°)	Sol. acids, ether, alc., NH_4OH; sl. sol. NH_3, acetone
$Cd(NO_3)_2 \cdot 4H_2O$	Prismatic white needles, hygroscopic	168 (20°)	Sol. alc., NH_3; insol. HNO_3
$Cd(NO_2)_2 \cdot H_2O$	White	V. sol.	
$CdC_2O_4 \cdot 3H_2O$	White	3.4×10^{-3} (0°)	Sol. acids, NH_4OH; insol. alk.
$Cd_3(PO_4)_2$	Amorphous white	Insol.	Sol. acids, NH_4 salts
$CdSO_4$	Rhombic white	77 (25°)	Insol. alc., acetone, NH_3
CdS	Hexagonal yellow-orange	Insol.	Sol. NH_4OH, acids
$CdSO_3$	White crystals	Sl. sol.	Sol. acids, NH_4OH; insol. alc.
$CdS_2O_3 \cdot 2H_2O$	White	Sol.	Sol. acids
Co	Cubic silvery-gray metal	Insol.	Sol. acids
Co_2O_3	Grayish-black powder	Insol.	Sol. acids; insol. alc.
CoO	Cubic grayish-brown	Insol.	Sol. acids, NH_4OH; insol. alc.
$Co(OH)_3$	Brownish-black powder	Insol.	Sol. acids; insol. alc.
$Co(OH)_2$	Rhombic rose-red	Insol.	Sol. acids, NH_4 salts; insol. alk.

Formula	Color and Form	Solubility in H_2O (g. per 100 g. H_2O)	General Solubility
$Co(C_2H_3O_2)_2 \cdot 4H_4O$	Monoclinic reddish-violet, deliquescent	Sol.	Sol. acids, alc.
$Co(BrO_3)_2 \cdot 6H_2O$	Octagonal red	45.5 (17°)	Sol. NH_4OH
$CoBr_2$	Green crystals, deliquescent	199 (60°)	Sol. alc., ether
$CoCO_3$	Trigonal red	Insol.	Sol. acids; insol. NH_3
$Co(ClO_3)_2 \cdot 6H_2O$	Cubic red, deliquescent	268 (20°)	Sol. alc.
$CoCl_3$	Ruby-red crystals	Sol.	Sol. alc.
$CoCl_2$	Blue crystals	51 (20°)	Sol. alc.
$CoCl_2 \cdot 6H_2O$	Monoclinic red	94 (20°)	Sol. alc., acetone
$CoCrO_4$	Yellowish-brown powder	Insol.	Sol. acids, NH_4OH
$Co(CN)_2 \cdot 2H_2O$	Buff	Insol.	Sol. KCN, HCl, NH_4OH
$Co_3[Fe(CN)_6]_2$	Red	Insol.	Sol. NH_4OH; insol. HCl
$Co_2Fe(CN)_6 \cdot 7H_2O$	Gray-green	Insol.	Sol. KCN; insol. HCl
$CoF_2 \cdot 4H_2O$	Monoclinic rose-red	Sol.	Sol. HF
CoF_3	Green powder	Dec.	
$Co(IO_3)_2$	Blue-violet needles	0.46 (20°)	Sol. HCl, HNO_3
CoI_2	Brownish-red, deliquescent	319 (40°)	Very sol. alc., acetone
$Co(NO_3)_2 \cdot 6H_2O$	Monoclinic red, deliquescent	161 (20°)	Sol. alc., acetone; sl. sol. NH_3
CoC_2O_4	Reddish-white	Insol.	Sol. acids, NH_4OH
$Co_3(PO_4)_2$	Reddish	Insol.	Sol. H_3PO_4, NH_4OH
$Co_2(SO_4)_3$	Black crystalline powder	Sol., dec.	Sol. H_2SO_4
$CoSO_4$	Red powder	36 (20°)	Insol. NH_3
Co_2S_3	Black crystals	Insol.	Sol. acids
CoS	Hexagonal black	Insol.	Sol. acids, alc.
$CoSO_3 \cdot 5H_2O$	Red	Insol.	Sol. H_2SO_3
$Co(SCN)_2 \cdot 4H_2O$	Dark blue crystals, hygroscopic	Sol.	
Ni	Cubic silvery metal	Insol.	Sol. dil. HNO_3; sl. sol. HCl, H_2SO_4

Formula	Color and Form	Solubility in H_2O (g. per 100 g. H_2O)	General Solubility
NiO	Cubic greenish-black	Insol.	Sol. acids, NH_4OH
$Ni(OH)_3$	Black amorphous powder	Insol.	Sol. acids, NH_4OH, NH_4Cl
$Ni(OH)_2$	Green amorphous or crystals	1.3×10^{-3} (cold)	Sol. acids, NH_4OH
$4Ni(OH)_2 \cdot H_2O$	Light green powder	Insol.	Sol. acids, NH_4OH; insol. alk.
$Ni(C_2H_3O_2)_2$	Green prisms	16.6 (cold)	Insol. alc.
$Ni(BrO_3)_2 \cdot 6H_2O$	Monoclinic green	28 (cold)	
$NiBr_2$	Yellowish-brown, deliquescent	133 (20°)	Sol. alc., ether, NH_4OH
$NiCO_3$	Rhombic light green	9.3×10^{-3} (25°)	Sol. acids
$Ni(ClO_3)_2 \cdot 6H_2O$	Dark red	198 (20°)	
$NiCl_2$	Yellow scales, deliquescent	60 (20°)	Sol. alc., NH_4OH; insol. NH_3
$NiCl_2 \cdot 6H_2O$	Monoclinic green, deliquescent	109 (20°)	Very sol. alc.
$Ni(CN)_2 \cdot 4H_2O$	Light green plates or powder	Insol.	Sol. KCN, NH_4OH, alk.; sl. sol. dil. acids
$Ni_2Fe(CN)_6 \cdot 11H_2O$	Greenish-white	Insol.	Sol. NH_4OH, KCN; insol. HCl
NiF_2	Quadrilateral green	0.02 (cold)	Insol. acids, alc., ether, NH_3
NiI_2	Black, deliquescent	147 (20°)	Sol. alc.
$Ni(NO_3)_2 \cdot 6H_2O$	Monoclinic green, deliquescent	153 (20°)	Sol. alc., NH_4OH
$NiC_2O_4 \cdot 2H_2O$	Light green powder	Insol.	Sol. acids, NH_4 salts
$Ni_3(PO_4)_2 \cdot 7H_2O$	Green powder	Insol.	Sol. acids, NH_4 salts
$NiSO_4$	Cubic yellow	37 (20°)	Insol. alc., ether, acetone
$NiSO_4 \cdot 7H_2O$	Rhombic green	67 (20°)	Sol. alc.
NiS	Trigonal or amorphous black	Insol.	Sol. HNO_3, KHS, aqua regia; sl. sol. acids
$NiSO_3 \cdot 6H_2O$	Tetrahedral green	Insol.	Sol. HCl, H_2SO_4
Mn	Cubic or tetragonal gray-pink metal	Reacts slowly	Sol. dil. acids
MnO	Cubic green	Insol.	Sol. acids, NH_4Cl

Formula	Color and Form	Solubility in H_2O (g. per 100 g. H_2O)	General Solubility
MnO_2	Rhombic black or brownish black powder	Insol.	Sol. HCl; insol. HNO_3, acetone
$Mn(OH)_2$	Trigonal white-pink	2×10^{-4} (18°)	Sol. acids, NH_4 salts; insol. alk.
$Mn(C_2H_3O_2)_2 \cdot 4H_2O$	Monoclinic pale red	Sol.	Sol. alc.
$MnBr_2$	Rose-red	142 (20°)	Insol. NH_3
$MnBr_2 \cdot 4H_2O$	Monoclinic rose-red, deliquescent	189 (20°)	
$MnCO_3$	Trigonal rose-pink or amorphous light brown powder	6.5×10^{-3} (25°)	Sol. dil. acids; insol. NH_3, alc.
$MnCl_2$	Cubic pink, deliquescent	75 (20°)	Sol. alc.; insol. ether, NH_3
$MnCl_2 \cdot 4H_2O$	Monoclinic rose, deliquescent	117 (20°)	
$Mn_2Fe(CN)_6 \cdot 7H_2O$	Greenish-white powder	Insol.	Sol. HCl; insol. NH_4 salts
MnF_2	Red quadrilateral prisms or reddish powder	Insol.	Sol. acids; insol. alc., ether
MnF_3	Red crystals	Dec.	Sol. acids
MnI_2	Yellowish-brown crystalline mass, deliquescent	Sol., dec.	
$MnI_2 \cdot 4H_2O$	Monoclinic rose-red, deliquescent	Sol.	
$Mn(NO_3)_2 \cdot 6H_2O$	Monoclinic rose-white	252 (25°)	V. sol. alc.
$MnC_2O_4 \cdot 2\frac{1}{2}H_2O$	White	0.03 (25°)	Sol. dil. acids
$Mn_3(PO_4)_2 \cdot 7H_2O$	White-pink amorphous powder	V. sl. sol.	Sol. acids; insol. alc.
$Mn_2(SO_4)_3$	Green crystals, deliquescent	Dec.	Sol. HCl, dil. H_2SO_4; insol. conc. H_2SO_4, HNO_3
$MnSO_4 \cdot 4H_2O$	Monoclinic or rhombic pink, efflorescent	95 (20°)	Sol. alc.; insol. ether

Formula	Color and Form	Solubility in H$_2$O (g. per 100 g. H$_2$O)	General Solubility
MnS	Cubic green or amorphous pink	4.7×10^{-4} (18°)	Sol. dil. acids, alc.; insol. (NH$_4$)$_2$S
Mn(SCN)$_2 \cdot$3H$_2$O	Deliquescent	Sol.	V. sol. alc.
Al	Cubic silvery-white metal	Insol.	Sol. alk., HCl, H$_2$SO$_4$; insol. HNO$_3$, HAc
Al$_2$O$_3$	Hexagonal or trigonal white	Insol.	V. sl. sol. acids, alk
Al(OH)$_3$	Monoclinic or amorphous gelatinous white ppt.	1.5×10^{-4} (20°)	Sol. acids, alk.; insol. alc.
Al$_2$O(C$_2$H$_3$O$_2$)$_4 \cdot$ 4H$_2$O	White amorphous powder	Insol.	Sol. acids; insol. NH$_4$ salts
Al(BrO$_3$)$_3 \cdot$9H$_2$O	White crystals, hygroscopic	Sol.	Sl. sol. acids
AlBr$_3$	Trigonal white plates	Dissolves with violence	Sol. alc., CS$_2$, acetone
AlBr$_3 \cdot$6H$_2$O	White-yellowish needles, deliquescent	Sol.	Sol. alc., CS$_2$, amyl alc.
AlBr$_3 \cdot$15H$_2$O	White needles	Sol.	Sol. alc.
Al(ClO$_3$)$\cdot$6H$_2$O	Rhombohedral white, deliquescent	V. sol.	Sol. dil. HCl
AlCl$_3$	Hexagonal white, very deliquescent	70 (15°); dissolves with violence	Sol. CCl$_4$, ether, alc.; insol. C$_6$H$_6$
AlCl$_3 \cdot$6H$_2$O	Trigonal white, deliquescent	Sol.	Sol. ether, alc.
Al$_4$[Fe(CN)$_6$]$_3 \cdot$ 17H$_2$O	Brown powder	Sl. sol.	Sol. dil. acids
AlF$_3$	Triclinic white	Sol.	Insol. acids, alc., alk., acetone
AlI$_3 \cdot$6H$_2$O	White-yellow crystals	V. sol.	Sol. alc., CS$_2$
Al(NO$_3$)$_3 \cdot$9H$_2$O	Rhombic white, deliquescent	113 (25°)	Sol. alc., alk., acetone, CS$_2$, HNO$_3$
Al$_2$(C$_2$O$_4$)$_3 \cdot$4H$_2$O	White powder	Insol.	Sol. acids; insol. alc.
AlPO$_4$	Rhombic plates	Insol.	Sol. acids, alk.; insol. alc.

Formula	Color and Form	Solubility in H_2O (g. per 100 g. H_2O)	General Solubility
$AlK(SO_4)_2 \cdot 12H_2O$	Cubic or monoclinic white	10.8 (20°)	Sol. dil. acids; insol. alc.
$Al_2(SO_4)_3$	White powder	36 (20°)	Sol. dil. acids; sl. sol. alc.
$Al_2(SO_4)_3 \cdot 9H_2O$	Monoclinic white	53 (20°)	Sol. acids, alk.
$Al_2(SO_4)_3 \cdot 18H_2O$	Monoclinic white	70.6 (20°)	Insol. alc.
Al_2S_3	Hexagonal yellow	Dec.	Sol. acids; insol. acetone
Cr	Cubic steel gray, very hard metal	Insol.	Sol. HCl, dil. H_2SO_4; insol. HNO_3
Cr_2O_3	Hexagonal green	Insol.	Insol. acids, alc., alk.
CrO	Black	Insol.	Insol. dil. HNO_3
CrO_3	Rhombic red, deliquescent	168 (20°)	Sol. ether, alc., H_2SO_4
$Cr(OH)_3$	Blue-gray green gelatinous or violet amorphous	Insol.	Sol. acids, alk.; sl. sol. NH_4OH
$Cr(OH)_3 \cdot 2H_2O$	Green	Insol.	Sol. acids, alk., $NaHSO_3$
$Cr(OH)_2$	Yellowish-brown	Dec.	Sol. acids
$Cr(C_2H_3O_2)_3 \cdot H_2O$	Gray-green powder or bluish-green pasty mass	Sol.	Insol. alc.
$CrBr_3$	Hexagonal olive-green	(1) 200 (cold) (2) Insol. (insol. modification)	V. sol. alc.; dec. by alk.
$CrBr_3 \cdot 6H_2O$	Hexagonal green plates, deliquescent	200 (cold)	V. sol. alc.; sol. fused Na_2O_2; insol. ether
$CrCO_3$	Amorphous gray-black	V. sl. sol.	Insol. ether, alc.; sol. mineral acids
$CrCl_3$	(1) Insol. violet plates (2) Sol. deliquescent crystals	Insol. 233 (25)°	Insol. acids, CS_2, acetone, alc.
$CrCl_3 \cdot 10H_2O$	Green crystalline powder	V. sol.	V. sol. alc.

Formula	Color and Form	Solubility in H_2O (g. per 100 g. H_2O)	General Solubility
$CrCl_2$	White needles, deliquescent	V. sol.	Sl. sol. alc.; insol. ether
CrF_3	Rhombic green	Insol.	Sl. sol. acids; insol. alc., NH_3
$CrF_3 \cdot 4H_2O$	Cubic octahedral green	Sol.	Sol. acids; insol. alc., NH_3
CrF_2	Green crystals	Sl. sol.	Sol. hot HCl; insol. alc.
CrI_2		V. sol.	
$Cr(NO_3)_3 \cdot 7\frac{1}{2}H_2O$	Monoclinic purple	Sol.	
$Cr(NO_3)_3 \cdot 9H_2O$	Monoclinic purple	Sol.	Sol. acids, alc., alk., acetone
$CrC_2O_4 \cdot H_2O$	Yellow crystalline powder	Sol. (hot)	
$CrPO_4 \cdot 3H_2O$	Violet crystals	Sl. sol.	Sol. acids, alk.; insol. HAc
$CrPO_4 \cdot 4H_2O$	Green crystals	Sl. sol.	Sol. acids
$CrPO_4 \cdot 6H_2O$	Triclinic violet	Sl. sol.	Sol. acids, alk.; insol. HAc
$CrK(SO_4)_2 \cdot 12H_2O$	Cubic octahedral red or green	43.9 (25°)	Sol. dil. acids; insol. alc.
$Cr_2(SO_4)_3$	Violet or red powder	Insol. and sol.	Insol. acids; sol. alc.
$Cr_2(SO_4)_3 \cdot 5H_2O$	Green amorphous	Sol.	V. sol. alc.; sol. H_2SO_4
$Cr_2(SO_4)_3 \cdot 15H_2O$	Dark green amorphous scales	Sol.	Insol. alc.
$Cr_2(SO_4)_3 \cdot 18H_2O$	Cubic octahedral, blue-violet	120 (20°)	Sol. alc.
$CrSO_4 \cdot 7H_2O$	Blue	12.3 (0°)	Sl. sol. alc.
Cr_2S_3	Brownish-black powder	Insol., dec.	Sol. HNO_3; dec. by alc.
CrS	Black powder	Insol.	V. sol. acids
Fe	Cubic silvery metal	Insol.	Sol. acids; insol. alk., alc., ether
Fe_2O_3	Hexagonal red-brown to black	Insol.	Sol. HCl
FeO	Black	Insol.	Sol. acids; insol. alk., alc.

Formula	Color and Form	Solubility in H_2O (g. per 100 g. H_2O)	General Solubility
Fe_3O_4	Cubic black or reddish-brown powder	Insol.	Sl. sol. acids; insol. alc., ether
$Fe(OH)_3$	Red-brown	Insol.	Sol. acids; insol. alc., ether
$Fe(OH)_2$	Hexagonal pale green or white amorphous	6.7×10^{-4} (cold)	Sol. acids, NH_4Cl; insol. alk.
$Fe(C_2H_3O_2)_2 \cdot 4H_2O$	Needles	V. sol.	
$FeOH(C_2H_3O_2)_2$	Brown-red powder	Insol.	Sol. acids, alc.
$Fe(NH_4)_2(SO_4)_2 \cdot 6H_2O$	Monoclinic green	26.9 (20°)	Insol. alc.
$FeBr_3$	Dark red-brown deliquescent	Sol.	Sol. alc., ether; sl. sol. NH_3
$FeBr_2$	Hexagonal greenish-yellow	112 (20°)	Sol. alc.
$FeCO_3$	Trigonal gray	6.7×10^{-3} (25°)	Sol. aq. CO_2, acids
$FeCO_3 \cdot H_2O$	Amorphous white	Sl. sol.	Sol. acids, aq. CO_2
$FeCl_3$	Hexagonal blackbrown	92 (20°)	Sol. alc., ether, acetone
$FeCl_2$	Hexagonal green to yellow, deliquescent	66 (20°)	Sol. alc., acetone; insol. ether
$FeCl_2 \cdot 4H_2O$	Monoclinic bluegreen, deliquescent	103 (20°)	Sol. alc.
$Fe_2(Cr_2O_7)_3$	Red-brown granular	Sol.	Sol. acids
$Fe_3[Fe(CN)_6]_2$	Deep blue	Insol.	Insol. alc., dil. acids
$Fe_4[Fe(CN)_6]_3$	Dark blue crystals	Insol.	Sol. HCl, H_2SO_4; insol. alc., ether
$Fe_2Fe(CN)_6$	Amorphous bluewhite	Insol.	
FeF_3	Rhombic green	Sl. sol.	Sol. acids; insol. alc., ether
$FeF_3 \cdot 4\frac{1}{2}H_2O$	Yellow crystals	Sl. sol.	Insol. alc.
$FeF_2 \cdot 8H_2O$	Green-blue	Sl. sol.	Sol. acids, HF; insol. alc., ether
FeI_2	Hexagonal gray	Sol.	
$FeI_2 \cdot 4H_2O$	Gray-black crystals, deliquescent	V. sol.	Sol. alc., ether

Formula	Color and Form	Solubility in H_2O (g. per 100 g. H_2O)	General Solubility
$Fe(NO_3)_3 \cdot 6H_2O$	Cubic yellowish-white	Sol.	
$Fe(NO_3)_3 \cdot 9H_2O$	Monoclinic white to pale violet, deliquescent	Sol.	Sol. alc., acetone; sl. sol. HNO_3
$Fe(NO_3)_2 \cdot 6H_2O$	Rhombic green	134 (20°)	
$Fe_2(C_2O_4)_3$	Amorphous yellowish-white	V. sol.	Sol. acids; insol. alc.
$FeC_2O_4 \cdot 2H_2O$	Rhombic pale yellow	0.022 (cold)	Sol. acids
$FePO_4 \cdot 2H_2O$	Yellowish-white amorphous	V. sl. sol.	Sol. HCl, H_2SO_4
$Fe_3(PO_4)_2 \cdot 8H_2O$	Monoclinic blue-white	Insol.	Sol. acids; insol. HAc
$Fe_2(SO_4)_3$	Rhombic yellow	Sl. sol.	Insol. H_2SO_4, NH_3
$Fe_2(SO_4)_3 \cdot 9H_2O$	Rhombic, deliquescent	V. sol.	Sol. alc.
$FeSO_4 \cdot 7H_2O$	Monoclinic blue-green	48.4 (20°)	Insol. alc.
Fe_2S_3	Yellow or green	V. sl. sol., dec.	Dec. by acids
FeS	Hexagonal brown-black	6.2×10^{-4} (18°)	Sol. acids; insol. NH_3
$FeSO_3 \cdot 2\frac{1}{2}H_2O$	Green	V. sl. sol.	Sol. H_2SO_3; insol. alc.
FeS_2	Yellow	Insol.	Sol. HNO_3; insol. dil. acids
$Fe(SCN)_3 \cdot 3H_2O$	Cubic red-black, deliquescent	Sol.	Sol. alc., ether
$Fe(SCN)_2 \cdot 3H_2O$	Rhombic green	V. sol.	Sol. alc., ether, acetone
$FeS_2O_3 \cdot 5H_2O$	Green crystals, deliquescent	V. sol.	V. sol. alc.
Zn	Hexagonal bluish-white metal	Insol.	Sol. acids, alk., HAc
ZnO	White or yellowish amorphous powder	1.6×10^{-4} (29°)	Sol. mineral acids, dil. HAc, NH_4OH
ZnO_2	Yellowish-white powder	2×10^{-3} (cold)	Dec. by acids
$Zn(OH)_2$	Rhombic white	4.2×10^{-4} (18°)	Sol. acids, alk.
$Zn(C_2H_3O_2)_2$	Monoclinic white	30 (20°)	Sol. hot alc.

Formula	Color and Form	Solubility in H_2O (g. per 100 g. H_2O)	General Solubility
$ZnBr_2$	Rhombic white, hygroscopic	445 (20°)	V. sol. alc., ether, NH_4OH
$ZnCO_3$	Trigonal white	1×10^{-3} (15°)	Sol. acids, alk., NH_4 salts; insol. NH_3, acetone, pyridine
$Zn(ClO_3)_2 \cdot 4H_2O$	Cubic yellowish-white, deliquescent	262 (20°)	Sol. alc., glycerine, ether
$ZnCl_2$	Cubic white, deliquescent	431 (25°)	Sol. alc., ether; insol. NH_3
$ZnCr_2O_7$	Orange-yellow powder	Insol.	Sol. acids; insol. alc., ether
$Zn(CN)_2$	Rhombic white	Insol.	Sol. alk., KCN, NH_3; insol. alc.
$Zn_2Fe(CN)_6$	White powder	Insol.	Sol. excess alk.; insol. dil. acids
ZnF_2	Monoclinic or triclinic white	Sl. sol.	Sol. hot acids, NH_4OH; insol. alc., NH_3
$Zn(IO_3)_2$	White crystalline powder	Sl. sol.	Sol. HNO_3, alk.
ZnI_2	Cubic white or white powder, hygroscopic	431 (15°)	Sol. acids, alc., ether, NH_3, $(NH_4)_2CO_3$
$Zn(NO_3)_2 \cdot 6H_2O$	Tetragonal white	185 (20°)	V. sol. alc.
$ZnC_2O_4 \cdot 2H_2O$	White powder	7.9×10^{-4} (18°)	Sol. acids, alk.
$Zn_3(PO_4)_2$	Rhombic white	Insol.	Sol. acids, NH_4OH; insol. alc.
$Zn_2P_2O_7$	White powder	Insol.	Sol. acids, alk., NH_4OH
$ZnSO_4 \cdot 6H_2O$	Monoclinic or tetragonal white	103.3 (20°)	
ZnS	Hexagonal white	6.9×10^{-4} (18°)	V. sol. acids; insol. HAc
$ZnSO_3 \cdot 2H_2O$	White crystalline powder	V. sl. sol.	Sol. H_2SO_3; insol. alc.
$Zn(SCN)_2$	White powder	Sol.	Sol. alc., NH_4OH
Ba	Yellowish-silvery metal	Reacts	Sol. alc., acids; insol. C_6H_6
BaO	Cubic or hexagonal white; yellowish-white powder	4.2 (25°) forms $Ba(OH)_2$	Sol. dil. acids, alc.; insol. NH_3, acetone

reduction of $Bi(OH)_3$ to black
metallic Bi by treatment of an
alkaline solution of Sodium Stannite

Conf. for Bismuth

$$2Bi(OH)_3 + 3Sn(OH)_4^{=} \rightarrow 2Bi' + 3Sn(OH)_6^{=}$$

$$3e + Bi^{+3} \rightarrow Bi^0 \quad 2$$
$$2e + Sn^{+4} \rightarrow Sn^{+6} \quad 3$$

Confirm. for manganese

$$MnO + H_2O_2 + 2H^+ \rightarrow Mn^{++} + O_2 + 2H_2O$$

$$5HBiO_3 + 2Mn^{++} + 9H^+ \rightarrow 4Mn^- + 5Bi^{+++} + 7H_2O$$

$$5e - Mn^{++} \rightarrow Mn^{+7}$$
$$2e + Bi^{+5} \rightarrow Bi^{+3}$$

Purple sol.,
shows presence
of Mn^{++}

$HgNH_2Cl + 2H^+ + 3Cl^- \Rightarrow HgCl_4^= + NH_4^+$

sol boiled to eliminate excess Bromate

$2BrO_3^- + 10Cl^- + 12H^+ \rightarrow Br_2 + 5Cl_2 + 6H_2O$

$2HgCl_4^= + SnCl_4^= \rightarrow Hg_2Cl_2 + SnCl_6^= + 4Cl^-$

$Hg_2Cl_2 + SnCl_4^= \rightarrow 2Hg + SnCl_6^=$

Precipitation of Manganesum

$HPO_4^= + NH_4OH \rightarrow PO_4^{\equiv} + NH_4^+ + H_2O$

$PO_4^{\equiv} + Mg^{++} + NH_4^+ \rightarrow$ <u>$MgNH_4PO_4$</u> white

Confirmation for Mg

$MgNH_4PO_4 + 2H^+ \Rightarrow Mg^{++} + NH_4^+ + H_2PO_4^-$

the

Formula	Color and Form	Solubility in H_2O (g. per 100 g. H_2O)	General Solubility
BaO_2	Gray-white powder	V. sl. sol.	Sol. dil. acids; insol. acetone
$Ba(OH)_2 \cdot 8H_2O$	Monoclinic white	8.7 (25°)	Sl. sol. alc.
$Ba(C_2H_3O_2)_2 \cdot H_2O$	Triclinic white	80 (30°)	Sl. sol. alc.
$Ba_3(AsO_4)_2$	Black	0.055 (cold)	Sol. acids, NH_4Cl
$Ba(BrO_3)_2 \cdot H_2O$	Monoclinic white	0.83 (25°)	Insol. alc., acetone
$BaBr_2 \cdot 2H_2O$	Monoclinic white	117 (25°)	V. sol. CH_3OH; sol. alc.
$BaCO_3$	Rhombic or hexagonal white	2×10^{-3} (18°)	Sol. acids, NH_4Cl; insol. alc.
$Ba(ClO_3)_2 \cdot H_2O$	Monoclinic white	35.7 (25°)	Sl. sol. alc., acetone, HCl
$Ba(ClO_4)_2$	Hexagonal white	286 (20°)	V. sol. alc.
$BaCl_2 \cdot 2H_2O$	Rhombic white	42 (20°)	Sl. sol. HCl, HNO_3; insol. alc.
$BaCrO_4$	Rhombic yellow	3.4×10^{-4} (16°)	Sol. mineral acids
$BaCr_2O_7$	Monoclinic red	Sl. sol.	Sol. hot conc. H_2SO_4
$Ba(CN)_2$	White crystalline powder	80 (14°)	
$Ba_2Fe(CN)_6 \cdot 6H_2O$	Monoclinic yellow	0.17 (15°)	
BaF_2	Cubic white	0.17 (10°)	Sol. acids, NH_4Cl
$Ba(IO_3)_2 \cdot H_2O$	Monoclinic white	2.3×10^{-2} (20°)	Sol. HCl, HNO_3; insol. alc., acetone, H_2SO_4
$BaI_2 \cdot 2H_2O$	Rhombic white deliquescent	222 (20°)	Sl. sol. alc.; sol. acetone
$Ba(NO_3)_2$	Cubic white	9.4 (20°)	Sl. sol. acids; insol. alc.
$Ba(NO_2)_2 \cdot H_2O$	Hexagonal yellowish-white	72 (20°)	V. sol. HCl; sl. sol. alc.; insol. acetone
$BaC_2O_4 \cdot H_2O$	White	8.5×10^{-3} (25°)	Sol. acids, NH_4Cl; insol. alc.
$Ba_3(PO_4)_2$	Cubic white	Insol.	Sol. acids
$BaSO_4$	Rhombic white	2.5×10^{-4} (25°)	Sl. sol. H_2SO_4
BaS	Cubic white	Hydrolyzes	Insol. alc.
$BaSO_3$	Cubic white	2.0×10^{-2} (20°)	V. sol. HCl; sol. alc.
$Ba(SCN)_2 \cdot 2H_2O$	Needles, white	43 (20°)	Sol. alc.
Sr	Cubic silvery pale yellowish-white metal	Reacts	Sol. acids, alc., NH_3

Formula	Color and Form	Solubility in H_2O (g. per 100 g. H_2O)	General Solubility
SrO	Cubic grayish-white	0.68 (20°) Forms $Sr(OH)_2$	Sl. sol. alc.; insol. ether, acetone
SrO_2	White powder	8×10^{-3} (20°)	V. sol. alc., NH_4Cl; insol. acetone
$Sr(OH)_2 \cdot 8H_2O$	Tetragonal white	1.74 (20°)	Sol. acids, NH_4Cl; insol. acetone
$Sr(C_2H_3O_2)_2 \cdot \frac{1}{2}H_2O$	White crystalline powder	42.9 (20°)	Sl. sol. alc.
$Sr(BrO_3)_2 \cdot H_2O$	Monoclinic yellowish-white	33 (16°)	
$SrBr_2 \cdot 6H_2O$	Hexagonal white, hygroscopic	142 (20°)	Sol. alc.; insol. ether
$SrCO_3$	Rhombic white or white powder	1.1×10^{-3} (18°)	Sol. acids, NH_4 salts
$Sr(ClO_3)_2$	Rhombic white or white powder	175 (18°)	Sol. alc.; insol. absolute alc.
$SrCl_2 \cdot 6H_2O$	Trigonal white	89 (20°)	Sl. sol. alc.
$SrCrO_4$	Monoclinic yellow	0.12 (15°)	Sol. HAc, HCl, HNO_3, NH_4 salts
$Sr(CN)_2 \cdot 4H_2O$	Deliquescent crystals, white	V. sol.	
$Sr_2Fe(CN)_6 \cdot 15H_2O$	Monoclinic yellow	50 (cold)	
SrF_2	White cubic or powder	0.012 (27°)	Sol. hot HCl; insol. HF
$SrI_2 \cdot 6H_2O$	Hexagonal yellowish-white, deliquescent	238 (20°)	Sol. alc.; insol. ether
$Sr(NO_3)_2 \cdot 4H_2O$	Monoclinic white	106 (25°)	Insol. HNO_3
$Sr(NO_2)_2 \cdot H_2O$	Hexagonal white	65 (15°)	
$SrC_2O_4 \cdot H_2O$	White	5.7×10^{-3} (25°)	Sol. HCl, HNO_3
$SrSO_4$	Rhombic white	1.14×10^{-2} (30°)	So. sol. acids; insol. dil. H_2SO_4, alc.
$SrSO_3$	White crystals	3.3×10^{-3} (17°)	V. sol. H_2SO_3; sol. acids
SrS	Cubic light gray	Sol., hydrolyzes	Sol. acids, alc.; insol. acetone
$SrS_2O_3 \cdot 5H_2O$	Monoclinic needles	25 (13°)	Insol. alc.

Formula	Color and Form	Solubility in H_2O (g. per 100 g. H_2O)	General Solubility
Ca	Cubic silvery white soft metal	Reacts	Sol. acids; sl. sol. alc.; insol. C_6H_6
CaO	Cubic white	0.122 (20°) Forms $Ca(OH)_2$	Sol. acids, alc.
$Ca(OH)_2$	Rhombic trigonal white	0.161 (20°)	Sol. acids, NH_4Cl soln.; insol. alc.
$Ca(C_2H_3O_2)_2$	White	35 (20°)	Sl. sol. alc.
$Ca_3(AsO_4)_2 \cdot 3H_2O$	White powder	Insol.	Sol. acids
$Ca(BrO_3)_2 \cdot H_2O$	Monoclinic white	V. sol.	
$CaBr_2 \cdot 6H_2O$	Hexagonal white	219 (20°)	Sol. acids, alc., acetone
$CaCO_3$	White	1.5×10^{-3} (25°)	Sol. acids, NH_4Cl
$Ca(ClO_3)_2 \cdot 2H_2O$	Monoclinic yellowish-white, deliquescent	209 (18°)	Sol. alc., acetone
$CaCl_2$	Cubic white, deliquescent	82 (25°)	Sol. alc., HAc
$CaCl_2 \cdot 6H_2O$	Trigonal white, deliquescent	162 (25°)	Sol. alc.
$Ca(OCl)Cl$	White powder, strong Cl_2 odor	Dec.	Dec. by acids
$CaCrO_4 \cdot 2H_2O$	Yellow monoclinic prisms	α form 18.6 (20°) β form 13.0 (20°)	Sol. acids, alc.
$Ca(CN)_2$	Cubic white	Sol.	
$Ca_3[Fe(CN)_6]_2 \cdot 12H_2O$	Red needles, deliquescent	V. sol.	
$Ca_2Fe(CN)_6 \cdot 12H_2O$	Triclinic yellow	89 (25°)	
CaF_2	Cubic white	1.6×10^{-3} (18°)	Sl. sol. acids; sol. in solns. of NH_4 salts
$Ca(IO_3)_2 \cdot 6H_2O$	Rhombic	0.33 (20°)	Sol. HNO_3
CaI_2	Yellowish-white plates, deliquescent	206 (20°)	Sol. acids, alc., acetone
$Ca(NO_3)_2$	Cubic white, hygroscopic	339 (20°)	Sol. alc., acetone
$Ca(NO_2)_2 \cdot 4H_2O$	White	119 (20°)	Sol. alc.
$CaC_2O_4 \cdot H_2O$	White	7.1×10^{-4} (25°)	Sol. acids

Formula	Color and Form	Solubility in H_2O (g. per 100 g. H_2O)	General Solubility
$Ca_3(PO_4)_2$	Amorphous white powder	0.002–0.003 (cold)	Sol. acids; insol. alc.
$Ca(PO_3)_2$	White	Insol.	Insol. acids
$CaSO_4$	Rhombic or monoclinic white	0.209 (25°)	Sol. acids, $Na_2S_2O_3$, NH_4 salts, glycerine
$CaSO_4 \cdot 2H_2O$	Monoclinic white	0.265 (25°)	Sol. acids, $Na_2S_2O_3$, NH_4 salts, glycerine
CaS	Cubic white	2.1×10^{-2} (20°)	Dec. by acids
$CaSO_3 \cdot 2H_2O$	Hexagonal white	4.3×10^{-3} (18°)	Sol. H_2SO_3
$Ca(SCN)_2 \cdot 3H_2O$	White crystals, deliquescent	V. sol.	V. sol. alc.
$CaS_2O_3 \cdot 6H_2O$	Triclinic white	71 (9°)	Insol. alc.
Mg	Hexagonal silvery white metal	Insol.	Sol. acids, NH_4 salts
MgO	Cubic white	8.6×10^{-4} (29°)	Sol. acids, NH_4 salts; insol. alc.
$Mg(OH)_2$	Trigonal white	9×10^{-4} (18°)	Sol. acids, NH_4 salts
$MgNH_4PO_4 \cdot 6H_2O$	Rhombic white	2.3×10^{-2} (0°)	Sol. acids; insol. alc.
$Mg(C_2H_3O_2)_2 \cdot 4H_2O$	Monoclinic white, deliquescent	61 (15°)	V. sol. alc.
$Mg_3(AsO_4)_2 \cdot 22H_2O$	White	Insol.	Sol. acids, NH_4Cl
$Mg_3(AsO_3)_2$	White	Sol.	Sol. acids, NH_4Cl; insol. NH_4OH
$Mg(BrO_3)_2 \cdot 6H_2O$	Cubic white	73 (18°)	Insol. alc.
$MgBr_2 \cdot 6H_2O$	Hexagonal white	153 (20°)	Sol. alc., acetone; sl. sol. NH_3
$MgCO_3$	Trigonal white	9×10^{-2} (19°)	Sol. acids, aq. CO_2; insol. acetone, NH_3
$Mg(ClO_3)_2 \cdot 6H_2O$	White crystals or powder, deliquescent	206 (20°)	Sol. alc.
$MgCl_2 \cdot 6H_2O$	Monoclinic white, deliquescent	117 (20°)	Sol. alc.
$MgCrO_4 \cdot 7H_2O$	Rhombic yellow	138 (18°)	
$Mg_2Fe(CN)_6 \cdot 12H_2O$	Pale yellow crystals	33 (cold)	

Formula	Color and Form	Solubility in H₂O (g. per 100 g. H₂O)	General Solubility
MgF_2	Tetragonal white	8.7×10^{-3} (18°)	Sol. HNO_3; sl. sol. acids; insol. alc.
$Mg(IO_3)_2 \cdot 4H_2O$	Monoclinic white	9.9 (20°)	
$MgI_2 \cdot 8H_2O$	White deliquescent powder	212 (20°)	Sol. alc., ether
$Mg(NO_3)_2 \cdot 6H_2O$	Monoclinic white, deliquescent	128 (20°)	Sol. alc.
$MgC_2O_4 \cdot 2H_2O$	White powder	1.51×10^{-2} (18°)	Sol. acids
$Mg_3(PO_4)_2 \cdot 4H_2O$	Monoclinic white	2×10^{-2} (cold)	Sol. acids; insol. NH_4 salts, NH_3
$MgSO_4 \cdot 7H_2O$	Rhombic white	71 (20°)	Sol. alc., glycerine
MgS	Cubic white	Hydrolyzes	Sol. acids
$MgSO_3 \cdot 6H_2O$	White crystalline powder	1.25 (cold)	Insol. alc., NH_3
$MgS_2O_3 \cdot 6H_2O$	White prisms	V. sol.	Sol. alc.

INDEX

Acetate ion, hydrolysis 177, 199
Acetic acid,
  ionization constant 97, 103, 497
  ionization equilibrium 96–101
Acid radicals (See Anions; Negative ions)
Acidity, testing of 297
Acids,
  common ion effect 100
  ionization constants of weak 104, 106, 497
  ionization of strong 20
  ionization of weak 95, 104
  list of 497
  polybasic 152
Adsorption 140
Alkali metal group, 312
  analysis of 317
  preliminary experiments 315
Alkali metal ions,
  equilibria involving 313
Alkaline earth group,
  analysis of 412
  carbonates 403
  chromates 405
  equations 416
  flame test 406
  oxalates 405
  phosphates 406
  precipitation of 413, 424
  preliminary experiments 408
  sulfates 404
Alloy, solution of 434
Aluminate ion 248, 370
Aluminon 372, 497
Aluminum compounds, properties 525
Aluminum hydroxide, amphoteric properties 248
Aluminum ion, 370
  hydrolysis of 184
  properties of 370–372
  test for, 398
Aluminum-zinc group, 369
  analysis of 385
  equations 400

Aluminum-zinc group (Cont'd)
  precipitation of 392, 423
  preliminary experiments 388
Americium 55
Amide ion 219
Ammonates 220
Ammonia, liquid 217
Ammonia complexes 232
Ammonium,
  arsenomolybdate 347
  compounds, properties 508
  molybdate solution 477
  polysulfide 230, 346, 349
  sulfide 253, 369
Ammonium ion, 218, 312–317
  hydrolysis of 179
  test for 315
Amphoteric elements 246
Amphoteric hydroxides 247
  as coordinated complexes 255
Amphoteric substances 245
  application to analysis 253
  and equilibrium 248
Amphoteric sulfides 251
Analysis, general 416
  anion 426
Anions (See also Negative ions),
  complex 226
  elimination chart 441
  homoatomic 229
  identification of 437
Antimonic ion, 347–349, 515
  properties of 347
Antimonic oxide 348
Antimonic sulfide 349
Antimonous ion, 347, 515
  properties of 347–349
  test for 367
Antimonous oxides 348
Antimonous sulfide 349
Apparatus, list of 476
Argenticyanide ion 227
Arsenate ion
  properties of 470
  test for 450
Arsenic acid 345

TABLES OF LOGARITHMS

ANSWERS TO PROBLEMS

800.

LOGARITHMS

No.	0	1	2	3	4	5	6	7	8	9	1	2	3	4	5	6	7	8	9
10	0000	0043	0086	0128	0170	0212	0253	0294	0334	0374	4	8	12	17	21	25	29	33	37
11	0414	0453	0492	0531	0569	0607	0645	0682	0719	0755	4	8	11	15	19	23	26	30	34
12	0792	0828	0864	0899	0934	0969	1004	1038	1072	1106	3	7	10	14	17	21	24	28	31
13	1139	1173	1206	1239	1271	1303	1335	1367	1399	1430	3	6	10	13	16	19	23	26	29
14	1461	1492	1523	1553	1584	1614	1644	1673	1703	1732	3	6	9	12	15	18	21	24	27
15	1761	1790	1818	1847	1875	1903	1931	1959	1987	2014	3	6	8	11	14	17	20	22	25
16	2041	2068	2095	2122	2148	2175	2201	2227	2253	2279	3	5	8	11	13	16	18	21	24
17	2304	2330	2355	2380	2405	2430	2455	2480	2504	2529	2	5	7	10	12	15	17	20	22
18	2553	2577	2601	2625	2648	2672	2695	2718	2742	2765	2	5	7	9	12	14	16	19	21
19	2788	2810	2833	2856	2878	2900	2923	2945	2967	2989	2	4	7	9	11	13	16	18	20
20	3010	3032	3054	3075	3096	3118	3139	3160	3181	3201	2	4	6	8	10	13	15	17	19
21	3222	3243	3263	3284	3304	3324	3345	3365	3385	3404	2	4	6	8	11	12	14	16	18
22	3424	3444	3464	3483	3502	3522	3541	3560	3579	3598	2	4	6	8	10	12	14	15	17
23	3617	3636	3655	3674	3692	3711	3729	3747	3766	3784	2	4	6	7	9	11	13	15	17
24	3802	3820	3838	3856	3874	3892	3909	3927	3945	3962	2	4	5	7	9	11	12	14	16
25	3979	3997	4014	4031	4048	4065	4082	4099	4116	4133	2	3	5	7	9	10	12	14	15
26	4150	4166	4183	4200	4216	4232	4249	4265	4281	4298	2	3	5	7	8	10	11	13	15
27	4314	4330	4346	4362	4378	4393	4409	4425	4440	4456	2	3	5	6	8	9	11	13	14
28	4472	4487	4502	4518	4533	4548	4564	4579	4594	4609	2	3	5	6	8	9	11	12	14
29	4624	4639	4654	4669	4683	4698	4713	4728	4742	4757	1	3	4	6	7	9	10	12	13
30	4771	4786	4800	4814	4829	4843	4857	4871	4886	4900	1	3	4	6	7	9	10	11	13
31	4914	4928	4942	4955	4969	4983	4997	5011	5024	5038	1	3	4	6	7	8	10	11	12
32	5051	5065	5079	5092	5105	5119	5132	5145	5159	5172	1	3	4	5	7	8	9	11	12
33	5185	5198	5211	5224	5237	5250	5263	5276	5289	5302	1	3	4	5	6	8	9	10	12
34	5315	5328	5340	5353	5366	5378	5391	5403	5416	5428	1	3	4	5	6	8	9	10	11
35	5441	5453	5465	5478	5490	5502	5514	5527	5539	5551	1	2	4	5	6	7	9	10	11
36	5563	5575	5587	5599	5611	5623	5635	5647	5658	5670	1	2	4	5	6	7	8	10	11
37	5682	5694	5705	5717	5729	5740	5752	5763	5775	5786	1	2	3	5	6	7	8	9	10
38	5798	5809	5821	5832	5843	5855	5866	5877	5888	5899	1	2	3	5	6	7	8	9	10
39	5911	5922	5933	5944	5955	5966	5977	5988	5999	6010	1	2	3	4	5	7	8	9	10
40	6021	6031	6042	6053	6064	6075	6085	6096	6107	6117	1	2	3	4	5	6	8	9	10
41	6128	6138	6149	6160	6170	6180	6191	6201	6212	6222	1	2	3	4	5	6	7	8	9
42	6232	6243	6253	6263	6274	6284	6294	6304	6314	6325	1	2	3	4	5	6	7	8	9
43	6335	6345	6355	6365	6375	6386	6395	6405	6415	6425	1	2	3	4	5	6	7	8	9
44	6435	6444	6454	6464	6474	6484	6493	6503	6513	6522	1	2	3	4	5	6	7	8	9
45	6532	6542	6551	6561	6571	6580	6590	6599	6609	6618	1	2	3	4	5	6	7	8	9
46	6628	6637	6646	6656	6665	6675	6684	6693	6702	6712	1	2	3	4	5	6	7	7	8
47	6721	6730	6739	6749	6758	6767	6776	6785	6794	6803	1	2	3	4	5	5	6	7	8
48	6812	6821	6830	6839	6848	6857	6866	6875	6884	6893	1	2	3	4	4	5	6	7	8
49	6902	6911	6920	6928	6937	6946	6955	6964	6972	6981	1	2	3	4	4	5	6	7	8
50	6990	6998	7007	7016	7024	7033	7042	7050	7059	7067	1	2	3	3	4	5	6	7	8
51	7076	7084	7093	7101	7110	7118	7126	7135	7143	7152	1	2	3	3	4	5	6	7	8
52	7160	7168	7177	7185	7193	7202	7210	7218	7226	7235	1	2	2	3	4	5	6	7	7
53	7243	7251	7259	7267	7275	7284	7292	7300	7308	7316	1	2	2	3	4	5	6	6	7
54	7324	7332	7340	7348	7356	7364	7372	7380	7388	7396	1	2	2	3	4	5	6	6	7
	0	1	2	3	4	5	6	7	8	9	1	2	3	4	5	6	7	8	9

LOGARITHMS

No.	0	1	2	3	4	5	6	7	8	9	1	2	3	4	5	6	7	8	9
55	7404	7412	7419	7427	7435	7443	7451	7459	7466	7474	1	2	2	3	4	5	5	6	7
56	7482	7490	7497	7505	7513	7520	7528	7536	7543	7551	1	2	2	3	4	5	5	6	7
57	7559	7566	7574	7582	7589	7597	7604	7612	7619	7627	1	2	2	3	4	5	5	6	7
58	7634	7642	7649	7657	7664	7672	7679	7686	7694	7701	1	1	2	3	4	4	5	6	7
59	7709	7716	7723	7731	7738	7745	7752	7760	7767	7774	1	1	2	3	4	4	5	6	7
60	7782	7789	7796	7803	7810	7818	7825	7832	7839	7846	1	1	2	3	4	4	5	6	6
61	7853	7860	7868	7875	7882	7889	7896	7903	7910	7917	1	1	2	3	4	4	5	6	6
62	7924	7931	7938	7945	7952	7959	7966	7973	7980	7987	1	1	2	3	3	4	5	6	6
63	7993	8000	8007	8014	8021	8028	8035	8041	8048	8055	1	1	2	3	3	4	5	5	6
64	8062	8069	8075	8082	8089	8096	8102	8109	8116	8122	1	1	2	3	3	4	5	5	6
65	8129	8136	8142	8149	8156	8162	8169	8176	8182	8189	1	1	2	3	3	4	5	5	6
66	8195	8202	8209	8215	8222	8228	8235	8241	8248	8254	1	1	2	3	3	4	5	5	6
67	8261	8267	8274	8280	8287	8293	8299	8306	8312	8319	1	1	2	3	3	4	5	5	6
68	8325	8331	8338	8344	8351	8357	8363	8370	8376	8382	1	1	2	3	3	4	4	5	6
69	8388	8395	8401	8407	8414	8420	8426	8432	8439	8445	1	1	2	2	3	4	4	5	6
70	8451	8457	8463	8470	8476	8482	8488	8494	8500	8506	1	1	2	2	3	4	4	5	6
71	8513	8519	8525	8531	8537	8543	8549	8555	8561	8567	1	1	2	2	3	4	4	5	5
72	8573	8579	8585	8591	8597	8603	8609	8615	8621	8627	1	1	2	2	3	4	4	5	5
73	8633	8639	8645	8651	8657	8663	8669	8675	8681	8686	1	1	2	2	3	4	4	5	5
74	8692	8698	8704	8710	8716	8722	8727	8733	8739	8745	1	1	2	2	3	4	4	5	5
75	8751	8756	8762	8768	8774	8779	8785	8791	8797	8802	1	1	2	2	3	3	4	5	5
76	8808	8814	8820	8825	8831	8837	8842	8848	8854	8859	1	1	2	2	3	3	4	5	5
77	8865	8871	8876	8882	8887	8893	8899	8904	8910	8915	1	1	2	2	3	3	4	4	5
78	8921	8927	8932	8938	8943	8949	8954	8960	8965	8971	1	1	2	2	3	3	4	4	5
79	8976	8982	8987	8993	8998	9004	9009	9015	9020	9025	1	1	2	2	3	3	4	4	5
80	9031	9036	9042	9047	9053	9058	9063	9069	9074	9079	1	1	2	2	3	3	4	4	5
81	9085	9090	9096	9101	9106	9112	9117	9122	9128	9133	1	1	2	2	3	3	4	4	5
82	9138	9143	9149	9154	9159	9165	9170	9175	9180	9186	1	1	2	2	3	3	4	4	5
83	9191	9196	9201	9206	9212	9217	9222	9227	9232	9238	1	1	2	2	3	3	4	4	5
84	9243	9248	9253	9258	9263	9269	9274	9279	9284	9289	1	1	2	2	3	3	4	4	5
85	9294	9299	9304	9309	9315	9320	9325	9330	9335	9340	1	1	2	2	3	3	4	4	5
86	9345	9350	9355	9360	9365	9370	9375	9380	9385	9390	1	1	2	2	3	3	4	4	5
87	9395	9400	9405	9410	9415	9420	9425	9430	9435	9440	0	1	1	2	2	3	3	4	4
88	9445	9450	9455	9460	9465	9469	9474	9479	9484	9489	0	1	1	2	2	3	3	4	4
89	9494	9499	9504	9509	9513	9518	9523	9528	9533	9538	0	1	1	2	2	3	3	4	4
90	9542	9547	9552	9557	9562	9566	9571	9576	9581	9586	0	1	1	2	2	3	3	4	4
91	9590	9595	9600	9605	9609	9614	9619	9624	9628	9633	0	1	1	2	2	3	3	4	4
92	9638	9643	9647	9652	9657	9661	9666	9671	9675	9680	0	1	1	2	2	3	3	4	4
93	9685	9689	9694	9699	9703	9708	9713	9717	9722	9727	0	1	1	2	2	3	3	4	4
94	9731	9736	9741	9745	9750	9754	9759	9763	9768	9773	0	1	1	2	2	3	3	4	4
95	9777	9782	9786	9791	9795	9800	9805	9809	9814	9818	0	1	1	2	2	3	3	4	4
96	9823	9827	9832	9836	9841	9845	9850	9854	9859	9863	0	1	1	2	2	3	3	4	4
97	9868	9872	9877	9881	9886	9890	9894	9899	9903	9908	0	1	1	2	2	3	3	4	4
98	9912	9917	9921	9926	9930	9934	9939	9943	9948	9952	0	1	1	2	2	3	3	4	4
99	9956	9961	9965	9969	9974	9978	9983	9987	9991	9996	0	1	1	2	2	3	3	3	4
	0	1	2	3	4	5	6	7	8	9	1	2	3	4	5	6	7	8	9

ANSWERS TO PROBLEMS

CHAPTER I   Pages 29–33

(20) 1.37 M.

(21) 0.1 mole.

(22) 0.392 g.

(23) .0565 M.

(24) (a) 0.1 mole; (b) 0.1 M; (c) 0.2 M.

(25) (a) 3.15 g.; (b) 245.2 g.; (c) 5.30 g.; (d) 0.204 g.; (e) 13.0 g.

(26) (a) 1709 ml.; (b) 1176 ml.; (c) 368 ml.; (d) 310 ml.; (e) 40 ml.

(27) (a) 20 ml.; (b) 475 ml.; (c) 54 ml.; (d) 140 ml.; (e) 0.4 ml.

(28) 75 ml. 0.1 M $AgNO_3$ and 175 ml. water.

(29) 75 ml.

(30) 37.5 ml.

(31) 10 ml.

(32) 7.5 ml.

(33) (a) 17.4 M; (b) 6.15 M; (c) 13.15 M; (d) 4.72 M.

(34) 152 cm.

(35) (a) 92.8%; (b) 86.6%; (c) 89.6%; (d) 90.7%.

(36) 6.4 g.

(37) Fe_2O_3.

(38) 478.4 g.

(39) 6.6 g.

(40) 1398 lbs.

(41) 2 atoms; Cu_2S.

(42) Cr_2O_3.

(43) 19.9.

(44) 11.0 M.

(45) 9.1 ml.

(46) 58.9 ml.

(47) 200 ml. each of $AgNO_3$, $Pb(NO_3)_2$ and $Hg_2(NO_3)_2$ solutions.

CHAPTER II   Pages 56–57.

(1) (a) Xe; (b) Xe; (c) Kr; (d) n or He; (e) Ne; (f) none; (g) none; (h) Xe; (i) Ne; (j) none.

(4) Na.
(8) (a) .00070 gm.
    (b) 5.85 fold.
    (c) 0.34 per cent.

CHAPTER IV Pages 92–94.

(2) 256 times faster.
(4) 16 times faster.
(11) 105.
(12) $K = 0.4$; (1) $d = 3$; (2) $d = 1.5$; (3) $a = 1.5$;
     (4) $a = 6$; (5) $b = 8$; (6) $b = 16$; (7) $d = 24$; (8) $d = 96$.

(13) (1) $\dfrac{(CN^-)(H^+)}{(HCN)} = K$;   (2) $\dfrac{(NH_4^+)(OH^-)}{(NH_4OH)} = K$;

(3) $\dfrac{(H^+)^2(S^{--})}{(H_2S)} = K$;   (4) $\dfrac{(Fe^{++})^2(Hg^{++})^2}{(Hg_2^{++})(Fe^{+++})^2} = K$;

(5) $\dfrac{(CO)(H_2O)}{(CO_2)(H_2)} = K$;   (6) $\dfrac{(NO)^2(O_2)}{(NO_2)^2} = K$;

(7) $\dfrac{(NH_3)^2}{(N_2)(H_2)^3} = K$.

(17) Absorbed.
(18) More soluble.

CHAPTER V. Pages 124–127.

(7) (a) 5; (b) 9; (c) 1; (d) 7.38; (e) 2.1.
(8) (a) $1.36 \times 10^{-3} M$; (b) $4.3 \times 10^{-4} M$; (c) $4.3 \times 10^{-3} M$;
    (d) $1 \times 10^{-5} M$;   (e) $1.93 \times 10^{-3} M$; (f) $2 \times 10^{-3} M$;
    (g) $1.4 \times 10^{-4} M$; (h) $1 \times 10^{-2} M$;   (i) $2.9 \times 10^{-6} M$;
    (j) $5.5 \times 10^{-5} M$.
(9) (a) $4.2 \times 10^{-3} M$; (b) $1.3 \times 10^{-3} M$; (c) $4.2 \times 10^{-4} M$;
    (d) $1.3 \times 10^{-4} M$; (e) $8.5 \times 10^{-4} M$; (f) $2.2 \times 10^{-3} M$;
    (g) $1.2 \times 10^{-2} M$; (h) $7.5 \times 10^{-3} M$; (i) $9.6 \times 10^{-7} M$.
(10) (a) 1.85×10^{-5};   (b) 1.84×10^{-5};   (c) 1.80×10^{-5};
     (d) 1.80×10^{-5};   (e) 4.5×10^{-4};   (f) 2.1×10^{-9};
     (g) 2.1×10^{-9}.
(11) $8 \times 10^{-4} M$ each.
(12) $(H^+) = 2.5 \times 10^{-5} M$; $(Ac^-) = 2.4 \times 10^{-2} M$.
(13) (a) .068; (b) .00046; (c) .019; (d) .03; (e) .08.
(14) .074 M.   (15) .003 M.
(16) 0.72 M.   (17) 0.18 mole.

(18) $8.5 \times 10^{-6} M$.   (19) $1.2 \times 10^{-5} M$.

(20) (a) 1×10^{-5}; (b) $3.2 \times 10^{-4} M$; (c) .032; (d) $1 \times 10^{-5} M$.

(21) .011 M.   (22) .21 M.

(23) $5.5 \times 10^{-6} M$.   (24) $1.9 \times 10^{-6} M$.

(25) $9 \times 10^{-6} M$.   (26) .02 M.

(27) $2.6 \times 10^{-5} M$.   (28) $2.9 \times 10^{-5} M$.

(29) (a) 1; (b) 1.56; (c) 2.87; (d) 4.75.

(30) Condition necessary for correct answer is that

$$\frac{(Ac^-)}{(HAc)} = 0.185.$$

(31) (a) one-half; (b) .05 M; (c) .05 M; (d) $1.8 \times 10^{-5} M$.

(32) First addition of NaOH: (a) one-tenth; (b) .01 M;
      (c) .09 M; (d) $1.67 \times 10^{-4} M$; (e) 3.78.

(33) (a) 10^{-4}; (b) 10^{-6}; (c) 10^{-7}; (d) 10^{-9}; (e) 10^{-10}.

CHAPTER VI. Pages 147–151.

(3) $1.25 \times 10^{-7} M$.

(14) (a) 1.56×10^{-10};   (b) 7.7×10^{-13};   (c) 1.5×10^{-16};
      (d) 1.1×10^{-10};   (e) 9.0×10^{-12};   (f) 8.9×10^{-9};
      (g) 3.6×10^{-9}.

(15) (a) 9.0×10^{-4} g. per 100 ml.; (b) 1.8×10^{-3} g. per
      100 ml.; (c) 4.35×10^{-3} g. per 100 ml.; (d) 5.2×10^{-9} g.
      per 100 ml.; (e) 0.106 g. per 100 ml.; (f) 9.9×10^{-3} g.
      per 100 ml.; (g) 4.3×10^{-5} g. per 100 ml.; (h) 2.0×10^{-5}
      g. per 100 ml.

(16) 6.0×10^{-9} mole per liter. 1.9×10^{-7} g. per 200 ml.

(17) 1.58×10^{-4} g. per 100 ml.

(18) (a) 0.363 g.; (b) 5.8×10^{-15} mole.

(19) (a) 1.56×10^{-9} mole; (b) 7.8×10^{-10} mole.

(20) (a) 7.7×10^{-12} mole per liter; (b) 9.5×10^{-6} mole per
      liter; (c) 1.5×10^{-13} mole per liter.

(21) (a) $(Pb^{++}) = 1.5 \times 10^{-3} M$, $(I^-) = 3.0 \times 10^{-3} M$;
      (c) 1.4×10^{-8}.

(22) (a) $5.1 \times 10^{-5} M$; (b) 6.5×10^{-3} g.

(23) 4.5×10^{-3} g. per 200 ml.

(24) $1.26 \times 10^{-4} M$.

(25) 1.5×10^{-4} g.

(26) 1.56×10^{-5}.

(27) $1 \times 10^{-3} M$; $5 \times 10^{-6} M$.

(28) (a) 4.7×10^{-7} g.; (b) 6.75×10^{-6} g.

(29) (a) 1.56×10^{-9} mole; (b) 1.25×10^{-5} mole;
  (c) 1.25×10^{-5} mole; (d) 1.56×10^{-9} mole;
  (e) 8.5×10^{-6} mole.

(30) 203.

(31) (a) $1.5 \times 10^{-15} M$; (b) $1.56 \times 10^{-9} M$; (d) $9.6 \times 10^{-8} M$;
  (e) $9.6 \times 10^{-5}\%$; (f) 1.04×10^{6};   (g) $3.1 \times 10^{-9} M$;
  $4.8 \times 10^{-8} M$; (h) 1.04×10^{6}.

(32) (a) $1.5 \times 10^{-14} M$; (b) $1.2 \times 10^{-3} M$; (d) $1.27 \times 10^{-13} M$;
  (e) 7.9×10^{10};   (f) $1.67 \times 10^{-3} M$; (g) $9 \times 10^{-14} M$;

  (h) 5.5×10^{10}; (i) $\dfrac{(\mathrm{Pb}^{++})^{\frac{1}{2}}}{(\mathrm{Ag}^{+})} = 7.9 \times 10^{11}$;

  (j) due to the fact that $\dfrac{(\mathrm{Pb}^{++})^{\frac{1}{2}}}{(\mathrm{Ag}^{+})}$ rather than $\dfrac{(\mathrm{Pb}^{++})}{(\mathrm{Ag}^{+})}$ is
  constant.

(33) 0.13 mole.   (34) 0.11 mole.

(35) 4.6 g./50 ml.   (36) 53.5 g.

(37) 22 moles per liter — impossible.

CHAPTER VII. Pages 169–172.

(8) $5 \times 10^{-5} M$. No.

(9) $(\mathrm{S}^{--}) = 1.2 \times 10^{-15} M$; $(\mathrm{H}^{+}) = 6.7 \times 10^{-5} M$.

(10) $6.3 \times 10^{-4} M$.

(11) (a) $1.9 \times 10^{-4} M$; (b) $5.9 \times 10^{-5} M$; (c) $3 \times 10^{-5} M$;
  (d) $6.6 \times 10^{-6} M$; (e) $2.1 \times 10^{-5} M$; (f) $1.3 \times 10^{-4} M$;
  (g) $.016 M$; (h) $.024 M$; (i) $4.6 \times 10^{-2} M$.

(12) (a) $1.1 \times 10^{-15} M$; (b) $1.1 \times 10^{-17} M$; (c) $1.1 \times 10^{-19} M$;
  (d) $1.1 \times 10^{-21} M$; (e) $1.1 \times 10^{-23} M$.

(14) (a) $0.285 M$; (b) $1.36 \times 10^{-22} M$; (c) yes; (d) no.

(15) $8.3 \times 10^{-7} M$.

(16) 7.5×10^{-9} mole.

(17) (a) $4.4 \times 10^{-35} M$; (b) $2.9 \times 10^{-26} M$; (c) $1.6 \times 10^{-20} M$;
  (d) $4 \times 10^{-47} M$; (e) $2.2 \times 10^{-25} M$.

(18) $6.5 \times 10^{-3} M$.

(19) $6 \times 10^{-18} M$.

(20) (a) $1.54 \times 10^{-2} M$; (b) $1.54 \times 10^{-2} M$; (c) $6.3 \times 10^{-8} M$;
  (d) $1.5 \times 10^{-18} M$.

(21) 7.6×10^{-16} mole Cu^{++} per 200 ml.; 2.2×10^{-6} mole Cd^{++}
  per 200 ml.

(22) 6 Hg^{++} per 100 li.

(23) (H^+) = .096 M or about 0.1 M.

(24) (H^+) = 1.8 × 10⁶ M; no.

(25) (H^+) = .01 M.

CHAPTER VIII. Pages 212–215.

(15) (a) 5.6 × 10^{-10}; (b) 5.4 × 10^{-10}; (c) 2.0 × 10^{-11}; (d) 1.5 × 10^{-10}; (e) 4.8 × 10^{-6}; (f) 1 × 10^{-4}; (g) 2.2 × 10^{-11}; (h) 4.8 × 10^{-11}; (i) 1.4 × 10^{-11}; (j) 7.1 × 10^{-10}.

(16) (a) *0.1 M solutions:*

(a) 7.5 × 10^{-6} M; (b) 1.4 × 10^{-9} M; (c) 1.4 × 10^{-6} M; (d) 2.6 × 10^{-9} M; (e) 1.4 × 10^{-11} M; (f) 3.2 × 10^{-12} M; (g) 6.7 × 10^{-9} M; (h) 4.6 × 10^{-9} M; (i) 1.2 × 10^{-6} M; (j) 1.2 × 10^{-9} M.

(b) *.01 M solutions:*

(a) 2.4 × 10^{-6} M; (b) 4.3 × 10^{-9} M; (c) 4.5 × 10^{-7} M; (d) 8.1 × 10^{-9} M; (e) 4.5 × 10^{-11} M; (f) 1.0 × 10^{-11} M; (g) 2.1 × 10^{-8} M; (h) 1.4 × 10^{-8} M; (i) 3.7 × 10^{-7} M; (j) 3.8 × 10^{-9} M.

(17) (a) *0.1 M solutions:*

(a) 5.13; (b) 8.86; (c) 5.86; (d) 8.59; (e) 10.86; (f) 11.50; (g) 8.17; (h) 8.34; (i) 5.92; (j) 8.92.

(b) *.01 M solutions:*

(a) 5.62; (b) 8.37; (c) 6.35; (d) 8.09; (e) 10.35; (f) 11.00; (g) 7.68; (h) 7.86; (i) 6.43; (j) 8.42.

(18) (a) *0.1 M solutions:*

(a) 7.5 × 10^{-5}; (b) 7.4 × 10^{-5}; (c) 1.4 × 10^{-5}; (d) 3.9 × 10^{-5}; (e) 6.9 × 10^{-3}; (f) 3.2 × 10^{-2}; (g) 1.5 × 10^{-5}; (h) 2.2 × 10^{-5}; (i) 1.2 × 10^{-5}; (j) 8.4 × 10^{-5}.

(b) *.01 M solutions:*

(a) 2.4 × 10^{-4}; (b) 2.3 × 10^{-4}; (c) 4.5 × 10^{-5}; (d) 1.2 × 10^{-4}; (e) 2.2 × 10^{-2}; (f) 0.1; (g) 4.7 × 10^{-5}; (h) 6.9 × 10^{-5}; (i) 3.7 × 10^{-5}; (j) 2.7 × 10^{-4}.

(19) 15.2 g.   (20) 9.6 g.

(21) 0.38 mole.
(22) $1.85 \times 10^{-5}\ M$.
(23) $2.3 \times 10^{-5}\ M$.
(24) 2.1×10^{-9}.
(25) Impossible — $100\ M$.
(26) (a) 1.4×10^{-4}; (b) $2.6 \times 10^{-12}\ M$; (c) 3.8×10^{-2}.
(27) $0.56\ M$.
(28) FeS.
(29) (a) $5.3 \times 10^{-6}\ M$; (b) $1 \times 10^{-7}\ M$; (c) $.018\ M$;
(d) $4.3 \times 10^{-9}\ M$; (e) $2 \times 10^{-13}\ M$.
(30) $(CO_3^{--}) = 1.4 \times 10^{-4}\ M$; $(OH^-) = 2 \times 10^{-6}\ M$.
(31) $MgCO_3$.
(32) *Neglecting hydrolysis:* (a) $1 \times 10^{-14}\ M$; (b) $2 \times 10^{-19}\ M$;
(c) $2.6 \times 10^{-15}\ M$; (d) $4.6 \times 10^{-18}\ M$; (e) $3.2 \times 10^{-14}\ M$;
With hydrolysis: (a) $9 \times 10^{-11}\ M$; (b) $1.7 \times 10^{-15}\ M$;
(c) $2.4 \times 10^{-11}\ M$; (d) $2.5 \times 10^{-15}\ M$; (e) $2.9 \times 10^{-10}\ M$.
(33) $\dfrac{(Ac^-)}{(HAc)} = 1.85$.
(34) $1.6 \times 10^{-6}\ M$.
(35) $\dfrac{(HPO_4^{--})}{(H_2PO_4^-)} =$ (a) $.063$; (b) 0.63; (c) 6.3.

CHAPTER IX. Pages 243–244.

(11) AgCl precipitates.
(12) Yes.
(13) $2 \times 10^{-10}\ M$.
(14) $Ag(CN)_2^-$ gives $(Ag^+) = 2.7 \times 10^{-8}\ M$; $Ag(NH_3)_2^+$ gives $(Ag^+) = 1.1 \times 10^{-8}\ M$.
(15) No.
(18) $9.5 \times 10^{-4}\ M$.
(16) No.
(19) $2.5 \times 10^{-8}\ M$.
(17) 2.72 g. per 100 ml.
(20) $3.6 \times 10^{-4}\ M$.
(21) $1.8 \times 10^{-3}\ M$.
(22) (a) $Cd(NH_3)_4Cl_2$ solution; (b) 92.
(23) $(Cu^+) = 2.4 \times 10^{-22}\ M$; $(Cd^{++}) = 1.3 \times 10^{-9}\ M$.
(24) (a) $Ag(CN)_2^-$ ion first formed; later AgCl precipitates;
(b) .05 mole; (c) $(Cl^-) = 0.1\ M$; $(Ag^+) = 1.56 \times 10^{-9}\ M$;
$(CN^-) = 5.1 \times 10^{-8}\ M$.

CHAPTER X. Pages 259–261.

(14) .034 mole.
(15) $(Zn^{++}) = 2.3 \times 10^{-6}\ M$; $(ZnO_2^{--}) = 2 \times 10^{-12}\ M$;
$(H^+) = 2.2 \times 10^{-9}\ M$; $(OH^-) = 4.6 \times 10^{-6}\ M$.

(16) $(Zn^{++}) = 5 \times 10^{-13} M$; $(ZnO_2^{--}) = 1 \times 10^{-5} M$.

(17) $(Pb^{++}) = 2.5 \times 10^{-14} M$; $(HPbO_2^-) = 2.1 \times 10^{-3} M$; $(H^+) = 1 \times 10^{-13} M$.

(18) No.

(19) $(OH^-) = 2.5 \times 10^{-4} M$.

CHAPTER XI. Pages 283–285.

(1) (a) $10^{20.2}$; (b) $10^{20.4}$; (c) $10^{-56.4}$; (d) $10^{1.6}$; (e) 10^{125}; (f) 10^{51}; (g) 10^{79}; (h) 10^{99}; (i) 10^{-6}; (j) 10^0; (k) $10^{-15.5}$; (l) $10^{21.6}$; (m) 10^{201}.

(2) $K_{eq} = 10^{140}$.

(3) $K_{eq} = 10^{-2.4}$; should be dissolved somewhat.

(4) No: $(Cr^{+++})^2 \times (Cl_2)^3 = 10^{-27}$.

(5) $K_{eq} = 10^{-6.6}$.   (9) $10^{-9.5}$.

(6) $K_{eq} = 10^{40}$.   (10) $10^{11.2}$.

(7) 10^{-9}.   (11) No. $K_{eq} = 10^{-127}$.

(8) $10^{-10.8}$.

MATHEMATICAL OPERATIONS

(1) (a) 10^6; (b) 4×10^5; (c) 5×10^4; (d) 9×10^3; (e) 6×10^2; (f) 7×10^1; (g) 1.45×10^6; (h) 9.46×10^5; (i) 5.9×10^4; (j) 9.627×10^3; (k) 4.5×10^2; (l) 5.632×10^5; (m) 10^{-2}; (n) 3.2×10^{-3}; (o) 7×10^{-6}; (p) 1.07×10^{-3}; (q) 9×10^{-10}; (r) 6.78×10^{-6}; (s) 1.03×10^{-1}; (u) 1×10^{-1}; (v) 4.5×10^{-4}; (w) 6×10^{-6}.

(2) (a) 1.26×10^9; (b) 5×10^3; (c) 6.06×10^{17}; (d) 2.8×10^{-6}; (e) 5×10^{-4}; (f) 10^{-1};   (g) 7×10^4; (h) 3×10^8;   (i) 6.25;   (j) 1.8×10^{-7}; (k) 5×10^2.

(3) (a) 5×10;   (b) 10^7;   (c) $3.2 \times 10 = 32$;   (d) 3×10^{-1}; (e) 4.5×10^{-5}; (f) $2 \times 10 = 20$; (g) 5×10^9; (h) 6×10^{-12}; (i) 2×10^{-12}; (j) 5×10^{-1}; (k) 3.2×10^{-1} (l) 5×10^{13}; (m) 2×10^{-8}; (n) 5×10^{-2}.

(4) (a) $1885.$; (b) 16.5; (c) 16.45; (d) 3×10^{-4}; (e) $X = 10^{-4}$.

(5) (a) 3.33372; (b) 2.5315; (c) $.0149$; (d) $\overline{6}.826$ (or -5.174); (e) 1.8277; (f) $\overline{1}.5877$ (or $-.4123$); (g) $\overline{3}.6$ (or -2.4); (h) 2.602.

(6) (a) 4726; (b) 273.0; (c) 1.939; (d) .2226; (e) .0002905; (f) .0001861; (g) .004337; (h) .5302.

(7) (a) $V = 310$; (b) $N = 3.56 \times 10^{22}$; (c) $M = 367$; (d) $X = 3.1 \times 10^{-4}$.

(8) (a) 6.45×10^{10}; (b) 1.30×10^{-7}; (c) 1.73×10^{-9}; (d) 5.3×10^{14}; (e) 5.7×10^{14}.

(9) (a) 2×10^{-3}; (b) 4×10^{-6}; (c) 6×10^{4}; (d) 5×10^{-3}; (e) 1.58×10^{-2}; (f) 83.32; (g) 1.578×10^{-3}; (h) 1.20×10^{-7}.

(10) (a) (imaginary); (b) $+ 1.52, - 1.67$; (c) $18.5 \times 10^{-4}, - 19.5 \times 10^{-4}$; (d) $\pm 1.34 \times 10^{-3}$.

(11) (a) 4; (b) 11.70; (c) 5.46; (d) 7; (e) 4.59; (f) .871.

(12) (a) 10^{-7}; (b) 4×10^{-9}; (c) 5.0×10^{-6}; (d) 1.35×10^{-7}; (e) 5.62×10^{-10}; (f) 3.47×10^{-3}.

(13) (a) $P = \dfrac{K}{V}$; (b) $V = KT$; (c) $P = KT$; (d) $S = \dfrac{K}{\sqrt{m}}$;

(e) $F = \dfrac{K(m_1 \times m_2)}{d^2}$.